Richa~
Har~

D1133136

SEQUENCE IN LAYERED ROCKS

The quality of the materials used in the manufacture of this book is governed by continued postwar shortages.

SEQUENCE
IN LAYERED ROCKS

A Study of Features and Structures Useful for
Determining Top and Bottom or Order of Succession
in Bedded and Tabular Rock Bodies

by ROBERT R. SHROCK

Associate Professor of Geology
Massachusetts Institute of Technology

FIRST EDITION

NEW YORK   TORONTO   LONDON

McGRAW-HILL BOOK COMPANY, INC.

1948

SEQUENCE IN LAYERED ROCKS

THE MAPLE PRESS COMPANY, YORK, PA.

PREFACE

One of the most important problems facing a field geologist is determining order of succession (top and bottom) and nature of the structure in folded layered rocks. As Mead (1940: 1007)[1] recently put it: "In a region of folded rocks the problem of the structural geologist is frequently the building of a reasonable three-dimensional picture of folded structure from the fragmental evidence afforded by scattered outcrops, drill holes, test pits, and mine workings. Dip, strike, and lithology of beds alone are inadequate because they do not afford unique solutions. Determinations of "top or bottom" of beds are of great value because they make possible unique solutions of many situations, and it is now generally recognized by structural geologists that every reasonable effort should be made to ascertain the stratigraphic sequence of beds."

In order to determine the tops and bottoms of beds and the architecture of folded layers, the field geologist must know not only where and how to search for the manifold record preserved in the different kinds of rocks but also how to interpret and use what he finds. In thus studying the structure of the earth's crust he has to determine, among other things, the sequence of bedded, or layered, rocks, i.e., the order of succession in which they were formed. The original sequence of the beds may not be obvious if the strata are steeply inclined or vertical. Under such conditions the investigator must search the exposed rocks for features that will indicate the original top or bottom of the sequence or, conversely, the relative order of succession of the units in the sequence.

This work has been prepared for the express purpose of describing and illustrating principles and features that can be used to establish order of succession (top and bottom) in layered rocks, especially where the strata are steeply inclined or vertical.[2] It has been prepared spe-

---

[1] We shall use the name-date-page method in citing references. Within the parentheses the first series of numbers refers to the date of the reference; the second series refers to the page or pages in the articles. All references cited are listed in the bibliography, which constitutes Chap. VIII. They are listed chronologically under the names of the authors, which are arranged alphabetically.

[2] The great importance of top and bottom features to geological field work was well summarized recently by M. E. Wilson of the Geological Survey of Canada, who stated in a lecture delivered before the New York Academy of Sciences on Nov. 5, 1945, that (Wilson 1945: 43–44): "Up to a few years ago, most geological maps of

cifically for students, but it also may well serve as a convenient review for mature and experienced field geologists.

It is published at this time because the author feels that the assembled data, even though incomplete and not so fully condensed as might have been possible with further effort, should be made available immediately to the many geologists who are searching for petroleum and metals in every part of the globe. It is hoped that the work will stimulate investigators to test in the field the many features that are described and illustrated and to search for and evaluate others that they themselves may find.[1]

In preparing this work the author has drawn heavily upon many sources for both text and illustrative matter. An expression of appreciation is due the following publishers for permission to quote excerpts and to reproduce illustrations from published works: D. Van Nostrand Company, Inc.; E. P. Dutton & Co.; Henry Holt & Co., Inc.; John Wiley & Sons, Inc.; Longmans, Green & Co., Inc.; McGraw-Hill Book Co., Inc.; Methuen & Co., Ltd.; Oxford University Press; Teachers College, Columbia University; University of Chicago Press; The Williams & Wilkins Company; and Thomas Murby and Co.

The following have kindly granted permission to use text and illustrative matter from their publications: American Association for the Advancement of Science (*Science*); American Geophysical Union (*Transactions*); American Institute of Mining and Metallurgical Engineers

---

Archaean areas in the southern part of the Canadian Pre-Cambrian Shield showed the distribution of formations, but gave little information regarding their structure. In recent years, it has been discovered, however, that Archaean rocks are characterized by features from which their structural succession can be determined. These are mainly pillow and brecciated flow tops in lavas and change of grain and cross-bedding in sediments.

Gruner (1941: 1635), in discussing the structural geology of the Knife Lake district of northeastern Minnesota, pointed out that top and bottom criteria that he and his associates found useful there should have wide application since the area studied " . . . is representative of large portions of the Canadian Shield. It contains metamorphic rocks which still permit the identification of certain primary sedimentary features such that the recognition of tops and bottoms of beds is possible. It is evident from inspection of the maps that without them it would have been impossible to interpret any but the simplest structures."

For unraveling the complicated structure of the district, Gruner and his associates, as well as the geologists who had previously worked in the area, found the following criteria most useful: horizon markers, gradational bedding, cross-lamination, scour and fill, "scalloping" (Art. 70), drag folds, and fracture cleavage.

[1] As Leith (1923: 187–188) pertinently remarks: "The keen observer will often discover other criteria which in particular cases will give the solution of this problem [*i.e.*, which is the top or bottom of a bed]."

(*Transactions*); Boston Society of Natural History; British Association for the Advancement of Science; Canada, Department of Mines and Resources (publications of the Geological Survey of Canada); Carnegie Institution of Washington (*Publications; News Science Bulletin*); *Economic Geology; Geological Magazine;* Geological Society of London (*Quarterly Journal*); *Journal of Geology; Journal of Paleontology; Journal of Sedimentary Petrology; Nature;* New York State Museum (*Bulletins; Memoirs;* etc.); Ontario Bureau of Mines; Quebec Bureau of Mines; Royal Irish Academy (*Proceedings*); Royal Society of South Australia (*Transactions and Proceedings*); *Science News Letter;* The American Association of Petroleum Geologists (*Bulletin*); *The American Journal of Science;* The Geological Society of America (*Bulletins; Memoirs; Special Papers*); The Geological Society of South Africa (*Transactions*); The Mineralogical Society of America (*The American Mineralogist*); The Quarry Managers' Journal, Ltd.; The Royal Society of Canada (*Transactions*); The University of Missouri School of Mines and Metallurgy; United States Geological Survey (*Bulletins; Professional Papers; Annual Reports;* etc.); and United States National Museum.

Not included in the foregoing list are a few publications from which brief abstracts were made or short excerpts quoted. Specific citations are given for all such source material, and it is hoped that these constitute satisfactory credit.

The author is deeply grateful to the many writers from whom he has abstracted ideas, quoted descriptions, or borrowed illustrations appearing in the foregoing lists of publications. He has preferred to quote excerpts rather than to abstract them in order that the original ideas or details may be recorded with complete accuracy. What may seem to a few readers to be overmeticulous attention to the proper crediting of these abstracts, quotations, and illustrations will, he is sure, be taken by most others as an indication of diligent effort to give credit fully where credit is due.

A special statement should be made about the photographs. Some of these were sent to the author at his request; others were prepared under his direction; and still others were obtained from published sources. Photographs furnished by individuals are acknowledged by placing the name of the person under the illustration. If the photograph has been published, that fact is noted in the caption. Those supplied by surveys and periodicals carry the appropriate credit line or are credited in the caption. Those from published sources alone are fully credited in the caption accompanying the illustration. All uncredited photographs are original with the author.

From the 18 persons who sent photographic prints or negatives, the author cannot forbear singling out for a special expression of gratitude Dr. R. L. Nichols, chairman of the Department of Geology, Tufts University. He not only furnished the 16 photographs reproduced in Chap. VI but also offered certain suggestions that were used in making several line drawings. A special acknowledgment is due to the Geological Survey of Canada for sending photographic prints used in Figs. 50, 115*B*, 123, 132, and 157. Similar acknowledgment is due the U.S. Geological Survey for providing prints of the subjects that appear as Figs. 189, 218, and 251. Finally, it is a pleasure to acknowledge the handiwork of F. P. Orchard of Peabody Museum, Harvard University, who prepared Figs. 68, 101, 103, 108, 109, 117, 124, 147, 160, 220, 281, and 287.

Except for a few, which are duly credited, all line drawings were prepared by the author. If the drawing is based on a published diagram, that fact is noted in the caption; if it is based on a colleague's suggestion, that colleague is duly credited in the caption.

The author has contracted a deep debt of gratitude to students and colleagues who have discussed with him many different aspects of top and bottom features, offered stimulating and helpful suggestions, challenged certain interpretations that necessitated restating them more clearly, collected specimens and photographs that have added to the value of the work, and called attention to certain obscure references that probably would have been overlooked. The list is much too long to include here, but the author cannot forbear expressing appreciation to the following; J. D. Allan, P. E. Auger, H. C. Dake, F. M. Grout, C. A. Malott, W. J. Mead, E. Mencher, W. D. Michell, W. H. Newhouse, R. L. Nichols, P. E. Raymond, O. Rove, H. C. Stetson, O. F. Tuttle, and S. A. Tyler. A special debt of gratitude is due to Prof. W. L. Whitehead, Prof. H. W. Fairbairn, and J. D. Allan, each of whom read the entire typescript critically and made many valuable suggestions.

Mrs. Margaret A. Frazier, librarian of the Museum of Comparative Zoology, Harvard University, rendered valuable bibliographic assistance. Sylvia Bateman, Barbara Fleming, and Anne K. Rodman deserve a vote of thanks for efficient stenographic work. Finally, grateful thanks are due Theodora Weidman Shrock for much tedious work on typescript and proof.

ROBERT R. SHROCK

LEXINGTON, MASS.
May, 1948

CONTENTS

CHAPTER IV. FEATURES OF SEDIMENTARY ROCKS (II)

II. FEATURES ON UPPER- AND UNDERSURFACES
OF SEDIMENTARY BEDS

CHAPTER V. FEATURES OF SEDIMENTARY ROCKS (III)

III. INTERNAL FEATURES

CHAPTER VIII. BIBLIOGRAPHY

CHAPTER I

INTRODUCTION

This chapter introduces the reader to the purpose and scope of the present work, *i.e.*, to describe and illustrate top and bottom features in all kinds of bedded and layered rocks. The features are considered in four groups comprising six chapters as follows: Chapter II—those Gross Relationships that have long been recognized and used as a basis for the accepted geologic time scale (*e.g.*, superposition, faunal succession, and unconformity), Chapters III, IV, and V—Features of Sedimentary Rocks, Chapter VI—Features of Igneous Rocks, and Chapter VII—Features of Metamorphosed Rocks.

We define how the terms *bed*, *layer*, *stratum*, and *lamina* are to be used, point out the nature and variations displayed by top and bottom features, and consider the limitations that must be imposed on the use of these features. It is emphasized that the features are developed on all scales, ranging from microscopic to grossly macroscopic, and that they lie on the upper or lower surface of a layer as well as within it.

We further emphasize the importance of determining stratification or bedding and list a few features that are useful for this purpose, define the way *dip* and *facing* (or *face*) are to be used, call attention to the value of carefully collected rock specimens, and suggest a few simple rules to be followed in taking samples.

Finally, the better known textbook and journal references to top and bottom features are cited and tabulated for easy reference.

1. Purpose and Scope.—This work has the single primary purpose of describing and illustrating features, structures, and relations of rocks that might be useful in determining original order of succession (top and bottom) in stratified or layered rocks, relative age of contiguous beds and layers, or direction of original verticality (up or down).

Order of succession, relative age of contiguous layers, and original verticality (*i.e.*, the direction in which gravity was acting at the time the feature was formed) are intimately related, and the determination of one may inferentially indicate one or both of the others. For example, any feature indicating the relative ages of sequential strata, presumably deposited in conformable succession and in essentially horizontal position, likewise indicates the top or bottom surface of a particular layer in the sequence and the original order of succession.[1] In the same way, by discovering which is the original top- or the original undersurface of a layer in a continuous sequence, one can infer the true original order of succession and the relative ages of contiguous beds in the sequence.

The features to be described will be useful in determining top and bottom in

1. Sequences of stratified sedimentary rocks that have been folded and faulted
2. Layered bodies of igneous rock that have been deformed
3. Sequences of layered metamorphosed rocks in which many original features have been altered or destroyed and new ones developed as a result of deformation and metamorphism
4. Massive bodies of any kind of rock that lack apparent layered structure or have such a structure developed only on a grand scale

The present work is designed primarily for advanced students and field investigators who expect to be or actually are faced with the problem of top and bottom determination. The problem usually offers little difficulty in a terrane that shows only minor deformation, but it is often a difficult one and of critical importance in regions of intense folding and faulting (see footnote below).

The investigator needs first to know something about the mode of

---

[1] As an example of a significant feature, let us consider primary and secondary cavities. If these are contemporaneous with beds or layers formed in horizontal position and are partly filled before there is any subsequent deformation, the flat surface of the incomplete filling marks original horizontality and is itself an original bedding plane (Fig. 1G). If these cavities are contemporaneous with layers formed on a slope and are partly filled before subsequent deformation, the horizontal plane of the incomplete filling makes with the bedding an acute angle that is the amount of initial dip of the layer (Fig. 1H). If, in the situation just described, the flat surface of the incomplete filling is inclined to the horizontal, the initially dipping layer has been modified in dip by compaction or folding (Fig. 1I). Secondary cavities in either flat-lying or initially dipping layers, if incompletely filled, show the same relations and have the same top and bottom significance as primary cavities (Fig. 1G). In fact, the two kinds of cavities may be indistinguishable. However, if they occur in tilted beds assumed to have been formed in horizontal position, the flat surface of the incomplete filling makes with the bedding plane an acute angle that shows the amount of tilting the bed underwent before the filling started. If there was tilting during the period of filling or afterward, the stratification planes in the incomplete or composite filling are tilted in the same direction as the inclination of the containing layer (Fig. 1J). If a stratified cavity filling is a primary feature in a massive body of undeformed rock (e.g., a thick flow or a pluton), its stratification indicates horizontality. The same stratification may or may not indicate which direction is up or down in the rock mass (see Arts. 217 to 220).

origin and the typical characteristics of any feature before he can fully appreciate its usefulness and limitations. Consequently, we discuss these aspects at considerable length in order to furnish the reader with a good basis for interpretation and evaluation. Each feature is evaluated, and the limitations that must be imposed on its use are discussed. Since it is likely that many investigators who may find occasion to test certain of the features discussed in this work will be in the field, often far removed from libraries and laboratories, the individual features, structures, and relationships are described in detail and illustrated fully. It is hoped that this elaboration will make the work a field manual more or less complete in itself. Those who wish to obtain additional information on a specific feature will find leading references in the Bibliography (Chapter VIII).

2. Plan of Presentation.—The features to be discussed have been divided into the following four categories:

1. *Gross Relationships*. Regional relationships involving principles that have formed the basis of all correlation and of the geologic column for the entire world (Chap. II).

2. *Features of Sedimentary Rocks*. Features, structures, and relations of rocks that were deposited as sediments. These will be of special interest and value to geologists investigating folded and faulted sedimentary rocks and their little-altered metamorphic derivatives (Chaps. III, IV, and V).

3. *Features of Igneous Rocks*. Features associated with vulcanism and the emplacement and crystallization of magmas. These will be found in terranes where igneous rocks predominate (Chap. VI).

4. *Features of Metamorphosed Rocks*. Features developed in rocks of different kinds during metamorphism (dynamic, hydrothermal, etc.). These may or may not be related to primary features that were present in the parent rock. They will be of chief value to geologists working in terranes where metamorphosed and deformed rocks predominate (Chap. VII).

Many of the features to be described have important significance and use aside from their value as indicators of the top or bottom of the layer in which they appear. Reference will be made to this aspect at appropriate places.

Each topical heading below the rank of chapter title has a number (*e.g.* **13. Collection of Field Samples**) for ease of reference. The numbers run consecutively from the beginning to the end of the work without regard for chapter divisions. Illustrations are keyed to these numbers. When a specific topic is referred to, the number is preceded by Art., the abbreviation for article (*e.g.* Art. 12).

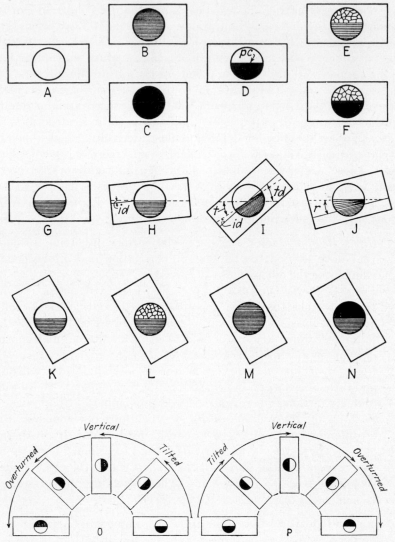

Fig. 1.—Filled cavities and their use as indicators of top and bottom.   In all figures the longer sides of the rectangles indicate bedding.   *A.* Unfilled primary cavity.   This might be geodized, and if the internally incrusting crystals were concentrated in or limited to the lower part of the cavity they would then have top and bottom significance.   *B.* Complete filling of laminated material.   The laminae indicate horizontality and a direction perpendicular thereto—*i.e.*, verticality—but this type of filling generally cannot be used for top and bottom determination.   *C.* Complete filling of massive material.   *D.* Incomplete filling of massive material.   The plane of composition *pc* defines horizontality and marks the upper side of the incomplete filling.   *E.* Composite filling composed of a laminated lower part and a crystallized upper part, the two separated by the plane of composition.   *F.* Composite filling composed of a massive lower part and a crystallized upper part, the two separated by the plane of composition. *G.* A primary or secondary cavity incompletely filled with stratified material.   Since the plane of composition is parallel to the bedding and the bedding is horizontal, it follows that the cavity may be either primary or secondary, and likewise the incomplete filling, and that the bed has not been disturbed since being formed in a horizontal position.   *H.* An incompletely filled cavity in a bed with a few degrees of

References are cited by author, date, and page [*e.g.*, Leith (1923 : 236)]. The complete name of the author, the title of his work, and the date and place of publication are included in the Bibliography, which constitutes Chap. VIII. References there are arranged alphabetically by authors and chronologically under the author's name and are numbered consecutively from 1 to 737. An Index to References precedes the list of authors and indicates by number the chief references on the more important topics of the several chapters.

Footnotes are used extensively. They contain information supplementary to the topic being discussed or appropriate comments concerning certain aspects of that topic and constitute an integral part of the general plan of presentation.

An attempt has been made to give adequate illustrations for nearly all the features and structures mentioned. An unusually large number of sketches and photographs have been used for certain features that show many variations. Unless otherwise stated, all illustrations were prepared by the author. Illustrations borrowed from published works or furnished in the original are fully credited in the legend for the figure (also see Preface).

Many features and structures are discussed in considerable detail, for it is hoped that this work will find its chief use in the field, and there, all too often, the geologist has no reference works available. The laboratory investigator has not been forgotten, however; he will find a large bibliography in Chap. VIII and many lists of selected references throughout the text.

3. Use of Bed, Layer, Stratum, and Lamina.[1]—*Bed* and *layer* will be used interchangeably in referring to any tabular body of rock lying in a

---

[1] For a detailed discussion of bed, layer, stratum, lamina, and other similar terms, see Calkins (1941 : 345–349). An excellent discussion of "Classification and Nomenclature of Rock Units" has been published by a group of specialists (Ashley *et al.*, 1933, *Bull. Geol. Soc. Am.*, **44** : 423–459; *Bull. Am. Assoc. Petroleum Geologists*, **17** : 843–868, 1933, **23** : 1068–1098, 1939), and Tomlinson (1940 : 2038–2046) has discussed the "Technique of Stratigraphic Nomenclature." These two important articles provide useful guides to modern usage of stratigraphic nomenclature.

---

initial dip *id*. The amount of initial dip is the angle between the horizontal plane—*i.e.*, the plane of composition—and the bedding. *I*. A steeply tilted layer that had some initial dip as indicated by the slightly inclined orientation of the plane of composition with reference to bedding. The amount of initial dip *id* is the angle between the bedding and the plane of composition of the filling. The amount of tilting *t* is the angle between the present horizontal plane and the plane of composition, which was the original plane of horizontality at the time the bed was deposited. Total dip *td* is the angle between the horizontal plane and the bedding *id* + *t*. *J*. A partly filled cavity with convergent laminae showing that filling took place as the bed tilted. The total amount of tilting is represented by the angle *r*. (See Fig. 339.) *K*. Cavity in a steeply tilted bed that was partly filled after folding. *L*. Cavity in a steeply tilted bed that was partly filled with laminated material and later completely filled with crystallized material. *M*. Cavity in a steeply tilted bed completely filled with stratified material. *N*. Cavity in a tilted bed composed of a composite filling—stratified material below and massive above. Cavity fillings like those shown in *K* to *N* have no top and bottom significance, as the relation of their plane of composition to bedding is indeterminable. *O*, *P*. Diagrams showing the use of partly filled cavities in determining the top or bottom of folded beds. A bed could be rotated through more than 180°, though such overturning is not common, and for this reason the situation is not included in the diagram. See Figs. 285 and 286, footnote 1 on page 2, and Arts. 1, 158, 174, 180, 182, 199, 217, 219, 265.

position essentially parallel to the surface or surfaces on or against which it was formed, whether these be a surface of weathering and erosion, planes of stratification, or inclined fractures. The body need not have been formed in a horizontal position, although generally its original position will have closely approached horizontality. Used in this broad sense, the terms apply to stratified and massive sedimentary rocks and their metamorphic derivatives, clastic dikes and the fillings of crevices, and tabular masses of igneous rock such as flows, sills, sheets, and dikes. The additional terms *stratum* and *lamina* will be used in discussing certain sedimentary and metamorphic rocks. Stratum will be used for a single bed, or layer, regardless of thickness; lamina, following the suggestion of Twenhofel (1932: 603), for a layer less than 10 to 12 mm. (0.5 in.) thick. A tabular body of igneous rock may be described as a bed or layer, but not as a stratum or lamina.

4. Nature and Variations of Features.—All sorts of features, structures, and relations are described and illustrated so as to provide the field geologist with a maximum number of criteria. Some have been recognized and used for a long time—so long, in fact, that there is uncertainty as to when they were discovered and first used. These have been mentioned repeatedly in published reports and will be considered fully in later chapters, especially with reference to their variations, limitations, and dependability. Others have been used without having been mentioned in print. These will be duly considered. Finally, for one reason or another, certain of the features probably have never hitherto been thought of in connection with top and bottom determination. Their possible use deserves consideration.

An attempt is made to describe and illustrate every feature fully enough so that it can be identified and tested in the field. It cannot be emphasized too strongly that the value of any top and bottom feature must be determined in the field or from carefully oriented specimens taken from actual outcrops and exposures (Art. 13). Until so tested, its limitations and reliability cannot be stated with certainty.

Top and bottom features vary greatly in nature and importance and are widespread in occurrence. Few of them if taken alone can be relied upon completely; hence corroborative evidence should always be sought. For this reason many features that ordinarily should be omitted from a discussion such as this are included to meet the rare occasion when they might corroborate an interpretation or conclusion based on another bit of evidence. No feature that might indicate the top or bottom of the rock in which it is present has been omitted intentionally.

The investigator who attempts to use top and bottom criteria in the field or in the laboratory should be forewarned that certain factors may limit or vitiate the usefulness and dependability of some features. Several comments are pertinent in this connection.

The feature or structure that is going to be used should be well enough developed and clearly enough outlined or exposed so that there is no doubt of its reality or of the fact that the containing rock is *in situ*.

The nature of the rock containing the feature should be determined with certainty to avoid errors arising from misidentification (*e.g.*, sills may be mistaken for flows or dikes, and a composite sill for a differentiated one, or vice versa).

After a significant feature or structure has been found and conclusions drawn from it, it is always advisable to search for other examples of the same nature or for certain associated features that can be used for corroboration.

5. Scale of Development of Features.—Inasmuch as some features show great range in the scale of development,[1] one must be on the alert at all times for microscopic development on the one hand and macroscopic on the other. Attention to only one phase of development, with disregard of the other, is likely to produce an incomplete or even misleading solution. It should be obvious, therefore, that detailed local field work and general reconnaissance must go hand in hand with laboratory investigations of carefully selected specimens taken in the field (Art. 13). In this way microscopic and macroscopic evidence can be intercorrelated.

Most top and bottom features are visible to the unaided eye. Many, however, are also developed on a microscopic scale, and geologic literature contains many references to these. A few such references are worth citing here.

Collins (1925: 66 *ff.*) describes and illustrates Pre-Cambrian examples of graded bedding in laminae less than a millimeter thick, tiny fragments buried along bedding planes, and filled cracks visible only when magnified. Shenon and McConnel (1940: 438) report that in some of the Pre-Cam-

---

[1] Cross-lamination is an example of a feature showing great range in the scale of development. It may be so minute that it is visible only in a thin section under microscopic magnification. At the other extreme, it may be developed on such a grand scale in great delta foresets that its very magnitude causes it to be overlooked entirely in a casual examination or, what is worse, to be mistaken for normal bedding which has been tilted (Fig. 19) [see Krynine (1937: 58) and Art. 11].

A second example worth citing is cyclic, or rhythmic, sedimentation. Individual laminae in a rhythmic sequence may be visible only in thin section. On the other hand, rhythmic bedding is easily visible to the unaided eye in typical varved sediments and rocks; it is even more obvious in the graded bedding of sandstones, siltstones, tuffs, and similar rocks; and in cyclothems and megacyclothems it is developed on such a grand scale as to escape cursory and localized observation.

brian Prichard beds of the Coeur d'Alene district in Idaho " . . . the alternating black and white laminae are so thin that gradation cannot be recognized in hand specimens, but thin sections cut at right angles to the bedding often show enough gradation in grain size to determine which were originally the upper sides of the laminae." Belyea and Scott (1935: 225–239) found many zones of tiny ripple marks, minutely developed cross-lamination, and microscopic graded bedding in the rhythmically bedded Halifax formation and used them as evidence that the 5,000-m. Pre-Cambrian sequence was all deposited in relatively quiet, shallow water in a slowly sinking trough. Krynine (1940: 1–134) illustrates microscopic cross-lamination, intraformational breccias, and compaction structures in the Upper Devonian Bradford sandstone of Pennsylvania and has informed the author in conversation that he has observed most of the common sedimentary features under the microscope.

Among the igneous rocks Walker and Parsons (1922a: 13) report that " . . . many sections [of basalt] show a well-marked amygdaloidal development on a microscopic scale." Moore (1930: 137–139) found microscopic pillow structure in the matrix of normal ellipsoids. It is hardly necessary to mention the importance of thin sections in the many investigations of igneous rocks (see Chap. VI). Many of the features observed in these studies are reliable top and bottom criteria.

Some of the most significant structures of metamorphosed rocks can be seen adequately only in thin section. Dale (1902: 564) long ago illustrated part of a cleavage band in slate that shows 360 slip planes in 25 mm. (1 in.) as well as the relation of these to bedding—a relation not readily visible to the unaided eye. Sander (1930: 222–223) recently described and figured microscopic tension cracks in thin quartz layers and in many mineral grains.

These examples, which could be multiplied if the discussion warranted, suffice to emphasize the fact that many useful top and bottom features are developed on a microscopic scale and that thin sections are necessary to detect them. The selection of oriented specimens from outcrops becomes a matter of critical importance if the specimens are to be used for microscopic work; hence a few suggestions on collecting are listed in Art. 13.

6. Positions of Features and Structures in the Rock.—Both primary and secondary features can be used in determining the top and bottom of layered rocks. These may be confined to a single layer, they may involve a succession of beds, they may lie in a massive tabular body of igneous rock, or they may occur in massive rock bodies lacking any apparent bedding. Furthermore, they may lie on the upper- or undersurface of a layer or anywhere within it. Consequently, it is a wise practice to scrutinize all exposed bedding surfaces and especially natural sections (joints, cracks, etc.) transecting layers, for such sections commonly reveal useful internal structures as well as any unusual contact relations between beds.

Many top and bottom features on the upper surface of a sedimentary bed or tabular igneous body record their presence by causing certain complementary structures to be formed in the basal materials of the overlying layer as they are deposited or emplaced or soon thereafter while they can still yield readily. Grabau (1924: 715) emphasizes the importance of recognizing this relation as follows:

The importance of discriminating between the original structure . . . and its reproduction in reverse, in the overlying stratum, will be appreciated when it is considered that strata often stand vertical, and are even overturned. The determination of the upper and lower surfaces of the strata may be the only means for recognizing the superposition of the strata of a region. In all cases, the surface on which the structure (ripple-mark, impression, etc.) was originally made is the upper surface of the stratum, while the surface having a reverse reproduction of the structure (raised footprint, mold of ripple-mark, etc.) is the lower surface of that stratum.

There are also features on the undersurface of sedimentary layers that come into existence as a result of plastic deformation of the upper part of the underlying bed. These may form during or after deposition of the overlying sediment and usually are the result of differential loading or current scouring. They cannot form, however, unless the material of the underlying layer can yield plastically (Art. 102).

Bedded rocks which have been folded and faulted and which stand at high angles with reference to their original horizontal position are commonly fractured or cleaved in such manner that it is rare to find an exposure which reveals either a bedding surface or a section approximately perpendicular to the bedding. This cleavage is especially characteristic of slaty rocks. The external and internal features that are preserved usually present an unfamiliar or distorted appearance on the inclined cleavage surfaces. Consequently, it is necessary to visualize such features in three dimensions so that their true configuration and construction are understood regardless of the way in which the cleavage plane transects them.

7. Determination of Stratification or Bedding.—It is not usually difficult to determine stratification in sedimentary rocks and their altered equivalents or to detect the layered nature of tabular masses of igneous rocks (*e.g.*, flows and sills) and their metamorphic derivatives. Determining stratification may be difficult, however, if the rock is unusually massive or has been intensely sheared. Since the determination of stratification or bedding is one of the initial steps in structural field work, it is appropriate to consider briefly the origin and nature of stratification and to suggest some relations that may be helpful in determining it.

When the eye cannot detect stratification on freshly fractured surfaces, it is advisable to search for weathered and eroded surfaces. On these the forces of weathering and erosion have differentially etched the strata. The surface will have a ribbed configuration with the more resistant layers protruding and the less resistant cut back into grooves. Resistance of a given rock to weathering and erosion is relative and varies with climatic conditions. A certain lithology may be quite resistant under one set of conditions and little resistant under another.

8. NATURE AND ORIGIN OF STRATIFICATION.—Stratification is the most characteristic structural feature of sedimentary rocks. It is produced by deposition of sediments in beds, layers, strata, laminae, lenses, wedges, and other essentially tabular units. It is due to many different causes—differences of texture, hardness, cohesion or cementation, color, mineralogical or lithological composition, and internal structure. Although it is the most apparent and widespread characteristic of sedimentary rock, no great amount of fundamental work seems to have been done on it.

Shaler (1884: 408–419) long ago ascribed separation planes and certain types of layers to several phenomena produced during earthquakes. Andrée (1915: 351–398) discusses bedding at some length, and McKee (1938: 684), pointing out how little is known about the mode of formation and environmental significance of stratification, summarizes the situation as follows:

To the student of sedimentary rocks, one of the best illustrations of present-day limitations due to lack of recorded observations of the processes is in the field of original structures, especially those classified as beds or laminae. Such structures are frequently the most apparent features with which a geologist has to deal when studying sedimentary rocks, yet their significance, for the most part, must remain obscure or be interpreted on the basis of pure speculation simply because a record of modern counterparts has not been made.
. . . the fact remains that today most bedding and lamination structures prove more puzzling than helpful to the geologist who endeavors to interpret the environment of their deposition.

Thompson (1937: 723–751) recently pointed the way toward a systematic classification and analysis of bedding types and showed that there is an inviting field for additional work on the general problem of stratification.

9. DETECTION OF STRATIFICATION IN UNDEFORMED ROCKS.—In the search for top and bottom criteria in thick bodies of sedimentary rock that have no apparent bedding as a guide (*e.g.*, thick limestones, conglomerates, tillstones, marbles, and quartzites) and in massive bodies of igneous rock, determining the general bedding constitutes one possible attack on the problem. Once bedding has been found, attention can next be directed to the search for features indicating which direction is up or down in the rock mass.

Careful examination of thick limestones often reveals thin stringers and layers of argillaceous material,[1] chert, or intraformational conglomerates; thin zones of fossils or concretions, either of which may weather

FIG. 2.—Conglomerate with two thin pebble layers and several zones of imbricate boulders. The layers and zones define the stratification in what is otherwise a massive conglomerate. The water flowed from right to left. The hammer handle is 30 cm. (12 in.) long. The photograph is a view of a Miocene interflow basaltic gravel taken a few miles west of Longview, Wash. (Arts. 9, 143.)

out and leave tiny holes; inconspicuous algal layers; zones of penecontemporaneous deformation; etc. Features of this sort are not usually apparent on fresh or dry surfaces but are apt to be rather well exhibited on weathered or wet surfaces.

Exposures of massively bedded conglomerates may be so limited in size that stratification is not apparent. If this is so, the investigator has a double problem. He must first determine the strike and dip (see Art. 12) of the bedding before proceeding to the determination of top and bottom. For strike and dip determination, many inconspicuous features may be utilized. Thin stringers and layers of pebbles (Fig. 2), sand-

[1] Prouty (1916: 115) reports that in certain Alabama marbles bedding is marked by thin layers of schist ranging in thickness from 2.5 to 5 cm. (1 to 2 in.). These probably represent mudstone layers in the original limestone.

stone, or siltstone commonly lie in the midst of coarse conglomerate and mark the general stratification (Fig. 3). Imbrication of pebbles and boulders shows the general plane of bedding (Fig. 2), and Pettijohn (1930: 568–573) was able to use this primary sedimentary feature in working out the structure of certain Pre-Cambrian conglomerates (Art. 143; Figs. 223, 224). Lenses of stratified or cross-laminated sand and pebbles may mark contemporaneous scouring and backfilling. Since these bodies are apt to be flat on top and convex downward, they can be used for top and bottom determination as well as for establishing the general plane of bedding. Internal features of the lens itself may prove similarly useful (*e.g.*, cross-lamination and gradational bedding) (Fig. 3).

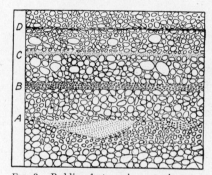

Fig. 3.—Bedding features in a massive conglomerate. *A.* General bedding is marked by two scour-and-fill structures. *B.* A pebble layer like that shown in Fig. 2. *C.* A thin sand layer. Note that some of the sand filtered downward between the boulders. *D.* A mud streak or shale film. (Art. 9.)

Massive sandstones and quartzites are commonly devoid of obvious bedding. Thin layers of snale and zones of argillaceous pellets may interrupt the monotonous homogeneity of a massive sandstone; rows of pebbles or concretions may mark the stratification; and the horizontal disposition of mica flakes, when the rock is viewed in thin section, usually indicates general stratification.[1]

Caution must be exercised in interpreting the orientation of mica flakes, however, for Woodworth (1901: 281–283) found that a type of false bedding is produced by their accumulation on the advancing fronts of sand ripples (see Arts. 68 and 82 and Fig. 60).

Argillaceous laminae commonly break the continuity of massive marbles (footnote, page 11) and salinastones (*e.g.*, anhydrock), thus indicating the general plane of stratification.

Ash and tuff deposits may be so massive as to lack obvious stratification but may contain mud pellets that are flattened in the plane of bedding. Allen and Nichols (1945: 25–33) recently reported such pellets in a water-laid Eocene tuff at Hobart Butte, Oregon (Fig. 388*A*). These

[1] In this connection Becker (1893: 54) commented as follows:
If a flat pebble or a mica flake is allowed to subside in relatively quiet water, the fluid may be considered as exerting a pressure on the lower side against a resistance due to the action of gravity on the stone. The disc will then tend to assume a horizontal position. It is for this reason that allothigenetic mica scales in sandstones and other rocks usually follow the direction of the bedding. In massive sandstones this is an assistance in determining the true stratification.

pellets are believed to represent eroded fragments of thin mud-crack polygons. The tabular polygons were ripped loose from a mud-cracked surface, transported some distance, and finally strewn out more or less parallel to bedding as they came to rest. The pellets appear to have been somewhat plastic at the time of deposition as they give evidence of having been flattened to some extent by the weight of overlying sediments. Further support for this conclusion is afforded by the molding of some pellets over particles on the bottom. This molding of pellets over underlying objects might be used in some cases to establish the top of the bed in which they lie. A somewhat comparable relationship is shown by accretionary lapilli in certain pyroclastic formations (see Art. 187 and Fig. 290B).

10. DETECTION OF STRATIFICATION IN METAMORPHOSED AND DEFORMED ROCKS.—Most bedding features are destroyed during intense metamorphism, especially if there is extensive recrystallization. Likewise, they are likely to be destroyed or made less obvious if the rock has been intensely deformed. Cleavage may be mistaken for bedding, particularly in argillaceous rocks. The search for bedding, therefore, must be concentrated on those features of stratification which can persist through metamorphism and deformation.

Thin layers of crumpled and distorted shale show general bedding in some marbles and salinastones, and algal layers commonly indicate original bedding in deformed salinastones. Shale partings are a common bedding feature preserved in deformed coal seams, and shale pebbles may indicate the general plane of stratification in folded sandstones (Art. 277; Fig. 388). Argillaceous layers alternating with thick sandstone beds usually develop conspicuous slaty cleavage during folding (Fig. 4). Original bedding in argillaceous rocks may be so obscured by cleavage that only faint traces of stratification remain. Dale (1896: 559–560) describes and illustrates some of these traces as follows:

Wherever bedding is obscured by cleavage one of the first things to be done is to distinguish, if possible, the bedding by tracing out the continuity of some minute line of sedimentary grains [Dale (1893: 322–323); Figs. 28, 29, 31]. When the sediment is homogeneous, this becomes impossible. In the Cambrian-Silurian shales and slates of Washington County, N.Y., lines of holes occur now and then on transverse joint faces [Figs. 5A, B, C]. Upon a closer inspection these are found to be due to a very slight calcareousness of the shale along certain bedding planes. Weathering attacks these planes more readily, but at irregular intervals, and the effect is as though small limestone pebbles had been dissolved out. Again, sometimes, in weathering, a slight parting in the stratification is sufficient to arrest vertical erosion for a time and expose the actual surface of a stratum, even where the cleavage foliation is the dominant one [Fig. 5D].

In [Fig. 6*A*] is shown a plicated bed of limestone in a mass of shale. In determining the dip of such a mass neither the dip of the cleavage nor that of the

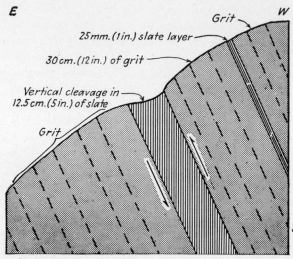

FIG. 4.—Vertical slaty cleavage in a red shale layer in coarse-grained Rensselaer sandstone as seen in a ledge at Grafton, N.Y. The cleavage is developed in only the thicker shale layer and does not extend into the grit. Arrows indicate direction of relative movement. (Art. 10.) [*Adapted from Dale*, 1896, *U.S. Geol. Survey Ann. Rept.*, **16** (1): 560, Fig. 86.]

separate limbs of the step-like folds of the limestone should be taken, but the general course of the limestone bed.

Van Hise (1896: 718) has described and illustrated how pebble beds in slates, even though intensely fractured, still indicate the plane of bedding (Fig. 7), for more intense deformation is required to destroy pebbles than to granulate the smaller particles. In such beds the pebbles tend to be rotated, so that their longer dimensions line up with the cleavage, but the pebble zones themselves maintain their original relative positions.

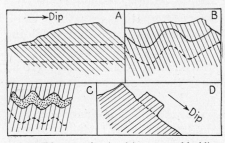

FIG. 5.—Diagrams showing faint traces of bedding in highly cleaved early Paleozoic shales of Washington County, New York. *A, B, C.* Bedding which is flat, though somewhat crumpled in *B* and *C*, is indicated by lines of small holes produced by differential etching of calcareous zones in the shale. It should be noted in *C* that the cleavage does not cut across the prominent thin calcareous layer. *D.* Bedding is shown by an uneven surface, which is continuous with a delicate parting in the stratification. (Art. 10.) [*After Dale*, 1896, *U.S. Geol. Survey Ann. Rept.*, **16** (1): 559, Fig. 84.]

11. FALSE STRATIFICATION.— Thick and extensive deltaic conglomerates and sandstones may exhibit cross-lamination on such a grand scale that it will be mistaken for true bedding. By such a mistake the conditions of deposition are not recognized, the true structure of the deposit is missed, and the thickness assigned to the sequence is likely to be grossly exaggerated. An excellent example of this error is illustrated by the Permian Nugush red-bed sequence

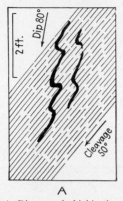
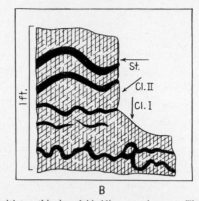

A   B

Fig. 6.—*A*. Diagram of a highly cleaved shale with two thin drag-folded limestone layers. The bedding dips to the left but faces the right; hence the beds are slightly overturned. The steeply inclined bedding is indicated by the general course of the plicated limestone layers. *B*. An exposure of chloritic sericite schist in Salem, Washington County, New York, showing quartz laminae in the plane of bedding and two sets of foliation across the bedding. The two upper quartz laminae may have been sandstone originally. (Art. 10.) [*Both sketches after Dale, 1896, U.S. Geol. Survey Ann. Rept.,* **16** (1): 560, *Fig. 85, and 565, Fig. 93.*]

of central Russia, which, according to an abstract by Krynine (1937: 58) of a recent paper by Pustovalov (1937: 963–964), consists of the foresets

of a great Permian delta. Previous to Pustovalov's investigations the sequence of inclined beds had been assigned a thickness of 7,500 m. (24,600 ft.) on the assumption that it represented a monoclinal succession. The measurements were made along a continuous line of outcrops showing what appeared to be a single monocline. Pustovalov proved by geophysical methods that the apparent "geologic" thickness of the deltaic blanket, if measured vertically, was actually only 1,200 m. (3,940 ft.) as compared with the previous estimate of 7,500 m.!

It is of critical importance, therefore, that some areal geology be done on any deposit suspected of being a delta in order to avoid the errors just mentioned [see Barrell (1912: 377–446)].

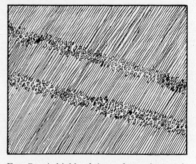

Fig. 7.—A highly deformed conglomeratic rock in which all traces of bedding have been destroyed except for two zones of crushed pebbles which still indicate the direction of bedding. The crushed pebbles tend to be rotated so that their longer dimensions lie parallel to the secondary cross foliation. The zones of pebbles, however, maintain their original relative positions. (Art. 10.) [*After Van Hise, 1896, U.S. Geol. Survey Ann. Rept.,* **16** (1): 718, *Fig. 140.*]

Some early American geologists, strongly prejudiced by views of the "authorities" of the times, mistook steep and vertical dips produced by folding for gigantic cross-bedding, being led to the mistake because there was no previous record of deformation in the area.   A case in point is the complex of steeply dipping and vertical Ordovician strata near Kentland, Ind., which Collett (1883: 58) believed was due to " . . . either serious dislocations or deposition under circumstances which gave origin to the most pronounced false bedding." [Also see Orton (1889) and Shrock (1937: 473–480).]

The quaquaversal initial dips on the peripheries of ancient bioherms [Cumings and Shrock (1928: 599; 1928a: 140–156)] and around buried hills [Powers (1922: 233–259) and Bridge and Dake (1929: 93–99)] commonly reach or exceed 30°.   Strata with such dips might well be mistaken for gigantic foresets if seen only in limited exposures.

An instructive example of pseudostratification is described by Louderback (1912: 21–31) from Santa Barbara County, California. Here, in a moderately dissected terrane sculptured out of massive friable Tertiary sandstone, a subsurface layer of cemented rock has formed parallel to the surface slope, especially on the sides of stream cuts and at the "shoulders" of canyons.   This layer, which is firmly cemented with opaline silica, ranges in thickness from less than to slightly more than a meter (2 to 5 ft.) and lies on an average of about a meter (1 to 5 ft.) below the surface, being overlain and underlain by friable sand similar to that of which it is composed.   Its formation is considered analogous to that of the familiar hardpan in soils.

Since the pseudostrata roughly parallel the hill slopes, in a cross section of a hilly area they would have the appearance of being folded if structural determinations were confined to the upper few meters, and they might be interpreted as original bedding.   This mistake could easily be made, for the sandstone generally lacks the usual features indicating stratification.   Louderback (1912: 25) states:

A test area of about two square miles, where the only exposures appeared to be those of pseudostratification, was worked over, and it was found that on the careful examination of the deeper slides and washes, and particularly of a series of excavations, a consistent group of observations could be obtained determining the original stratification and the attitude of the original beds.   It showed a very open syncline while the more evident exposures of pseudostrata gave consistent indications of an anticline (a pseudoanticline), the axis of the syncline being quite a distance south of the axis of the pseudoanticline.

Pseudostrata or surficial incrustations of the type just described are to be expected in drier areas where surficial debris can become firmly cemented with caliche and similar substances.

Care must be exercised in examining cores of soft sedimentary rocks (*e.g.*, mudstones and claystones) because of the tendency for false bedding to develop transverse to the core during drilling. Bramlette (1928: 1167–1169) cites an instructive example of this misleading phenomenon. As the core broke into cylindrical sections, drilling mud mixed with pulverized formation was forced into the rather regularly spaced horizontal partings. As the core came from the core barrel, it seemed to have well-developed stratification in a horizontal plane. Actually the true stratifi-

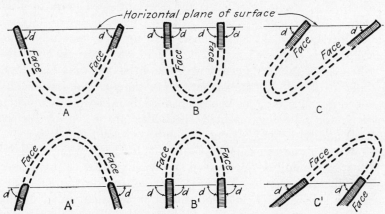

Fig. 8.—Diagrams illustrating use of *dip* (angle of inclination of a layer measured from the horizontal plane; *d* = angle of dip) and *face* (the original top surface of a layer). *A, A*[1]. Syncline with beds facing inward and anticline with beds facing outward; in both folds the beds face in the same direction as they dip. *B, B*[1]. Isoclinal syncline and anticline, respectively, with beds vertical. Dip may be measured on either side of the bed. *C, C*[1]. Overturned syncline and anticline, respectively. In each fold the steeper bed is overturned and faces in a direction opposite the dip, whereas the more gently inclined bed is merely tilted and faces with the dip. In all the folds diagramed, top and bottom features are needed to determine which surface of a layer is the face. (Art. 12.)

cation might well have been inclined and yet have been overlooked because of the more obvious false bedding.

From the examples just cited, it is obvious that determination of true bedding in sedimentary rocks is more than merely noting the attitude of the stratification. It must be demonstrated that the strata were deposited on a horizontal or gently inclined surface in the same way in which layers are added to a cake and that they were not deposited as fairly steeply inclined layers resting against some rigid mass—an arrangement such as that in a row of inclined books on a partly filled shelf—or as surface incrustations. In the first example true verticality is essentially perpendicular to stratification; in the latter examples it is not.

12. Definition of Dip and Face.—Two terms will be used in describing the inclination and surface of beds, layers, and other tabular masses. *Dip* refers to the angle of inclination of a layer with reference to the horizontal plane and has no other connotation (Fig. 8). *Face*, or *facing*, refers to the original upper surface of a layer [see Cooke *et al.* (1931: 50–51)]. If a bed dips 20° to the east and is right side up, it faces east; if vertical with top toward the east, it also faces east; if dipping west at an angle of 45°, but overturned, it still faces east. This usage has been adopted to avoid the confusion commonly arising over whether dip means merely inclination with reference to the horizontal, in which case it does not exceed 90°, or the angle, measured from the horizontal, through which the top surface of a bed has been rotated. In the latter usage, the angle of dip may range between 0 and 180°, or even more in unusual structures.

13. Collection of Field Specimens.—The need for carefully oriented field specimens is discussed in Art. 4. Such specimens are most useful when taken from thick masses of uniform lithology that lack obvious megascopic features. Keen observation and careful examination should be practiced in collecting rock specimens for laboratory study. Detailed instructions for selecting oriented specimens are given by Fairbairn (1942: 106) and with his kind permission are partly quoted in the footnote below.[1] Full notes on the exposure should always be written on the spot. Bedding should be determined and the direction of any suspected or obvious lineation should be recorded; strike, and direction and degree of inclination, are valuable data and should be indicated on the specimen with ink, paint, or colored pencil. If time and skill permit, it is a good

---

[1] The first step in petrofabric analysis, as in any geological investigation, is the selection of material to be used. The amount and kind of material collected in the field depends on the experience of the collector and the problem to be studied. In general it is better to collect too much than too little. Specimens may be taken with the object of studying in detail some special feature of mineral orientation, or for the purpose of obtaining a general picture of the regional orientation. In the latter case it is necessary to mark the specimen so that its field orientation can be reproduced in the laboratory. This is done as follows:—— Select a place on the outcrop and break off a piece of suitable size. Before attempting to trim it, fit it back into place. Then determine the strike of a foliation, bedding, or joint surface present in the specimen, and, holding the compass in the strike direction, mark this direction on the specimen, using the straight edge of the compass as a guide. (The Brunton model is especially useful for this work.) A colored pencil is convenient if the specimen surface is sufficiently dry and smooth; otherwise a dental pick or sharpened nail is preferable. Mark the dip at right angles to this line, using suitable symbols to denote an overturned or vertical dip surface. The geographic directions are thus established permanently for the specimen and may later be reproduced and correlated with fabric directions. In the laboratory it is advisable to mark the strike, dip, and specimen number with waterproof ink or wito paint.

In the usual case where lineation occurs, a record of its strike and pitch should be made. This may be done in three ways—1. By approximate compass measurement of the strike, and estimation of the dip. 2. By compass measurements and use of a Schmidt net. 3. By use of a universal clinometer and an accompanying graph.

practice to sketch the entire exposure in three dimensions, indicating exactly how the specimen fitted into the exposure.

Any gross lineaments of structure not apparent in small samples should be indicated on the specimen, for it often happens that an unmarked specimen, taken to illustrate some gross feature, later proves valueless because the collector has forgotten why he selected it.

It is always poor practice to trust the memory in reconstructing an observed feature. Recollection has a perverse way of bringing back an uncertain picture; notes and sketches made on the spot are much more reliable.

14. Sources of Information.—Certain top and bottom features have been used so long by geologists that only the most painstaking and exhaustive bibliographic research would establish who first recognized their significance or employed them for structural determination. Many others have been discovered in recent years. Most of these have been described and illustrated. Still others have been discovered and used widely without any published announcement. No attempt has here been made to search out the earliest reference to the use of any feature, though examples are cited that have come to the author's attention. It has seemed preferable to follow the general policy of citing and quoting from the more recently published works in which the features are described and illustrated.

Many of the features and structures considered in this work have undoubtedly been described in languages other than English (*e.g.*, Norwegian, Swedish, French, German, and Russian), but the author does not have the linguistic facility, nor has he had the time that would have been necessary, to make the laborious bibliographic search for such descriptions. He believes, however, that the literature cited represents sufficiently complete coverage of the general subject of top and bottom criteria so that the work does not suffer unduly from the lack of the additional citations.

Only a few articles in English deal at any length with the specific thesis of the present work. Cox and Dake (1916: 1–59) seem to have been the first American geologists to call particular attention to the top and bottom significance of certain primary sedimentary and igneous rock features and secondary metamorphic structures. They cite a few examples of earlier use of some of the criteria. Their important contribution has been almost universally overlooked so that reference to it in modern textbooks and articles is rare. Burling (1917: 208) and Belyea (1935: 154–155) published provocative abstracts, but neither appears to have written anything further on the subject. Stearn (1934: 146–156) describes a few minor primary sedimentary features that he used in working out the structure of vertical and steeply inclined clastic strata at the Parnell Hill quicksilver mine in southwestern Arkansas. The features he describes are of special interest because they occur in strata that lack such common features as cross-lamination, ripple-mark, and gradational bedding. In the most recent article seen, Shenon and McConnel (1940: 430–444) discuss how they used ripple-mark, cross-lamination, mud cracks, textural gradation, and cleavage to determine whether or not steeply dipping beds were overturned in the Belt series of the Coeur d'Alene district of Idaho.

The excellent reports on the Pre-Cambrian rocks of the Canadian Shield by Collins (1925), Cooke, James, and Mawdsley (1931), Gunning and Ambrose (1940), Gruner (1941), and others who are mentioned later contain many descriptions and illustrations of features and structures that proved useful. A thorough examination of Canadian geologic literature, especially that concerning the Pre-Cambrian, would yield many additional references not included in this work.

Much interest in top and bottom features was aroused in Scotland about 16 years ago when the discovery and interpretation of cross-lamination and graded bedding in a great sedimentary sequence, long considered to be lying right side up, showed that in actuality the section was overturned. An account of this interesting episode, in which American and Canadian geologists were instrumental in applying the criteria, is fully recorded by Bailey (1930: 77–92), who not only inspired papers by Tanton (1930: 73–76) and Vogt (1930: 68–73) but also enthusiastically went about teaching his colleagues [see Bailey (1930: 77–92; 1934: 462–525; 1936: 1713–1726)], thereby developing the so-called "Glasgow School," whose members are known for their application of top and bottom criteria.

Most authors of textbooks on structural geology and sedimentation emphasize the importance of certain features and structures as top and bottom criteria but seldom discuss them in detail. Older textbooks usually dismiss the subject after referring to a few of the more common sedimentary features. More recent books, however, contain fuller discussions [see especially Grabau (1924), Twenhofel et al. (1932), and Billings (1942)]. The interested reader is referred to the following list of textbooks and articles that contain information of differing degrees of detail about significant top and bottom features (the table following the list furnishes a ready means of finding a specific subject in the more important works):

BECKER, HANS, 1939, "Gebirgsbildung und Vulkanismus," Verlagsbuchhandlung Gebrüder Borntraeger, Berlin.
BILLINGS, M. P., 1942, "Structural Geology," Prentice-Hall, Inc., New York.

BRANSON, E. B., and W. A. TARR, 1941, "Introduction to Geology," 2d ed., McGraw-Hill Book Company, Inc., New York.

EMMONS, W. H., G. A. THIEL, C. R. STAUFFER, and I. S. ALLISON, 1939, "Geology," 2d ed., McGraw-Hill Book Company, Inc., New York.

FORRESTER, J. D., 1946, "Principles of Field and Mining Geology," John Wiley & Sons, Inc., New York.

GEIKIE, J., R. CAMPBELL, and R. M. CRAIG, 1940, "Structural and Field Geology, for Students of Pure and Applied Science," Oliver and Boyd, Edinburgh and London.

GRABAU, A. W., 1924, "Principles of Stratigraphy," 2d ed., A. G. Seiler, New York.

GROUT, F. F., 1932, "Petrography and Petrology," McGraw-Hill Book Company, Inc., New York,

HILLS, E. S., 1940, "Outlines of Structural Geology," Methuen & Co., Ltd., London.

KEILHACK, K., 1921, "Lehrbuch der praktischen Geologie," Vol. I, F. Enke, Stuttgart.

LAHEE, F. H., 1941, "Field Geology," 4th ed. rev., McGraw-Hill Book Company, Inc., New York.

LEITH, C. K., 1923, "Structural Geology," rev. ed., Henry Holt and Company, Inc., New York.

LONGWELL, C. R., A. KNOPF, and R. F. FLINT, 1939, "A Textbook of Geology," Pt. I, Physical Geology, 2d ed. rev., John Wiley & Sons, Inc., New York.

MILNER, H. B., 1940, "Sedimentary Petrography," 3d ed., Thomas Murby and Co., London.

NEVIN, C. M., 1942, "Principles of Structural Geology," 3d ed., John Wiley & Sons, Inc., New York.

SORBY, H. C., 1908, On the application of quantitative methods to the study of the structure and history of rocks, *Geol. Soc. London Quart. Jour.*, **64**: 171–233.

STOČES, B., and C. H. WHITE, 1935, "Structural Geology," D. Van Nostrand Company, Inc., London.

TWENHOFEL, W. H., and collaborators, 1932, "Treatise on Sedimentation," 2d ed. rev., The Williams & Wilkins Company, Baltimore.

TWENHOFEL, W. H., 1939, "Principles of Sedimentation," McGraw-Hill Book Company, Inc., New York.

VAN HISE, C. R., 1896, Principles of North American Pre-Cambrian geology, *U.S. Geol. Survey Ann. Rept.*, **16**(1): 571–843.

WILLIS, B., and R. WILLIS, 1934, "Geologic Structures," 3d ed. rev., McGraw-Hill Book Company, Inc., New York.

In addition to the foregoing list, there have appeared in recent years an appreciable number of papers devoted to detailed description and illustration of a broad range of sedimentary features in ancient rocks. The following references, selected at random, are typical of this rejuvenated interest in sedimentary rocks.

BUCHER, W. H., 1938, Key to papers published by an Institute for the study of modern sediments in shallow seas [largely German articles], *Jour. Geology*, **46**: 726–755.

COLLINS, W. H., 1925, North Shore of Lake Huron, *Geol. Survey Canada Mem.*, **143**: 1–160.

FENTON, C. L., and M. A. FENTON, 1937, Belt Series of the North: stratigraphy, sedimentation, paleontology, *Bull. Geol. Soc. Am.*, **48**: 1873–1970.

	Billings 1942	Cox-Dake 1916	E.T.S.A. 1939	Forrester 1946	Geikie 1940	Grabau 1924	Grout 1932
Stratification and superposition......	....	....	254, 260	72	105–120	697–701	260, 261, 278, 323, 324
Cyclic sedimentation............	72	....	201, 260	67, 68	115, 116	....	261, 342–344
Unconformity and conglomerates....	72–74, 240–245	30, 31	277–278, 364–367	31, 32, 72	112, 113, 183–185, 287, 288	530, 723–744, 784–785, 821–826, 1132	325
Ripple-mark............	69–71	7–26	257–258	67	117, 118	219, 429, 712–713	278–280, 324
Inorganically produced relief features.	75	31, 32	148, 258–259	70, 71	118–120	708–709, 712–714, 856–857	325
Organically produced relief features..	75	32	....	70	119	604, 861, 1124	325
Shrinkage cracks—mudcracks, etc...	74	37–50	256–257	66	92, 113, 114	530, 709–710, 776–779, 883–886	318–324
Cross-lamination............	71–72	26–30	63, 64, 154, 254–255	68	....	429, 570–578, 590, 701–706	278, 279, 324
Penecontemporaneous deformation..	72–74, 97, 98	30	350–351	33–35	....	529–531, 657–661, 756–759, 776–785	341
Buried fossils and organic structures..	67	33–35	283–284	70	....	375, 385–449, 514–519	....
Igneous intrusion............	316–318	....	303–309	....	....	309–311	....
Differentiation............	269, 270	....	320	....	....	....	135–136, 231–257
Pyroclastic deposits............	....	....	314–315	....	....	285	....
Lava flows............	75, 76, 313–315	52	294, 311–315	69	125, 213–216	311–320, 868	32, 93–95, 482
Sills and dikes............	269–270	....	303–309. 311	....	....	....	32
Folds and drag folds............	71–81	....	343–349, 351–352	57–64	....	....	....
Fracture and flow cleavage.........	223–233	52–59	390–395	37, 38, 65	84, 225–227, 295, 296	769, 793–795, 819–820	428, 429
Metamorphism............	....	....	384–400	....	....	746–755	....

Hills 1940	Lahee 1941	Leith 1923	L.K.F. 1939	Nevin 1942	Shenon-McConnel 1940	Stoces-White 1935	Tanton 1930	Twenhofel 1932	Willis-Willis 1934
1	55–59, 108, 187, 403	....	222–224, 234–236	8	....	....	....	432–439	35–40
2	89–92	185, 187	235, 236	74	430, 438	....	74	95, 435, 436, 439–444, 595	
11, 12	59, 67–73, 76–78, 95, 104–110, 187, 400, 403, 679	187, 278–284	247, 248, 320, 345–349, 468	74	....	13, 35, 320–330	74	69, 111, 159, 160, 163, 164, 184, 188, 445–451, 526, 589	43–45
7–10	49–51, 86	185, 187	183, 239, 240	74	430, 435–437	6	75	65, 444, 451–483	327, 328
9, 10, 13	22–33, 51–54, 74–79, 106, 111	49–51, 86, 95, 96, 98, 102, 103, 187	238	....	430, 438, 439	6–7	74	453, 483–492	327
....	33, 54	187	....	....	....	6	....	488–492	327
10–13	52–53, 79	50, 51, 187	238, 239	74	430, 433–435	6–7	74	106, 263, 492–496	
4–10	16, 80–88, 96, 98, 102, 103, 106, 183, 184, 187, 275, 276, 280, 406, 407	185, 187, 188	183, 240–242	74	430, 437, 438	9–12	74	442–445, 591, 592, 618–623	
14, 78–81	60, 63–64, 80, 189–194, 236–238	160, 201–217, 224–233	230	74–75, 186–204	....	111, 138, 140, 149, 150	74	73, 74, 521–529	
11	54, 96–97	160, 187	....	74	....	6, 7, 29–31	....	223–251, 437–438, 450, 531, 557, 608, 610	
....	114, 121–162, 678								
....	137, 147								
....	13, 22, 121, 261, 262								
129	9, 13, 117–118, 131, 133, 134, 152, 285, 286	....	258, 277–279, 296–297, 511	74	....	83, 85	75		
....	9, 11, 123, 127, 135, 149, 152–153, 155, 412								
82–91	59, 145, 148, 164–199, 212, 273, 274	179–181	....	68–74	....	148, 264, 265	76	....	97–100
97 98, 100–103	163–164, 200, 253, 258–259, 266–268, 271–275	113, 126–135, 148–158, 181–185	321, 377, 380–382, 515, 517	70, 74, 145–157	430, 440–444	....	75, 76	....	99, 100, 117, 263–272
....	138–149, 263–271, 278–282								

HADDING, A., 1929, The pre-Quaternary sedimentary rocks of Sweden, *Lunds Univ. Årsskrift*, N.F. Avd. 2, **25**(3): 1–287.

KRYNINE, P. D., 1940, Petrology and genesis of the Third Bradford Sand, *Bull. Penn. State Coll. Min. Indus. Exper. Sta.*, **29**: 1–134.

McKEE, E. D., 1945, Cambrian history of the Grand Canyon region, *Carnegie Inst. Washington Pub.*, **563**(1): 1–168.

PETTIJOHN, F. J., 1943, Archean sedimentation, *Bull. Geol. Soc. Am.*, **54**: 925–972.

STOCKDALE, P. B., 1931, The Borden (Knobstone) rocks of southern Indiana, *Indiana Dept. Cons., Div. Geology, Pub.*, **98**: 1–330.

————, 1939, Lower Mississippian rocks of the East-Central interior, *Geol. Soc. Am. Special Paper*, **22**: 1–248.

WANLESS, H. R., 1939, Pennsylvanian correlations in the Eastern interior and Appalachian coal fields, *Geol. Soc. Am. Special Paper*, **17**: 1–130.

————, 1946, Pennsylvanian geology of a part of the Southern Appalachian coal field, *Geol. Soc. Am. Mem.*, **13**: 1–162.

15. General Summary.—In years to come, as areas of relatively little known geology become more carefully surveyed, geologists will be forced to spend more and more time on smaller and smaller areas—a situation that has long existed in Great Britain.[1] In such intensive work the investigator has to take more careful note of minor features in rocks of every kind. It is hoped that the present work may be of help in the quest for both major and minor features.

Rocks are like the old-fashioned newspaper and magazine "face puzzles" in that the longer one studies them, with some idea of what to look for, the more becomes apparent. It has often been the experience of the author, after having seen and interpreted a certain feature in a rock for the first time, to see the same feature repeatedly in rocks where it had been overlooked in previous examinations.

It is never enough merely to recognize and describe interesting and significant features in rocks. The real value of these features has been realized only when they have been interpreted, for it is by interpretation that past conditions can be reconstructed and modes of formation determined. Reconstruction, in turn, requires an understanding of how and under what conditions a given feature was formed and leads to proper evaluation of that feature with reference to its reliability as a top and bottom criterion. He is a well-trained geologist indeed who knows which features of a rock can be used with confidence in determining tops and bottoms and which cannot be relied upon for this purpose.

[1] The author keenly regrets that he has not been able to make a thorough search of British and continental geologic literature for descriptions and illustrations of top and bottom features. That many such descriptions exist is obvious from the few references cited in the present work.

CHAPTER II

GROSS RELATIONSHIPS

The broader stratigraphic, structural, and intrusive relationships of rocks and the successions of faunas and floras that the rocks contain, have long been recognized and used by geologists the world over as a means of determining the order of stratigraphic succession and of geologic events. They are reviewed here to reemphasize the important role they have played in the gradual elucidation of the grander events of earth history. Recognition of the significance of these relationships has made it possible to determine the major divisions of geologic time and to construct a geologic column for the entire world. They are the indispensable and only means by which order of geologic events can be determined in an unexplored terrane. It is not until these events and major time divisions have been determined that the geological investigator can work out the many minor stratigraphic and structural features and correlate events and stratigraphic succession with those of neighboring regions.

The gross relationships discussed in this chapter are

1. *Superposition or Undisturbed Stratigraphic (Lithologic) Succession.* In a flat-lying, undisturbed sequence of stratified or layered rocks, the order of succession is from younger at the top to older at the bottom.

2. *Faunal Succession.* Upon acceptance of the principle of organic evolution, it follows that in a continuous sequence of fossiliferous strata the more highly developed plants or animals in a biological group lie stratigraphically above the simpler, less specialized forms of the same group.

3. *Unconformity.* Unconformity is that relationship between juxtaposed bodies of rock which indicates that one body, the older, was eroded before the other body, the younger, was deposited on the eroded surface. It therefore represents a lost record. In sedimentary rocks the record may have been lost because of nondeposition, or it may have been destroyed by erosion. In igneous sequences unconformities commonly indicate intervals of weathering and erosion between successive lava flows and ash falls.

4. *Intrusion.* Any rock mass that has been intruded by molten material is older than the intruding fluid. Likewise, any rock or sedimentary surface buried beneath lava or pyroclastics is older than the

volcanic material, hence lies beneath it so far as original position is concerned.

5. *Comparative Deformation.*[1]   In a sequence of rock units having different degrees of deformation, the part exhibiting the most intense deformation is the oldest, whereas the least disturbed rocks are the youngest.

If the intensity of deformation varies in degree laterally rather than across a rock unit or sequence, it probably has no significance with reference to order of succession.

6. *Comparative Metamorphism.*[2]   In a sequence of rocks exhibiting different degrees of metamorphism, in a direction transverse to the general plane of bedding, or layering, the part of the sequence showing the more

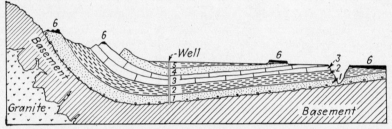

Fig. 9.—Diagrammatic cross section of a basin of deposition bounded on one side by a shore and on the other by a mountain range.   By determining original order of succession (superposition) in the essentially undisturbed part of the basin—natural outcrops, artificial exposures, mine-shaft sections, well cores and cuttings, etc., being used for this purpose—the geologic column of the basin can be constructed and then applied where strata are steeply inclined.   This illustrates how the principle of superposition can be applied.   (Art. 16.)

intense alteration, similar lithology being considered, is judged to be the older, hence to lie lower in order of succession.

If the degree of metamorphism varies laterally in the general plane of bedding, it is likely that the variation has no significance with reference to order of succession.

It should be emphasized that there are important exceptions to the generalizations stated above.   Certain of these exceptions, important for our present purpose, are discussed in later sections.

16. Superposition or Undisturbed Stratigraphic (Lithologic) Succession.—The first students of geology observed that sedimentary rocks are characterized by distinct beds, or layers, and they soon discovered that the top strata in a sequence of undisturbed flat-lying sedimentary rocks

[1] Deformation as here used refers to the mechanically produced structures associated with folding and faulting; compositional change is negligible.

[2] Metamorphism as we shall use the term embraces the secondary structures and compositional changes produced by the combined action of pressure, temperature, and solutions.

were the youngest, or most recent, whereas the basal strata of the same sequence were the oldest.

This principle, though old and elementary, is still widely employed in many kinds of stratigraphic work, as demonstrated by the extensive use of columnar sections. In a new area (such as a mining district or an oil field), the complete geologic column must first be constructed by piecing together all available sections of the region. Thereafter it is possible to locate any isolated section in the general succession by identifying the sequence of lithologic units. A good example is that illustrated in Fig. 9. The complete column is determined from cores or cuttings that have been taken from wells penetrating the subsurface succession or from scattered exposures along valleys trenching the terrane. With the complete column as a reference, it is possible to determine the order of succession in neighboring mountainous regions where the same strata have been folded and faulted.

It is true that an occasional bed or sequence of beds may be present in one area and absent in another, but the general lithologic succession is likely to be consistent. It is likewise true that some beds change lithologically from the central part of a basin toward the periphery or from the deeper water part of an aqueous environment to the shallow water and shore areas. This variation in lithology is to be expected and should occasion no difficulty if the investigator recognizes the general principle of lithologic facies in sedimentary rocks (Figs. 10 and 11).

The principle of superposition is invalid in those regions where sedimentary sequences have been inverted by recumbent folding and overthrust faulting. The inverted position of the strata will have to be determined by features in the beds themselves if regional relations do not suggest the structural complications. Inverted sequences are exposed in the Alps and Scottish Highlands, and the author has seen a similar sequence in the Mississippian siltstones along the Southwest Mabou River in Cape Breton Island, Nova Scotia. In the last cited example the siltstones show little metamorphism and only a suggestion of cleavage—strongly indicating deformation while they were still plastic (Fig. 12).

It should be evident, therefore, that a sequence of strata is not necessarily right side up because it is flat-lying or but slightly inclined. The investigator should always be certain that he is dealing with undisturbed rocks before basing conclusions on superposition per se. Once superposition has been established, however, similarity in lithologic succession becomes an important basis for correlation. As already stated, this means of correlating disturbed unfossiliferous strata has found worldwide usage.

An important aspect of the principle of superposition is the rhythmic

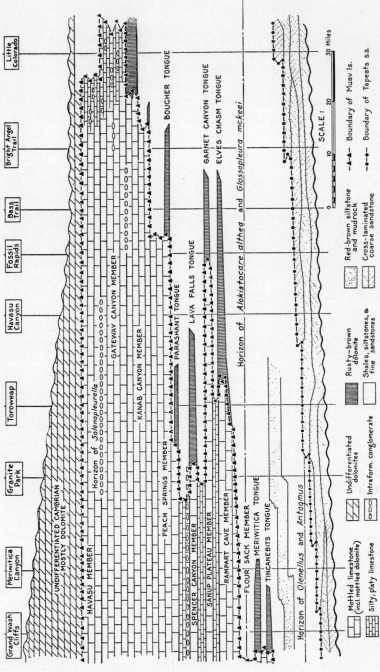

FIG. 10.—Diagram illustrating lithologic facies. Section of Cambrian rocks in Grand Canyon, showing stages in transgression and regression and distribution of facies from west (left) to east. Time planes are horizontal; actual thickness ranges from 460 m. (1,500 ft.) in the west to 245 m. (800 ft.) in the east. (Art. 16.) (*After McKee*, 1945, *Carnegie Inst. Washington Pub.*, **563**: 13, *Fig.* 1.)

nature of some sequences of rocks, in which a certain order of lithology or texture is repeated many times in a single section or in a basin of deposition. The cycle may concern single bipartite laminae of almost microscopic magnitude (*e.g.*, varves and graded beds) on the one hand or sections containing many different units (*e.g.*, cyclothems and mega-

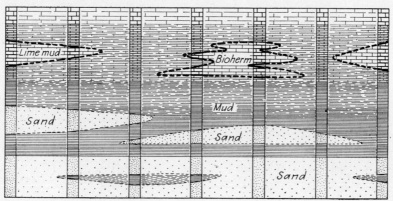

Fig. 11.—Diagram illustrating how columnar sections can be used to work out lithologic facies changes in a sedimentary sequence. (Art. 16.)

cyclothems) on the other. If the cyclic nature of a sequence of rocks can be established, the order of units in an individual cycle then becomes a criterion of top or bottom in that sequence.

Broderick (1935: 553–554) points out that the Pre-Cambrian Keweenawan lava flows of Michigan seem to show a succession of flow cycles

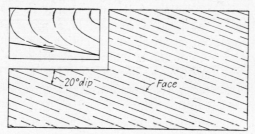

Fig. 12.—Overturned mudstone and siltstone of the Mississippian Windsor series along the Southwest Mabou River, Cape Breton Island, Nova Scotia. These beds were folded and faulted while soft and hence no cleavage developed, but the rock is closely jointed. The nature of the regional structure is shown in the inset. The gently inclined inverted layers lie in the under part of an overturned fold, which probably rests on a thrust-fault plane. Sedimentary features in thin intercalated limestone layers of the shale sequence reveal the true order of succession and prove that the beds are overturned. (Art. 16.)

in which a specific type of lava precedes or follows another type. It is not known, however, whether such cyclic extrusion is common or rare, but certainly the possibility of its occurrence should be kept in mind. An unusual cyclic sequence of lava flows alternating with glacial till is reported by Atwood (1933: 214) from the rim rocks of Crater Lake, Oregon. Gruner (1941: 1608) describes a pyroclastic section of the Pre-Cambrian Kekekabi formation of Minnesota that consists of a rhythmic alternation of tuffs and slates in layers averaging less than 40 cm. (16 in.) thick.

Barrell (1917: 745–904), in one of his classic papers, considered geologic rhythms at length and called attention to some of the grander sequences of sedimentary rocks showing cyclic sedimentation. For our present purpose it is necessary to consider only those aspects of rhythmic deposition which are of significance in top and bottom determination.

17. Successions Showing Cyclic Deposition.—Cyclic deposition of sediments produces a characteristic lithologic or textural sequence that is repeated many times in the stratigraphic column of a depositional basin or in a single section. This kind of sedimentation has been recognized in many parts of the world and in stratigraphic successions of widely different ages.

Apparently the grandest development is the sequence of conglomerate, sandstone, shale, and limestone that has so often been set forth in geologic literature as the typical geosynclinal succession [Grout (1932: 342–344)]. Rhythmic sandstone-shale sequences are known from widely separated regions, and the order of appearance of each unit in a cycle may be used to determine the top or bottom of the sequence (Art. 18). The remarkable cycles of Pennsylvanian sedimentation which produced characteristic sequences of sandstone, shale, underclay, coal, etc., and for which Weller [in Wanless and Weller (1932: 1003)] proposed the term *cyclothem*, represent a complicated sedimentational sequence in a coal basin (Art. 19). Inasmuch as a cyclothem consists of a more or less constant sequence of lithologic units, an observer, noting the order in which the several units appear in a section of steeply inclined rocks, can determine whether he is ascending or descending in the section. This criterion becomes useful in regions where coal-bearing strata are intensely folded (see statement relevant to this point in Wanless's letter quoted in Art. 19).

The examples thus far cited are of sequences involving formations or groups of formations. There is a second type of sequence resulting from cyclic deposition that is exhibited in pairs of beds or in a single bipartite stratum. The dominant feature of such beds is a textural gradation from coarse at the base to fine at the top. Barrell (1917: 799) called attention to this kind of rhythm as follows:

Passing to the smaller rhythms which characterize beds rather than members of formations, two beds which grade from coarse below to fine above are presumably continuous, but each such pair may be separated from adjacent pairs by a stage of scour or non-deposition, since each coarse bed must lie in turn on one of finer texture. It would be unsafe, however, to use it as an absolute criterion of minor discontinuity, as it is quite possible for sand to be washed over mud-beds without necessarily producing a down-scour.

The term *graded bedding* has long been applied to one kind of textural rhythm like that just described, and the feature provides a reliable top and bottom criterion when used with discrimination (Arts. 51, 52).

The familiar varved sediments so commonly associated with recent and ancient glacial deposits represent still another type of cyclic deposition. A single varve consists of a bipartite layer of which the lower part is coarser and the upper part finer. Each part grades into the other, but adjacent varves are distinctly separated. It is commonly possible to determine top and bottom in an ancient varved slate by noting in which direction the coarse material grades into the fine (Art. 53).

In a recent conversation with Dr. Henry Stetson the attention of the author was called to the following possibility of cyclic precipitation of calcium carbonate: On a bottom composed of fetid mud full of decomposing vegetable and animal matter considerable ammonia should be produced. This ammonia reacting with calcium bicarbonate in solution would cause some of the soluble carbonate to be precipitated:

$$CaH_2(CO_3)_2 + 2NH_3 = (NH_4)_2CO_3 + CaCO_3$$

If this reaction occurred repeatedly, a fetid black mud should be succeeded through transition by finely divided calcareous mud. There should, on the other hand, be an abrupt break between calcareous mud and the succeeding fetid mud since the former would rather quickly seal off the bottom materials and prevent further escape of ammonia. In a geologic column the phenomenon should be represented by successive bipartite layers composed of black shale in the lower portion grading upward to limestone at the top. This type of cyclic sedimentation does not seem to have been described. It should be sought in thin-bedded carbonaceous limestones.

18. *Rhythmic Sandstone-Shale Sequences.*—One of the conspicuous features of the Lower Mississippian Horton series of Cape Breton Island, Nova Scotia, is the repetition of a characteristic sandstone-shale sequence. Once the order of appearance of the units in the sequence has been established, it is thereafter possible, even in limited outcrops, to determine in which direction the top or bottom of the succession lies. This sedimentational phenomenon proved most helpful to the author in working out some of the complicated structure in the folded and faulted Horton beds, especially along the Southwest Mabou River.

Dr. W. L. Whitehead and the author measured the following section, in which the cyclic sedimentation is particularly well exhibited (the units are given in descending order, and thicknesses are only approximate because the strata show variable dips):

SECTION ALONG SOUTHWEST MABOU RIVER, CAPE BRETON ISLAND, NOVA SCOTIA
(Descending order)

Thickness		Lithology
M.	Ft.	
20	60	*Windsor series*—"ribbon" limestone—characteristized by laminae averaging 1 mm. or less in thickness
80	250	*Horton ser es*—red shale
75	230	Cross-laminated sandstone
95	300	Sandstone and red shale with 7 distinct sandstone beds
32	100	Massive sandstone
32	100	Shale
15	45	Massive sandstone—a falls maker
10	30	Shale
10	30	Sandstone—laminated, massive, rippled
65	200	Red shale
31	90	Sandstone
59	180	Shale with a few thin sandstone beds
57	175	Sandstone—a falls maker
38	115	Red shale
49	150	Sandstone
32	100	Red shale
10	30	Sandstone
		Sandstone, shale, and arkose to igneous basement

The above section shows a characteristic threefold cycle of sedimentation repeated seven times. The cycle consists of the following three units, in descending order (Fig. 13):

3. Red sandy shale and shaly sandstone in fairly thin beds with little or no cross-lamination and with some ripple marking.
2. Highly rippled and cross-laminated silty and fine-grained sandstone. The individual laminae are lenticular and average about 25 mm. thick. The variable dips of the foresets indicate currents and waves with frequently changing directions.
1. Massive, fine- to coarse-grained sandstone in one thick unit containing great foresets indicative of powerful waves or strong wind currents. Many of the cross-laminated parts are wedge-shaped or lenticular, indicating aeolian deposition. Upward the unit grades into No. 2. Downward it is separated sharply from the shale of the preceding cycle.

The cycle represented in the foregoing sequence seemingly includes the following events: First, the sand was shifted about by wind in dunes and by waves and currents on bars. Next, the shallow waters of a transgressing sea, greatly agitated by current and wave, constantly disturbed the bottom materials and shifted the incoming sediments from place to place. Finally, as the water deepened, only finer sediments were brought in, the bottom materials were less disturbed, and the last muds settled to the bottom through quiet water. Uplift terminated the cycle and initiated a new one, which began as sands were drifted across the uncovered mud surface.

An example closely similar to the one just cited was recently described from Australia by Hills and Thomas (1945: 52). In the Ordovician rocks of the gold fields of central Victoria, they found a definite gradational sedimentary unit consisting of the following materials in reverse order of deposition (*i.e.*, in descending order):

4. Argillaceous slates
3. Argillaceous slate with interbedded sandstone laminae or layers
2. Laminated sandstones
1. Quartzose sandstones and argillaceous sandstones

A third example of an ancient rhythmic sandstone-shale sequence proved useful to Stearn (1934: 146–156) in working out the structure of steeply folded Pennsylvanian Stanley clastics in the quicksilver district of Arkansas. The usual top and bottom features—cross-lamination, ripple marking, and graded bedding—are lacking, but the rocks of the district show a quadripartite lithologic succession that is repeated 15 times (4 in one sequence; 7 in another; etc.). The depositional cycle, representing a unique rhythm of sedimentation, begins with massive sandstone, grades through shaly sandstone into sandy

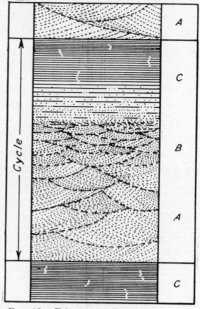

Fig. 13.—Tripartite sedimentary cycle repeated seven times in the Mississippian Horton formation along the Southwest Mabou River on Cape Breton Island, Nova Scotia. The cycle began with wind and water deposition of coarse quartz sand in great cross-laminated units of lenticular and wedge shape (*A*). The highly cross-laminated nature of this part of the cycle indicates vigorous and changeable currents. As deposition of sand continued, the units became smaller and smaller, giving a "choppy" appearance to the deposit (*B*). The overlapping lenses of *B* are composed of medium-grained sand. Upward they become smaller in size and finer in texture, grading finally into the sandy basal part of *C*. The cycle closed with deposition of a considerable thickness of silt in well-laminated layers (*C*). The red silt of *C* grades downward into *B*, becoming more and more sandy as it passes into the cross-laminated lenses. Upward it ends abruptly against the base of the overlying coarse, sandstone, which marks the initial deposit of the next cycle. The cycles range in thickness from less than 20 m. (60 + ft.) to more than 100 m. (300 + ft.). Part *C* is thicker than *A* and *B* together in some cycles; in others it is thinner. (Arts. 17, 18.)

shale, and ends with laminated clay shale. Stearn (1934: 248) noted:

The sharpest planes of demarkation [in beds dipping 72° or more to the south] are those between the south faces of shale layers and the north faces of the sand-stone layers. A gradation, four times repeated, occurs southward. . . .

He concluded that the beds are right side up because the sequence grades from coarse sand at the north face of the southward dipping sequence to laminated shale at the south. Fenton and Fenton (1937b: 1934–1935) report sand-mud rhythms in the Belt series of western North America. Some of the rhythms are on a scale commensurate with seasonal fluctuations, but others are much larger.

Multipartite rhythms of deposition have been mentioned in geologic literature but usually only in routine descriptions of flat-lying formations. Inasmuch as they are known to exist and to have been used for structural purposes in at least three widely separated regions where the strata are vertical or overturned, they constitute a top and bottom criterion worth consideration and further investigation.

19. *Cycles, Rhythms, Cyclothems, and Megacyclothems.*—Cyclic sedimentation is especially well displayed in the Pennsylvanian deposits of North America and Europe [Trueman (1946: lv–lxii)] and no doubt will prove on future investigation to be of common occurrence in other parts of the world. Inasmuch as an ideal cycle is composed of a sequence of lithologic units that have the same relative stratigraphic position, it is possible to determine whether one is ascending or descending in the section by noting the order of succession of the several units. The individual units may vary considerably in lithology, in thickness, and in certain other characteristics and may even be missing from the succession altogether, but if they are present their stratigraphic position and relations are consistent.

These repeated sedimentary sequences, variously designated cycles, rhythms, cyclothems, and megacyclothems, have been reported by many writers and have received considerable attention in recent years [Udden (1912); Savage (1930: 125–135); Weller (1930, 1931, 1931a, 1934); Ashley (1931); Moore (1931); Plummer (1931); Reger (1931); Stout (1931); Wanless (1931, 1938, 1939, 1946); Wanless and Weller (1932); Wanless and Shepard (1936: 1177–1206); Weller, Wanless, Cline, and Stooky (1942: 1585–1593)].

Udden (1912: 47) long ago recognized the remarkable cyclic nature of the Pennsylvanian strata of Illinois and in a single quadrangle differentiated 21 lithologic divisions which he grouped into quadripartite cycles (Fig. 14). He found that "Each cycle may be said to present four successive stages, namely: (1) accumulation of vegetation; (2) deposition of calcareous material; (3) sand importation; and (4) aggradation to sea level and soil making."

Wanless (1939: 8) gives the following complete sequence of beds as described by Weller (1930) for western Illinois (in descending order):

10. Gray shale with limestone concretions
9. Limestone with marine fossils
8. Black, hard, sheety shale, with large limestone concretions
7. Limestone with marine fossils
6. Gray shale
5. Coal
4. Underclay
3. Fresh-water limestone
2. Shale or sandy shale
1. Sandstone, with unconformity at base

This sequence is an ideal one and usually is not complete. Beds 1, 4, 5, 9, and 10 are the most common. To such a sequence, Weller [Wanless and Weller (1932: 1003)] applied the term *cyclothem,* pointing out that in the Eastern Interior coal basin it constitutes a formation which can be correlated readily from place to place. He visualized the cycle as beginning after uplift with deposition of sand and shale on an unconformity; the second stage was the deposition and formation of underclay; the third, formation of coal; the fourth and last stage began with submergence, continued with deposition of marine limestones and clastics, and ended with uplift.

The interpretation by Weller (1930: 100) of the original cyclic sequence of Udden (1912: 47) is shown in Fig. 14.

Moore (1936: 21), accepting the concept of the cyclothem but differing in his opinion as to how it should be bounded, pointed out that

The sedimentation cycle in the Mid-Continent region differs from that of Illinois and other eastern states in the greater prominence of the marine deposits, especially limestone, and in the absence in most cases of definitely recognizable disconformities [which mark the beginning and end of Weller's cyclothem]. There is perhaps some question as to the lines of division between certain cycles of the Kansas Pennsylvanian, but there is no doubt as to the definite relationship of each element in the succession of beds comprising the cycle.

Moore (1936: 24) considered an "ideal cyclothem" to have the following units, in descending order:

9. Shale (and coal)
8. Shale, typically with molluscan fauna
7. Limestone, algal, molluscan, or with mixed molluscan and molluscoid fauna

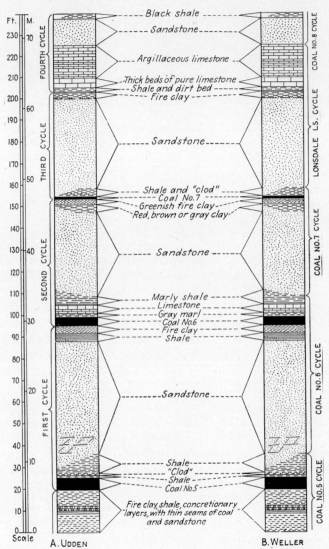

Fig. 14.—Cyclic sedimentation and cyclothems. A. The generalized section of Udden (1912: 47–50) for the Pennsylvanian rocks of the Peoria, Ill., quadrangle divided into the four cycles he recognized. B. Udden's column divided into the four cyclothems recognized by Weller (1930: 100).   Udden used a coal or if this was missing the overlying shale as the initial deposit of his cycle and an underclay as the closing deposit.   Weller, on the other hand, used unconformities to bound his cyclothem. (Arts. 17, 19.) (A and B adapted from Udden, 1912, Bull. U.S. Geol. Survey, **506**: 27, Fig. 2, and Weller, 1930, Jour. Geology, **38**: 100, Fig. 1.)

6. Shale, molluscoids dominant
5. Limestone, contains fusulinids, associated commonly with molluscoids
4. Shale, molluscoids dominant
3. Limestone, molluscan, or with mixed molluscan and molluscoid fauna
2. Shale, typically with molluscan fauna
1*c*. Coal
1*b*. Underclay
1*a*. Shale, may contain land plant fossils
0. Sandstone

He points out that in the Kansas Pennsylvanian there are several distinct cycles of cyclothems, and to these rhythms of larger order he applies the term *megacyclothem*.

Wanless (1939: 8–9) points out how "too close resemblance between corresponding strata leads to the erroneous correlation of different cyclothems" and goes on to say:

In areas with thicker section and geosynclinal facies of deposition, like southern Illinois, eastern Kentucky, Virginia, and West Virginia, the strata are in cyclic succession, but the sequences are notably different from those in western Illinois. Marine limestones are not common, and black shales and fresh-water limestones are generally absent. The sandstones are massive cliff-forming beds. The sandy shales (member 2) may be quite thick and may include several thin layers of sandstone and in some instances coal beds. The underclays are generally sandy and thinner than in the western Illinois cyclothems. The coals commonly split into several benches a few inches or several feet apart with shales and thin-bedded sandstones between. The gray shales over the coals (member 6) contain fossil plants at many horizons, while plants are rather uncommon in the areas of thinner section. There are large, flattened, oval masses of impure limestone with cone-in-cone on their upper surfaces at several horizons from a few feet to about 30 feet above the coals. They are wholly unfossiliferous in some places but contain marine fossils in others. These beds probably correspond to the marine limestone members. The upper gray shales (member 10) are not separated from the gray shales immediately over the coal (member 6) where black shales and limestones are absent.

Inasmuch as Dr. Wanless has investigated cyclothemic sediments for so many years and over such wide areas, the author asked him for comments on the extent to which cyclic sediments might be used for determining order of succession in steeply tilted strata. In reply (Feb. 20, 1940), he commented so significantly that, with his kind permission, most of his letter is repeated here verbatim:

It seems to me that there are many conditions present in Pennsylvanian sediments with which I have worked which would permit the recognition of the top and bottom of a sequence even though they should be overturned. I have actually seen Pennsylvanian strata dipping very steeply to vertically at a number of places and have had no trouble in determining the order of their sequence. At one locality which is especially noteworthy a whole series of beds seems to have been completely inverted. This feature was observed in the large, open pit of an anthracite coal mine at Summit Hill, Pennsylvania. The feature is illustrated in Lobeck's new book *GEOMORPHOLOGY* in the photograph on page 581 at the beginning of Chapter 17. The locality is there called, "near Coaldale." In the lower left of the picture are three sharp folds, apparently anticlines, from which the coal has been removed. We observed in the field that these structures consisted of a hard black shale with large pyritic concentrations, a sequence commonly found in the roof of a coal bed, and that above the coal stripped from there is a structureless clay with root traces. The impression is, therefore, that these structures are completely inverted synclines, the coal having been turned bottom side up.

I have also measured vertical Pennsylvanian sections at Pottsville Gap in Sharp Mountain in the anthracite field, and at several gaps in the Cumberland Mountains in Virginia, Cumberland Gap, Kentucky, and Big Creek Gap, Tennessee. At all of these places there were several very massive sandstones sharply demarcated from the beds below by a minor unconformity with a tendency for quartz pebbles to be concentrated in the lowermost parts of these sandstones.[1] In the Southern Appalachian coal field I have noted that many massive sandstone and coal sequences have a more or less constant relation to one another. I believe that a normal sequence might be illustrated by the following description taken more or less at random from a section on United States Route 119 where the route crosses the drainage divide between Tug Fork and Levisa Fork of Sandy River in Pike County, Kentucky.

Coal, rather slaty, 2″
Clay, medium gray, olive above, 1′8″
Shale, bony, 2″
Coal, 8″
Siltstone, light olive gray, shaly to fairly massive, 3′9″
Sandstone, massive light brownish gray, well jointed, medium gray, ledge forming, with some shaly lenses and finer grains in upper part, 35′
Unconformity
Coal, 7″
Clay, light gray, 6″
Shale, brownish, 2″
Underclay, light gray, 1′1″
Coal, 1½″
Clay, light gray, 10½″
Coal, 9″
Underclay, light gray, 10″
Siltstone, hard, well indurated, with root traces in upper part, 2′6″
Shale, silty, light olive gray, 3′

---

[1] The author has noted a similar lithologic assemblage in the basal Pennsylvanian (Mansfield) sandstone of Indiana.

Sandstone, very massive, poorly bedded, light brownish gray, medium grained,
  cliff forming, micaceous, upper part thin bedded, finer and more shaly, 37′
Shale, blue gray weathering olive, silty, with thin regular bands of ironstone
  concretions, 5′

You will notice that each sandstone rests unconformably on the beds below
and that it grades upward into a much finer grained or more shaly sandstone so
that if the overlying rock is a siltstone it is often difficult to tell where the two
should be separated. The coals almost always have an underclay, or a shale,
siltstone or sandstone floor, which contain stigmaria and other root traces. Such
material may form the roof of a coal bed, especially if the coal is split into several
benches, in which case the underclay of one bench may serve as the roof of the
next lower one. Limestones are almost never present below coals and in the very
few cases where I have found them in that position they also contained root
impressions along with the marine fossils. In the Appalachian coal field, the
roof of at least the uppermost bench of a coal is very commonly either a well
laminated shale, which often contains stem or leaf impressions, or an unconformable sandstone like that above the 7 inch coal in the section copied above.

If one is dealing with cyclic sediments including a larger component of marine
material than is found in the Southern Appalachian coal field, it is even easier to
determine the order of sequence of the beds than where the sediments are largely
non-marine, as in Illinois and adjacent states the strata of a cyclothem tend to
arrange themselves in the order which has been cited by Marvin Weller in his
papers. The hard black fissile shale, and marine limestones and gray shales with
flat ironstone bands, almost always occur above the coal bed, while the underclay,
nodular fresh water limestone, and sandy shale or sandstone almost invariably
occur beneath the coal. A part of these beds may be missing, but those which are
present will still preserve this order even when a coal bed is missing. [The]
position [of the coal] may be commonly identified at the contact of a limestone or
well bedded shale above with a structureless underclay below. We have observed
this condition in hundreds of localities in Illinois. The condition in the Mid-
Continent region is somewhat different in that coals are less frequent and marine
limestone more prevalent. There Raymond Moore has discovered a complex
sequence repeated many times involving three or more marine limestones and
intervening shales which permit one to determine very easily the upper and lower
sides of various beds. The stratum equivalent to our eastern underclays is
generally a non-laminated shale between what he calls the lower limestones and
the middle. This occasionally contains root traces, though such are often lacking.

In the Rocky Mountain region, coal beds are almost entirely lacking in the
Pennsylvanian and so are underclays and fresh water limestones. In many
parts of the Rocky Mountains, a basal sandstone is present and may be very thick
and conglomeratic. At many localities the pebbles include feldspar and crystalline rock fragments as well as quartz. The lowest parts of such sandstones or
conglomerates are generally more massive and coarser grained than the upper
parts, as was also true in the Appalachian area. The sandstone or conglomerate
grades upward into very fine sandstone or siltstone, often with calcareous cement

and marine fossils, and within such beds there may be thin bands of conglomerates similar to those lower down.   The marine limestones normally follow the siltstones and are commonly quite free from grit.   The limestone may be followed by shaly beds or it may be truncated by the basal sandstone or conglomerate of another cycle.   Where red beds are present, these commonly occur in alternation with either conglomerates or sandstones, or with limestones.   At the Red Rocks Park, Morrison, Colorado, there are fifty or more alternations of massive conglomeratic sandstones with red silty or sandy shales.   Elsewhere, both in the Rocky Mountain region and in the Conemaugh formation of the Eastern States, I have found red beds apparently occupying the position of the lower part of an underclay or the shales and sandstones below an underclay.

I think you will gather from the foregoing notes that it is possible to tell which is the upper and which the lower part of a cyclic Pennsylvanian section almost anywhere from the anthracite fields to the Rocky Mountains.

20. Faunal Succession.—By their classic investigations in England, William Smith and his followers discovered that diagnostic assemblages of fossils always occupied the same relative position in the geologic column which had been constructed on the basis of superposition.   This discovery of faunal succession, the significance of which became immediately apparent on the announcement of the Darwin-Wallace thesis that life evolved by orderly change from simple ancestral forms, gave to the scientific world for the first time a means of dating fossiliferous rocks.

Through the decades since the discoveries of Smith, Murchison, Sedgwick, Darwin, and Wallace, stratigraphers and paleontologists have been adding new formations to the geologic column and new faunas and floras to the geologic life record, so that now any reasonably large assemblage of fossils can be assigned its proper position in the geologic time scale without undue difficulty.

In a recent symposium on correlation by means of fossils, significant papers were read by Clark (1937: 389), Elias (1937: 374), Keen (1937: 390–391; 1937a: 396; 1939: 659–663), Mueller (1937: 373), and Thomas (1937: 373).   The recently published "Index Fossils of North America" [Shimer and Shrock (1944)] will be useful to paleontologists in dating North American fossils, and somewhat similar compendiums are available in certain foreign countries [see Neaverson (1928)].   There are, in addition, many published articles discussing the value of certain groups of fossils for correlation purposes.   An excellent recent example is the article by Ellison (1946: 93–110) on "Conodonts as Paleozoic Guide Fossils" [also see Schuchert (1924: 539–553)].

In addition to their broader use as time markers, fossils have a more restricted use as a criterion for determining order of succession in a sequence of fossiliferous strata that are steeply inclined or overturned.

In this use of fossils the bottom of the sequence is toward the older, less advanced faunas and floras, whereas the top is toward the younger, more highly developed organisms (Figs. 15, 16).

Stutzer and Noé (1940: 227) cite an instructive example of the value of fossils in determining original order of deposition in a coal-bearing series.

The identification of plant fossils in the Alais basin in central France helped not only in the recognition of the stratigraphic horizon but also in unraveling a complicated tectonic problem (Dannenberg, 1915). At first it was not realized that a tectonic problem existed. The various coal beds lay in apparently undisturbed position with a regular dip toward the east. During their study of plant

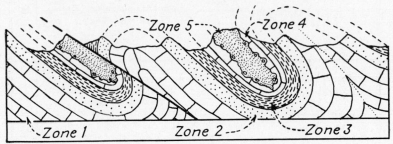

Fig. 15.—Diagrammatic geologic cross section showing how a succession of increasingly more advanced faunas can be used to determine stratigraphic sequence and regional structure. Zone 1 contains the oldest fauna; zone 5, the youngest and most specialized or advanced. This illustrates the use of the principle of faunal succession in structural work. (Art. 20.)

fossils the French paleobotanists, R. Zeiller and Grand 'Eury, came to the unexpected conclusion that the upper coal beds of the basin belong to an earlier horizon than the lower beds. Therefore the normal order of deposition, as has been assumed, did not exist. Bertrand believed that a horizontal thrust explained the relationship, on the assumption that a portion of the coal-bearing rocks had been pushed horizontally across an adjoining portion of the basin. Subsequent folding and erosion had so effaced the evidence that the tectonic structure of the Alais basin was recognized only after a study of the fossil plants which accompany the coal.

In addition to being used as components of an assemblage, for correlation and for determining order of succession, fossils are also useful as top and bottom criteria apart from their age significance. Individual fossils or fossil fragments commonly indicate the top of the containing bed by the way they are oriented in the rock (Arts. 159 to 179). Certain primary and secondary internal structures have proved useful in the same way (Arts. 180 to 183). It should be obvious, therefore, that the relation of a fossil to the materials surrounding it may be fully as significant as the age of the organism which made the hard part.

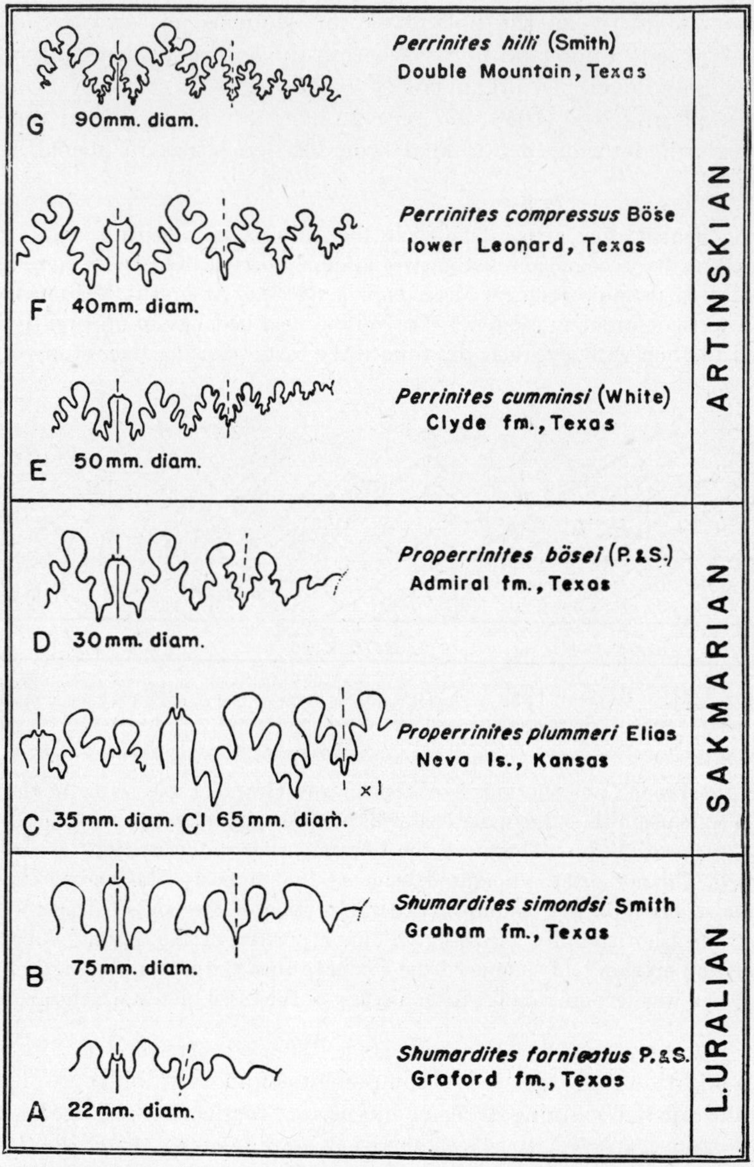

Fig. 16.—Diagram showing how the sutures of cephalopods can be used to determine faunal succession and superposition. The *Shumardites–Perrinites* evolutionary series extends from late Pennsylvanian (Graford, Graham, and Neva) into the Permian (Admiral–Double Mountain). (Art. 20.) (*After Plummer in Sellards, 1932, Texas Univ. Bull. 3232, Plate 6, as modified by Elias, 1938, Jour. Paleontology,* **12:** 103, *Fig. 2.*)

21. Unconformity.—Few geological phenomena are of more interest and importance to the field geologist than an unconformity, which represents a break in the geologic record. The record which is lost has to be determined from the age, lithology, and relations of the rocks above and below the unconformity. Inasmuch as the sequence of geologic events can usually be determined from unconformities, it follows that a study of them has a direct bearing on determination of sequence in layered rocks. The surface of unconformity between two bodies of rock represents an ancient subaerial or subaqueous surface on which many features were formed. These features, if preserved, not only reveal information about conditions on that surface but also show by their intimate relation to the surface that they are a part of it rather than of the covering materials.

22. DEFINITIONS.—An *unconformity* is a surface of weathering and erosion or nondeposition interrupting the continuity of a sequence of bedded or layered rocks. Such a break may indicate a long period of time or a short one, a profound gap in the fossil record or an insignificant one, extensive weathering and erosion or little of either, a conspicuous structural break or none at all, etc. [see Crosby (1899: 141–164), Blackwelder (1909: 289–299), and Twenhofel (1932: 108–110, 625–632)].

The concept of unconformity is exceedingly important in geology, for every unconformity, large or small and regional or local, was once a surface, and most of the surfaces were once exposed to the action of subaerial weathering and erosion. During this exposure, irregularities were produced on the surface. At the time when these were formed the surficial material may have been soft and unconsolidated or completely lithified. Some features now associated with unconformities may have developed in the rock long after the old surface was buried (*e.g.*, filled caves—Art. 131).

Joints and crevices opened up by thermal contraction, dehydrational shrinkage, or slight deformation may be backfilled with surficial detritus. Joints enlarged by solution and by erosion may be filled in the same manner. Channels, narrow defiles, potholes, and other similar erosive features may be preserved on old erosion surfaces. Soft clays, unconsolidated coaly matter, friable sands, and other easily eroded sedimentary material may be scoured out here and there and the excavation later backfilled with coarse, cross-laminated sand. All these features and many others, produced by subaerial weathering and by erosion, show, by their relation to contiguous beds, which stratum bears the true ancient surface and which was deposited on that surface (see Arts. 130 to 132, 190, 202, and 222 to 227).

The relation of unconformity is so variable and is manifested in so many different ways that only a long and detailed discussion with innumerable illustrations would cover the subject adequately.   Here we shall confine the discussion to those relations of unconformity which involve large rock units on a regional scale.   Unconformities of small magnitude are considered under sedimentary rocks in Arts. 130 to 132 and under igneous rocks in Arts. 190, 202, and 222 to 227.

An *angular unconformity* is the relation in which the strata overlying the surface of unconformity transect the beds lying below that surface (Figs. 17, 18).   The angle between the beds on the two sides of the unconformable contact may be 90° or any angle less than that to one so

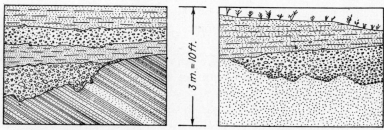

Fig. 17.

Fig. 18.

Fig. 17.—Angular unconformity in unconsolidated Tertiary clastics as observed in a road cut near Juan Santiago, Dominican Republic.   Horizontally bedded siltstones, sandstones, and gravels lie upon truncated, steeply inclined strata of a slightly earlier clastic series.   In adjacent areas this relationship is even more strikingly shown where the second or later series of clastics has undergone deformation since deposition.   (Arts. 21, 22, 38.)

Fig. 18.—Unconformity in unconsolidated Tertiary clastics as observed along the eastern bank of the Rio Yaqui del Sur in the Dominican Republic.   The underlying massive sandstone, in which bedding is not apparent, was channeled by erosion and the troughs then backfilled with gravel.   Gravel was followed by sand and silt, which were deposited in horizontal layers.   Since bedding cannot be determined in the lower sandstone, it is not possible to state whether the relation is that of angular unconformity or disconformity.   It is clear, however, that the gravel rests unconformably on the massive sandstone because of the shape and relations of the gravel lens.   This relationship can be used for top and bottom determination in near-by areas where beds with similar relations have been folded and faulted.   (Arts 21, 22, 38.)

small that accurate field mapping is necessary to determine whether or not there is any discordance whatever.   If an unconformity is interpreted as angular, deformation of the beds below the surface of unconformity is implied.   It should be obvious, however, that, if the angle of discordance between the juxtaposed beds is small, it may not be possible to determine whether that angular difference is to be ascribed to deformation or to low initial dip in the underlying beds.   If the discordance is ascribable to initial dip, the relation between beds is that of *disconformity* (Art. 28).

One example should be excepted from the above definition of angular unconformity.   If a pediment or erosional surface closely following a plane of stratification over an extensive area were buried by large sand dunes with great foreset units tens of feet thick, similar to those in the Coconino sandstone of the western United States or in the Mesozoic sandstone of the northern Shensi Province, China [see Twenhofel (1932,

Fig. 75)], a condition the exact reverse of angular unconformity would be produced (Fig. 19).

A *disconformity*[1] is the relation in which the strata both above and below the surface of unconformity are essentially parallel. There may be a slight discordance of angle between the beds because of initial dip in the underlying sequence, but no deformation other than vertical uplift and later subsidence is implied. It is also possible for disconformable relations to be brought into existence without any deformation. If a bottom of deposition is built or elevated to the profile of equilibrium and conditions are then stabilized, a long period of nondeposition may ensue, as pointed out by Twenhofel (1932: 106–108). Such depositional breaks of assumed minor duration have been named *diastems* by Barrell (1917: 794), who states

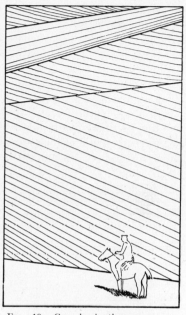

FIG. 19.—Cross-lamination on an unusually grand scale in great, wedge-shaped units many meters thick in Mesozoic red sandstone of northern Shensi Province, China. If only small parts of such a sequence were observable, the steeply inclined foresets might easily be mistaken for true stratification, which in this sketch is essentially horizontal. Each separation surface between adjacent cross-laminated units is an unconformity because it marks a break in the sedimentary record, but it is not an angular unconformity, as might well be concluded from the steep dip of the foresets if only a small exposure of the sequence were observed, because there was no deformation involved. (Arts. 21, 22, 30, 137, 139.) (*Adapted from a photograph by E. L. Estabrook published in "Treatise on Sedimentation" by W. H. Twenhofel et al., 1932. The Williams & Wilkins Company, Baltimore, p. 622, Fig. 75.*)

The term disconformity has come to refer to a well defined hiatus of larger value and essentially due to diastrophism in elevating the land or depressing the ocean level, although for lack of a separate term these minor breaks would also at present be included as minor disconformities. The distinctness of the two classes of lost intervals and the emphasis placed here on the class of smaller pauses, due largely to oscillations in the intensity of climatic factors, seem to justify the erection of a new term and the restriction of the class of disconformities to those breaks which have a large enough value to be recognized by change in fossils or marked contrast in sedimentation. A suitable name appears to be *diastem*, the word meaning a space or interval. It was formerly used in music as signifying

---

[1] Grabau (1924: 821; see also 1905: 534) proposed the term disconformity for that type of unconformable relation ". . . in which no folding of the older set of strata is involved. . . . "

an interval. The Latin form, *diastema*, is now used in zoology with the special meaning of a vacant space, or gap, between teeth in a jaw.

A disconformity marks a period of time which is represented in some other region by a deposit of formation value. A diastem is a break represented in other regions, often within the same formation, by a bed or series of beds. A disconformity is theoretically traceable over a broad area. For deposits of epeiric seas it means ordinarily a movement sufficient to more or less completely drain the sea-water from the continent. A diastem does not imply the draining of a shallow sea, but rather a shorter or longer downward oscillation of wave-base. The two classes of breaks, although typically distinct, must grade into each other. The assignment of a break to one or the other category must not depend on a doubtfully assigned cause, but must rest on the observable field evidence. Therefore the discrimination should rest for disconformities on breadth of occurrence and faunal or floral change, for diastems on breaks in continuity of lesser areal importance, of greater number, and not characterized by permanent faunal or floral change.

23. IDENTIFICATION OF UNCONFORMITY.—Unconformities have long served to indicate the older and younger of contiguous strata. Van Hise (1896: 725–734), in studying the Pre-Cambrian rocks of the Lake Superior region, found that the important phenomena to be sought in establishing unconformity are

1. Ordinary discordance of bedding
2. Difference in the number of orogenic movements to which the series has been subjected
3. Discordance of bedding of upper series and foliation of lower
4. Relations with eruptives
5. Difference in degree of crystallization
6. Basal conglomerates
7. General field relations

Stephenson (1929: 1325) found the following criteria useful in determining unconformity (disconformity) in the Upper Cretaceous rocks of Texas:

1. A thin conglomerate composed of pebbles, bones, teeth, or other hard objects at the base of the overlying formation
2. A thin layer of phosphatic nodules[1] or phosphatic fossil casts of organisms.
3. A phosphatic layer consisting of materials obviously derived from an older formation
4. Sharp differences in lithology of the materials above and below the contact between contiguous strata

[1] Some years ago, in discussing unconformities, Dr. E. O. Ulrich remarked to the author that he had indentified breaks in a black shale sequence by using phosphatic nodules, even though he did not know at the time that the faunas above and below the break were greatly different.

5. An eneven or undulating contact transecting the bedding planes of the underlying formation
6. Presence above and below a contact of faunal zones that elsewhere are known to be separated by other strata
7. Discordance of dip below and above a contact
8. Borings made by littoral organisms in strata below the contact and later filled with material similar to that in the overlying bed

Twenhofel (1932: 626) states that another " . . . criterion would be the occurrence in place of such littoral organisms as barnacles" and points out that, whereas the existence of the first seven features enumerated by Stephenson may suggest a disconformity or diastem, " . . . each feature may occur without indicating a disconformity." Several other relations and features should be added to the above lists, as shown by Lahee (1941: 67–70, 76–113) and Krumbein[1] in their discussions of unconformities. Many of these features not only indicate unconformity but also illustrate other geological phenomena of sufficient significance for them to be considered in separate sections later in this work.

24. UNCONFORMITY AS A CRITERION OF SUCCESSION.—In using the relation of unconformity as a criterion for determining order of succession in layered rocks or sequence of geologic events, it is not always enough merely to establish that juxtaposed rocks are unconformable. A careful search must be made along the line of contact or on the surface of unconformity for features showing which of the contacting bodies is the upper, or younger, and which the lower, or older.

Relations of unconformity that *ipso facto* show order of succession are considered in this chapter. Less obvious features, structures, and relations occurring on or adjacent to surfaces of unconformity are discussed in later chapters under sedimentary and igneous rocks.

25. REGIONAL UNCONFORMITY.—An extensive surface once exposed to subaerial weathering and erosion or subjected to subaqueous erosion may have certain surface and internal features that owe their origin to processes operating during the period of attack. Other features and relations come into existence in the materials that bury the old destructional surface. Such a buried surface of weathering and erosion is called a *surface of unconformity*, and the relations between it and the covering rock are designated *regional unconformity*. This relationship usually implies that a long period of denudation preceded deposition of the materials covering the unconformity and hence that rocks once lying at considerable depths have been laid bare on the surface of erosion.

---

[1] The reader will find an excellent summary of the criteria of unconformity in a recent article by Krumbein on "Criteria for Subsurface Recognition of Unconformities" [Bull. Am. Assoc. Petroleum Geologists, **26** : 36–62 (1942)].

A surface of prolonged erosion may expose plutonic igneous rocks, basements of intensely folded and altered schists, and less intensely affected sedimentary strata (Figs. 20*A* to *D*).   There is likely to be great difference in the lithology of the rock above and below the surface of unconformity.   Lava flows may cover such surfaces, contrasting sharply with underlying serpentenized basalts, etc. (Figs. 20*E* to *F*).   Large bodies of juxtaposed rocks may exhibit such confusing or vague contacts that areal mapping on a regional scale is necessary to determine the true relations between them (Figs. 20*G* to *H*).

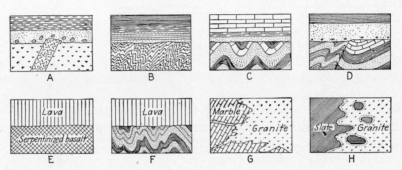

FIG. 20.—Unconformities.   *A*. A conglomeratic sandstone succeeded by laminated shale lying upon an eroded, dike-transected granite basement.   *B*. Sandstone-shale sequence overlying an eroded terrane of highly folded metamorphosed rock.   *C*. Sandstone-shale-limestone series lying upon a flat erosion surface truncating a series of folded sediments.   *D*. Sandstone-shale succession lying upon a folded and faulted sedimentary series.   *E*. A young lava flow resting on the eroded surface of an ancient flow that has been serpentinized.   *F*. Lava flow resting on a folded sedimentary succession.   *G*. Marble terrane invaded by a granite that sent dikes into the host rock.   *H*. Slate terrane invaded by a granite containing partly digested inclusions of the host rock.   (Arts. 21, 25, 32.)

Unconformable relations are common in volcanic rocks.   In a succession of ash falls (Fig. 21*A*) or lava flows (Fig. 21*B*), each surface of separation may mark an unconformity.   Ash deposits commonly rest unconformably on a weathered or eroded flow (Fig. 21*C*); in fact, flows and ash beds may be separated by old soils and forest beds that had time to develop between periods of volcanic activity (Fig. 21*D*).   New lava flows may bury preexisting ash plains, and the relation of lava and ash will then be that of unconformity, with a strong likelihood that the top of the ash bed will be distorted and baked (Fig. 21*E*).   Lava flows may alternate with glacial till layers as reported by Atwood (1933: 214) (Art. 16).

Many investigators have called attention to different kinds of regolithic deposits overlying ancient surfaces of weathering and erosion.   Such regolith is largely the insoluble residue from the parent rock (Figs. 21*F* to *K*).   Mechanical weathering alone may produce a regolith which grades downward into the parent rock so imperceptibly that no definite surface of unconformity exists (Fig. 21L). Such an example illustrates a *zone of unconformity*.

A transported regolith such as glacial till (Figs. 22A to C), stream-gravel, wind-blown sand (Fig. 22D), or silt (Fig. 22E) usually is quite different in lithology and mineralogy from the underlying material. The buried surface may be one that has been planed by glacial abrasion (Fig.

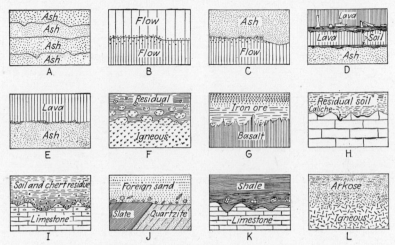

Fig 21.—Unconformity. *A*. A series of unconformable ash beds. *B*. A younger flow with thin basal zone of vesicles lying unconformably upon the eroded surface of an older flow. *C*. An ash deposit unconformably overlying a flow that shows erosion of its upper vesicular part. *D*. Diagram showing an ash bed and flow separated by a soil bed, which formed before the lava covered the ash, and a forest bed, which developed on the lava flow and later was overwhelmed by a younger flow. *E*. Lava flow unconformably overlying an ash deposit, the upper part of which was deformed and baked by the hot lava. *F*. Buried surface of weathering showing a residual deposit of clay and boulders derived from the underlying igneous rock. *G*. Residual iron-ore deposit, concretionary in the upper part and earthy in the lower, grading downward into basalt from which it was derived by weathering. *H*. Residual soil resting on the unevenly etched, caliche-incrusted surface of the limestone from which it was released by solution. *I*. Soil and chert residue lying on the uneven weathered surface of the cherty limestone from which they were released by solution. *J*. A basement of metamorphosed sedimentary rock unconformably overlain by a sandstone of foreign origin in the base of which are locally derived boulders. *K*. Weathered and eroded limestone surface overlain by laminated shale containing blocks derived from the underlying limestone. *L*. Residual arkose formed *in situ* by weathering of an igneous rock. The fresh igneous rock grades upward through weathered rock into arkose. (Arts. 21, 25.)

22A) or smoothed by wind erosion (Fig. 22F). On the other hand, it may be uneven because of weathering and erosion of rock or of unconsolidated sediment (Fig. 22G). Certain structures may be imposed on the unconsolidated materials (Fig. 22B).

Some unconformities, though exhibiting relief of tens of meters, were completely denuded of the regolith before burial. Hyde (1911: 557–560) called attention to the absence of soil along the Mississippian-Pennsylvanian unconformity in southern Ohio, commenting as follows (page 560):

. . . a soil bed or evidence of weathering at an erosional contact is not essential to its interpretation as a plane of subaërial erosion, even when the next succeeding beds appear to be of continental origin, and . . . the absence of such a bed at such a contact may demand a much more complicated explanation than that of simple submarine or subaërial erosion.

An unconformity may separate two glacial tills that differ greatly in age (Fig. 22C); the younger of these is likely to contain material derived from the older.   Sufficient time may have elapsed between ice advances

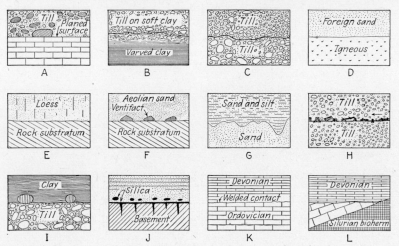

Fig. 22.—Unconformity. A. Bouldery till resting on a limestone surface planed smooth by glacial abrasion.   B. Till resting on a varved clay the upper laminae of which were disturbed by the glacier. C. Two till sheets with unconformable contact.   The upper has smaller boulders, contains materials from the lower, and has a different color.   D. A sandstone of foreign materials resting unconformably upon an eroded igneous basement.   E. Loess overlying an eroded rock substratum the surface of which may be smooth or uneven.   F. Ventifacts buried *in situ* on an erosion surface covered by wind-blown sand.   G. Eroded sand formation unconformably overlain by laminated sand and silt.   H. A forest bed preserved along the unconformity between two till sheets.   The arrow indicates the direction in which the second ice sheet moved.   I. Buried boulders along the unconformable contact between a till sheet and overlying clay.   J. Silicification along an unconformity between an old basement and overlying quartzite.   The silica extends downward along enlarged joints in the basement rocks, and boulders of it are incorporated in the overlying quartzite.   K. Thin-bedded Devonian limestone resting unconformably on more thickly bedded Ordovician limestone with a welded contact that is not readily apparent.   L. Horizontal Devonian limestone overlying the truncated marginal layers of a Silurian bioherm.   (Arts. 21, 25, 28.)

to allow the formation of a soil and development of a forest.   If so, the intercalated forest layer shows by undisturbed stumps which till is the younger and by prostrate logs in which direction the overwhelming ice moved (Fig. 22H).

A varved clay may overlie an earlier till (Fig. 22I), or a late glacial readvance may deposit a layer of till upon such a clay (Fig. 22B).   In the latter situation the clay is almost certain to show surficial deformation caused by ice shove and by being loaded when still soft.

Relations of the several kinds of glacial deposits are especially valuable in working out an ancient glacially deposited sequence of tillstones, outwash gravels, lacustrine deposits, etc.

26. INCRUSTATIONS ON REGIONAL UNCONFORMITIES.—Crusts of iron oxide, alumina, silica, and certain other relatively insoluble substances commonly are deposited on extensive surfaces of chemical weathering if conditions are favorable. Woolnough (1918, 1927, 1928, 1930), in a series of instructive articles, has discussed such deposits in Australia. These crusts are ubiquitous over the larger part of the Australian continent. They vary in chemical composition in strict conformity with the nature of the underlying rocks and seem to represent colloidal substances brought to and deposited at the surface in the process of subaerial decomposition. Woolnough (1927: 27) suggested that these several types of surface deposits be collectively named the *duricrust*.

In Australia the duricrust, which is commonly a hard and thoroughly cemented rock, rests on a completely leached substratum. Such a crust under favorable conditions might well be buried and preserved as an indicator of an ancient surface of weathering.

Leith (1925: 513–523) has called attention to silicification on and immediately below surfaces of unconformity[1] (Fig. 22*J*), and similar deposits of calcareous material have long been referred to as "caliche" in the southwestern United States and northern Mexico. Crusts of several alkali salts and of ferriferous and aluminous materials have also been described from various parts of the world and may be expected on surfaces of unconformity (Fig. 22*J*), where they show by their relations which formation they incrust. Soluble salts such as chlorides and nitrates, because of the ease with which they dissolve in ground water, are not likely to be preserved except under unusual conditions [see Whitehead (1920: 187–224) and Tarr (1926: 511–513)].

27. PROFILES OF WEATHERING BELOW UNCONFORMITIES.—Under conditions favoring dominantly chemical weathering, the surface is not greatly eroded, and the prolonged circulation of ground water alters the rock to great depths. Feldspars are thus kaolinized, ferromagnesian minerals and biotite bleached or otherwise decomposed, and other min-

---

[1] Leith (1925: 515, 516) describes conditions along silicified unconformities as follows:

On this surface are patches and veins of cherty and jaspery quartz, filling the openings and depressions. They tend to spread out along the erosion surface, but projecting downward are root-like veins, which usually end less than ten feet below the surface. . . .

It is clear that the silicification took place mainly prior to the deposition of overlying sediments, because in all cases the chert is conspicuously represented in all its phases in pebbles in the basal conglomerate. The manner in which the chert follows the details of the old erosion surface, filling joints and other irregularities, crossing the secondary structure and bedding of the underlying rocks, shows clearly that it was introduced after the underlying rocks were deformed, and during or after their erosion. The fact that it appears in so many different kinds of rocks would seem to indicate that it was related to a widespread condition like weathering . . . [see Fig. 22*J*].

erals, as well as glasses, altered in response to the conditions of the environment.   In this way is developed a deep zone of weathering marked by a thick cover, or loipon,[1] of insoluble oxides, hydroxides, and hydrated silicates.   Commonly occurring in this residuum are bands of concretions, layers made dense and hard by concentrated colloids and mineral cements, zones of enrichment, and zones of reduced, oxidized, or hydrated minerals.

If the surface of weathering persists for a long time, the loiponic cover on the source rock is thick.   In mid-latitudes the typical residuum is red clay containing residual quartz grains, mica flakes, and chert fragments released from the parent rock[2] [Kerr (1881: 345–358)].   In the tropics it is more likely to be a lateritic ore of iron, aluminum, manganese, nickel, or chrome.[3]   Weathering less intense in nature than that described in the preceding paragraphs may have little effect on the rock other than to discolor it.   Such weathering may be seen along the uncon-

___

[1] The author (Shrock 1947: 1228) has suggested the term *loipon* for those regolithic deposits resulting from intense and prolonged chemical weathering of rocks.

[2] An excellent example of an ancient soil, or loipon, is the Lower Cretaceous Little Bear residuum, which lies on the unconformity transecting upper Paleozoic rocks and beneath the overlapping Tuscaloosa conglomerate.   This residual deposit, which is composed of a mixture of insoluble materials accumulated *in situ* from decomposition of Paleozoic strata, extends from Kentucky to northern Alabama along the eastern side of the Mississippi Embayment [Mellen (1937: 8)].   In western Kentucky, according to Sutton (1931: 449–452), this ancient soil horizon is represented by internally contorted arenaceous shale that lacks apparent bedding and contains quartz grains and mica flakes.   Here, as farther south, it rests on Mississippian and Pennsylvanian rocks and is overlain by Tuscaloosa gravel.

[3] The lateritic iron ores of Cuba and Puerto Rico are examples of weathering profiles developed on serpentinized igneous rocks, the bauxite of Bintan Island (near Singapore) is an aluminous laterite derived by weathering from an aphanitic hornfels [van Bemmelen (1941: 638) recently published an instructive profile of the deposit], and the bauxite deposits of Arkansas represent *in situ* and *transported* accumulations resulting from the weathering of nepheline syenite [Mead (1915)].   Incomplete laterization of Columbia River basalt in northwestern Oregon produced a considerable loipon of high-silica ferro-aluminous laterite, recently described in some detail by Libbey, Lowry, and Mason (1945: 1–97; 1946).   In all these examples, and in many similar ones that could be cited, the weathering profile shows gradual loss of silica and alkalies, from the source rock upward, and increase, in the same direction, of iron or alumina or both concomitant with loss of silica.   Residual lateritic deposits now buried along ancient unconformities may be expected to show the same general profile.

Extensive deposits of ferro-aluminous "laterite" have been discovered recently in Jamaica, Haiti, and the Dominican Republic, resting on a prominent karst surface etched into early Tertiary limestone.   These deposits are believed to be ancient soils left as a residual cover from limestone long since dissolved away [see Goldich and Berquist (1947: 53–84)].   Similar deposits along ancient buried karst unconformities have been reported from several localities and are probably widely scattered over the earth.

formity between the Mississippian Horton series and underlying basement rocks and is described by Bell (1929: 31) as follows:

The composition of the basal contact beds is in direct relation to that of the underlying rock. Where the latter is slate . . . the Lowermost Horton bed of several feet thickness is a breccia consisting of angular or sub-rounded fragments of the underlying rocks embedded in a paste of the same material and with but occasional waterworn pebbles from distant localities. These underlying slates show the effects of weathering for several tens of feet—weathering that took place

before the Horton was laid down, as it is reflected in the colour of the material included in the Horton breccia. The effect of weathering was to oxidize the iron and to remove the carbon so that purplish or reddish shades of colour were produced.

If a loiponic complex were preserved and later metamorphosed, it would contain an unusual suite of minerals and would exhibit abnormal relations to the enclosing rocks. Some of the metamorphic effects might be mistakenly ascribed to introduction of foreign substances if the residual nature of the original material were not recognized.

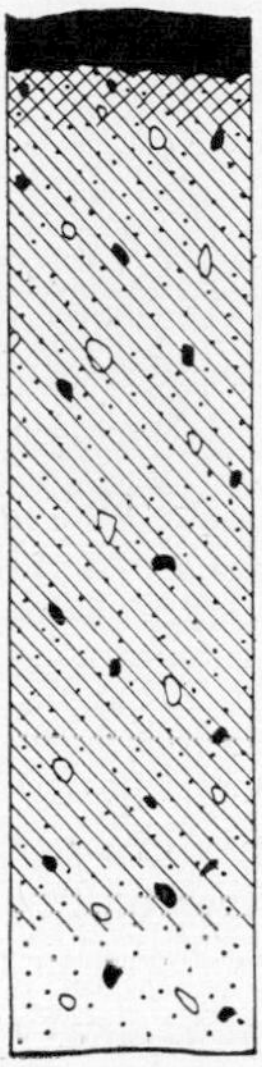

Another type of weathering profile is that found in the glacial tills of Iowa where, according to Kay (1931: 435), the succession is from unaltered till at the base of a sheet, through oxidized material in the upper part, to gumbotil[1] at the top (Fig. 23). If such a profile were repeated

Gumbotil
Transition zone
Oxidized and leached phase
Zone of concretions

Oxidized and unleached phase

Transition zone

Unoxidized and unleached phase

Fig. 23.—Weathering profile in Pleistocene till. The diagram shows the relation of gumbotil to the underlying altered and unaltered zones in the weathered till. (Art. 27.) (*After Kay*, 1931, *Bull. Geol. Soc. Am.*, **42**: 457–458, *Fig. 8*.)

[1] Kay (1931: 456) discusses the formation of gumbotil as follows:

The development of gumbotil from unoxidized and unleached till requires a comparatively long time under proper topographic conditions [see Kay and Pearce (1920: 89–125); Kay and Apfel (1929: 139–141); Leighton and MacClintock (1930: 28–50)].

As soon as drift became exposed after the retreat of an ice-sheet marginal vegetation undertook almost at once to occupy the new territory, and as soon as the climatic conditions became sufficiently congenial this vegetation no doubt spread rapidly over the surface. Even before the coming of vegetation wind and rain, sun and frost, and other weathering agencies had begun to alter the newly exposed glacial drift. The air and water oxidized the iron compounds in the drift and changed the color from the drab or gray of the fresh drift to the yellow, brown and red colors of iron oxides. As the oxidation extended downward from the surface other changes followed. The underground water began to dissolve those rock minerals which were the most soluble, and as the water passed downward the

several times and were preserved in ancient tillites, as it is in the Pleistocene tills of Iowa and elsewhere, the sequence could be used to determine the top of the tillite complex.

The common podsolic soil profile of the pedologists is introduced here so that the student can become acquainted with its essential sequence (Fig. 24). It is probable, however, that an ancient soil with a fully developed podsolic profile or, for that matter, with only a partly developed profile would show its stratigraphic position by its relations to the adjacent rocks [see Nikiforoff (1943: 194–200)].

Robinson (1936: 54, 56) describes the formation of a soil profile as follows:

We have now to examine a series of processes whereby, under the influence of water movements within the soil, the inorganic products of weathering and the organic matter undergo differentiation into definite layers or *horizons*, some characterized by impoverishment, and others by enrichment in certain constituents. The complete succession of horizons down to the undifferentiated parent material is called the *soil profile*. . . .

We may refer to the translocation of material, either mechanically or in solution, as *eluviation*, and two main types of eluviation may be distinguished, namely, (a) *mechanical eluviation*, in which, apart from any chemical differentiation, the finer fractions of the mineral portion of the soil are washed down to lower levels, and (b) *chemical eluviation* in which decomposition occurs and certain products thus liberated are translocated in true or colloidal solution, to be deposited in other horizons.

It is customary to refer to those horizons from which material has been removed by eluviation as the A or *eluviated* horizons, and to those horizons enriched by the deposition or precipitation of material from the eluviated horizons as the *illuvial* or B horizons. The undifferentiated parent material lying below is termed the C horizon.

28. Disconformity.—Parallel and contiguous strata in a sedimentary section may be separated by an unconformity that is not apparent

---

soluble materials were carried from the soil into the subsoil. Thus, limestone and other calcareous materials were leached out, first from the surface zones and then from deeper and deeper horizons. Oxidation extended itself downward much more rapidly than did leaching, and hence in the course of time the unchanged fresh till had two zones developed above it, the oxidized, unleached zone and the overlying oxidized and leached zone. But the maximum change had not yet been reached. Vegetation was growing on the surface and the vegetal products of previous seasons were undergoing decay. Organic acids were formed, which, together with the other agents of weathering, brought about additional chemical changes. The result was a reversion to the darker colors of reduced iron compounds, the breaking down of fine materials into still finer—with many of them reduced to colloidal size—and the disintegration and decomposition of many of the complex minerals of which the drift is composed. Thus gumbotil and related underlying zones were formed. . . .

because of the welding of the two layers (Fig. 22K). Such a welded contact is not uncommon in limestone sequences and may escape notice altogether unless discovered by regional stratigraphic tracing of superposed lithological units or by finding fossils of widely different ages near the line of contact. There are examples of this kind where an entire geological system is represented by the hiatus along the welded contact.

Another interesting type of disconformity is that which Ulrich (1924: 93) long ago described and used in locating the contact between certain contiguous massive sandstones in the Upper Cambrian section of the upper Mississippi valley (Fig. 47). As the advancing sea reworked the fairly well graded massive sand deposit on which it was encroaching, the currents carried to deeper water the smaller and lighter grains and left on the bottom a thin sheet of the coarsest grains. As the water deepened and sand was washed in, the incoming grains transported from a distant beach were gradually mixed with the upper part of the coarse concentrate, forming a basal transition zone. In this way was formed what might be considered a residual basal sandstone, marking, by its abrupt termination downward, the depth of reworking by the invading sea as well as the imaginary plane of unconformity (Art. 57).

29. LOCAL UNCONFORMITIES.— Many features and relations come into existence locally on a surface of weathering and erosion and may be preserved when that surface is buried. These include small deposits of locally derived basal conglomerates spread over the surface of unconformity as thin lenses

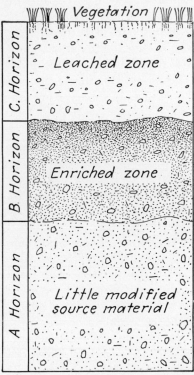

Fig. 24.—Diagram illustrating the essential features of a podsol profile. The C horizon is a leached zone of light-colored material from which the potassium, calcium, and iron salts and carbonaceous matter have been largely removed. Descending waters carry the latter two substances into the underlying materials of the B horizon, developing an enriched zone much darker in color than either the C or A horizon and containing a concentration of carbonaceous matter and the sesquioxides of iron. The A horizon consists of the raw source material, which has been little modified by the weathering. Under certain conditions ascending solutions carry soluble salts from the A horizon into the enriched zone of the B horizon. Podsol profiles are probably preserved under only exceptional conditions, but they should be expected in argillaceous formations suspected of being ancient soils. Compare with Fig. 23. (Art. 27.)

or collected nestlike in depressions and erosion channels on that surface; scoured-out depressions backfilled with cross-laminated gravels and sands, water-sorted sands with the heavier grains at the base of the deposit, or differentially compacted muds; buried and filled sinkholes of an ancient karst surface (*e.g.*, in the Tri-State lead and zinc district); original mounds and other similar irregularities buried beneath stratified sediments, which may be deposited quaquaversally around and over them; and other equally significant features. Most of the features of this kind are large enough to be detected easily, but some are so minute that they can be seen only in thin or polished section under the microscope. It should be obvious, therefore, that specimens taken to include an unconformable contact should be marked for orientation in the field before removal from the collecting site.

Since these features are local rather than regional in their extent and are, for this reason, likely to be restricted largely to one general type of lithologic terrane, they are discussed in detail later under sedimentary and igneous rocks.

30. FALSE UNCONFORMITY.—Attention has already been called to certain relations which, interpreted at face value, would be misleading in their indication concerning order of succession in two unconformable formations (Art. 22). Cross-lamination is probably the structure most likely to give trouble in this way; hence formations exhibiting it on a grand scale should be studied carefully with this fact in mind (Fig. 19).

An instructive example of the confusion that can be caused by a false unconformity is the Pre-Cambrian Ramsey Lake formation of the Sudbury district in Ontario. This coarsely clastic formation is the third oldest of the seven members of the Sudbury-Bruce series and was considered a conglomerate by Coleman (1905: 14), who named it. Fairbairn (1944: 5) points out, however, that the formation is typically a grit with scattered pebbles and boulders and numerous quartzite lenses. The commonest boulders are granite, presumably derived from the pre-Huronian basement. Transecting the entire Sudbury-Bruce series, along an irregular line that tends to parallel the strike of successive formations, is a zone of brecciation marked by patches of fairly well rounded fragments. This breccia is developed in all the formations cut by the line of disturbance but has caused most confusion where derived from the Ramsey Lake and overlying Mississagi formations. Lawson (1929: 374), misinterpreting the breccia as the conglomeratic phase of the Ramsey Lake, inverted the entire sequence, placing the McKim graywacke *above* and the Mississagi unconformably below. Later workers have pointed out Lawson's mistake not only in inverting the section but also in placing a nonexistent unconformity between the Ramsey Lake and Mississagi formations [Fairbairn (1944: 6–9)]. Lawson's error was seemingly ascribable, at least in part, to the fact that the rounded fragments of the breccias bear superficial resemblance to true conglomeratic boulders [Fairbairn and Robson (1944: 20–23)].

False unconformable relations may also be produced in a series of rocks long after burial, as illustrated by truncated color bands, which simulate cross-lamination or scour-and-fill structure (Art. 142), and by stylolite seams (Art. 135) and fillings of underground caverns, sinkholes, and crevices produced by subterranean drainage (Art. 131). Relations such as the last-named should be expected in soluble rocks such as limestones, dolostones, and salinastones.

31. SUMMARY OF UNCONFORMITIES.—Because they represent ancient surfaces, unconformities are unsurpassed by any other geologic features insofar as interest and general significance are concered. Almost every separation plane in a stratigraphic sequence is an unconformity of some duration; hence most examinations of bedding surfaces and of their profiles in cross section will show relations useful in interpreting the geological history of the rocks. Unconformable surfaces with spectacular relief are not the rule, but if present in a region they are likely to exhibit many relations that cannot exist on surfaces that are flat or only gently undulating. On the other hand, flat or undulating surfaces are more likely to transect folded, faulted, and altered beds and for this reason may reveal more of the past geologic events. All basal deposits which lie on an unconformity should be studied carefully, for they are commonly helpful in indicating the kind of rock terrane that was being destroyed, the conditions under which the rock was being disrupted, and something about the means of transport and the environment of deposition.

32. Igneous Intrusion.—It has long been recognized that the rock invaded by magma is older than the intruding material; hence, where the margins or peripheries of intruding bodies can be examined, it is usually possible to determine the older and younger of contacting rocks. An intrusive contact can be mistaken for an unconformity if the relations of the contacting bodies are confused or indistinct. If a sedimentary or igneous rock rests unconformably on a plutonic rock such as a granite, there should be no contact metamorphic effects in the covering rock (Fig. 20*G*). If, on the other hand, the contact is an intrusive one, dikes from the main igneous body should cut the invaded rock, altered blocks of the latter may be expected as xenoliths or roof pendants in the intrusive rock (Figs. 20*H*, 25), and the invaded rock is almost certain to show alteration along its contact margin (Fig. 25).

If the intrusive body is of tabular shape and if it crystallized in a position approaching horizontality, it may contain within itself structures and textures that indicate the direction of the force of gravity at the time of cooling. With this known, it is usually possible to determine the top or bottom of the sedimentary sequence in which it lies (*e.g.*, a thick sill intruded essentially parallel to the stratification). These internal features, most of which are microscopic, are discussed fully in Chap. VI on Features of Igneous Rocks.

33. Comparative Deformation.—In a sequence of rocks in which one part exhibits much more intense folding and faulting than the other, especially where conspicuous faults or other structures of one part do not cross the contact into the adjacent rocks, age relations usually are

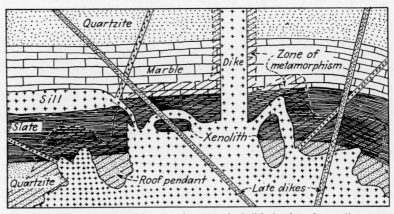

FIG. 25.—Diagram showing marginal features of a granite batholith that intrudes a sedimentary series. The complex is cut by two lamprophyre dikes that represent a late phase of intrusion. A zone of metamorphism in the sediments is shown along the contact with the granite. (Arts. 32, 248.)

obvious. In comparing degrees of deformation, however, similar lithologies should always be considered; for under a certain intensity of deformation shales, for example, yield readily, whereas sandstones and quartzites do not (Figs. 26, 382*E*).

Van Hise (1909: 102), in outlining the principles he and his associates found useful in working out the classification and correlation of the highly deformed beds of the Lake Superior Pre-Cambrian, stated

> The amount and nature of the deformation are of assistance in correlation within limited areas. Upon the whole, the older a series the greater and more intricate the deformation. The difference in the amount of deformation in the pre-Cambrian series wherever there is a somewhat full succession of formations is sufficiently great to make this an important factor in the classification and correlation of the formation.

In an earlier report he [Van Hise (1896: 632–633)] described three cases of comparative deformation as follows:

In the first and simplest case the lower formations have been subjected to either simple or complex folding, while the upper formations are undisturbed or very slightly disturbed. In this case the upper formations are likely to be found as inliers upon the other, and the structural break between the two is comparatively easy to determine. Phenomena of this kind are found at many localities between the Paleozoic and pre-Paleozoic sediments, and less frequently they are found wholly within the pre-Paleozoic formations.

The second case is that in which the lower formations were folded by one or more movements before the upper series was deposited, and subsequently the two were again folded. If the second folding was of a comparatively simple character, and the earlier was rather complex, it is usually comparatively easy to

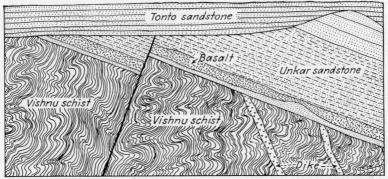

Fig. 26.—Comparative deformation. Section of the north wall of the Grand Canyon of the Colorado, as seen from the south side near the mouth of Congress Canyon. The Vishnu schist of Pre-Cambrian age is greatly deformed, whereas the overlying Unkar formation, also Pre-Cambrian in age, has only been tilted and faulted, and the Middle Cambrian Tonto sandstone is essentially horizontal. (Art. 33.) [*Modified after Walcott, 1894a, U.S. Geol. Survey Ann. Rept.,* **14** (2): 507, *Fig.* 52.]

separate the two series. For instance, the lower formations may have been rather closely folded by the first orogenic movement, and the two sets of formations together may have been gently folded by the second movement. The discrepancy between the two may often be detected, even when the movements were in the same direction, as they so frequently were. But the discordance may be more easily discovered if the second movement was in a different direction from the first, so that the first folds of the lower formations became complexly folded at the second period of folding, the newer formations at the same time being simply folded.

Third, in more complicated cases the lower formations were folded one or more times before the upper series was deposited, and after the deposition of the latter the two series were again folded in a complex fashion, either by a single orogenic movement or else by successive movements. In proportion as the folding of the later formations becomes complicated the criterion of folding for separating series is more and more difficult to apply, and where the folding of the upper formations is at all intricate it is usually of little value. The criterion of folding for separating unconformable series is to be considered in all cases in connection with other criteria given upon subsequent pages [cleavage, joints, etc.].

Deformation is seldom so intense that it blots out all previously existing features and structures; hence, in deformed sedimentary and igneous rocks, some original structures may still be obvious enough to allow determination of order of succession within the sequence.

Cleavage and foliation made in an earlier period of deformation may be accentuated beyond usefulness by later folding. If metamorphism accompanies the later deformation, only traces of the earlier cleavage may remain.

34. Comparative Metamorphism.—In a sequence of rocks exhibiting different degrees of metamorphism, those strata or bodies showing the greater or more intense alteration are judged to be the older; hence, within such a sequence it is frequently possible to determine the top by starting at the contact between the differently metamorphosed rocks and continuing upward into the less altered, hence younger, or upper, beds. In applying this criterion successfully, the same lithologic type must be considered in comparing two rocks, for dissimilar types show different degrees of alteration if subjected to the same conditions of metamorphism (*e.g.*, shale and sandstone respond quite differently under similar conditions).

Fortunately for the structural geologist, it commonly happens that other features along or associated with the unconformity between two masses of differently metamorphosed rocks aid in determining which of the contacting masses is the older (Fig. 27).

Van Hise (1896: 707–708) long ago pointed out the usefulness and limitations of comparative metamorphism in working out structural relations in the metamorphosed terranes of the Pre-Cambrian. He wrote as follows on the subject:

The amount and character of the metamorphism of a series of formations may be an important guide in structural work. It may serve to separate one series from another and assist in determining the structure within a series. The criterion has limitations, however, which are readily deducible from the manner in which metamorphic action occurs.

Since metamorphism is produced by consolidation, welding, cementation, injection, metasomatism, and mashing, any one process acting separately or combined with others, it follows that a series of rocks may be profoundly metamorphosed locally and the metamorphism be less or of a minor character in an adjacent area. Not only is this so, but different parts of the same fold are in most cases metamorphosed to a different degree, depending upon the position within the fold. Still further, one set of beds may be more readily metamorphosed than another, so that one formation may become completely crystalline while the adjacent formation may still be plainly fragmental; as, for instance, a shale may change to a mica-slate or mica-schist and an interbedded quartzite be but little affected by any process except cementation. As pegmatization is so frequently dependent upon the presence of an intrusive rock, it follows that an extreme phase of metamorphism engendered by this, combined with other processes, may have a very local character.

Notwithstanding all of these limitations, if a set of formations be superimposed upon another set of formations, and one has become crystalline throughout, while

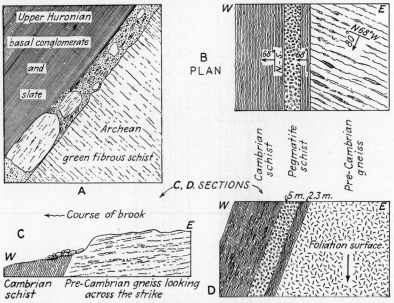

Fig. 27.—Comparative metamorphism. *A.* Contact between Huronian slate and Archean schist on the Potato River in Wisconsin. The basal conglomerate, which averages about a meter in thickness, rests on the truncated fibrous schist and gives way upward to slate. It should be noted that the strike of the fine-grained slate is almost perpendicular to the foliation of the schist. Even if the narrow conglomeratic zone were covered, the more intensely altered rock—*i.e.*, the schist—would be considered the older. *B-D.* Diagrams illustrating the unconformable contact between Pre-Cambrian gneiss and Cambrian schist in Downer Glen, Manchester, Vt. *B.* Plan of a part of the contact. *C.* Diagrammatic sketch along axis of Bourn Brook. The strike of the foliation is parallel with the course of the stream, whereas the micaceous Cambrian quartzites strike almost at right angles to the brook. In these examples the truncation of the gneissic foliation, together with the more intensely altered nature of the gneiss, indicates that this rock is older than the schistose quartzite. *D.* Cross section of *B.* (Art. 34.) [*A modified after Van Hise,* 1896, *U.S. Geol. Survey Ann. Rept.,* **16** (1): 722, *Fig.* 144. *B-D modified after Dale,* 1902, *Bull. U.S. Geol. Survey,* **195**: 18, *Fig.* 7.]

the other shows little or no change, it is probable that the first series underwent a period of metamorphism before the new series was deposited. But in order to make this conclusion at all certain the superior formations should be of kinds which are equally likely to be metamorphosed; and further, it must be certain that it is a case of superposition, for laterally the metamorphosing forces may die out rapidly and the altered rocks pass quickly into those but little changed. Still further, if the metamorphism be due to pegmatization as a consequence of the intrusion of great batholites of granite the process may die out rapidly in a vertical direction, so that the extremely metamorphosed lower formations would gradually pass into the unmetamorphosed beds higher up, with no structural break. . . . It is further clear that metamorphism is much more dependent upon environment, dynamic action, and igneous intrusion than upon age. Age affects metamorphism largely in that old rocks are more apt to be deeply buried, folded, and intruded by igneous masses than are younger rocks.

35. Summary.—The gross relationships discussed in preceding sections have chief value as aids in determining broad regional relationships. Two or more of them are quite likely to be present in the same sequence of rocks and may be supplementary to each other in indicating order of succession or of geologic events. Conclusions based on the grander relations between adjacent bodies of rock may often be corroborated by internal features in the rocks themselves. These internal features, which also may prove useful in determining order of succession, are considered in detail under the several kinds of rocks in the following chapters.

CHAPTER III

FEATURES OF SEDIMENTARY ROCKS (I)

I. LITHOLOGICAL—TEXTURAL—MINERALOGICAL SEQUENCES

36. Introduction.—Most of the folded structures of the world are in sedimentary rocks and their metamorphosed equivalents. These rocks, therefore, deserve careful study because of the light their features, structures, and relations may throw on the order of succession in terranes where deformation has occurred. Fortunately for this purpose, sedimentary rocks are variable both vertically and horizontally, and they contain innumerable features that are useful in determining the top or bottom of a single stratum or the order of succession in a stratigraphic sequence. Kindle (1919: 339) has emphasized that "in both its time and space relations sedimentation is highly variable" and has pointed out that as a result of this variability sedimentary rocks, rather than being uniform over great areas and through considerable thickness, are quite the opposite. Barrell, Twenhofel, and the students of these great teachers of sedimentation have long emphasized the variability of environmental conditions on bottoms of deposition and of the sedimentary deposits made there.

It is to the many small and commonly rather insignificant sedimentary features that geologists often must turn for some clue as to which is the top or which the bottom of a bed that is steeply inclined or vertical. Although most of these features are of small magnitude and usually of limited geographic and stratigraphic extent, they are, nonetheless, frequently of the greatest usefulness in determining local structure. Furthermore, since small folds and faults are commonly miniatures of much larger regional structures, solving local structure may at the same time aid in working out major features on a regional scale.

In applying sedimentary criteria to the problem of top and bottom determination, it is not enough that the geologist be able to recognize the individual features and structures and to appreciate that they have practical value. He must also determine, if he can, whether the feature is of primary or secondary origin and under what environmental conditions it was formed, so that he can evaluate the extent of its use and its limitations for structural work. Erroneous conclusions may be drawn unless

63

proper discrimination is exercised in applying certain top and bottom criteria.

The sedimentary features to be discussed are divided into the following categories:

1. *Lithological—Textural—Mineralogical Sequences.* These include variations in lithology and texture, basal formations, and cyclic sediments (Chap. III).

2. *Features on Upper- and Undersurfaces of Sedimentary Beds.* These include primary and secondary structures and features present on the upper- and undersurfaces of layers or penetrating the layer from either of the surfaces (Chap. IV).

3. *Internal Sedimentary Features.* These include primary and secondary features and structures lying mainly or entirely within a bed or transecting a sequence of beds (Chap. V).

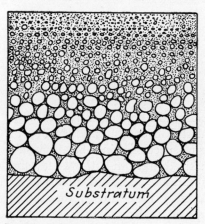

FIG. 28.—Textural variation in a coarse conglomerate lying unconformably upon an eroded substratum. Note that the components decrease in size upward from the unconformity. The boulders and pebbles may be composed of the same rock as that in the substratum or of other kinds. A marble, quartzite, or argillite substratum can yield boulders, whereas a schist, gneiss, or slate is not so likely to yield large fragments because of the ease with which they can be disintegrated. (Art. 37.)

In this chapter we shall consider the top and bottom features included in division 1 of the foregoing list. A brief review of these is appropriate as an introduction. Order of succession is commonly obvious in many kinds of lithological sequences. Basal conglomerates are quite likely to be coarsest at the base and to have many boulders derived from the underlying rock; graded bedding in sandstones and siltstones and rhythmic stratification or varves in finer grained sediments usually consist of sharply separated bipartite layers that are coarsest in the basal part and finest at the top; accessory minerals not uncommonly appear abruptly in a stratigraphic section, often in great abundance, and then decrease gradually upward in the section; and saline sequences may be layered in accordance with the reaction series of precipitation.

The several names that will be used in discussing sedimentary rocks are shown in the accompanying table "A Classification of Sedimentary Rocks" [Shrock (1946b: 1231; 1948)].

37. Textural Variation in Conglomerates.—It may be possible to determine order of succession in a sequence containing a conglomeratic unit by noting whether or not the conglomerate exhibits an abrupt contact

A CLASSIFICATION OF SEDIMENTARY ROCKS

	Nature of sediments			Sedimentary rocks		
Dominantly fragmental	Angular particles more than 2 mm. in greatest dimension	Rubble composed of sharpstones		Sharpstone	CONGLOMERATE	
	Rounded particles more than 2 mm. in greatest dimension	Gravel composed of roundstones		Roundstone		
	Angular and rounded particles of rocks and minerals ranging in greatest dimension from 2 mm. to 0.06 mm.	Volcanic fragments = Tuff Mixture of rock and mineral fragments Quartz + Feldspar Quartz + other minerals in large amount Quartz + other minerals in small amount		Tuffstone Graywacke Arkose Normal Quartzose	SANDSTONE	
	Rock and mineral particles ranging in greatest dimension from 0.06 mm. to 0.001 mm. and colloidal particles less than 0.001 mm. in greatest dimension	Volcanic ash Silt particles — 0.06 to 0.001 mm. Clay materials less than 0.01 mm. Silt + Clay + Water = Mud		Ashstone Siltstone Claystone Mudstone	SHALE	
Partly fragmental	Fe^{II} and Fe^{III} compounds precipitated inorganically and organically as concretions, nodules and layers Impurities commonly present in the layers	Iron concretions Iron compounds + mud, silica, etc.		Concretionary Precipitated	IRONSTONE	**Partly precipitated**
	Siliceous inorganic fragments less than 0.06 mm. in greatest dimension Siliceous organic hard parts and their fragments Silica precipitated as oölites, pisolites, etc. Silica precipitated from suspensions and solutions	Inorganic fragments Diatom frustules, radiolarian skeletons and sponge spicules Siliceous concretions Chert, flint, sinter, etc.		Fragmental Concretionary Precipitated	SILICASTONE	
	Plant structures—spores, fronds, leaves, wood, etc. Inorganic sediment Waxes, resins, etc., from decomposition of plants	Plant debris; inorganic impurities Plant fluids		COAL		
	Calcite and Aragonite fragments Calcareous organic hard parts—shells, exoskeletons, plates, spines, and fragments Organically and inorganically precipitated concretions Inorganically precipitated CaCO$_3$—Evaporation, etc. Organically precipitated CaCO$_3$—(1) by NH$_3$ from decomposition; (2) loss of CO$_2$ to plants; etc.			Fragmental Concretionary Precipitated	LIMESTONE	
	Dolomite fragments Dolomitized organic hard parts Dolomitic concretions Inorganically precipitated dolomite Organically precipitated dolomite			Fragmental Concretionary Precipitated	DOLOSTONE	
Possibly fragmental	Fragments of anhydrite, gypsum, halite, alkali, nitrate caliche, etc.			Fragmental		**Dominantly precipitated**
	Evaporites—minerals precipitated during evaporation of saline waters	Anhydrite Gypsum Chlorides Nitrates Other rare salts	Precipitated	Anhydrock Gyprock	SALINA-STONE	

along one surface and a gradual decrease in size of fragments from that surface through the layer (Fig. 28). Although there are exceptions to this rule [Twenhofel (1936: 677–703)], the general condition, as pointed out by Twenhofel (1932: 210), is that "the base of a conglomerate is usually more sharply limited than the top, since the conglomerate grades upward to finer sediments."

38. Uneven Base of Some Conglomerates.—The base of certain types of conglomerates is likely to be uneven, as compared with the top of the same unit, and this condition should be true generally whether the conglomerate is widespread or local. Continental conglomerates are more likely to rest on irregular surfaces than are marine ones, for a stream having enough competency to carry coarse pebbles and boulders also has

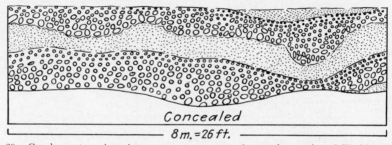

Fig. 29.—Conglomerate and sandstone sequence as exposed near the crossing of Washington and Morton Streets, Dorchester, Mass. One good example of scour-and-fill structure and two prominent gravel-filled channels are present in the sandstone. The larger boulders tend to be concentrated in these channels. The uneven base of the higher conglomerate is a common feature and contrasts with the more even top of most conglomeratic layers in the vicinity. (Art. 38.)

enough erosive power to excavate the surface materials differentially, especially if the latter are unconsolidated gravel and sand. In the later stages of gravel deposition, the stream's competency decreases with loss of volume and velocity, so that the last materials transported are finer in grade and make a relatively smooth top to the conglomerate layer.

The uneven base of conglomerates has been observed repeatedly in many stratigraphic sections in the United States and abroad, *e.g.*, in the Roxbury conglomerate and Squantum tillite of the Boston region (Fig. 29); in the several conglomerates of the Narragansett Basin; and in the much folded Tertiary beds of Haiti and of the Dominican Republic (Figs. 17, 18). It is undoubtedly a feature of common occurrence and should be expected in ancient gravel deposits of any age.

39. Residual Basal Sharpstone Conglomerates.—The basal part of a sedimentary sequence commonly consists of a sharpstone conglomerate, which, in its typical development, varies in thickness and grades from coarse texture at the base to finer texture at the top. Such conglomerates can be formed in several ways.

A terrane that has undergone a prolonged period of weathering without appreciable accompanying erosion is characteristically covered by a veneer of blocks, slabs, and generally angular fragments of the underlying rock, together with similar fragments of more resistant nodules or layers

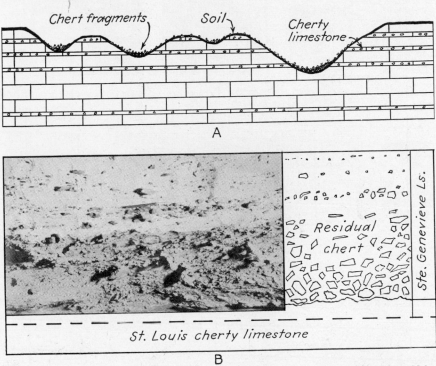

Courtesy of C. A. Malott

Fig. 30.—Residual sharpstone conglomerates. *A.* Karst surface developed on a cherty limestone. A thin veneer of residual soil and chert fragments covers most of the surface. It is thinnest on the higher areas and thickest in the solution sinks and other depressions. In the later stages of the karst, when there is little relief, most of the surface is likely to be covered with residual material. Ancient buried surfaces of this kind have been discovered recently in drilling for oil. *B.* Residual chert rubble, derived from the underlying St. Louis limestone, forms a basal sharpstone conglomerate at the base of the Ste. Genevieve limestone. Upward the chert fragments decrease in size and number. The bedding is essentially horizontal. The photograph was taken in the Cumberland Caverns, Sloans Valley, 5 miles southeast of Burnside, Pulaski County, Kentucky. As indicated in the diagram at the right, the top of the St. Louis is only a few feet below the base of the photograph. The sharpstone zone ranges in thickness from 2.5 to 4.5 m. (8 to 14 ft.). (Art. 39.)

(*e.g.*, chert), released from the parent rock as it dissolved (Figs. 30, 31). If surficial mantles like these become cemented and preserved as the basal phase of the covering formation, they indicate by their lithological nature that they were derived from the underlying rock, through weathering and slight erosion, and that they are therefore younger than the rock on which they rest.

Surficial accumulations such as those just described are common and

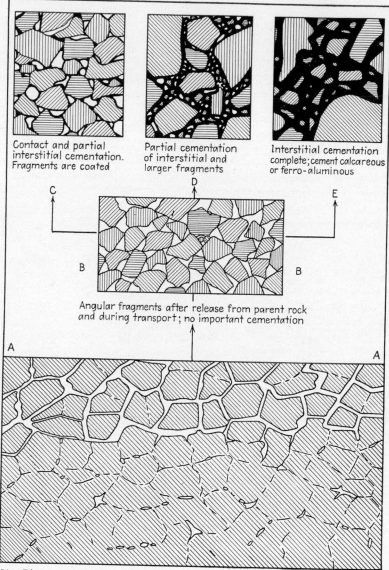

FIG. 31.—Diagrams showing the development of three types of basal sharpstone conglomerates ("weathering breccias") from the weathering and disruption of massive Eocene limestone near Mont La Selle, Haiti. (Art. 39.) (*Modified after Shrock, 1946a, Indiana Acad. Sci. Proc.,* **55**: 107, *Fig.* 1.)

are referred to frequently in conventional descriptions of geological conditions. Leith (1925: 513–523) mentions them in discussing the silicification of erosion surfaces, and Kerr (1881: 345–358) and Sharpe (1938: 21 –48) point out their importance as surface deposits. The author has observed red clay–chert mantles over deeply weathered limestones at many places in the Appalachian Valley and in the karst belt of Indiana and Kentucky. Similar cherty mantles are common in the lead and zinc district of Missouri. The surface of karst areas in tropical regions is characteristically covered with red soil or limestone rubble, and similar material should be expected along ancient karst unconformities.

Professor C. A. Malott of Indiana University has called the attention of the author to an instructive example of a residual basal sharpstone conglomerate that he found while mapping the Cumberland Caverns in Sloans Valley near Burnside, Ky. In the wall of the cave he found a prominent chert rubble at the base of the Mississippian Ste. Genevieve limestone where that formation rests unconformably on the irregular surface of the cherty St. Louis limestone, also of Mississippian age. (Fig. 30*B*). The chert fragments, derived from the older limestone, are concentrated in the basal meter or so of the younger and decrease upward in number as well as in size. They are strewn out along the bedding, thus affording evidence of some transport.

A striking example of an ancient karst topography, which is now buried beneath a thick section of Pennsylvanian sediments, was recently described by Walters (1946: 660–710) from Barton County, Kansas. Many of the sinkholes and other depressions on this old surface contain deposits of residual and transported debris originally derived from the weathering of the rocks exposed at the time the topography was formed.

40. Penecontemporaneous Sharpstone Conglomeratic Zones.—A second type of sharpstone conglomerate is that formed by fragmentation of the upper part of a deposit while the material composing it is still essentially unconsolidated.

Under certain bottom conditions, partly indurated muds, silts and calcareous materials, and incipiently cemented sands are ripped up by unusually strong tides, tsunamis,[1] storm waves and storm-produced currents, and other similar phenomena which cause temporary depression of the base level of submarine erosion (Fig. 32). The disturbed bottom materials ultimately come to rest on the reestablished bottom of deposition as a brecciated mass with chaotic arrangement of fragments. The larger and heavier fragments settle first, making the coarser basal part of the deposit; the finer fragments and particles settle last, making the

---

[1] Tsunamis—the powerful waves of translation produced by submarine earthquake shocks—may rip up sediments on shallow bottoms (*i.e.*, on the continental shelf as well as in the shallower littoral zone) and transport them seaward. As soon as the waters have quieted, the transported materials sink to the bottom, which may be far below the reach of ordinary waves, and there make a vertically graded series of clastic materials, coarsest at the base and finest at the top. Such series should be sought especially in offshore deposits.

finer upper part of the deposit. The finely comminuted material, together with the sediment that is brought in and deposited later, filters down into the interstices between the angular fragments, and the two ultimately serve as a cement for the brecciated mass (Fig. 33).

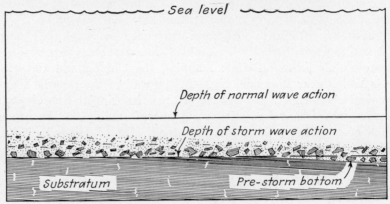

FIG. 32.—Diagram illustrating how a penecontemporaneous sharpstone conglomerate can be produced under storm conditions. The storm waves reach down below the depth of normal wave action and rip up some of the partly indurated substratum. The fragments so produced are transported locally and mixed with whatever sediments are brought in by the storm waves. The deposit thus made rests unconformably upon the eroded substratum, and its constituents grade upward from coarse fragments that lie upon the substratum to small bits along the upper boundary of the conglomerate. Compare this diagram with Fig. 33. The laminae of the substratum have been given an initial dip of about 3° to indicate how part of the bottom may escape erosion while an adjacent area is eroded. (Art. 40.)

Certain brecciated layers (sharpstone conglomerates) and some so-called "intraformational" and "edgewise" conglomerates probably were formed in the manner just described. If they were, their texture and internal structure should furnish the clue necessary to establish which is the top of the brecciated body.

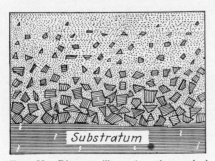

FIG. 33.—Diagram illustrating the gradual upward decrease in size and number of fragments in a sharpstone conglomerate derived from the materials of the substratum. The base of such sharpstone layers is usually marked off sharply, and the upper boundary is uneven because of the scattered fragments. Compare this diagram with Fig. 34. (Art. 40.)

This sedimentary feature must be used with considerable caution, however, for it is first necessary to establish that the bottom sediments were fragmented under conditions favorable for settling and crude sorting. Brecciated lenses, wedges, and layers formed in the manner just described should grade laterally and upward into normal sediments—

—calcareous material, muds, silts, and sands. Downward they should be sharply separated from material like that of which the constituent fragments are composed.

41. Imbricate Structure at Base of Conglomeratic Zones.—The larger platy fragments of thin conglomerates intercalated with other sediments commonly exhibit conspicuous imbrication (Fig. 34). The slabs are inclined upstream and may touch or be separated by sand and other sediment. Coarse gravel or sand may be concentrated in a small pocket at the base of the inclined fragment. This deposit represents material that was too coarse for the current to wash out by its turbulence on the downstream edge of the inclined fragment.

Fig. 34.—Imbricated sandstone slabs constituting an intraformational sharpstone conglomerate in the Upper Cambrian Dresbach (Galesville) sandstone near Coon Valley, Wisconsin. The base of the conglomerate is marked by the three largest slabs. Upward the sharpstones are much smaller. The conglomerate lies in the midst of a fairly massive sandstone and appears to have been formed by the penecontemporaneous fragmentation of a few layers of fairly well cemented sand. The rule is 17.5 cm. (7 in.) long. (Arts. 40, 41.)

The base of this kind of deposit tends to be rather sharply marked off from the underlying sediment by the abrupt appearance of platy fragments. Upward the conglomerate usually shows considerable variation in thickness, depending on the original supply of fragments. The interstitial sediment is likely to vary greatly in texture. In general, however, it becomes less variable upward, and fragments likewise decrease gradually in size and number in that direction. The author has observed this imbricate structure in Upper Cambrian strata of both Wisconsin (Fig. 34) and Vermont (Fig. 168), and it probably is of common occurrence.

The mode of formation of imbrication such as that just described is not certain. Field evidence in some exposures indicates that a sand-transporting current ripped up partly indurated mud bottoms and then imbricated the platy fragments. Certain controversial "edgewise" conglomerates may have been formed in this way, but others that have been described clearly require a different explanation.

42. Residual Basal Roundstone Conglomerates.—Partly exhumed monadnocks rising above ancient surfaces of weathering and erosion commonly have on their flanks great wedgelike masses of conglomerate composed entirely of boulders derived from the hills themselves. These deposits have been called "plaster" conglomerates, and the term is not inappropriate, for they truly are plastered against the old hill slope (Fig. 35). Not uncommonly the boulders of such conglomerates are of gigantic size and could not have moved far from their source; yet they

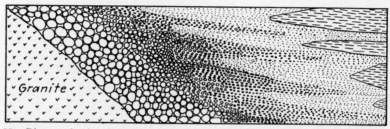

Fig. 35.—Diagram showing the sedimentary facies in a series of clastics deposited offshore from an island. The thick conglomerate, which lies directly upon the granite, climbs the stratigraphic section. At any given level in the conglomerate the components are older than the sediments present offshore at the same level because of the strong initial dip. Although the conglomerate forms a steeply inclined layer that is plastered against the old land mass, its bedding dips gently away from the granite. The diagram is based on the relations of the Pondville conglomerate and Wamsutta red beds to the Quincy granite along the south slope of the Blue Hills in eastern Massachusetts. Many of the larger boulders near the granite have long since been weathered to rounded forms by spheroidal weathering of somewhat angular original blocks that once formed a great talus deposit at the base of a steep granite slope. (Art. 42.)

are fairly well rounded. It seems likely that weathering, more than erosion during transportation, produced the rounding.

Conglomerates of this type form sheets of variable thickness on the flanks of the hills from which they came and may even completely cover them. They cut across all bedding and other structural features in the hills; hence, their basal relations are almost certain to be those of angular unconformity (Art. 21). Considered as a layer, the conglomeratic mass also climbs the stratigraphic section and at any given time level grades laterally into other kinds of sediments (Figs. 35, 36).

Conglomeratic bodies of this type are significant and important because they reveal so much of the destructional history of mountain roots and of the history of the time during which the roots were buried. Local studies usually are sufficient to establish the true relations of this type of conglomerate, but if these prove inadequate it may be necessary to conduct regional stratigraphic and structural investigations.

43. Basal Mixedstone Conglomerates.—The broadly spread basal conglomerate that covers a regional unconformity is usually a mixture of several kinds of boulders, for its materials were gathered from different lithologic terranes. Long-traveled fragments are well rounded, whereas those derived from near-by sources are little rounded or angular. Hence the final deposit consists of both sharpstones and roundstones and is therefore a mixedstone conglomerate (Fig. 37).

Mixedstone conglomerates may also be expected in sequences flanking old mountain ranges of complex lithology and in ancient glacial complexes (Art. 44). Whatever their nature, however, they rest on an old

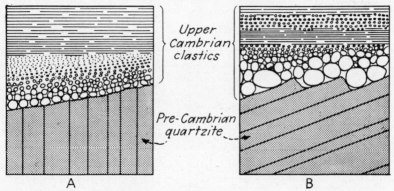

Fig. 36.—Basal quartzite roundstone conglomerates of Cambrian age resting with angular unconformity on folded Pre-Cambrian quartzite beds from which they were derived. The conglomerate grades upward through sandstone into siltstone. *A*. Ableman's Gorge in the Baraboo Range, Wisconsin. *B*. Devil's Lake, in the Baraboo Range, Wisconsin. The largest boulders exceed a meter in diameter. The rounding of the boulders is ascribed to the erosive action of waves that pounded against the ancient quartzite hills. Most of the boulders were derived locally. (Art. 42.)

erosion surface and are indicative of extensive rock destruction in adjacent regions.

44. Tillstones, Tillites, and Their Substrata.—Tillstones and tillites resting on a planed and grooved substratum are known to be present in a few scattered localities [Coleman 1926: 122].[1] If the substratum and superincumbent conglomerate were rotated into a steeply inclined or vertical position, the relationship just described would indicate the order of succession of the contiguous rocks, but care would be necessary to differentiate the relationship from a somewhat similar one that might occur along a steeply inclined fault plane. Longwell, Knopf, and Flint (1939: 336, Fig. 224) describe and illustrate such a fault from the Spotted Range in Nevada.[2] If there is doubt about the relation of conglomerate

[1] Du Toit (1939, Plate 24) illustrates the Permian Dwyka tillite resting on a smooth striated floor of diabase at Nooitgedacht, near Riverton, in the Kimberley district of Rhodesia, and there are probably other examples fully as spectacular.

[2] Their Fig. 224 on p. 336 bears the following caption: "Part of an old fault surface, with slickensides, uncovered by erosion. The striations and flutings indicate that the movement was directly down the dip of the surface."

and substratum, the presence of gouge material, friction breccias, drag folds, and other dynamically produced features should suffice to identify the polished and grooved surface as one produced by faulting.

45. Characteristics of Coal Sequences.—Coal sequences offer many problems to stratigraphers and to structural geologists because of their great lithological diversity and the relative ease with which the different beds deform during folding.   In regions of folded coal-bearing strata an investigator must closely observe the order of succession of beds, for the sequence commonly has top and bottom significance.   Unconformities that are common and likely to be conspicuous locally should be sought. Individual coal seams may exhibit compositional variations across the vein, and commonly they contain internal lithological and structural features that can be used as top and bottom criteria.   Inasmuch as coal-bearing strata are intensely folded in many parts of the world (*e.g.*, Appalachian Valley of the United States, Cape Breton Island in Nova Scotia, Belgium, and Germany), the geologist who is called upon to determine the structure of coal veins in these regions will need to take

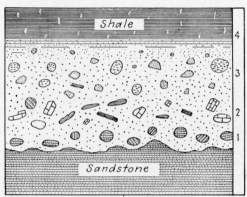

FIG. 37.—Diagram of a conglomerate with heterogeneous components.   In this kind of conglomerate it is important to determine the lithologic sequence of the boulders since they can be used to determine the date when certain formations were first eroded, when igneous masses were unroofed, etc.   Here the sandstone was first eroded and boulders of the rock incorporated in the basal part of the conglomerate (1).   Then followed a period when marble and slate boulders and pebbles were brought in (2).   The last components to come in were quartzite boulders, quartz fragments, and large masses of granite (3).   Inasmuch as the period of gravel deposition ended with sand followed by mud deposition, it is to be concluded that after the batholith had been uncovered the local conditions changed and erosion of the land produced only finer clastics.   (Art. 43.)

advantage of every feature of the coals and their contiguous strata in his investigations.   A few of these features are considered briefly in following paragraphs.

46. Roof and Floor of Coal Beds.—The stratigraphic position of a coal bed, with reference to underlying and overlying lithological units, in a typical cyclothem is fully discussed in Art. 19 and need not be considered here.   The generally expected relations are well stated by Stutzer and Noé (1940: 211, 213) as follows:

> The rocks overlying bituminous beds are usually very uniform, thinly laminated, and of dark color.   Well-preserved plant fossils are commonly contained in them.

The rock beneath the coal bed is less uniform.   It is lighter than the roof. Well-preserved plant fossils are rare, but roots are commonly present.

When the coal is mined, the roof rock usually breaks into parallel slabs; the floor rock, into irregular pieces, like soil.   These are only general characteristics of roof and floor material.   In particular, every seam has a distinctive variety of floor material.

In North American coal sequences, coal beds, as Wanless points out in his letter quoted in Art. 19,

. . . almost always have an underclay, or a shale, siltstone or sandstone floor which contain stigmaria and other root traces.   Such material may form the roof of a coal bed, especially if the coal is split into several benches, in which case the underclay of one bench may serve as the roof of the next lower one.   Limestones are almost never present below coals and in the very few cases where I have found them in that position they also contained root impressions along with the marine fossils.   In the Appalachian coal field, the roof of at least the uppermost bench of a coal is very commonly either a well laminated shale which contains stem or leaf impressions or an unconformable sandstone. . . .

[See also Wanless (1934: 115–116) and Grim (1939: 1998).]

In one area in southwestern Indiana thin irregular coal beds rest directly on an undulating sandstone surface and in another on an eroded limestone (Fig. 38).   The literature on coal contains references to many other kinds of material known to lie directly beneath coal beds [Twenhofel (1932: 355–357)].

In sequences of intensely deformed coal-bearing strata, therefore, the relations of a coal seam to adjacent beds and to the lithology of those beds may indicate the top or bottom of the sequence.   Wanless (see letter quoted in Art. 19) recently called the author's attention to an example of completely inverted strata in a Pennsylvania anthracite mine.   The inversion was discovered by noting the relation of coal to underclay and to overlying black shale with pyritic concretions.

47. RELATIONS OF COALS TO CONTIGUOUS STRATA.—Coal beds and the adjacent strata associated with them exhibit an amazing diversity of structural and sedimentary unconformity (Figs. 38, 39).   Furthermore, coal seams themselves contain many unusual structural features which prove that coal is easily deformed and that the deformation can be carried to such extremes that the material flows readily under differential stress.   Some of the deformation was essentially contemporaneous, some took place shortly after the coal layer was covered, and some was much later [Stutzer and Noé (1940: 331–334)].

A few of the many instructive relations of coal beds that are particularly pertinent to the purpose of the present work are discussed in following paragraphs, but anyone who plans to do geological work in a coal-bearing region should first acquaint himself with such standard works on coal as those of Ashley (1899), Moore (1940: 228–250), Stutzer and Noé (1940), Thiessen,[1] Stevenson, David White, and others.

48. VERTICAL COMPOSITIONAL VARIATION IN COAL BEDS.—Brief

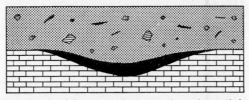

FIG. 38.—A miniature coal basin in a depression eroded into Pennsylvanian limestone. The lenticular coal seam lies at the base of the Merom sandstone and is exposed near Merom, Indiana. The basin is about 5 m. (16 ft.) across, and the coal seam at the thickest point about 0.3 m. (1 ft.). (Arts. 46, 47, 132.) (*Modified after Kindle in Ashley*, 1899, *Indiana Dept. Geol. Nat. Resources Ann. Rept.*, **23** : 909, *Fig.* 625.)

notice should be taken of the possibility that there may be vertical compositional variation in some thick beds of coal. It has been reported that the lower part of a thick seam is quite likely to be considerably more woody in nature than the upper part. Furthermore, Stutzer and Noé (1940: 229) cite a sequence of nine coals in which the gas content on a pure coal basis decreases downward from 33 to 27 per cent. There are probably other compositional variations that might have top and bottom significance, but this general subject has not been investigated in the present work.

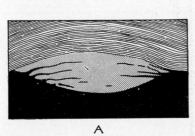
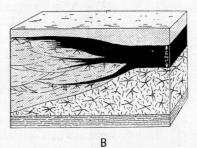

| A | B |

FIG. 39.—Relations of coal beds to contiguous strata (Arts. 47, 147). *A.* Sandstone "roll," or channel filling (much reduced), that apparently was formed during or soon after deposition of the coal. The subsequent shale arches gently over the sandstone body and shows no evidence of deformation. There should be deformation if the sand had been deposited on mud, and the shale laminae should be flat and cut out if the sand had been deposited in a channel eroded into shale. *B.* Sketch showing marginal relations of a 1.2-m. coal bed in one of the German coal basins. The coal bed lies upon stigmarian shale, interfingers laterally with cross-laminated sandstone, and is overlain by massive sandstone. (*A adapted from Ashley*, 1899, *Indiana Dept. Geol. Nat. Resources Ann. Rept.*, **23** : 47, *Fig.* 8. *B after Kukuk*, 1936, *Glückauf*, **72** : 1026, *Abb.* 15.)

49. Seasonal Banding in Carbonaceous Sandstone.—At the 501st meeting of the Washington Academy of Sciences, David White (1933: 567 –568) is reported to have " . . . exhibited specimens of layered grits of

[1] Consult this author's name, and those which follow, in the several bibliographies of the U.S. Geological Survey—*Bulls.* 746, 747, 823, 937, 938, and 949—for many important articles on coal and coal-bearing strata.

Lower Pennsylvanian age from Orange and Perrin [Perry] counties, Indiana," which were described as follows:

Lighter colored layers, about ⅜ inch thick, which are used in the manufacture of whetstones, are separated by thinner zones in which there are two dark bands richer in carbonates and organic matter. The dark bands, correlated by Dr. White with times of slack sedimentation, are believed by him to reflect a seasonal hot dry climate, since xerophytic plant fossils are found associated with them [Fig. 40].

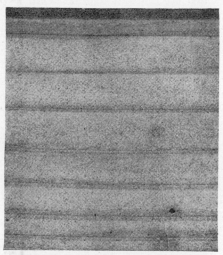

Griswold (1892: 158) and Kindle (1895: 349) had previously described these unusual whetstone rocks,[1] and it would appear from their descriptions that the layers not only have a double band of carbonaceous matter in the upper part but also grade from fine sand at the base to argillaceous material in the top portion (Fig. 40). This unusual example of possible seasonal banding may have been formed in somewhat the same way

FIG. 40.—Hindostan whetstone rock from Pennsylvanian Mansfield sandstone of Indiana (X2). The individual layers show coarse texture in the lower three-fourths; this grades upward into much finer and lighter colored material of argillaceous nature. The top is marked by a single or double film of dark-colored carbonaceous matter, which David White (1933: 567–568) has ascribed to seasonal changes. (Art. 49.)

as the lamination reported by Johnston (1922: 115–129) in the subaqueous

[1] Griswold (1892: 158) studied the fine-grained sandstone in thin section and reported on it as follows:

Specimen yellowish gray in color, homogeneous, and presenting the appearance of a very fine-grained sandstone. A few cavities exist between the grains. Small quartz grains .02 mm. in diameter constitute the greater part of the groundmass. The uniform size of the quartz grains is remarkable; there are no large grains of quartz, but some of the small ones are thick enough to give low polarization colors. Besides the quartz there is much iron and earthy material, and a little muscovite mica present. The earthy material and iron are in small masses about the size of quartz fragments, and it is undoubtedly the large amount of these substances present which gives the stone its softness, though at the same time the iron acts as a cement to bind the grains of silica together.

Kindle (1895: 349) described the rock as follows:

. . . the stone is a bluish-gray color, and contains some argillaceous matter with very thin layers of clay between the strata. The surfaces of the strata have the rough or wavy appearance of ripple marks. The upper surface of the layer is always slightly softer than the lower. This fact is recognized and taken advantage of by the quarrymen, who always rule the slab with a scribe awl on the upper surface. The greater softness of the upper part of the stratum is probably due to that portion containing a larger per cent. of earthy matter than the lower.

topset beds of the Fraser River delta. In the deltaic deposits thin layers of vegetable matter alternate with tidal laminations formed during freshets, which brought in silt and fine sand. The bipartite laminae, which are interpreted as seasonal deposits, average about 50 mm. (2 in.) thick.

50. Vertical Variation in Texture of Medium- and Fine-grained Clastic Rocks.—One of the most widely used sedimentary criteria for top and bottom determination in clastic rocks of medium- to fine-grained texture is graded bedding, or the gradation in texture from coarse at the base to fine at the top within a single bed. The use of this feature in coarser clastics is discussed in Art. 37. Here we shall consider sediments in the sandstone and shale ranges of texture.

The principle of graded bedding may be stated as follows: *In a single bipartite layer, the texture grades from coarse in the lower part of the stratum to fine in the upper part, the finer upper part ending abruptly against the coarse base of the next overlying layer.* Textural variation of this sort occurs in all types of clastic sedimentary rocks from conglomerates to claystones and is developed on a scale ranging from microscopic to grossly macroscopic. Where repeated many times in an unbroken succession, the feature is obviously due to repetition of similar conditions of deposition. The ultimate cause of the repetition has been ascribed to seasonal changes, rhythmic rise and fall of sea level, tidal variations, periodic earthquakes[1] and seaquakes,[2] and other less probable phenomena. To judge from the different aspects of graded bedding, it seems likely that more than one cause can produce it.

When used with discrimination and with an understanding of its limitations, textural variation of the graded bedding type is a reliable top and bottom criterion. Used indiscriminately, however, it is almost certain to give confusing and perhaps even erroneous results. A case in point is cited by Cooke (1931: 71–74)[3], who found the texture of certain coarse Cambrian quartzites to grade from fine at the base of a layer to coarse at the top—the reverse of the normal textural profile in graded

---

[1] Derry (1939: 133) recently suggested that the graded bedding of the Pre-Cambrian Timiskaming graywackes of Canada " . . . might be due to earthquakes accompanying geosynclinal deposition."

[2] Bailey (1930: 89) has suggested " . . . that graded sandstone beds are often the records of sea-quakes (movements communicated to sea water during disturbances of the bottom). The coastal fringe of unconsolidated current-carried sand and mud would provide a source for the material."

[3] Cooke (1931: 71) seriously questions the reliability of the generally accepted rule that, "when a sedimentary bed varies in grain from coarse on one side to fine on the other, the coarse-grained side was the bottom, the fine-grained side the top," for he found the reverse to be true in beds of the supposed Cambrian Caldwell quartzite of the

bedding. From this he pertinently emphasized that graded bedding can be relied upon for top and bottom determination only in those formations having a succession of layers showing concordant textural change. In addition to this important warning, another should also be heeded. It should always be established that the textural variation present in a layer is original and the result of deposition, for in some metamorphosed sediments the grain-size variation has been reversed by development of large crystals in the finer, more argillaceous portion of the bipartite layer (Art. 260).

51. RHYTHMIC GRADED BEDDING.—Uniform and constant textural variation in each layer of a sequence of medium- and fine-grained clastic sedimentary rocks can often be used successfully to determine the order of succession. Typical graded bedding is best developed in single bipar-

---

Thetford district, Quebec. Individual layers of pebbly to coarse or coarse to fine quartzite, ranging in thickness from a few centimeters to a meter ("a few inches to several feet thick"), alternate with layers of slate up to 0.3 m. (1 ft.) thick, and the whole sequence is closely folded, with some dips vertical.

He found that textural gradation in the quartzite layers gave evidence diametrically opposed to that indicated by drag folds and cleavage-bedding relations. Because of this disparity, Cooke (1931: 73) states:

. . . we can only conclude, therefore, that in the deposition of moderately thick beds of sediments such as these quartzites, conditions not yet understood may cause reversal of the normal variation of grain between top and bottom. This being the case, it is evident that it is unsafe to use variation of grain as evidence for structure, unless thoroughly checked by the more reliable methods of drag-folds and cleavage-bedding relationships.

Discussion at the time when Cooke read his paper brought out the fact that P. S. Warren had observed similar textural gradation in flat-lying sedimentary rocks of Alberta. W. A. Johnson suggested that [Cooke (1931: 73)] ". . . the sequence of coarse to fine grain within a bed should be used for determining structure only in those beds whose material was all fine enough to be taken into suspension in water." Cooke (1931: 73) then adds that "if this prove true, it will seldom be possible, from megascopic examination in the field, to distinguish the top and bottom of a bed by this means."

Barrell (1917: 803) long ago reported reversal of the normal ascending coarse to fine gradation in the rhythmically banded "ribbon slates" of Pennsylvania. These slates are characterized by regularly spaced bipartite layers consisting of a lower soft black shale overlain by a layer of clear gray sand. Barrell concluded that the thythmic banding represented periodic storms which produced unusually powerful waves which stirred up the bottom. He was led to this conclusion by the experimental work of Kindle (1917c: 906–909), who had shown that if silt is allowed to settle, after being stirred up in fresh water, the coarsest particles are deposited first and the finest last, whereas, if the experiment be repeated in salt water, the order of deposition is reversed, because the finest particles coagulate into masses (flocks), which settle quickly, so that the slimes are deposited first and the very fine sand last. This can hardly be an explanation of the case Cooke (1931: 71–74) describes, however, because of the coarseness of the original sediment involved.

tite layers or laminae.   In each layer coarse material forms the basal part, beginning abruptly and grading upward into finer and finer material, whereas the finest material forms the upper part, grading downward into coarser particles and ending upward sharply against the base of the overlying layer (Figs. 41, 42).

Individual bipartite laminae and layers range from thickness so small that the variation is microscopic [Leith (1913: 132)] to units over 1.5 m. (5 ft.) thick [Read (1936: 472–473)].[1]   Sequences of rocks with graded bedding have been reported as thick as 10,000 m. (over 30,000 ft).   The Pre-Cambrian Halifax formation of Nova Scotia is reported by Beylea and Scott (1935: 225) to have such a thickness and to " . . . have been laid down in a broad sinking geosyncline," which received seasonal floods of sand and silt that were deposited under shallow-water conditions to form the succession of classified laminae.   The laminae themselves average several centimeters in thickness. Douglas, Milner, and MacLean (1938: 37–38) measured one sequence containing 684 bipartite layers and attempted a statistical analysis of these to determine whether or not they exhibited any periodicity like that in varves, growth rings of trees, and

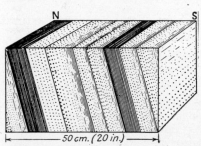

Fig. 41.—Graded bedding in the Carboniferous Cambridge shale-sandstone sequence lying upon the Squantum tillite in Boston Harbor, Massachusetts. Thin beds of well-graded sand and silt alternate with layers of siltstone and uniformly textured sandstone. Each of the layers exhibiting graded bedding is sharply separated from the underlying shale or fine sandstone and grades from coarsest material at the base to finest at the top. In some exposures the sandstone layers grade upward into siltstone without a conspicuous break. In some parts of the same sequence as many as a dozen layers with graded bedding may succeed each other without interruption by a shale layer or a bed of uniformly textured sand. (Art. 51.)

sunspots.   Their results were inconclusive other than to support the hypothesis of seasonal deposition.

Theoretically, particles in a mobile medium should come to rest with those of similar size and shape or weight settling together, the coarser and

---

[1] Graded bedding in unusually thick strata is well developed in the highly altered Dalradian rocks (Pre-Cambrian) of Banff, Scotland.   Read (1936: 472–473) states that, in a series of coarse grits and andalusite schists dipping steeply to the east and southeast,

. . . the western edge of each grit band is coarsely pebbly, and that toward the east in each band the pebbles become finer and that at the east margin of each bed a few crystals of andalusite appear.   The change in grain-size and abundance of pebbles takes place perfectly gradually from one side to the other of innumerable grit bands up to 5 feet in thickness.   This can be interpreted only as graded bedding, however disquieting the scale may be. . . . All the observations on graded bedding in grits hereabouts point to an upward succession towards the east or east-south-east.

heavier going down first and the finer and lighter last.   Hence, under ideal conditions (*i.e.*, in a large body of relatively quiet water), graded bedding should form often.   It should be least well developed on bottoms stirred up each time by the influx of sediment, as determined experimentally by Cox and Dake (1916: 50–52), and better developed in wind-laid ash and tuff deposits[1] and should attain its greatest perfection in

Courtesy of J. D. Allan

Fig. 42.—Graded bedding in graywacke of early Pre-Cambrian Yellowknife group of Wray Lake area, Northwest Territories, Canada. The tops of beds, as determined by gradation in grain size, is in the direction of the arrow.   J. D. Allan, who took the photograph, describes the outcrop as follows (personal communication, Apr. 18, 1941): "The rock is a fairly fine-grained sediment.   It is well-bedded and in places the beds are highly crenulated.   The thickness of the beds in this outcrop is about three to six inches as indicated by the scale of the compass.   Each bed shows a gradation from a relatively coarse sandy phase to a fine shaly phase.   In general from three-fourths to four-fifths of the bed is sandy material and the rest is shaly.   The gradation from sand to shale is rapid in any one bed.   The repeated gradation is believed to show a cyclic bedding of some sort, and the finer material is believed to indicate the tops of the beds.   In many outcrops the gradation is evident, as the change in grain size can be seen and also the finer material is darker in color than the coarser material.   The photograph shows the change in grain size with a color difference.   The arrow indicates the top of the bed.   If a hammer is scratched across the outcrop, it gives a gritty sound on the sandy part and a softer sound on the shaly part.   Thin sections show that the shaly part consists mainly of fine-grained chlorite and sericite, whereas the sandy part contains grains of detrital quartz."   Where metamorphosed by granitic intrusives the textural gradation of this rock is reversed as shown in Fig. 377.   (Arts. 51, 262.)

sedimentary deposits laid down originally in quiet or but little disturbed bodies of water.

When employed with discrimination, rhythmic graded bedding has been found to be a fairly reliable top and bottom criterion.   There are some conditions of sedimentation, however, under which textural varia-

[1] In a visit to the active volcano El Parícutin, in southwestern Mexico, in the summer of 1944, the author saw along the road from Uruapan to the volcano several exposures of ash showing excellent graded bedding.   The individual layers, presumably representing successive ash falls, averaged 1 to 5 cm. thick and consisted of a black, coarser lower part, usually constituting more than half the thickness of the layer, and a lighter colored finer grained upper part.   The coarser basal part graded into the finer upper part in layer after layer.

tion in contiguous strata can range from fine material below to coarse
above.   Therefore, the criterion should always be checked against other
evidence if possible [see Kindle (1917: 907–908) and Twenhofel (1932: 613
–614)].

Graded bedding appears to have been first used early in the present
century by both British and North American geologists investigating the
Pre-Cambrian rocks of Scotland and of the Canadian Shield, respectively.
Bailey (1930: 85) states: "I first recognized graded bedding—and its
significance as a criterion of succession—in a gritty quartzite . . . in
the Spring of 1906. . . . I have never lost sight of this observation."
Leith (1913: 132) mentioned the feature in the first edition of his "Structural Geology" in 1913, and 3 years later Cox and Dake (1916: 50)
stated that so far as known to them it was first employed some years
earlier in northern Wisconsin under the direction of W. O. Hotchkiss,
state geologist.

During the intervening years from these early citations to the present,
graded bedding has been mentioned in countless publications by Canadian
and American geologists[1], but it does not appear to have been used abroad
to any extent previous to 1927.   In that year, the well-known Scottish
geologist, E. B. Bailey, was invited by R. M. Field to join the Princeton
Summer School in an excursion across Canada.   During this trip Bailey
(1930: 77) had an opportunity to study the field use of both graded
bedding and cross-lamination (current bedding), so that when he returned
to Scotland, he immediately applied the criteria to determining the attitude
of certain deformed rocks in the Scottish Highlands.   Some 3 years
earlier, in 1924, Vogt had studied these rocks in the field with S. Buckstaff
and O. N. Rove, two geologists from the University of Wisconsin, and the
party had found many examples of cross-lamination which showed clearly
and unequivocally that Bailey's previously published section was
inverted.   Upon further field examinations, Bailey himself (1930: 77–92)
applied the criteria of graded bedding and cross-lamination and readily
accepted the conclusions of Vogt, Buckstaff, and Rove, meanwhile also
publishing an excellent discussion of the nature and mode of formation of
the two features.   Since Bailey's enthusiastic application of graded
bedding as a top and bottom criterion, it has been referred to frequently
by British and Continental geologists [Bailey (1930: 77–92; 1936: 1713–
1726), Becker (1939: 6), and Hills (1930); see also Tanton (1930: 74)].

---

[1] Among the more important articles and reports are those of Barrell (1917: 799),
Collins (1925: 66–67), Tanton (1926: 44–45; 1930: 74), Bailey (1930), Grout (1932:
261), Allison (1933), Beylea (1935), Beylea and Scott (1935), Douglas, Milner, and
MacLean (1938), Shenon and McConnel (1940), Gruner (1941: 1621), Lahee (1941:
89–90), Nevin (1941), and Billings (1942: 72).

A few examples of typical graded bedding are cited here in order to present the general nature and distribution of the feature.

Merritt (1934: 365) reports that graded bedding is common in the Pre-Cambrian Seine clastics of the Rainy Lake and Seine River regions of Canada and that it proved a reliable top and bottom criterion, showing concordant results when checked against cross-lamination. Attention is called to the fact that graded bedding and cross-lamination do not occur together in the same bed, but rather in different though closely contiguous strata. Bailey (1930: 84–85) had emphasized this fact earlier and had pointed out that, whereas the two sedimentary features do not ordinarily occur together, one may give way to the other or the two may alternate in successive layers. In his words (page 85), " . . . graded bedding and current bedding are the distinguishing marks of two different sandstone facies, the one facies as important as the other." Collins (1925: 66) reports a variation of graded bedding in the Pre-Cambrian Gowganda formation as follows:

The greywacke matrix is in regular layers usually about ⅛-inch thick, but ranging from that down to ¼₀ of an inch. In some cases a coarse-grained layer alternates with a fine one, but ordinarily each layer is coarsest at the bottom and becomes steadily finer grained towards the top [Fig. 123]. This produces a structure comparable to the annual rings of wood, and gives rise on weathered surfaces to a delicate banding. . . . The lower part of each lamina is somewhat gritty or sandy owing to an abundance of quartz and feldspar grains; towards the top the material becomes finer-grained and more like an indurated mud. This progression from coarse material upward into finer in each layer affords a means of distinguishing top from bottom in upturned strata.

Bell (1929: 23–24) describes the remarkable graded bedding of the Pre-Cambrian Halifax formation as follows:

. . . a uniform sequence of fine, quartzitic, chloritic, and micaceous slates of prevailing dark green-grey colour, but with a marked rhythmic banded appearance due to rapid alternation of dark carbonaceous micaceous layers with lighter siliceous bands. The siliceous layers are commonly minutely crossbedded.

Bell, like Beylea and Scott (1935: 225) and Douglas, Milner, and MacLean (1938: 34), cites the recurrent cross-lamination as evidence that the 10,000-m.-thick section of clastics was deposited in shallow water in a slowly subsiding geosyncline.

Ruedemann (1942: 38) recently described a division of the Lower Cambrian Nassau formation of New York as " . . . an endless repetition of greenish gray shales with thin greenish quartzite bands (from an inch to half a foot [25 to 150 mm.]). . . . " Several rhythmically banded formations with graded bedding are mentioned in the "Lexicon of Geological Names" by Wilmarth (1938).

52. INTERRUPTED GRADED BEDDING.—Some sedimentary rocks have thin sequences of strata with graded bedding, alternating with thick or thin, uniformly textured beds of sand and silt. The two types of bedding are usually separated by local erosional unconformities. A succession of this kind is found in the stratified clastic beds overlying the Squantum tillite and in the Wamsutta red-bed sequence of the Narragansett Basin of Rhode Island (Fig. 43). It is believed to have been deposited in an environment where conditions favorable for development of graded bedding were occasionally interrupted by erosion of the bottom.

Interrupted graded bedding is just as useful as rhythmic bedding in determining order of succession and has been employed successfully in this way for structural work. Similar sequences of sandstone and shale, with some units showing graded bedding, should be expected in close association with ancient tillstones and tillites and in deltaic sediments.

An unusual case of what appears to be excellently developed, interrupted graded bedding in laminated glacial sands, silts, and clays of the northern glacial drifts of Britain is, according to Carruthers (1939: 315–316), who has studied them in great detail, really a "pressed melt" produced by shear. The graded layers are interpreted as "banded dirts" that represent " . . . englacial detritus, released by the rising bottom melt [page 326]." Carruthers' explanation is challenging and should be seriously considered by those interested in the study of laminated sediments in recent and ancient glacial complexes.

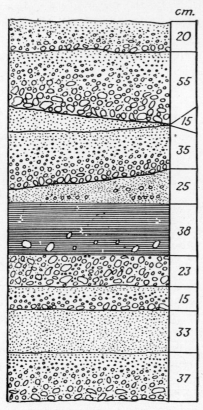

cm.

20

55

15

35

25

38

23

15

33

37

FIG. 43.—Interrupted graded bedding in Pennsylvanian Wamsutta formation along east side of Great Pond, Braintree, Mass. Conglomerate layers with graded bedding alternate with uniformly textured conglomeratic and sandstone layers. A shale layer, midway in the section, interrupts the coarser clastics. The largest pebbles in the conglomeratic layers rarely exceed 5 cm. (2 in.) in greatest dimension, and the sand particles range from very coarse to very fine. The graded bedding in this section is a reliable top and bottom criterion, for the direction of textural gradiation is the same in each of the several layers. (Art. 52.)

53. VARVED SEDIMENTARY ROCKS.—Many Pleistocene glacial deposits of silty clays are composed of thin layers called varves that give the deposit a characteristic rhythmically banded appearance. Each varve, which is now generally accepted to be an annual layer, consists of a basal part of coarser material, deposited during the summer, which grades upward into a finer textured and somewhat darker colored part, which supposedly is the winter deposit. The finer material ends abruptly against the base of the next summer's deposit (Figs. 44, 45). Order of succession usually is obvious from the texture in undisturbed sections of Pleistocene varved clays, and Sayles (1914, 1919, 1924, 1929) has demonstrated that the same textural variation holds for the ancient varved slates associated with the Carboniferous Squantum tillite.

There are many publications dealing directly or indirectly with the nature, mode, and environment of deposition, distribution, and geological significance of varved sediments and rocks. A few of these are cited here, but no attempt has been made to accumulate a comprehensive bibliography.[1] It now seems to be generally accepted that varved sediments represent sequences of annual deposits made in quiet waters of either fresh or brackish waters [possibly even salt waters; see Fraser (1929: 49–60)].

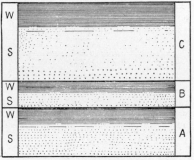

FIG. 44.—Diagram showing the typical bipartite or didactic nature of varves. The summer deposit *S* is coarse to fine silt; the winter deposit *W*, very fine silt and some clay. The contact of the winter layer with the deposit of the preceding summer is somewhat transitional; with the succeeding summer deposit, sharp. Varve *A* shows a summer deposit of moderate thickness; *B* has the two parts nearly equal; *C* has a considerable thickness of summer deposit as compared with that of winter. In general the thickness of the summer deposit has a greater range than that of the winter deposit. See Fig. 45. (Art. 53.)

Erratic boulders found embedded in Pleistocene and older varved sediments usually have been interpreted as ice-rafted [Sayles (1914, 1919, 1929) and Brigham (1932: 373–378)].

Early Pre-Cambrian varved slates have been reported from northern Ontario by Pettijohn (1936: 621–628; 1943: 949–954); late Pre-Cambrian or early Cambrian ones from Virginia by Thiesmeyer (1939: 109–118); late Paleozoic varved sediments are associated with the Squantum tillite of eastern Massachusetts (Sayles 1914, 1919, 1924, 1929); and Coleman

[1] See Sayles (1914, 1919, 1924, 1929); Johnston (1922: 115–120; 1922a: 376–390); Reeds (1923: 371–380); Antevs (1922: 1–6; 1925: 171–172); Coleman (1926: xxxviii, xxxix, 37, 233–235); Tanton (1926: 44); Wallace (1927: 109–118); Fraser (1929: 49–60); Bradley (1931a: 318–330; 1937: 32–42); Twenhofel (1932: 606–618); Rubey (1933: 325–338); Rittenhouse (1934: 110–120); Pettijohn (1936: 621–628; 1943: 949–957); Burwash (1938: 3–6); Thiesmeyer (1938: 326–327).

(1926) has reported ancient varved rocks from many parts of the world.

54. MISCELLANEOUS RHYTHMIC BEDDING.—Geological literature contains many references to rhythmically bedded sedimentary rocks consisting of large numbers of thin varvelike laminae. The rhythmic stratification in these rocks has usually been ascribed to seasonal deposi-

A   B

Courtesy of F. J. Pettijohn

FIG. 45.—Varved sediments. *A.* Pleistocene glacial-lake varved clay in an exposure on the shore of Wabigoon Lake, near Barclay, Ont. The darker bands are stiff winter clay; the lighter, summer silt. *B.* Archean varved slate. The darker bands are slate; the lighter, siltstone. The squarish pits in the siltstone band near the knife blade are cavities left by weathering out of pyrite cubes. Note the diagonal fracturing of brittle siltstone, which does not pass through the less competent slate bands. (Art. 53.) (*After Pettijohn*, 1943, *Bull. Geol. Soc. Am.*, **54**: 949, *Plate 8, Figs.* 1, 2.)

tion of some kind. All have in common a constant change in lithology, texture, or some other physical characteristic from the top of the lamina to the bottom. Several representative examples are cited in the following paragraph. Their use as top and bottom criteria is uncertain. Each must be judged on its own merits.

Many years ago Davis (1918: 386–394) described the remarkable rhythmic banding of the Franciscan radiolarian cherts, and several writers have since discussed the nature and cause of the rhythms. Bramlette (1934: 575) has described somewhat similar rhythmic bedding in the Monterey shale as follows:

. . . the beds are generally between one and two inches thick, and each shows a distinct sequence of deposition with sand at the base, grading upward through finer clastic material to an upper zone of organic deposition—largely diatoms. The various processes that might produce such bedding have been considered and the tentative conclusion reached that annual cycles best fit the evidence, that is, that these layers are marine varves. [See also Bramlette (1946).]

Twenty years ago Wallace (1927: 118) reported that the Dakota sandstone of northwestern Manitoba has successions of 1-in. (25-mm.) lignite bands separated by 2- to 3-in. (50- to 75-mm.) sand layers. He suggested that these alternating layers might represent seasonal banding. A few years earlier Johnston (1922: 115–129) had reported seasonal lamination in the deposits of the Fraser River delta. More recently David White (1933: 567–568) explained as seasonal banding an unusual alternation of dark and light layers in Pennsylvanian whetstone sandstones of southern Indiana (Art. 49), and Vanderhoof (1934: 332) ascribed to the same cause the banding in an asphalt deposit at McKittrick, Calif. Bradley (1931a: 318 330; 1937: 32–42) described and listed the literature on nonglacial marine varves and in a later paper (1938: 162–163) gave a brief annotated bibliography on cyclic variations in climates as indicated by pre-Pleistocene nonglacial varves. About the same time Thiesmeyer (1938: 326–327) summarized the criteria of seasonal and annual accumulations in sediments, and with Storm [Thiesmeyer and Storm (1938: 1964)] pointed out certain features that indicate seasonal banding in silicified argillites at Chapel Hill, N.C. An unusual varvelike deposit was recently described by Keller (1939: 32–35). It was discovered in a solution channel.

55. Textural Variation Due to Importation of Foreign Material.— Foreign materials such as quartz and feldspar grains and tiny rock fragments may suddenly appear in abundance in a limestone section and then gradually die out upward in succeeding layers, completely disappearing within a few centimeters. Such a condition indicates a sudden importation of particles from some near-by source by wind or water currents.

Several quartz-flooded limestone units of this sort are present in the basal part of the Platteville formation in Wisconsin. In dolomitic limestone of the same age at Kentland, Ind. (Fig. 46), where the strata are almost vertical, this criterion was used, along with other features, to establish the top and bottom of the tilted sequence [Shrock (1937: 471–531)]. Quartz sand, blown from the Adirondack land mass into the

Cambrian seas along its eastern shore, makes its appearance in certain Upper Cambrian limestones of Vermont and diminishes upward in the same way as described in the previous examples.

56. Textural and Volumetric Variation in Accessory Minerals.— Suites of light or heavy accessory minerals and of rock fragments may appear abruptly and in abundance in a stratigraphic sequence, indicating the uncovering or renewed erosion of a particular terrane, and individual minerals may increase for some distance upward before fading out and disappearing (Fig. 47). As a general rule the suite will decrease upward gradually rather than abruptly. This criterion, which needs extensive testing in the field, should serve successfully over basins or parts of basins where the accessory mineral succession has already been determined. It should also be tested on massive sandstones lacking the usual sedimentary features [see Krynine (1940)].

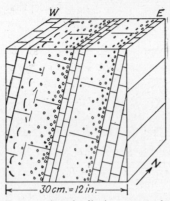

Fig. 46.—Steeply dipping, westward facing, thin-bedded Ordovician limestones exposed in the north wall of the main quarry near Kentland, Ind. Two of the thicker layers contain a concentration of rounded quartz grains, which are abundant in the basal part but sporadic in the upper. The quartz-bearing layers have a sharp contact with the underlying lithographic bed, and the scattered quartz grains do not reach upward to the next succeeding layer. The quartz grains were washed in from near-by areas, where the St. Peter sandstone was being eroded, and are characteristically most abundant in the earlier, or lower, part of the beds in which they occur. One of the beds also contains scattered brachiopod valves, most of which show, by their westward convexity, that the sequence is not overturned. Here two sedimentary criteria are mutually corroborative. (Arts. 55, 178.)

57. Textural Variation along Contact of Reworking between Massive Sandstones. A sea, encroaching on a sand terrane, resorts the material it encounters, removing to a distant area the finer and lighter grains and leaving as a residue the coarser and heavier grains. The depth of such reworking is determined by wave and current action. Burial of the coarse sand as the water deepens leaves it to mark an abrupt textural change downward (Fig. 47). Upward it is likely to merge into the fine sand and silt brought in from the adjacent shore as the strand moves inland. Ulrich (1924: 93) used this criterion as a means of locating the disconformable contact between the Galesville (Dresbach) and Ironton sandstones in the Wisconsin Upper Cambrian section (see Art. 28). He described the relation as follows:

The Ironton member is composed mainly of reworked washed and relatively coarse residual grains of Dresbach sandstone, the surface of which had previously been subjected to subaërial leaching and wear. The line of the break between the two formations—Dresbach and Franconia—lies at the undulating plane where washing and sorting of the loose quartz grains of the underlying formation is first indicated.   In other words, the Ironton sandstone member extends downward to the lowest plane indicating reworking and redeposition of the weather-loosened top sands of the underlying Dresbach formation.   Commonly the new deposit includes a few grains of glauconite and other material that is not present in the undisturbed underlying beds of Dresbach sandstone.

Some of the geologists who came after him disagreed with Ulrich on the reliability of this criterion for determining order of succession and unconformity.   Certainly it deserves a rigorous field test before it can be fully accepted or rejected.

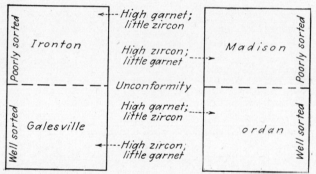

Fig. 47.—Diagrams showing how textural variation and change in content of heavy accessory minerals can be used to identify unconformities and determine tops and bottoms of beds in certain Upper Cambrian formations of Wisconsin.   The materials comprising the upper part of each of the lower sandstones were reworked and mixed with the incoming sediments, producing a poorly sorted sandstone flooded with a heavy accessory mineral not abundant in the underlying sand.   (Arts. 28, 57.)   (*Diagrams based on information furnished by G. O. Raasch.*)

58. Salinastone Sequences.—Much has been written on the general subject of salt deposits, and attention has been called to the order of succession that sometimes obtains in a salt sequence (*e.g.*, the Stassfurt deposit).

Numerous writers have pointed out that, if a large body of sea water were cut off and completely evaporated, the deposit of salts on the bottom would have the following units, in descending order (or reverse order of precipitation):

> Salts of last bitters
> NaCl (rock salt)
> $CaSO_4 \cdot nH_2O$ (anhydrite or gypsum)
> $CaCO_3$ + iron oxide (limestone and iron oxide)

The $CaSO_4$ unit would merge with $CaCO_3$ downward and with NaCl upward.   The rock salt unit would merge downward into the sulphate layer and mingle upward with bittern salts. This is an ideal sequence and probably is rare in nature. Repetition of the lower two units, however, is not so uncommon and might, under special conditions, serve as a criterion of succession. A case in point is illustrated by the following section from the Mississippian Windsor series of Nova Scotia [Bell (1921: 166–167)]:

The following generalized lithological section illustrates the rhythmic recurrence of mud deposition with chemical and organic deposits:

D. Kennetcook limestone...................................... 100′+
     Gypsum and anhydrite with *Nodosinella* bands.
     Red shale, etc.
C. Avon River limestone..................................... 45′+
     Gypsum? and red shale.
     Dolomitic and calcareous shales and sandstones, oölites, algal and *Modiola*
     bands.
B_2. Miller limestone.. 35′+
     Gypsum, anhydrite, and red shale.
B_1. Maxner limestone.. 80′+
     Gypsum, anhydrite, and red shale.
A. Basal limestone, conglomerate and quartzite.

It seems highly unlikely that folded (hence, probably recrystallized) salinastones such as gyprock and anhydrock would retain within the body of the rock important original sedimentary features which would indicate the top of the sequence. Even if some did escape destruction during folding, it is not probable that they would be useful in a typically deformed salinastone sequence because of the intense flowage usually developed [see Grabau (1920), Lindgren (1928: 328–360), and Twenhofel (1932: 460 –509)].

Strong (1937: 398) found that the position of polyhalite in certain salinastone sequences he had investigated was near the base. In discussing the mineral, he states:

This occurs as a bedded deposit sometimes intercrystallized with anhydrite.
In normal successions it is seldom found more than once, and then low down towards the base of the main rock salt deposit.

Udden (1924: 347–354) has reported, from the Permian Castile salinastone of Texas, a 450-m. (1,262-ft.) succession of rhythmically laminated anhydrite in which the laminae average less than 2 mm. in thickness. Each lamina, which is interpreted as a cycle of precipitation and sedimentation in a body of quiet water, is bipartite in nature. About 1.5 mm. is composed of clear anhydrite and 0.5 mm. consists of bituminous films and calcite or dolomite crystals. Although no statement is made concerning the relations of these two parts of a cycle, if Udden's photomicrographs are used as a basis, the thinner layer seems to grade into the anhydrite in one direction and to be more sharply separated from it in the opposite direction. It seems possible, therefore, that careful study of the core on which Udden's article is based might indicate whether or not the rhythmic lamination does provide a top and bottom criterion.

59. Tuff-Ash-Silicastone Sequences.—It has been suggested[1] that silicastones, such as cherts and radiolarites, might immediately succeed deposits of water-laid tuff and ash, inasmuch as, during and immediately after volcanic activity, there is much readily soluble silica available to streams for transport to adjacent bodies of water. Unusual numbers of Radiolaria, diatoms, sponges, and other silica-precipitating organisms might well indicate strong influx of silica.

This criterion has not been tested in the field or by study of the literature, but it is mentioned here with the hope that some investigator will be interested enough to study the suggestion further.

[1] Oral discussion with R. J. McEwen, June 16, 1943, at that time head of the Mercury Section of the Miscellaneous Minerals Division of the War Production Board at Washington, D.C.

CHAPTER IV

FEATURES OF SEDIMENTARY ROCKS (II)

II. FEATURES ON UPPER- AND UNDERSURFACES OF SEDIMENTARY BEDS

60. Introduction.—In Art. 6 attention is called to the fact that many useful and reliable top and bottom features and structures are preserved on the upper- and undersurfaces of sedimentary layers. It follows, therefore, that exposed bedding surfaces are ideal places to search for these features. If such surfaces are not exposed, the next possibility is a section transecting the contacts between contiguous beds. It is commonly possible, from such transverse sections alone, to identify top and bottom.

Surface features are of many kinds and of both primary and secondary origin. They range in size from microscopic on the one hand to large, easily visible, and readily identifiable features on the other. They exhibit different degrees of efficacy for determining on which surface of the bed they lie.

They include ripple marks and all sorts of similar regular and irregular ridges and depressions; surface irregularities made by boulders and masses of sand sinking into soft muds; mud cracks and associated features resulting from their disruption (*e.g.*, penecontemporaneous sharpstone conglomerates); inorganic markings including wave marks and impressions of many kinds; organic markings and objects such as tracks, trails, and coprolites; pit and mound structures; and surface effects (fulgurites) of lightning and of forest fires.

Inasmuch as many of the features are formed on or in beach sands, the possibility of their being preserved is determined to a large extent by the conditions on the beach. Kindle (1936: 16–22) and Thompson (1937: 723–751) have discussed these conditions in some detail. Features formed in a humid climate are not likely to be preserved except under unusual conditions [Krynine (1935: 96–97)].

61. Ripple-mark.—The familiar ridge and trough configuration—ripple marks—on surfaces of loose granular materials such as snow and sand has long been recognized as the result of wind or water moving across such surfaces. The ridges and intervening troughs exhibit great range in size and variation in shape and pattern. Because they are one of the commonest and most widespread of original sedimentary features, they have been described and illustrated in countless reports. Certain of them are quite useful in determining tops and bottoms of beds, whereas others may be misleading unless their variations are recognized.

In the present work ripple-mark will be used to signify the surface sculpture produced by individual ridges and troughs. Ripple mark, written without the hyphen, refers to a single complete ripple, and ripple marks is the plural designation.

62. *Definition.*—Ripple-mark refers to the undulating surface sculpture produced in noncoherent granular materials by the wind, by currents

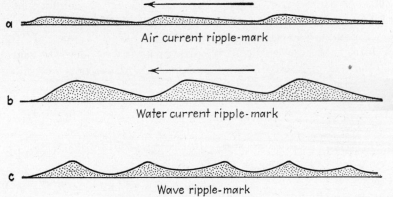

FIG. 48.—Diagrammatic profiles of the three common types of ripple-mark. (Arts. 62, 67.) (*Modified after Kindle, 1917c, Bull. Geol. Soc. Am., 28: 912, Fig. 7.*)

of water, and by the agitation of water in wave action. The usual sculpture consists of low ridges separated by shallow troughs and is of two fundamental types. The current-produced ripple has an asymmetrical form; the wave-produced, a symmetrical form (Fig. 48). These may be superimposed upon each other to produce many compound patterns. Certain types of ripple marks are reliable as top and bottom criteria; others are indeterminate; and still others are useless for this purpose (see Arts. 64, 72, and 74).

The ridges may anastomose or parallel each other, they may be symmetrical or asymmetrical in transverse section, and their crests may be sharp, rounded, or flattened. They may be far apart in proportion to their height above troughs, in which case the ripple is said to have a high index, or they may be close together, making a ripple of low index (Fig. 49). They may constitute a single system of equally developed parallel ridges, a single system of alternating large and small ridges, a double system in which one set of minor ridges superimposed transversely on a major set results in a reticulate structure, or a double system with the two sets about equally strong and the reticulation essentially uniform over the entire surface; or the ridges may be so disposed as to make a confused sculpture in which no orderly arrangement is obvious.

The troughs may be rounded or slightly flattened by filling, symmetrical or asymmetrical in transverse section, and anastomosing or parallel in plan. They exhibit the same symmetry or asymmetry as the adjacent ridges and the same general ground plan. In addition, they may contain accumulations of organic debris, silt particles, mica flakes,

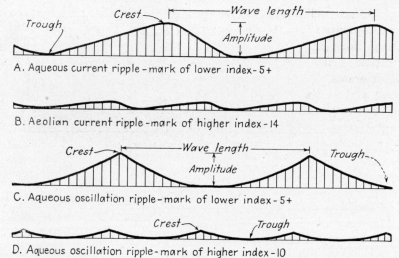

FIG. 49.—Diagrams showing range of index in ripple-mark. The ripple index is the number obtained in dividing the wave length by the amplitude. Indexes of aqueous-current ripple-mark range from less than 5 to more than 15; those of aeolian ripple-mark are considerably greater. Oscillation ripple marks have indexes ranging from less than 5 to 8 or 10. (Arts. 62, 67.)

grains of heavy minerals and bits of rock, and coarse quartz grains, because of being depressions where these materials can be trapped and buried (Fig. 50).

Ripple marks range from microscopic features to gigantic undulations with wave lengths of several kilometers and amplitudes of several meters [Kindle (1917, 1936) and Bucher (1919)]. The commonest and most useful for the present purpose are those which are developed on a relatively small scale with wave lengths of a few centimeters and amplitudes of a few millimeters.

Lobate and scalloped structures are commonly associated with ripple-mark and probably form under essentially similar conditions. Several of these are described in Arts. 67, 75, and 78.

Ripple-marked surfaces on fine sand and silt are commonly sculptured by rill marks and other miniature erosional features, imprinted with the tiny craters formed by falling raindrops and hailstones, and tracked up with the footprints made by passing animals and fowls or crawling and burrowing lowlier organisms (Fig. 51).   Similar assemblages of significant surface markings are to be expected in such formations as the Upper Devonian clastics of New York and Triassic red beds of the eastern United States.   The red bottom sediments of the Bay of Fundy have often been cited for the well-preserved features that commonly appear on the surface between tides (Fig. 132).

Ripple marks are preserved in conglomerates, sandstones, and siltstones, and in clastic limestones and dolostones.   It is uncertain whether or not they can be formed in clays,[1] especially under water.   Many examples have been described from rocks of all ages, and the more important references are cited in Art. 65 or in the following pages.

63. *Mode and Environment of Formation.*—Ripple marks are formed by currents of air and by movements of water.   These motions disturb the upper part of a noncoherent granular deposit, causing the individual particles to be heaped into several kinds of ridges.   Ripple marks produced by wind are ephemeral, and because the sediment in which they are formed is dry they are seldom preserved [Bagnold (1942: 144–187)].   Most subaqueous ripple marks appear to

Courtesy of Geological Survey of Canada

Fig. 50.—Asymmetrical, or current, ripple marks that were modified by waves moving oblique to the direction of the current.   The more prominent sculptured ridges, disposed horizontally on the photograph, are current ripples; the finer sculpturing, represented by the vertically disposed ridges, are the result of wave action.   Coarser and heavier particles and carbonaceous debris have been concentrated in the troughs along the fronts of the current-ripple ridges.   Current movement was from the top toward the bottom.   Scale is indicated by the watch at the bottom of the picture.   Locality: The Avon River below Windsor, N.S.   (Arts. 62, 66, 67, 71.)   (*After Kindle*, 1917, *Geol. Survey Canada. Mus. Bull.*, **25**: 29, 30, *Plate 9A, Photograph*, 30779, *furnished by the Geological Survey of Canada.*)

be formed on shallow bottoms (strandline to 100 m.), but conditions favorable for their formation have been found at depths as great as 800 m. They form in any sort of granular sediment but do not form in mud or

---

[1] Coffrey (1909: 754–755) reports dunes of clay several miles long, 30 ft. high, and 200 to 300 ft. wide made by wind heaping up clay fragments and particles derived from disruption of dried lagoonal clay.   It seems entirely possible that ripples of clay in the same physical state might form, but none seems to have been reported.

in coherent granular material.   Their presence in a sedimentary rock, therefore, is conclusive evidence that the sediment was granular at the time the ripple-mark was formed.

64. *Use and Limitations of Use.*—In order to use ripple-mark to the fullest extent, it is necessary to consider not only the external form but also the internal structure of the individual ripple ridge.   Much attention has been devoted to the form, but little to the structure.   As a result, when ripple-mark is mentioned or discussed as a top and bottom criterion,

Courtesy of J. H. Maxson

Fig. 51.—Ripple marks, worm burrows, rill marks, and bird tracks on a silt bar at the mouth of Reference Point Creek near headwaters of Lake Mead, Boulder Canyon.   The light is from the left, and the rule is 12 in. (30 cm.) long.   This is an example of how organic and inorganic surficial features may be preserved together on the same surface.   (Arts. 62, 63, 76.)

emphasis is nearly always on the form and its modification (Arts. 72, 75, 76).

In following paragraphs it is shown that the form of either current or oscillation ripple marks can be useful provided that certain conditions prevail and also that internal structure can serve as a criterion even if the form has been partly destroyed.   The paleogeographic significance of ripple marks has been considered at length by Bucher (1919: 241–269). Students wishing to investigate this use of ripple-mark will find his paper an excellent guide.   They should also consult the instructive paper by Hyde (1911a: 257–269) in which he sets forth the results of mapping the regional orientation of many Mississippian ripple marks in Ohio.

65. *References on Ripple-mark.*—Since ripple-mark is one of the commonest surface features of sedimentary layers, it has been discussed to some extent by nearly every investigator who has done field work involving ripple-marked beds. Some of the writers, where the situation warranted, directed attention to the usefulness of certain types of ripple-mark for determining order of succession. Other investigators have written at length about the physical principles involved in the production of ripple-mark, and still others have described and illustrated the many kinds of ripple marks that can be observed on present-day depositional surfaces.

Among the many articles and discussions concerning ripple-mark, five merit special mention here because of their comprehensive nature and reference lists. "Recent and Fossil Ripple-mark" by Kindle (1917: 1–121) and "Bau und Bildung von gros-Rippeln in Wattenmeer" by Haentzschels (1938: 1–42) are especially noteworthy because of their excellent illustrations of every kind of common ripple-mark that may be seen on present beaches or along stream channels. "On Ripples and Related Sedimentary Surface Forms and Their Paleogeographic Interpretation" by Bucher (1919: 149–210, 241–269) is an analytical study of ripple formation and a discussion of the paleogeographic significance of the several kinds of ripple-mark. The article has an excellent list of references including many works by European writers. Kindle and Bucher (1932: 632–668) cooperated in preparing "Ripple Mark and Its Interpretation," published as a part of "Treatise on Sedimentation," and this treatment is probably the most comprehensive and best documented discussion of ripple-mark in English.

Many scattered references to local occurrences of ripple-mark in ancient rocks are not listed in the four comprehensive works cited in the preceding paragraph because of their relative unimportance or the fact that they appeared after 1932, but the majority of these previous to 1924 are listed in "Literature of Ripplemark," by Kindle and Edwards (1924: 191–203), which contains nearly 200 references.

Ripple-mark has been reported from rocks of all ages from the oldest intensely altered Archean sedimentary rocks of the Fenno-Scandian and Canadian shields to recently deposited sediments along present-day streams, shores, and beaches. The following examples are cited to give a general idea of the nature and extent of this sedimentary feature in ancient rocks as well as in recent sediments.

Sederholm (1899: 98) long ago reported ripple marks from the intensely altered Archean rocks of Finland and Sweden, thereby demonstrating the sedimentary nature of these ancient rocks.

Hore (1913: 59) and many geologists after him have mentioned the ripple-marked beds of Huronian age in Canada and the United States, and Ransome and Calkins (1908: 30) early in this century called attention to the grand development of ripple-mark in the Belt series of western

North America, where a peak is appropriately named Mt. Ripple and a formation is named Ripple after the mountain[1] [Daly (1912: 155–156); see also Fenton and Fenton in Chap. VIII, References].

The early New York and Wisconsin geological reports contain descriptions and illustrations of ripple marks from the Upper Cambrian (Potsdam) sandstones, and many writers of the early twentieth century mentioned the abundance of ripple marks in the Ordovician rocks of the Cincinnati region [Shannon (1895: 53–54); Moore and Hole (1902: 216–220); Culbertson (1903: 202–205); Prosser (1916: 456–475); *et al.*] and in the Mississippian rocks to the east [Hyde (1911*a*: 257–269)].

Cox and Dake (1916: 257–269), in an excellent discussion too often overlooked, described a wide variety of ripple marks from the early Paleozoic rocks of Missouri.

Gilbert (1899: 135–140) explained the giant ripples of the Silurian Medina sandstone as the product of 60-ft. waves, a conclusion not generally accepted by subsequent writers [see Kindle and Bucher (1932)]. Fairchild (1901: 9–14) later interpreted them as beach structures, and Branner (1901: 535–536) concluded they were due to seaward extension of beach cusps. Other references to these well-known ripple marks can be obtained by consulting the appropriate U.S. Geological Survey bibliographies.

Patton (1933: 77–82) reports typical oscillation ripple marks from the Texas Permian Merkle dolomitic limestone and from the Cretaceous Fredericksburg of the same state. Udden (1916: 123–129) and Scott (1930: 53–56) have reported unusual incomplete ripple ridges in the form of symmetrical and asymmetrical windrows of shell fragments (Arts. 70, 79).

Hitchcock (1858: 1–220, etc.) and many after him have made familiar the rippled formations of New England over which the Triassic dinosaurs trod and upon which they left their footprints.

Tarr (1935: 1498) discovered microripples in the summer layers of Pleistocene varves in the Connecticut Valley; Thiel (1932: 452–458)

---

[1] The Pre-Cambrian Ripple formation of British Columbia is characterized by exceptionally well preserved ripple-mark according to Daly (1912: 155–156), who states:

A principal feature of the quartzite is the occurrence of extremely well-preserved ripple-marks at various horizons. On Mt. Ripple itself these markings are exposed in a truly spectacular fashion. In bed after bed for a thickness of several hundred feet together the surfaces of the old sand were moulded into typical ripples of highly varied orientation. . . . As exposed on bedding-planes these marks are to-day apparently as sharply marked as they were when each bed was just covered by the next wash of sand. Whole cliffs are ornamented with the strong ridges and troughs of the ripples themselves or with their negative impressions.

described huge symmetrical *sand waves* " . . . that have changed their profiles to asymmetrical meta-ripples" like those discussed by Bucher (1919: 173) (Figs. 55, 56); and Gilbert (1884: 375–376) long ago described a 45-cm.- (18-in.-) thick deposit of laminated silt showing innumerable superimposed oscillation ripples (Fig. 52).

66. CURRENT RIPPLE-MARK.—To paraphrase Gilbert (1899: 137), it may be said that a current of air or water flowing over a surface of gravel, sand, or silt reacts on any prominence of the surface in the following manner: An eddy or vortex is created on the lee side of the prominence, and the return current of this vortex checks traveling particles, causing growth of the prominence on its down-current side. Simultaneously,

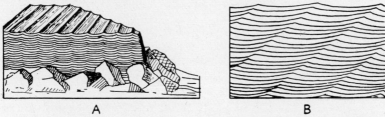

A   B

FIG. 52.—Superimposed oscillation ripple-mark   *A*. Oscillation ripple-mark in a bank of fine river silt. The sediment was deposited in a pool in which the water was periodically agitated as the silt settled to the bottom.   Successive laminae are inflected in the same way and hold a stable position so that a line connecting the angular crests is vertical.   The rippled deposit is 45 cm. (18 in.) thick.   *B*. Diagram of superimposed oscillation ripple-mark in which each successive lamina is slightly displaced horizontally so that a line connecting the angular crests is inclined to the surface.   The inclined alignment of the crests gives the appearance of false bedding to the deposit when it is viewed in transverse section. (Arts. 65, 68.)   (*A after Gilbert*, 1884, *Science*, **3** : 376, *Fig*. 1.   *B* original.)

the up-current side of the prominence is eroded, and its form thus travels down current. The prominences thereby produced are linear ridges of asymmetrical form, with short steep downstream slopes and comparatively long gentle upstream slopes. The crests and troughs are usually quite similar and asymmetrical (Fig. 53). Current ripple marks are characterized by wide variation in shape, amplitude, wave length, and ground plan [see Bagnold (1942: 144–187)].

On the basis of form alone, current ripple marks cannot be used to determine the top or bottom of a layer, for the counterpart presents the same appearance[1] (Fig. 50). Aspects that may serve as useful criteria are discussed in following paragraphs.

[1] Grabau (1924: 712) states:

The natural mold [counterpart, or obverse] of this type of ripple [aquatic current ripple] will be difficult to distinguish from the original ripple, though the directions of the slopes will be reversed. A careful examination, however, will show that, whereas the surfaces of the normal current ripple are gently convex, those of the mold [counterpart] will be gently concave.

But not all observers agree with him on the latter statement.

67. *Form and Variations.*—The fundamental form produced by current action is an asymmetrical ridge (Art. 66). Wind-current ripple marks are characterized by high indexes, whereas water-current ripple marks have relatively low indexes (Fig. 49). This means that for a given wave length (distance from crest to crest) the height[1] of a ripple produced by a water current is several times that produced by wind [Kindle (1917: 12)]. This difference in index gives a ready means of separating current ripple marks of aeolian and aquatic origin.

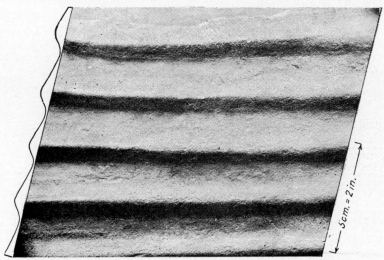

Fig. 53.—Current ripple marks on the upper surface of thin-bedded red Permian sandstone. A diagrammatic profile of the rippled surface is shown at the left. The ripple ridges have a wave length of about 25 mm. (1 in.). (Arts. 66, 67.)

In the formation of water current ripple marks, coarse sand grains and small pebbles are sometimes rolled up the gentle backslope, over the crest, and down the steep lee slope, at the base of which they finally come to rest (Figs. 50, 54). Platy organic debris may accumulate in similar fashion. If, now, the ripples be buried, the small accumulation of coarser and heavier grains in the trough indicates the top of the bed (Fig. 54). As a rule the finer material lies on and near the crest.

Aeolian current ripples, in contrast to those made by aquatic currents, not only are much flatter but also nearly always have the coarser material on and near the crests and the finer material in the troughs (Fig. 54). An interesting exception is that of heavy grains of such minerals as ilmen-

---

[1] Kindle (1936a: 861) uses the term *sand waves* for ripple ridges that differ from ordinary asymmetrical ripples only in having crests a foot or more high instead of an inch or so.

ite, magnetite, and garnet.[1] These tend to lie in the troughs, probably because a wind current strong enough to move quartz grains of similar size cannot move the heavier grains out of the trough once they have been rolled there.   As pointed out by Bucher (1919: 26ɹ), aeolian ripple-mark is probably of rare occurrence in sedimentary rocks.   McKee (1945: 313–325), however, in a recent article, reports an unusual type of aeolian ripple-mark from the Coconino sandstone of Arizona.[2] These ancient ripple marks lie on the foreset layers of dunes that have a leeward slope of 32 to 33° and a backslope of about 12°.

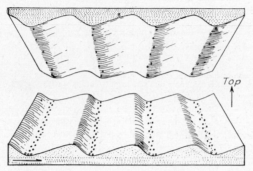

Fig. 54.—Aqueous current ripples with coarse sand grains and mica flakes concentrated in the troughs ahead of the advancing ripples. Some of the grains might adhere to the crest of the ridge representing the counterpart of the trough. In aeolian ripples the coarse particles tend to be concentrated on the crests rather than in the troughs. The much higher index of the aeolian ripple should suffice to differentiate it from one made by water. See Fig. 50. Note also that the ripple ridge has cross-lamination, whereas its counterpart has horizontal stratification. (Art. 67.)

In the latest comprehensive treatment of ripple marks, Kindle and Bucher (1932: 653–664) recognize the following types made by water currents (all are asymmetrical except pararipples, which may also be symmetrical):

1. *Normal*—simple asymmetrical ridges with various ground plans (Fig. 48) (Art. 66).   They are of no use in determining top and bottom of beds.[3]

[1] The author has observed this phenomenon on Ipswich Beach, east of Marblehead, Mass. Pink garnet grains are ommonly concentrated in the troughs of both water-current and wind-current ripple marks, the latter above high tide showing that they were not merely modified aqueous ripples. Bucher (1919: 155) reports a similar condition in sand dunes of northern Jutland, where the crests were covered with quartz, whereas the troughs held magnetite sand.

[2] These are tiny asymmetrical ripple marks, with index ranging from 17 to 98, that trend up and down parallel to the dip on dune foresets that are inclined from 32 to 33°. McKee ascribes them to wind action across the lee slope of a dune and mentions that the coarser grains are concentrated on or about the crests of the ripples.

[3] Berthololy, according to Bucher (1919: 155), observed that ". . . in active current-ripples the coarser grains accumulated on the lee-side" and exceeded those on the stoss side by as much as three or four times. Bucher (1919: 155, footnote)

2. *Rhomboid*—a rare form showing a reticular, scalelike pattern. It is too uncommon to be of importance in the present discussion [see Woodford (1935: 518–525) and Bethune (1936: 291–296].

3. *Linguoid*—a modified normal ripple-mark with unit forms characterized by tonguelike outline and producing counterparts resembling small mud flows. These might be confused with flow casts (Art. 102). They are not likely to be of any use in determining order of succession.

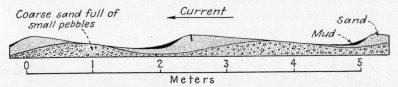

Fig. 55.—Cross section of metaripples observed on a sandbank in the Little Miami River after a flood. The foundation of the rippled surface consists of prominent symmetrical-ripple ridges composed of sand with small pebbles. The symmetrical profile was changed to one of asymmetry by the deposition of sand lenses on the down-current slopes of the original ridges. A thin layer of mud then paved the troughs and adjacent slopes to a thickness of 3 to 5 mm. Compare with Fig. 56. (Art. 67.) (*Modified after Bucher*, 1919, *Am. Jour. Sci.*, (4) **47**: 173, *Fig.* 4.)

4. *Metaripples*—large asymmetrical ridges of sand on an undulating base of coarser material, with small mud deposits in the troughs (Figs. 55, 56). The unusual relation of mud, sand, and gravel in this type of ripple may be useful in identifying the top or bottom of some sequences.

5. *Pararipples*—large symmetrical and asymmetrical ripples found in limestones. Because of their magnitude it is doubtful that they would ever be exposed in highly inclined beds over sufficient bedding surface for it to be possible to use

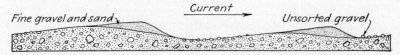

Fig. 56.—Metaripples in glacial sediments, representing unusually large symmetrical "sand waves" that have had their profiles changed by localized deposition under swift-current conditions. The foundation material is unsorted glacial gravel and sand. The finer gravel and sand were deposited asymmetrically on the downstream limbs of the ripples to make the observed profile. The wave length of the ripples ranges from 8 to 20 m. (25 to over 60 ft.), and the average form index is 12. Compare with Fig. 55. (Art. 67.) (*Modified after Thiel*, 1932, *Jour. Geology*, **40**: 457, *Fig.* 8.)

them to determine top and bottom. In addition they are not at all common as compared with the smaller types of current ripple-mark.

---

points out, however, that similar distribution of heavier grains has been observed on aeolian ripples in which the crests were covered with white quartz sand, whereas the troughs carried black magnetite sand.

This latter condition should not occasion concern, however, for such aeolian ripples would have little chance of being preserved and, even if they were, they could probably be distinguished readily from aquatic current ripples by their flatter profile and stratigraphic setting.

It might be possible, therefore, to use the distribution of coarse and fine or heavy and light sand grains to determine the top of a rippled layer (Art. 72 and Figs. 50, 54).

68. *Internal Structure.*—The typical internal structure of current ripple ridges is a special kind of cross-lamination,[1] as illustrated in Fig. 57. The lamination is inclined down current and is roughly parallel to the steeper down-current slope of the ridge. Hence, even if the ripple mark were partly destroyed, it should be possible to determine the up or down direction across the eroded ridge if cross-lamination is preserved

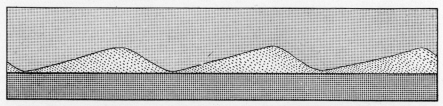

Fig. 57.—Diagram to illustrate cross-lamination in a small ripple ridge or large sand dune. The internal structure of the ridges provides a reliable top and bottom criterion since the intervening troughs are filled with horizontally laminated sandstone. If the beds were vertical or overturned, the top of the sequence could be determined by noting that the convexity of the cross-laminated ridges is toward the surface or up. The ridges should not be mistaken for a series of symmetrical scour-and-fill structures (see Fig. 59). (Arts. 68, 132.)

(Fig. 58). Structure such as that shown in Fig. 57 closely resembles the cross-laminated filling in an asymmetrically eroded trough but may be differentiated by careful study of the details. The cross-lamination of the ridge is truncated along the curved upper boundary and is also likely to show angular contact along the plane surface, whereas that of the scoured trough shows conspicuous tangency with the curved boundary

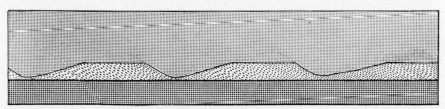

Fig. 58.—Eroded ripple ridges and dunes. Although the crests of the cross-laminated ridges were transected before the overlying sand was deposited, the cross-lamination of the rippled layer allows restoration of the original bottom profile and this makes it possible to determine the top of the sequence as illustrated in Fig. 57. If the sequence is viewed in an inverted position, the relations between the cross-laminated layer and the contiguous sandstones are obviously impossible if it were suspected that the beds were right side up. (Arts. 68, 69.)

surface and truncation along the flat boundary (Figs. 59, 192). Bucher (1919: 154–155) states: "The structure of a current-ripple should, there-

---

[1] Kindle (1917: 55–56) states:

Cross bedding represents in many instances one phase of a phenomenon called sand waves which are nothing more than current made ripple-mark of mammoth proportions that appear to be formed instead of ripple-mark when the current is overloaded with sediment. The crests are often 15 to 35 feet apart and rise 2 to 3 feet above the troughs. . . . A set of beds which have been laid down in a zone characterized by sand-wave formation

fore, in the most typical case, consist of laminae of deposition parallel to the lee-slope, cut at an oblique angle by the up-stream slope."

Woodworth (1901: 281) has described an unusual kind of cross-banding in ripple-marked sandstone produced by the deposition of mica flakes on the steeper slope of current ripples (Fig. 60). The flakes, coming to rest on the advancing front of the ripple ridge, lie parallel to the

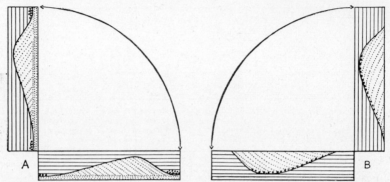

Fig. 59.—Diagrams showing how a cross-laminated ripple ridge can be differentiated from a scour-and-fill structure. In the ripple ridge (A) the foreset laminae are parallel to the shorter and steeper slope and are sharply truncated along the gentler slope. They may be angular or asymptotic along the plane forming the base of the ridge. Furthermore, coarser and heavier sand grains commonly collect in the deepest part of the trough at the foot of the steeper slope. In typical scour-and-fill (B) structure the foreset laminae are asymptotic with the gentler slope, do not parallel the steeper slope, rather leaning against it, and are sharply truncated on the upper side. The coarser and heavier particles are not limited to the deepest part of the excavation but generally are distributed along the gentler slope lying at the bases of the foreset laminae. Since scour-and-fill structures may have about the same magnitude as current-ripple ridges and may also occur in similar sedimentary sequences, features like cross-lamination and coarser particles provide reliable means of determining not only the nature of the cross-laminated feature but also the top or bottom of the bed in which it lies. Here both beds have been turned on end to show the similar appearance of the two features. (Arts. 68, 132.)

cross-lamination of the ridge itself, but in addition they make prominent bands simulating bedding across the true stratification. The slight forward advance of each successive horizontal layer causes the band of

---

may not preserve the outlines of any single set of sand waves but the steep foreset beds which are formed as these waves travel with the current will be preserved as the familiar cross bedding so common in many coarse sandstones. Cross bedding is thus characteristic of both river and tidal current laid beds. . . .

Cross bedding on a much finer and smaller scale than that developed in connexion with sand waves may characterize sandstones formed under water velocities suitable for the formation of ordinary asymmetrical ripple-mark.

Bell (1929: 36) points out that in the Mississippian Horton of Nova Scotia

Confirmatory evidence of the prominence of [current] rippling is afforded by the presence of minute crossbedding characteristic of much of the finer siliceous and arenaceous material of the middle and upper members of the Horton Bluff formation.

[For additional discussion of ripple marks and cross-lamination, see Gilbert (1899: 135–140)].

mica flakes to have a pronounced upstream inclination. If this phenomenon were present in micaceous metamorphosed rocks, it might well be mistaken for true bedding.

Lahee (1941: 96) has pointed out that mica flakes may accumulate in similar manner on the leeward slopes of sand dunes, causing the foreset beds to contain more mica than the topset.

Twenhofel (1932: 623–624) and McKee (1938a: 80–81) have described and illustrated a peculiar kind of pseudo cross-lamination produced by successively deposited ripple laminae, showing lee-side concentration of sediment (Fig. 221), and Gilbert (1899: 139–140) many years before described a similar kind of structure produced by gradual shifting of a

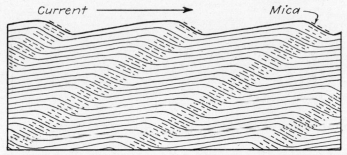

Current ⟶ Mica

FIG. 60.—False bedding caused by concentration of mica flakes on the steeper down-current slopes of successive ripples. The flat mica flakes, swept along by the current, come to rest in a stable position on the front slope of the slowly advancing asymmetrical ripple, and as successive thin layers are deposited the profile of the ripple ridge slowly advances down current so that the zones of mica concentration have a strong up-current inclination simulating inclined bedding. The flakes themselves lie parallel to the foreset laminae of the ripple ridge. (Arts. 68, 142.) (*Sketch based on figures by Woodworth*, 1901, *Am. Geol.*, **27**: 281–283, *Figs.* 1, 2.)

wave-ripple profile (Figs. 61, 221). If the wave ripple does not shift position, each successive lamina is deposited on the preceding and the superimposed angular crests give the deposit a vertically banded appearance [Fig. 52; Gilbert (1884: 376)].

An unusual, supposedly genetic association of ripple-mark and crossbedding has been reported by Spurr (1894: 43–47; 1894a: 201–206) in the outwash of a glacial plain. The deposit, which has well-developed current ripple marks, consists of graded sand and gravel layers with an upstream inclination of about 40° (Fig. 61). According to Spurr (1894a: 202), "The ripple-marked laminae generally nearly coincide with one another, crest for crest, and trough for trough, except for the slight forward advance of each new crest and trough." The slight advance accounts for the upstream inclination of the graded layers, which Spurr believed were genetically related to the ripple ridges.

Jaggar (1894: 199–201) doubted that current rippling of the type Spurr described would persist through a thickness of sediment as great as the 3 or 4 m. deposited and suggested that the cross-bedded nature of the deposit really represented foreset bedding similar to that which Davis (1890: 195–202) had described some years before as being well developed in the stratified parts of glacial sand plains.

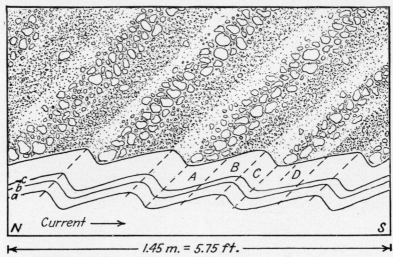

Fig. 61.—Cross-bedding of an unusual type produced in Pleistocene gravels and sands by strong current action. *A* = coarse gravel; *B* = compact sand; *C* = loose sand; *D* = loose sand with some gravel. If the crude graded bedding of this deposit were used as a top and bottom criterion, the layers would appear to be overturned. Spurr (1894: 43–47) considered the cross-bedded structure to have been formed by maintenance of ripple formation as successive increments were deposited on the bottom. As successive layers of sediment were deposited, each with a rippled upper surface (*a, b, c*), the coarsest material was concentrated in the trough, the finest in the crest region. Slight forward advance of each successive rippled layer produced the upstream inclination of the coarse and fine "beds." (Arts. 68, 142.) (*Modified after Spurr, 1894, Am. Geol.,* **13**: 43–47, *Figs.* 1, 2.)

Since the true bedding in the deposit consists of nearly horizontal, faintly rippled surfaces, the inclined layers are the result of continuous deposition on such a surface. The site of a certain grade of material advanced slightly downstream as each successive horizontal layer was added. It should be noted that, whereas neither the cross-bedded structure nor the textural profile of the inclined layers can be used for top and bottom determination, the profile of each ripple ridge can be used for that purpose because the trough contains the coarse material, whereas the crest is marked by the finest sediment (Fig. 61).

It is clear from the foregoing examples that conditions of deposition play a major part in determining the nature and extent of internal structures such as cross-bedding in ripple ridges. An important responsibility of the field investigator is to determine as far as he can the nature of the conditions under which a given depositional feature was formed. Inasmuch as the internal structure of cross-laminated or cross-bedded deposits differs from place to place and even from bed to bed, it follows that the conditions of deposition also differed. As an example, conditions of a dune-covered surface would be quite different from those on a broad outwash plain in front of a glacial lobe.

69. *Ripples Modified by Erosion.*—Attention is called to the possible use of eroded subaqueous ripple-mark in Art. 68 and Figs. 57 and 58, where the top of the ripple ridge has been transected by erosion. The profile of the eroded ripple ridge should suffice for top or bottom identification even if internal structure is lacking.

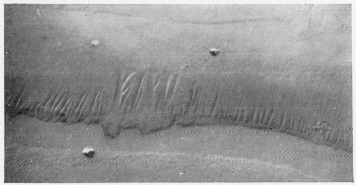

(Courtesy of Z. M. Kirman.)

Fig. 62.—Current-ripple ridge sculptured by seaward-flowing water, observed on the beach at Lynn, Mass. The ripple ridge has its steeper slope facing the sea, which is toward the bottom of the photograph. As the tide is ebbing, water, trapped behind the ridge on the landward side, aided at first to some extent by the tidal current itself, cuts transverse grooves into the ridge and deposits the sand in tiny lobate deltas at the foot of the steep slope of the ridge.

The incoming wave, visible in the lower quarter of the photograph, is dying out before reaching the sculptured ripple ridge. A second ridge shows faintly at the top of the picture. The wave length is about 50 cm. (20 in.) and the height of the ridges about 2 or 3 cm. The two small pebbles, which are less than 50 mm. (2 in.) across, indicate the approximate scale of the transverse rill marks. (Art. 69.)

A second modification produced by almost contemporaneous erosion is shown in Fig. 62. On a gently sloping sandy beach the seaward moving water produces ripple ridges with the steeper slope toward the sea. As the tide is going out, water, temporarily trapped behind the ridge, transects it a little later, producing a characteristic pattern of dendritic grooves terminating seaward in lobate deltaic masses of sand, which festoon the base of the ridge.[1] This feature, often observed in the process of formation along Massachusetts beaches, is similar to the miniature

---

[1] McKee (1945: 313–325) describes as "slump mark" an interesting feature in the Coconino sandstone, which he ascribes to avalanching, or slumping, of wetted sand on the lee slope of dunes. These marks wipe out the ripple-mark elsewhere preserved on the leeward slope. They are probably not common enough to warrant serious consideration as a criterion for top and bottom determination, but they do indicate the direction in which gravity was acting at the time they were formed.

deltas described and illustrated by Kindle (1917: 36, 37, Plate XVIA) but is not formed in the same way. If such a sculptured ripple ridge were preserved, the surface should be easily distinguishable from the counterpart on the bottom of the covering layer.

Brown (1912: 536–547), reporting on the well-preserved ripple-mark in Sandwich Bay, Labrador, mentions an unusual type of erosional modification of current ripples here illustrated in Fig. 63.

Kindle (1917: 36–38) describes a number of peculiarly sculptured sand

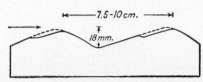

surfaces produced by current erosional modification of ripples and uses for them the term *current mark* originated by Jukes (1872: 163–164). These unusual features, ascribed by Jukes to currents of troubled water, may well be confused with certain similar sand structures discussed in Art. 102, Flow Casts, but careful examination of the

Fig. 63.—Current-ripple ridges eroded on the back side of the ridge to produce an unusual profile. (Art. 69.) (*After Brown*, 1912, *Acad. Nat. Sci. Philadelphia Proc.*, **63**: 539, *Fig. 2.*)

lithology of the contiguous bed should prove the nature of the structure in question.

70. *Incomplete Current Ripples.*—Under certain bottom conditions, particularly if there is an insufficient supply of sand to cover the entire surface, currents heap sand into windrows that constitute incomplete ripples. The shape and relations of these can be used to determine the top or bottom of a stratigraphic sequence as illustrated in Figs. 64 and 65.

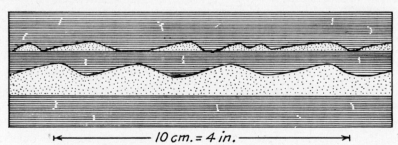

Fig. 64.—Complete and incomplete aqueous-current ripple ridges of fine sand buried by mud (now shale) in the transition beds between the Carboniferous Squantum tillite and overlying Cambridge slates on Squantum Head, eastern Massachusetts. Compare with Fig. 233. (Art. 70.)

Scott (1930: 53–56) has described and illustrated large, essentially incomplete current-ripple ridges from the Walnut limestone member of the Texas Cretaceous Fredericksburg formation. These ridges, which are really asymmetrical windrows of shell fragments, rest unconformably on the Paluxy sandstone and are buried beneath a shell layer (Fig. 65). Incomplete current-ripple ridges composed of sand are common in the stratified beds associated with the Squantum tillite on Squantum Head (Figs. 64, 233).   In both examples just cited, the flat base and discontinuous profile of the incomplete ripples furnish criteria for determining top and bottom.

They are probably to be accounted for as Gilbert (1899: 136; 1914: 243; see also 1899: 136) suggests:

In certain experiments on flume traction a slow current, moving over a smooth channel bed of wood, swept along a small quantity of sand.   With increase of the load of sand local deposits were induced, which took the form of thin straggling patches, similar to one another in outline and separated by approximately equal bare spaces.   These moved slowly downstream, the mode of progress being similar to that of dunes, and with further increase of load they acquired the typical profile of dunes.

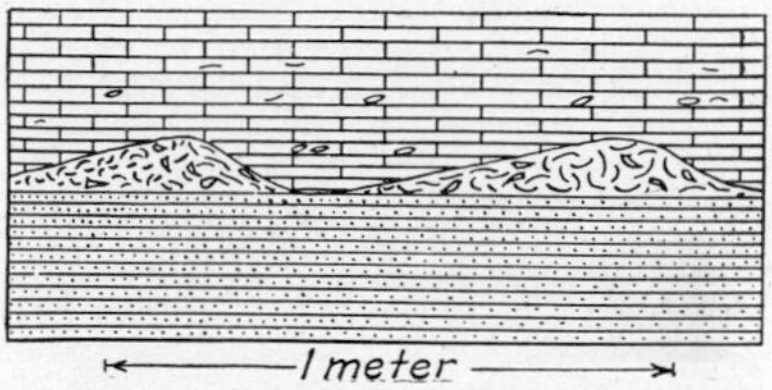

According to Bucher (1919: 153), Baschin (1889: 420) called attention to " . . . a similar arragement of wind-blown sand in parallel elongated patches," but it seems quite unlikely that a feature of such ephemeral nature would be preserved often enough to be of any importance in the present discussion.

71. *Mud-buried Ripple-mark.*—A ridged surface, such as that produced by current or wave ripple-mark or by uneven erosion and deposition

Fig. 65.—Incomplete current ripple ridges in a fossiliferous Cretaceous limestone (Walnut) of Texas. The ridges are composed of shell fragments that were heaped up by bottom currents. In some places on the bottom the shell detritus was so thin that a continuous sheet of ripple-mark could not form; instead there developed a series of disconnected ripple ridges. It should be noted that these incomplete ripples are many times larger than similar ridges of sand present in the Carboniferous Cambridge formation of eastern Massachusetts as illustrated in Fig. 64. (Arts. 70, 177.) (*Adapted from Scott, 1930, Texas Univ. Bull.*, **3001**: 53, *Fig.* 12.)

of bottom sands, may when buried by an influx of mud show the relations illustrated in Figs. 66 to 68.   As the mud settles out of the water, the greater thickness accumulates in the troughs between the ripples, whereas little or none remains on the crests.   This manner of deposition is probably caused partly by slumping and partly by slight currents of water, which wash off some or all of the mud from the crests and deposit it in the troughs.[1]

The resulting discontinuous shale layer, lying in a sandstone sequence, is a good criterion for top and bottom determination as shown in Figs.

[1] Cox and Dake (1916: 25) refer to the partly filled troughs of ripple-marked beds in Missouri and state:

Observation of a considerable number of these filled ripple marks in place in beds known not to be disturbed shows that the filling material accumulated in the troughs.   For practical purposes, then, when such material fills the depression, it may safely be assumed to be the trough of a true ripple mark . . . ; while if more rarely it is found capping a ridge . . . , the ridge may be assumed to be the cast which formerly filled the trough.

66 to 68.   When viewed in transverse section, the concave lenses of shale are conspicuous, symmetrical in the troughs of wave ripples and asymmetrical in the troughs of subaqueous current ripples and in irregular

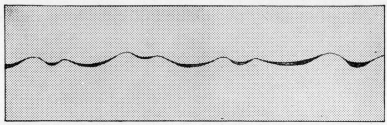

Fɪɢ. 66.—Diagram showing lenticular shale deposits in the depressions of an irregularly rippled surface in the midst of a massive sandstone.   At the time when the mud was deposited the sand bottom had considerable irregularity because of local deposition and erosion.   Many of the ridges are wave ripples. The mud was washed off the higher prominences and ripples and concentrated in the depressions, where it was compressed by the incoming sand.   This feature can be developed on a microscopic scale or on a scale measurable in meters.   (Arts. 71, 76, 80.)

depressions.   When viewed in plan, after separation of the sandstone layers, the shale is seen to lie in broad bands—the trough fillings— separated by narrow bands of sandstone alone or sandstone with small

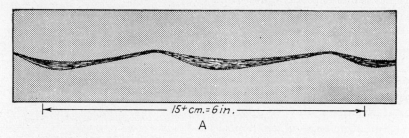

A

B

Fɪɢ. 67.—Mud-buried ripple-mark.   *A.* Current ripples buried by red mud in the Carboniferous Roxbury conglomerate along Hammond Pond Parkway, Newton, Mass.   The shale layer is thinnest over the crests and thickest in the troughs.   When taken with the shape of the shale layer, the current-ripple ridges provide a top and bottom feature.   *B.* Wave-ripple ridges from the same locality as *A.* (Arts. 71, 76, 80.)

patches of attached shale.   On complexly rippled surfaces and on those of irregular relief, the shale-sandstone relation is likely to be less simple. Plant remains and other organic debris may also be expected to concentrate in the troughs and, if buried, to form a thin carbonized layer (Fig. 50).

Kindle (1936a: 867), in discussing certain irregularities of shallow-water sand bottoms, cites an instructive example bearing on the present discussion. His description, abstracted from notes made by Kellogg (1905: 38) along the Gulf Coast, follows:

[After wading] perhaps 1500 feet across slightly elevated ridges with hard bottom the same traverse was repeated two days later when the depressions were found to be three or four inches deep with very soft mud and the ridges free of

Fig. 68.—Mud-buried ripple ridge. Transverse section of a symmetrical ripple ridge of coarse sand overlain successively by red clay, reddish-brown silt, and gray sand. It should be noted that the sequence just given is the reverse of the usual textural succession of coarse to fine. Both clay and silt layers show prominent thinning over the ripple crests and thickening in the intervening troughs (see Fig. 67). This phenomenon occurs in the Carboniferous Roxbury conglomerate along the Hammond Pond Parkway in Newton, Mass. The specimen is reduced to about two-thirds natural size. (Arts. 71, 80.)

mud. It thus appears that a complete change in the character of the material in the upper three or four inches of these trough structures may take place in 48 hours.

72. *Limitations in Use of Current Ripple-mark.*—In general, well-preserved current ripple-mark of either aeolian or aquatic origin is of little use and reliability in determining the top or bottom of a stratigraphic sequence.

On the other hand, certain primary and secondary features of the ripples themselves are quite useful and should always be sought. The more important of these are (1) coarser and heavier particles concentrated in the troughs of aquatic ripples and on the crests of aeolian ones (Art. 67); (2) metaripples, with small mud deposits in the troughs (Art. 67); (3) cross-lamination with laminae parallel to the steeper slope of the ripple ridge (Art. 68); (4) flat-topped ripples transected by erosion, hence possessing an unusual profile (Art. 69); (5) transversely grooved ridges with miniature deltas at the ends of the grooves and at the base of the steeper slope of the ripple ridge (Art. 69); (6) incomplete ripples (Art. 70); and (7) concave lenticular shale layers in the troughs of ripple-marked surfaces (Art. 71).

73. ANTIDUNE RIPPLE-MARK.—If a current of water reaches that velocity at which its effects extend below the sand surface over which it is flowing, a moving layer of mixed sand and water comes into existence. This layer grades downward by transition into the motionless substratum. If the velocity is increased beyond this so-called "smooth phase," the sand surface again becomes undulatory with symmetrical ripples having

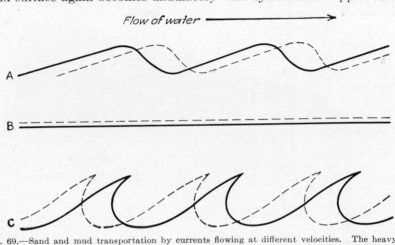

FIG. 69.—Sand and mud transportation by currents flowing at different velocities. The heavy line marks the first position; the broken line, the second position. *A.* Transport by asymmetrical ripple ridges that advance downstream. *B.* The sediment moves along the bottom in a thin sheet as velocity increases over conditions in *A* and the ripple ridges are destroyed. *C.* With still greater velocity, there is development of turbulence followed by antidune transport in which the sharp-crested ridges are eroded on the downstream side and, as a consequence, advance upstream. Preservation of *A* gives asymmetrical ripple-mark; of *B*, laminated siltstone and sandstone; of *C*, antidune ripple ridges. (Art. 73.) (*Modified after Lamont, 1941, Quarry Managers' Jour.*, **24**, *Fig.* 9.)

flattened or gently rounded crests (Fig. 69). These ripples, termed *antidunes* by Gilbert (1914: 11, 31) and *regressive sand-waves* by Bucher (1919: 165), differ from ordinary current ripples by traveling upstream, the movement being " . . . accomplished by erosion on the downstream face and deposition on the upstream face" [Gilbert (1914: 11)]. Lamont (1941: 127) points out: "These rush back against the flow of the stream, erosion taking place on the concave sides and deposition on the convex . . . " (Fig. 69).

It is not likely that regressive sand waves would commonly be preserved, for they are almost certain to be destroyed as current velocity decreases. They are mentioned here, however, because structures interpreted as antidunes have been described[1] and illustrated (Fig. 70).

[1] Lamont (1938: 14–15; 1941: 135) describes and illustrates an unusual kind of

74. WAVE (OSCILLATION) RIPPLE-MARK.—Jukes and Geikie (1872: 63) appear to have been the first to point out the use of wave ripple-mark for determining top and bottom of beds. Since then many writers have mentioned the features, among them Van Hise (1896: 719–721), Cox and Dake (1916), Kindle (1917: 54–55), Bucher (1919: 184–185; 1932: 635), and many later authors of textbooks on structural geology.

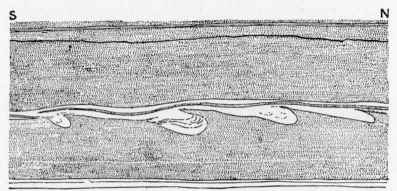

FIG. 70.—Antidunes in the Posidonomya limestone, County Dublin, Ireland (×0.6). This structure is exposed in a rock face that is inclined steeply seaward. The bed containing it is on the northward dipping limb of an anticline. Returned to horizontal position, the feature indicates a current that flowed from the north. (Art. 73.) (*After Lamont, 1938, Royal Irish Acad. Proc.,* **45**: 15, *Fig.* 4.)

75. *Form and Variations.*—The oscillation of water in wave action produces distinctive ripple-mark characterized by marked symmetry of crest and trough.[1] The crests are fairly sharp or slightly rounded and

---

rippled structure, which he suggests was formed in the same way as antidunes, (see Fig. 70).

[1] Gilbert (1899: 137–138) has described the formation of wave ripple-mark as follows:

The ordinary ripple-mark of beaches and rock faces is produced by the to-and-fro motion of the water occasioned by the passage of wind waves. During the passage of a wave each particle of water near the surface rises, moves forward, descends, and moves back, describing an orbit which is approximately circular. The orbital motion is communicated downward, with gradually diminishing amplitude. Unless the water is deep the orbits below the surface are ellipses, the longer axes being horizontal, and close to the bottom the ellipses are nearly flat, so that the water merely swings forward and back. It is in this oscillating current, periodically reversed, that the sand-ripples are formed. A prominence occasions vortices alternately on its two sides, and is thereby developed in a symmetric way, with equal slopes and a sharp apex. There is a strong tendency to produce the mole laterally into a ridge, the space between ridges is definitely limited by the interference of vortices, and in time there results a regular pattern of parallel ridges, equally spaced.

It has been found experimentally that by varying the amplitude of the water oscillation, and also by varying its frequency, the size of the resulting ripples can be controlled; but the precise laws of control have not been demonstrated. Evidently the frequency of the natural oscillation equals the frequency of the wind waves, and its amplitude is a function of the size of the waves and the depth of the water; so that a relation will ultimately be

the troughs gently rounded (Figs. 71, 72). Hence with well-preserved wave ripple-mark there should seldom be any question as to the top of the sequence containing it (Fig. 73).

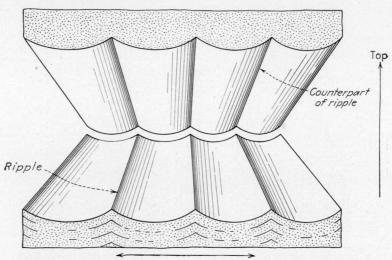

FIG. 71.—Block diagram showing typical wave ripples and their counterparts. The chevron structure below the ripple crests is not present, in reverse, in the overlying bed since it is a feature of the ripple ridge only. See Fig. 82. (Arts. 75, 77.)

FIG. 72.—Diagrammatic sections of wave ripple marks. *A–D.* Original ridges. *E.* Original ridges rounded and modified by erosion. *F.* Ridges like *A* or *B*, flattened by erosion of the crests. *G.* Original ridges deformed by lateral compression. (Arts. 75, 76.) (*After Fenton and Fenton, 1937, Bull. Geol. Soc. Am.,* **48**: 1913, *Fig.* 5.)

Some wave ripples have a secondary ridge of small magnitude along the axis of the trough (Fig. 74), and Van Hise (1896: 720) has pointed

---

established between wave-size, wave-period, and water-depth as conditions and ripple-size as a result.

Evans (1941: 41) has recently pointed out that

. . . wave-formed ripple marks should be placed in two classes: symmetrical oscillation ripples, which do not travel, formed by waves of oscillation which act on the bottom but are not distorted, and asymmetrical oscillation ripples, which usually do travel, and which are formed by distorted oscillation waves.

out the usefulness of this feature in determining the top side of steeply inclined beds:

Normal ripple-marks consist of a series of sharp ridges separated by rounded hollows, each of which, however, often has a slight sharp ridge in its center. . . .

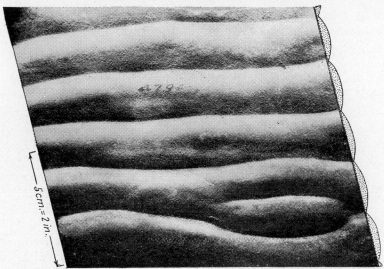

FIG. 73.—Counterpart of oscillation ripple-mark as preserved on the undersurface of a thin sandstone layer of Permian age. Since this is the reverse of a rippled surface, the crests of the ridges are broad and rounded, whereas the troughs are narrow and angular, as shown in the diagrammatic profile. (Art. 75.)

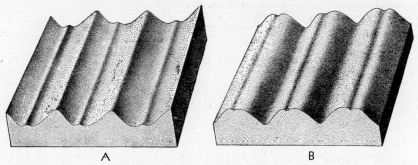

A   B

FIG. 74.—Ripple-mark composed of two sets of parallel ripple ridges differing greatly in magnitude. *A.* Original rippled surface. *B.* Obverse of rippled surface or undersurface of layer covering *A.* (ART. 75.) [*After Van Hise, 1896, U.S. Geol. Survey Ann. Rept.,* **16** (1): 719–720, *Figs.* 141, 142.]

The obverses or casts of such ripple-marks have an entirely different appearance. They consist of broad rounded ridges, each of which has a slight depression in its center, and the ridges are separated by steep depressions. . . . The profile of either of these figures is shown by [Fig. 75], which is placed in a vertical position. One side represents the ripple-marks as normally formed, the other their cast or obverse.

Other similar complications [see Kindle and Bucher (1932: 650 *ff.*)] need not affect the usefulness of a wave ripple as a criterion so long as its essential form is apparent. It is only when the crests have undergone considerable erosion that the wave ripple becomes of questionable reliability. These modifications are discussed in Art. 76.

Many kinds of compound ripple-mark are formed by the interaction of waves and currents. Two sets of ripples may be formed simultaneously, or a second may be formed after completion of the first. Such complicated systems are common but usually are not reliable for determining the top of the sequence in which they lie because of the confusion of crests and their modification by erosion. If the profile of the sharp crest is preserved, however, it is a reliable top and bottom indicator (Figs. 76, 77). The several complicated systems of ripples are discussed fully by Bucher (1919), Kindle (1917: 29–36), and Kindle and Bucher (1932: 653–655).

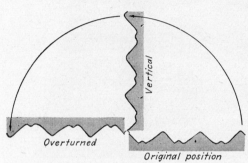

Fig. 75.—Diagram showing profile of ripple-mark like that illustrated in Fig. 74. With the fact in mind that the second-order ripple ridges lie along the axes of the major troughs, it is possible to determine at a glance whether the profile is normal or overturned and, in vertical beds, the direction in which the beds face. (Art. 75.) [*Sketch based on Van Hise,* 1896, *U.S. Geol. Survey, Ann. Rept.,* **16** (1): 721, *Fig.* 143.]

Wave ripples are typically small features with wave lengths seldom exceeding a meter and amplitudes of only a few centimeters. Ripples larger than these are usually given special designations (*e.g.*, pararipples, metaripples). Kindle (1936*a*: 861–869) describes "ridge and trough structures," which are essentially like wave ripples except that they are spaced many meters apart instead of a few centimeters.

76. *Modifications of Form.*—Wave ripple-mark is commonly modified by penecontemporaneous erosion with consequent rounding or flattening of the sharp crests, as illustrated in Figs. 78 and 79, and by partial filling of the troughs as discussed in Art. 71 and illustrated in Figs. 66 to 68. A wave-rippled surface may be completely covered with a thin layer of mud which, indurated to shale, sharply outlines the ripple profile and suggests the top in a sequence of coarse and fine sand, as shown in Fig. 80 (Art. 80).

Oscillation ripple marks developed in fine argillaceous silt may be so modified by wind drift acting on a thin film of water overlying them that they take the form of " . . . rounded flat-topped blobs not unlike tar creeping on a sloping surface. . . . " Bucher (1938: 735), from whose

FIG. 76.—Interference ripple-mark on Pennsylvanian sandstone from Cape Breton Island, Nova Scotia. This sharp-crested symmetrical type of ripple-mark provides an excellent top and bottom criterion. (Art. 75.) (*After Kindle, 1917, Geol. Survey Canada Mus. Bull., **25**: 43, Plate 30A. Photographic print, 36046, furnished by the Geological Survey of Canada.*)

FIG. 77.—Interference wave ripple-mark on an ancient, fine-grained quartzite. The sharp crests and rounded troughs show that this is the original surface. The specimen is about 30 cm. (12+ in.) long, and the average wave length of the main ripple ridges is about 35 mm. (1.4 in.). (Art. 75.)

article the preceding quotation was taken, reported such modified ripples from the tidal flats at Wilhelmshaven, Germany, and pointed out that "in the fossil record this [*i.e.*, the modified ripple form] has been thought to indicate viscous flow of sediment on relatively steep slopes on the sides of geosynclines." In a recent article, however, Pringle and Eckford (1945: 7) ascribe to penecontemporaneous erosion of oscillation ripple marks a system of uniformly directed linguoid ridges on the top surface of a steeply dipping Silurian graywacke bed in Scotland. Had

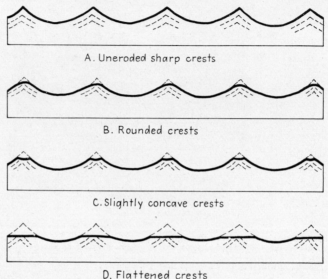

A. Uneroded sharp crests

B. Rounded crests

C. Slightly concave crests

D. Flattened crests

Fig. 78.—Diagrams showing change in profile of wave ripples by transection of the crests. Even though wave ripples are commonly eroded to some extent, the resultant profile is ordinarily usable as a top and bottom criterion. (Arts. 76, 77.)

these features been described a decade or so earlier, they very likely would have been ascribed to viscous flow.

Animals wading and crawling over a ripple-marked bottom commonly leave footprints, trails, and other evidences of their travel, and these markings may be so related to the troughs as to indicate the top surface of the rippled bed (Fig. 51).

If contiguous rippled strata separate, a part of the sharp crest of a ripple ridge may adhere to the underside of the covering layer, resulting in imperfect ridges and in irregular rough bands on the counterpart where the impression of the crest should be (Figs. 81*A*, *B*).

The modifications just described may increase the reliability of wave ripple marks as criteria of superposition, or they may render them completely useless. The limitations of their use are indicated in the captions accompanying the figures.

77. *Internal Structure.*—The typical wave ripple has a distinctive internal structure characterized by superimposed chevronlike laminations, the surfaces of successive ridges (Fig. 82). Since wave ripples maintain a fixed position so long as the conditions producing them remain unchanged, successive crests may be directly superimposed through sandstone beds as much as 15 cm. (6 in.) thick, as reported by Kindle (1917: 27) in the Joggins section, and Gilbert (1880: 61–62) describes an example in which the lamination of the beds shows that a set of ripples held the same position during the deposition of 0.6 m. (2 ft.) of sediment. Under certain conditions one slope of the chevron may be better preserved than the other so that the ripple ridge appears to have imperfect unidirectional cross-lamination (Fig. 52B).

Fig. 79.—Eroded symmetrical ripple marks on the top surface of a layer of Lower Ordovician New Richmond sandstone from Wisconsin. The ripples have a wave length of about 3 to 4 mm. (⅛ to ⅙ in.). The ripple ridges have a flattened crest, whereas the troughs between are round-bottomed (*cf.* Fig. 78). (Art. 76.)

If the sharp crest of the ripple has been truncated by erosion, the chevrons show similar truncation. Furthermore, if most of the rippled surface has been worn away or if it is poorly preserved, the internal structure should be nonetheless useful in indicating the upward angularity of the original crests (Fig. 78). Unfortunately, the internal structure of many ripple-marked beds is indistinct or lacking, and its use is thus definitely limited.

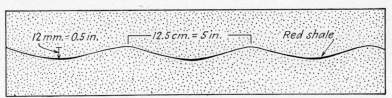

Fig. 80.—Wave ripples marked by a thin red shale film in the Pennsylvanian Wamsutta red beds near Big Pond, Braintree, Mass. The shale film is less than a millimeter thick over the crests and several millimeters thick in the troughs. Inasmuch as the sandstone containing the shale film is homogeneous in texture and structureless, the thinly lenticular trough parts and the ribbon-thin crest parts of the film provide a means of determining top and bottom in the bed. Compare with Fig. 86. (Arts. 76, 80.)

It is probable that some of the so-called "compound foreset" type of cross-lamination represents the internal structure of interference, or compound, ripple-mark. In many deposits it is possible to determine the top surface of a compound rippled sand layer by observing the cross-lamination visible in a transverse section (see Art. 132).

A further warning should be sounded with reference to internal structure. The chevron structure of wave ripple-mark should not be

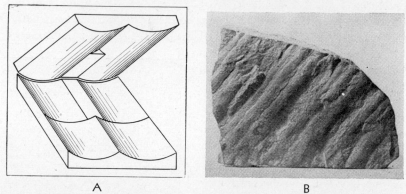

A   B

FIG. 81.—Wave ripples and counterparts.   *A.* Block diagram showing how the crest of a wave-ripple ridge may break along the stratification and adhere to the underside of the covering layer.   *B.* Underside of a thin sandstone layer with counterparts of wave ripples and several adhering crests that separated from their parent layer.   Inasmuch as steeply inclined ripple-marked layers commonly separate along the surface of contact between ripples and their counterparts, a surface like the one shown here—which is a counterpart—is fully as useful as the original surface itself for determining top and bottom. The specimen is from the Mississippian Horton sandstone of Nova Scotia and is about one-third natural size.   (Art. 76.)

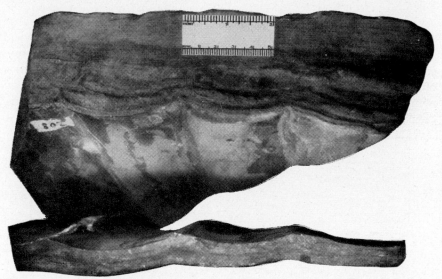

FIG. 82.—Wave ripple-mark and counterpart in an argillaceous sandstone.   The layers lie in a normal position, the top being toward the top of the illustration.   Note the several superimposed laminae in the rippled layer.   The scale is 5 cm. (2 in.) long.   Compare with Figs. 71 and 81.   (Art. 77.)

mistaken for quite similar structure in certain types of calcareous algae (Fig. 83; Art. 161).   The latter structure is produced by direct precipitation of calcium carbonate, whereas ripple-mark depends on the granular nature of the sediment. Therefore, textures should be carefully noted along with other features mentioned later in Art. 161.

78. *Scalloping.*—Gruner (1941: 1621–1622), in discussing sedimentary features that he found useful for top and bottom determination in the

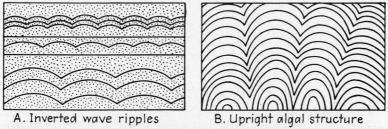

A. Inverted wave ripples   B. Upright algal structure

Fig. 83.—Comparison of inverted wave ripple-mark and upright algal structure. Wave ripple-mark is confined to granular sediments—silts, sands, calcareous muds, etc.—whereas algal structure is typically composed of crystalline calcareous rock. Wave ripple-mark is characteristically confined to thin layers measurable in centimeters of thickness, whereas algal structure commonly extends through meters of thickness. Furthermore, a single ripple lamina is flat over considerable areas, whereas a lamina of an algal mass is characteristically conoidal or hemispheroidal. Typical wave ripples have a much lower index of curvature than algal laminae. Except in limited exposures, it should not be difficult to make a positive differentiation between wave ripple-mark and algal structure. (Art. 77.)

Minnesota Pre-Cambrian, mentioned a feature that he called *scalloping* and described as follows:

A new, but uncommon, kind of criterion was discovered by Dutton [one of Gruner's field associates]. It looks like ripple marks at first glance. Close inspection shows that it occurs only in slates and is connected with neither ripple marks nor mud cracks. As in ripple marks it has a concave side which is always toward the top of the beds. The writer believes that it has some connection with differential expansion or shrinkage of adjoining layers before complete consolidation. For want of a better name it was called "scalloping."

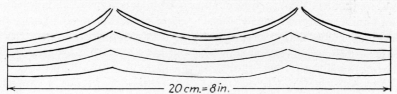

← 20 cm. = 8 in. →

Fig. 84.—Sketch showing transverse section of "scalloping" structure developed in fine-grained Pre-Cambrian sediments of probable tuffaceous origin. The crest part looks broken in some instances. Although the origin of this structure is uncertain, it is a useful top and bottom criterion. (Art. 78) *(Sketch and description furnished by J. W. Gruner.)*

In response to the author's request Dr. Gruner kindly sent the sketch which is reproduced here as Fig. 84 and with it the descriptive matter on which the caption is based. According to Dr. Gruner's letters (Nov. 30 and Dec. 11, 1942), the best exposure of the feature is in Section 8, Township 65 North, Range 6. West, north of Star Lake, in northeastern Minnesota, where

The scallops are visible only in transverse sections. The slates have a dip of about 90 degrees and, since the outcrops are glaciated, almost horizontal exposures are the rule. The scallops are definitely not parts of mud cracks. I do not believe they are oscillation ripples though one might debate that point.

The striking chevron structure is at once suggestive of that in wave ripple-mark. It may also represent an unusual preservation of shrinkage cracks in which successively higher laminae became more concave—somewhat similar, perhaps, to those found south of the Blue Hills in Massachusetts (Fig. 86). Whatever its origin, however, scalloping appears to have proved a useful feature in the field and deserves further investigation.

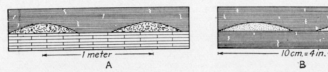

A   B

FIG. 85.—Incomplete wave- (oscillation-) ripple ridges formed on a bottom where there was insufficient granular material to form a continuous sheet of ripple-mark. *A.* Cross section of large incomplete ripples in the Cretaceous Goodland formation of Texas. The ridges are composed of shell fragments that were heaped up on the shallow bottom and then buried by yellow calcareous clay. The ridges trend in a northeast-southwest direction parallel to the old Cretaceous shore line. Compare these with Fig. 65. (*Adapted from Scott,* 1930, *Texas Univ. Bull.,* **3001**: 54, *Fig.* 13.) *B.* Incomplete wave-ripple ridges of sand in the Carboniferous Cambridge slate of eastern Massachusetts. These are only about one-fifteenth as large as those shown in *A.* (Art. 79.)

79. *Incomplete Wave Ripple-mark.*—On firm bottoms covered with a thin layer of loose sand, wave motion tends to heap the grains or particles into small and more or less symmetrical windrows similar, except in profile, to those described in Art. 70 and illustrated in Figs. 64 and 65. If these ridges with sharp or rounded crests were buried by mud, they would be just as useful as, and in all probability not easily distinguishable from, similar current-formed ridges. Sand ridges believed to have been formed as incomplete wave ripples are common in the coarse bedded clastics overlying the Squantum tillite (Figs. 85, 233) and were long ago reported by Gilbert (1899: 136) from the Medina sandstone of New York. Scott (1930: 53–56) has reported small more or less symmetrical ridges of shell debris from the Goodland limestone of the Texas Cretaceous (Fig. 85).

Incomplete wave ripples are probably more common in ancient sedimentary rocks than the existing literature would indicate. Their usefulness as a top and bottom criterion is dependent on the shape of the ridge and its relations to contiguous strata.

80. *Mud-buried Wave Ripples.*—If a limited amount of mud is deposited on a wave-rippled surface, the undulating lamina may be buried with little change in its over-all thickness. More commonly, however, it thins slightly over the crests and thickens somewhat in the troughs, as shown in Figs. 66 to 68. In the latter case the layer itself becomes a significant feature by its profile, quite apart from the profile of the ripple-mark it covers. In fact, in some rocks the sharp part of the crest has been eroded away, and the shale layer then appears as a line of concave lenses with sand above and below (Fig. 86).

This feature has been used successfully in determining the top of massive sandstone bodies in the Roxbury conglomerate south of Boston.

81. *Textural Variation in Wave Ripples.*—Bucher (1919: 184) states:

All oscillation ripples show a more or less perfect assortment of grains, with the lightest grains forming the crests and the heaviest the bottoms of the troughs. . . . Off the west side of the Island of Bourbon in the Indian ocean, the French engineer Siau observed ripples the crest of which was formed by white coral sand, the troughs by black basalt sand. The presence of this assortment of grains is perhaps the most reliable characteristic of oscillation ripples.

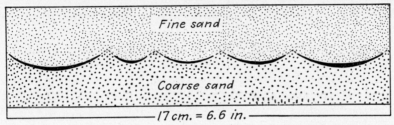

Fig. 86.—Red shale crescents in the Pennsylvanian Wamsutta red beds near Big Pond, Braintree, Mass. The crescents represent cross sections of shale fillings in the troughs between symmetrical ripple ridges. The actual crests of the ripples are not well preserved but can be reconstructed from the curvatures of the shale layers. It is probable that the crests were denuded of the original mud, which was washed into the adjacent troughs [see Cox and Dake (1915: 25)]. (Arts. 76, 80.)

It might well be added that this textural difference in crest and trough is significant if the former has been rounded or flattened by erosion (see Figs. 78, 79). Another kind of textural variation might be present in the chevron structure described in Art. 77 if mica flakes were deposited on the two slopes of a crest. However, no published notice of this phenomenon has come to the attention of the author.

82. PSEUDO RIPPLE-MARK.—Certain bedding-surface features consisting of more or less parallel ribs and ridges have been erroneously identified as ripple marks. One such feature is the sharply ridged surface of a competent bed such as quartzite which is in contact with an argillaceous layer having fracture or slaty cleavage (Fig. 87). A case in point is illustrated by the Pre-Cambrian Vishnu schist of the Grand Canyon of Arizona. Maxson and Campbell (1934: 298–303, Fig. 2) described and illustrated a ribbed surface on a vertical quartzite bed in contact with a layer of mica schist and, because of the symmetry and general plan of the ridges, interpreted the configuration as oscillation ripple-mark. This interpretation was challenged by J. T. Stark, who suggested a deformational origin. Accordingly, appropriate specimens were collected and submitted to E. Ingerson for petrofabric analysis. Ingerson (1939: 1953; see also 1940: 557–569) reported on his findings as follows:

Without exception the axes of the pseudo ripple marks are important fabric directions, both for quartz and mica, whereas the axes of the actual ripple marks appear to bear little or no relation to the fabric.

. . . Fold axes can be determined, or confirmed, from the microscopic fabric when megascopic data are not clear, and the direction of motion during deformation can be inferred.

Maxson and Campbell (1939: 606), accepting the results of Ingerson's analysis, closed the matter by stating that " . . . the crenulations of Archean quartzite described as ripple mark [Maxson and Campbell (1934: 298–303)] are only 'pseudo ripplemark,' for in reality they are drag folds formed by deformation in the Vishnu series during late Archean metamorphism."

A second example of this kind of pseudo ripple-mark was recently called to the attention of the author by Prof. W. J. Mead, who observed the phenomenon in the Pre-Cambrian Ocoee quartzite of Tennessee and collected the specimen illustrated in Fig. 87*B*. The ribbed surface, which has the configuration of the reverse of a true ripple-marked surface, was observed in an area of several hundred square yards (or square meters) on a rather steeply dipping bedding plane. The phenomenon first attracted attention because of its striking resemblance to ripple-mark. Close inspection showed that the riblets are the surface expression of gently inclined imbricating platelets bounded by fractures which die out into the quartzite within a centimeter of the surface. Our specimen shows this relation of riblet and fractures very clearly (Figs. 87*B*, *C*). This kind of pseudo ripple-mark, which seems to be similar to the crenulated structure described by Maxson and Campbell (1934: 298–303; 1939: 606), is unquestionably of tectonic origin.

Bucher (1919: 203) describes a peculiar ridged surface produced by friction in brick mud being cut by wire and cites Geinitz (1911: 640–643), who reported " . . . delicate ruffling of the surface of schistosity of many slates, which may represent an analogous phenomenon of friction."

Bucher (1919: 203) adds the following note of caution in a footnote:

This rippling of the cleavage surface may attain larger dimensions in slates and schists (*cf.* Henke, *Zeitschr. Deutsch. Geol. Ges. Monatsberichte*, 1911, p. 104). True ripple-mark must, however, not be mistaken for it in rocks showing slaty cleavage in argillaceous layers.   For an interesting discussion see Krause, *Zeitschr. Deutsch. Geol. Ges. Monatsberichte*, 1911, p. 196–202.

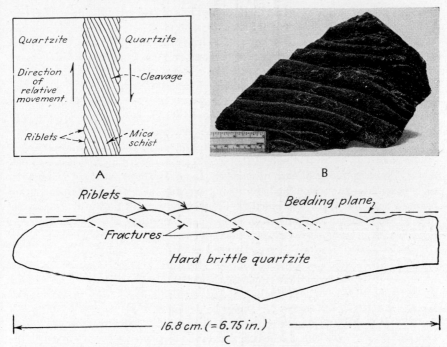

FIG. 87.—Pseudo ripple-mark—a system of dynamically produced, more or less symmetrical riblets bearing a striking resemblance to the typical ripple-mark made by wave action.   *A.* Diagrammatic section across a zone of mica schist between vertical massive beds of quartzite in the Pre-Cambrian Vishnu formation of the Grand Canyon region.   As a result of the deformation that rotated the strata to their vertical position, riblets were formed on the surfaces of the two quartzite layers bounding the schistose zone, whereas the incompetent argillaceous material of the zone was altered to mica schist. Although we cannot be certain, it is probable that the riblets are the surface expression of short inclined platelets bounded by fractures, as illustrated by Fig. 87*B*.   The riblets, which are single or forked in plan, are 12 to 18 mm. (½ to ¾ in.) across and have relief of 6 to 9 mm. (¼ to ⅜ in.); those shown in *B* are of about the same magnitude.   *B.* View of the surface of a small specimen of Pre-Cambrian Ocoee quartzite from the Cheo Dam site on the Little Tennessee River at Tapoca, Tenn.   The surface configuration, which might readily be mistaken for the reverse of a ripple-marked surface, consists of essentially parallel and symmetrical riblets with well-rounded crests and sharply angular troughs (see *C*). It is to be noted that the riblets vary considerably in width and curve somewhat in plan—two features not especially characteristic of wave ripple marks—and that they are the surface expression of gently inclined imbricating platelets bounded by parallel fractures which die out into the quartzite within 10 to 12 mm. (about ½ in.) of the surface.   *C.* Diagrammatic cross section along one of the longer sides of the specimen illustrated in *B*, showing the profile of the ribbed surface and the relation of the fractures to the riblets.   The fractures are inclined about 30° to the general plane of the ribbed surface.   (Art. 82.)   [*A is based on a description and a photograph by Maxson and Campbell, 1934, Am. Jour. Sci.,* (5) **28**: 299, *Fig. 2.   B represents a specimen collected by W. J. Mead.*]

Certain types of algal structures may also be mistaken for ripple-mark if the symmetrically crenulated structure is not observed carefully (Art. 177).

83. SUMMARY OF RIPPLE-MARK.—There is probably no better way of summarizing the importance and limitations of the *form* of ripple-mark as a top and bottom criterion than to quote from one of the ablest observers, E. M. Kindle (1917: 54–55), who writes:

In areas of excessive orogenic disturbances it is often very difficult to ascertain with certainty the original order of superposition of the beds.   The discovery in such beds of ripple-mark often serves to clearly indicate which is the top and which is the bottom of the section.   A reversed or overturned bed of ripple-mark would, of course, indicate a corresponding reversal of the original order of the beds of the section.   This use of ripple-mark in determining order of superposition, of course, assumes that the trough and crest in ripple-mark are unlike and distinguishable.   Certain kinds of ripple-mark which have ridges and troughs distinctly unlike may be used in this way.   Where the crest and trough show a similar degree of curvature as in the case of some wave-made ripple-mark it would be impossible to distinguish the sandstone mould from the original ripple-mark.   Most examples of current made ripple-mark exhibit the same characteristic of contour of the trough and crest being so nearly identical that discrimination between a mould and the original would be very difficult and often impossible in the case of fossil ripple-mark in beds where the order of superposition was unknown. . . . It is, therefore, evident that current ripple-mark with crests and troughs of similar contour cannot be used as criteria for determining the true order of superposition in areas of complex structure.   The type of ripple-mark, which is very common in wave ripple-mark, characterized by sharp angular crests separated by wide rounded troughs . . . or rounded hollows, each of which has a low sharp ridge in the centre . . . may be depended upon, however, to furnish decisive evidence regarding the order of superposition in disturbed areas.[1]   There appears to be no exception to the rule that in the type of ripple-mark in which the profile shows a series of gentle curves connected by angles the angles will represent the crests. . . . Since no examples of ripple-marks with rounded crests and angular troughs are known, the angular parts of the profile can be considered to represent the crests when found in beds whose order of superposition is unknown.   While the evidence of this kind of ripple-mark is entirely trustworthy it should be clearly understood that the interpretation of the evidence of the other types referred to is difficult and generally of no value.

In the foregoing discussion, considerable attention has been given to certain detailed structural and textural features of the several types of ripple-mark because of the importance and reliability of some of these as

[1] Regarding wave ripple-mark as a top and bottom criterion, Bucher (1919: 183–184) remarks:

The profile . . . is strictly symmetrical, with sharp crests and broad round hollows. The contrast between the original and the cast is therefore marked and offers to the geologist a means to distinguish the upper and lower surface of strata in regions of complicated structure.   A good illustration of this use of ripples in structural geology is offered by the controversy of Rothpletz and Stuchlik on the structure of the Oligocene lignite beds of Peissenberg, in the foothills of the Bavarian Alps, which also serves as illustration for the fact that, although pointed out long ago [Jukes and Geikie (1872: 63)], this difference between cast and original is not as familiar to geologists as it should be.

top and bottom criteria. Not uncommonly they are significant when no dependence whatsoever can be placed in the form of the ripple of which they are a part.

Whether form or some detailed feature of the ripple ridge or trough is being considered as a top and bottom criterion, it is always good practice to work out first how the particular feature was made and then determine whether it is reliable. If such judicial use of ripple-mark is practiced, the original sequence of many steeply tilted sedimentary strata can be definitely established.

84. Inorganically Produced Ridges and Depressions.—Careful examination of the upper and lower surfaces of the more thinly bedded sedimentary rocks usually reveals a variety of ridges and depressions. Some of these features were obviously produced inorganically; others, by organisms (Art. 110); and some are of problematical origin.

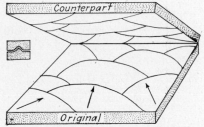

Pits, irregular depressions, and linear troughs are common and may furnish a clue to the top or bottom of the layer on which they occur, provided that their origin can first be determined or their significance established in a known sequence. The counterparts of these depressions, which commonly are preserved on the surface of the contacting layer,

Fig. 88.—Swash marks left on the fine sand of a beach by the lobate fronts of incoming waves. They are formed as the tide goes out, with each wave advancing less and less up the beach. The enlarged diagram at the left shows the swash mark to be a tiny ridge that leaves a groove in the covering layer. The arcs of the swash marks are typically less than 1 m. (3+ ft.) in length, though they may range widely from that figure. The sketch is based on observations along sandy New England beaches. Many ancient clastic formations contain well-preserved swash marks, which prove their littoral origin. (Art. 86.)

may be just as useful as the depressions. They must be differentiated, however, from original low mounds, irregular blisterlike bumps, curved and linear ridges, and other raised features. Likewise, the counterparts of the latter original positive features must not be confused with original depressions. In short, the features discussed in the following paragraphs must be studied carefully and used with discrimination in order to avoid mistakes of interpretation.

The positive and negative features next to be discussed constitute a heterogeneous assemblage of structures that are not necessarily related in origin. Many of them have been proved reliable for top and bottom determination when used properly; others remain to be tested and evaluated in actual field use. All require keen observation and careful study.

85. Features Made on Beaches by Waves and Tidal Streams.— Along the shore where the sea impinges on the land, the moving waters, changing frequently in direction, volume, and velocity, produce certain characteristic erosional and depositional features, which, if buried, may prove useful for determining top and bottom. The Silurian Medina sandstone of New York is well known for its excellently preserved features of this kind, many of which were first adequately described and illustrated by James Hall in his Part IV of the Geology of New York (1843: 52–57).

Waves, undertow, tidal currents, and other water motions both erode and make deposits on the shallow littoral bottoms. Swash marks, rill marks, current marks, and scour-and-fill structures are the most common features. These can be observed in the making along almost any shore that has a beach of some extent.

86. *Swash Mark.*—Along many present strands the lobate fronts of waning waves, advancing over sandy beaches,[1] form a system of tiny imbricating sand ridges that are convex landward and mark the line of farthest advance (Fig. 88). These curved ridges, seldom exceeding a millimeter or two in height and composed of very fine sand grains, form an integral part of the surficial irregularity of the stratum on which they lie. Their counterpart on the underside of a covering stratum is a system of tiny imbricating grooves (Figs. 88, 89).

Care should always be taken that such marks, when viewed in transverse section, are not mistaken for minute ripple marks. This danger can be avoided by examining extensive areas of bedding surfaces.

Swash marks have been reported from many thin-bedded sandstones [Fairchild (1901: 10); Clarke (1918: 199–238)], siltstones, and limestones and may be observed in the process of formation on nearly any existing beach [Hall (1843: 54–55); Grabau (1924: 708); Twenhofel (1932: 669–670); Lahee (1941: 51)].

87. *Rill Mark.*[2]—Four closely related features of the strand, or beach, region are included under the term *rill mark*.

The first of these is a seaward-facing dendritic system of tiny grooves or channels made by a small stream that splits into numerous distributaries and dies out as it flows seaward down a muddy or sandy beach (Figs. 90*B*, 91).

The second type, a landward-facing miniature river system, is composed of many tiny, quickly widening grooves that join a main channel which conducts the water seaward (Fig. 90*A*). This system of rill marks is made as the waters from a dying wave or ebbing tide gather themselves

[1] For a discussion of the "Dominant Factors in the Formation of Firm and Soft Sand Beaches," see Kindle (1936: 16–22).

[2] LAUDERMILK, L. D., and A. O. WOODFORD, 1932, Concerning Rillensteine, *Am. Jour. Sci.*, **23** (5): 135–154; Abstract, *Bull. Geol. Soc. Am.*, **43**: 227.

A   B

Courtesy of New York State Museum

FIG. 89.—Swash marks in the Devonian Portage sandstone of New York (much reduced). These represent tiny curvilinear ridges of sand pushed up the beach by successive overriding waves. *A.* Plaster replica of the original surface, showing the delicate ridges. *B.* Undersurface of overlying bed—counterpart of true surface—from which *A* was made. On this surface the counterparts of the original ridges are shallow, narrow curvilinear grooves. (Art. 86.) (*After Clarke, 1918, Bull. N.Y. State Mus.,* **196**: 229, *Plates* 24, 25.)

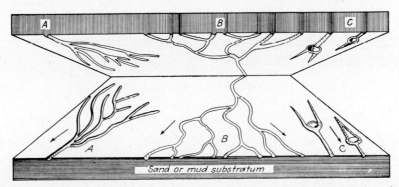

FIG. 90.—Diagram showing rill marks made by water flowing seaward as the waves recede or the tide falls. *A.* A dendritic system of small grooves joining seaward into a single channel. *B.* A large system of grooves that split seaward into many small distributaries (see Fig. 91). *C.* Grooves made upstream and downstream from a small object like a stone or shell. In some cases a moat develops around the object as shown in the left figure. The counterpart of a rill system is a similar system of tiny ridges. (Art. 87.)

into rills that join other rills at an acute angle to form the characteristic dendritic pattern.

These two types of rill mark are likely to be preserved if the sediment in which they are excavated hardens enough so that they can maintain their form while being buried. The counterparts of such rill marks constitute a dendritic system of ridges that, as Grabau (1924: 708) and Twenhofel (1932: 671) point out, might be mistaken for a fossil plant.

FIG. 91.—Rill marks made on the sand of a modern beach by receding tidal currents. The water flowed toward the upper right corner. In this type of rill mark the distributaries bifurcate downslope toward the sea. The sediment of the beach is very fine sand. It should be noted that the zone of well-formed marks is only a meter or so wide and is roughly parallel to the water's edge. Its inland margin is sharply marked, whereas its seaward margin is less distinct because of the greater amount of erosion in that direction. See Fig. 90*B*. (Art. 87.)

A third type of rill mark, reported by Hall (1843: 55) and Grabau (1924: 708) from the Silurian Medina sandstone, is formed when water flowing down a sandy or muddy beach is locally checked and diverted by partly buried shells or pebbles. The water, flowing down against and on either side of the obstacle, excavates a moatlike depression around it on the upper side, and then cuts a tiny channel seaward for a short distance (Fig. 90*C*). A tiny ridge of sediment may be left or built on the downstream side of the obstruction.[1]

[1] Hall (1843: 55) describes this sort of rill mark as follows:

The surface beyond the highest point where the water flowed smoothly down, was covered with pebbles, some fragments of shells, and the bones and scales of fishes. Every

Scrutiny of the facing beds containing this type of rill mark and its counterpart should reveal which surface is the original one and which the obverse. It is not likely that the feature is very commonly preserved, but it should be expected in ancient beach and playa deposits.

The fourth type of rill mark, commonly developed on a conspicuous scale, consists of aligned asymmetrical depressions cut into the materials of the strand by ebbing tidal currents or retreating storm waves (Fig. 92).

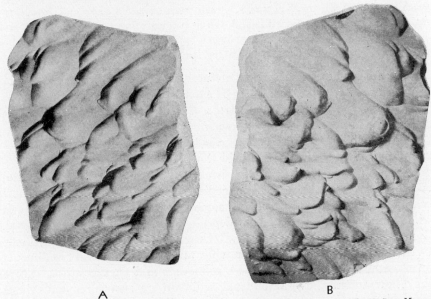

A   B

Courtesy of New York State Museum

Fig. 92.—Lobate rill marks in the Devonian Portage sandstone of New York (much reduced). *A*. Plaster replica of true surface with asymmetrical depressions eroded "by rills following the fall of the tide or possibly the retreat of heavy storm waves on a strand of low pitch." The current flowed from lower left to upper right. *B*. Counterpart of rilled surface, represented by the undersurface of the overlying sandstone layer, showing the lingual ridges formed by sand backfilling the original depressions. This type of surface has been cited mistakenly as mudflow structure. It must be differentiated from flow casts, to which it bears considerable resemblance (see Art. 102, Fig. 117). (Art. 87.) (*After Clarke, 1918, Bull. N.Y. State Mus.*, **196**: 217, *Plates* 13, 14.)

This type of rill mark is well developed in the Devonian Portage beds of New York [Clarke (1918: 203–204)], Mississippian Horton-Windsor series of Nova Scotia, and Pennsylvanian Allegheny sandstones of Indiana and probably is common the world over in similar deposits. The counterpart of the rill-marked surface, which appears to be the more commonly preserved aspect of the rill mark, has been mistakenly called "mud-flow" structure. It bears close resemblance to what we call "flow casts" in a

one of these had offered some obstruction to the advancing water; and in that direction, and on each side, there was a depression or shallow excavation, while beyond the obstacle extended a little ridge of sand narrowing and sloping down to the general surface.

later article (Art. 102) but differs in having preferred orientation of the lingual ridges and in lacking certain minute details of structure.

88. *Current Mark.*—Twenhofel (1932: 668) applies the term *current mark* to certain irregularities produced by current erosion. He states:

A current mark which is common on some tidal mud flats uncovered at low tide is made by the aggregation of the retiring waters into channels, with the result that the surface becomes eroded into rectangular, triangular, etc., high places separated by these channels. Such were observed in splendid development in Ellis Bay on Anticosti Island, the elevations being 4 to 5 inches high and 2 to 70 feet across. After becoming covered by succeeding sediments, the channel fillings in some instances resemble casts of logs.

The author has seen similar structures, which may have had the same origin, in steeply tilted beds of the Horton-Windsor series of Nova Scotia, in the flat-lying Pennsylvanian strata of Indiana, and in folded beds of similar age in northeastern Alabama.

The reliability of current mark for top and bottom determination is uncertain. It deserves a rigid field test before being discarded.

There are many other bottom irregularities produced by waves and currents on beaches and on the immediately adjacent bottoms. As these come to be studied and described, some may well prove reliable criteria when found preserved in ancient deposits [see Kindle (1936a: 861–869)].

89. PITS MADE BY ASCENDING CURRENTS OF GAS AND LIQUID.—Currents of gases and liquids moving upward through soft sediments form certain features within those sediments and on the surface where they flow forth. Several unusual sedimentary structures have been ascribed to such ascending currents, and it is quite likely that some features which can be observed today in the making may ultimately be discovered in ancient rocks. Pit and mound structures, spring pits, gas pits, and certain other papillose features on the surfaces of sedimentary layers have possible use as top and bottom criteria and deserve brief consideration.

90. *Pit and Mound.*—Kindle (1916: 542–547) and Twenhofel (1932: 680–681) have summarized several articles that describe certain pit and mound structures commonly found in recently deposited muds and occasionally identified in ancient shales. The feature may often be seen forming in rapidly settling mud of low viscosity.[1] Gas bubbles and

[1] Schofield and Keen (1929: 492–493), in the course of purifying clay fractions of soil, observed a phenomenon, during flocculation and sedimentation of the material in dilute hydrochloric acid, that produced pit and mound structure on the surface. They describe the phenomenon as follows:

When the concentration of the suspension exceeds a certain critical value—the significance of which will appear later—a number of sharp ramifying fissures develop containing

water currents, moving vertically upward through the mud and emerging at the surface, produce at the point of emergence a shallow crater simulating a raindrop impression or, less commonly, a blisterlike mound with a tiny central pit or crater (Fig. 94). The little crater, or pit, leads downward to the vertical tube along which the bubble or current ascended, but

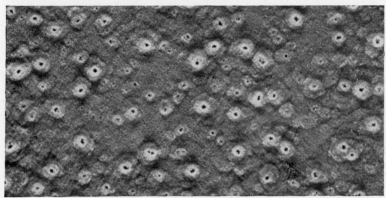

Courtesy of Nature

FIG. 93.—Pit-and-mound structure in soft sediment. The mounds average about 1 mm. in height and 10 mm. across. Each mound has a well-defined hole at the summit. This sort of structure has been found in ancient shales (*cf.* Fig. 95) and if well enough preserved provides a reliable criterion for determining the top surface of a bed. (Art. 90.) (*After Schofield and Keen*, 1929, *Nature*, **123** : 492, *Fig.* 1. *Copy of photograph furnished by editor of Nature.*)

the tube itself is rarely apparent, especially in consolidated muds and in shales, for it exists only as long as the rising column of gas or water can keep it open. As soon as current action ceases, the surrounding soft mud closes in and the tube disappears.

---

clear liquid. The density of this being less than that of the surrounding clay-laden liquid, a circulation is set up, clear liquid rising through the fissures while the remainder sinks. Some of the fissures form against the glass walls of the vessel, so the progress of sedimentation can be watched in detail. Near the bottom of the vessel the fissures tend to close, and to enlarge progressively towards the top of the column into conical chimneys, through which the motion of the ascending liquid can be traced by the movement of floccules detached from the walls of the fissures. The circulation is completed by the deposition of these floccules in a crater or ring around the exit of the chimney. There is no doubt that the suspension has acquired rigidity. The descending surface retains the initial form impressed on it by the curvature of the meniscus and by occasional air bubbles floating on the water. Marks deliberately made on the clay surface are also retained.

Weaker concentrations settle much more rapidly; in those less than one-quarter of the critical, the floccules fall individually, whereas at half the critical value the floccules settle *en masse* leaving a clear supernatant liquid. In the latter case the suspension subsides, with a perfectly flat surface, which, when disturbed, shows no sign of rigidity. But as the flocks settle on the bottom of the vessel, a layer is built up which has a concentration great enough to show rigidity. The chimneys already described then form, and extend progressively upwards towards the descending surface. When this is still about 1 cm. above the tops of the chimneys, discrete domes, often exceeding 1 mm. in height and 1 cm. across, are formed over them, and finally each mound develops a well-defined hole at the summit. This stage is shown in the accompanying photograph [Fig. 93].

The top of a layer containing this interesting feature can be differentiated from the counterpart preserved on the bottom of the covering layer by noting the appearance of the contacting surfaces—pits and mounds on the original, or top, surface; counterparts of these on the underside, as illustrated in Figs. 94 and 95.

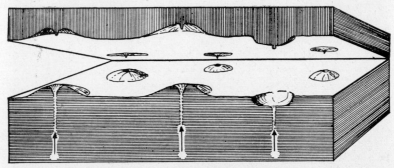

Fig. 94.—Diagram showing pit-and-mound structure on the surface of a shale bed and counterparts on the underside of the overlying stratum. These features are supposed to be formed by gas bubbles rising through water-filled mud along chimneylike tubes. The ascending currents carry with them tiny particles of mud that are deposited around the orifice of the tube in the form of an encircling ridge, giving rise to a low mound with a central pit. The tubes are never apparent in shale because of destruction during compaction. At the right-hand front corner of the diagram is a craterlike pit formed by a springlike current of water that excavated the mud instead of building it up. The individual structures shown in the diagram are seldom over 2 or 3 mm. across and 1 mm. or so high. Compare this diagram with Fig. 95, on which it is based. (Art. 90.)

Probable pit and mound structure has been reported from the ancient Belt series of western North America by Fenton and Fenton (1937b: 1924) and from the Carboniferous Cambridge slate[1] [Clark 1923: 482], and

[1] The rock containing the structure is finely banded shale composed of alternating dark and light layers averaging about a millimeter thick. Clark (1923: 483) states that "[the pits] are surrounded by a raised ring within which is a sunken annular area from which the surface rises conically to a central apex or ridge. None of our specimens shows much elevation, 2 mm. being the maximum."

The pits are considered to mark the "sites of vents from which gas escaped." The gas probably came from the decomposition of organic matter originally present in the mud, although it may also have been air trapped in the sediment.

A more detailed description of probable pit and mound structure is given by Madigan (1928: 213), who reports extensive pitting on bedding surfaces of early Paleozoic beds in Australia and remarks that they resemble raindrop impressions.

These little pits are from one-tenth to one-twentieth of an inch [2.5 to 1.2 mm.] across, and almost in contact. They average about 45 to the square inch. They are better seen in most cases as little blobs the size of shot on the underside of the overlying layer. . . . The bands showing this phenomenon are about half an inch thick, and it was noted that there were pits on one side of the slab and projections on the other. A thin section unexpectedly disclosed that the depressions went right through the half-inch slabs, and that a pit on one side was connected with a projection on the other. It was noted in the field that the pits were on the upper side of the slabs in situ. The thin-section of the half-inch slab shows it to be composed of very fine material in bands of varying fineness, as many as six bands being definable. The section is marked by vertical lines, the cores of each pit,

specimens containing the feature, collected by Clark from glacial drift near Hingham, Mass., show clearly which is top and bottom (Fig. 95, 96).

A   B

FIG. 95.—Pit-and-mound structure in Carboniferous Cambridge slate from eastern Massachusetts. *A.* Original surface, showing the characteristic pits, which have the appearance of tiny doughnuts. *B.* Undersurface of overlying layer, showing counterpart of pitted surface. Individual counterparts appear as tiny circular moats surrounding a central mound. (Art. 90.)

Shenon and McConnel (1940: 438–440) describe and illustrate an interesting corrugation resembling pit and mound structure, which seems to be present on only the undersurface of some quartzite laminae. They are not certain of its origin. They describe the structure as follows:

The bottoms of some of the light gray and more quartzitic laminae of the Prichard formation [Belt series of Idaho] are marked by sharply defined, crinkled surfaces, whereas the tops of these laminae join smoothly with the overlying black laminae. . . . Careful checking against

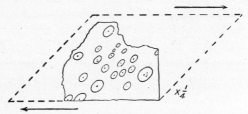

FIG. 96.—Ancient pit-and-mound structures in the Carboniferous Cambridge slate of eastern Massachusetts. These were originally circular in outline but have been distorted to such an extent that now they have elliptical outlines. (Art. 90.) (*Modified after Clark*, 1923, *Boston Soc. Nat. History Proc.*, **36**: 484, *Fig.* 2.)

evidence presented by mud cracks, cross-bedding and cleavage demonstrates that the crinkled surfaces are always at the base of the gray quartzitic layers.

in the form of conical depressions at each surface between the bands, down which the material of the band above has sunk into that below in a long tapering cone. . . . The upward path of air bubbles in mud is suggested, but material has been carried from each layer downwards, and also the pits are so numerous and uniform in size and spacing.

The origin of this crinkly surface is obscure, but in plan it resembles the pit and mound structures described by Twenhofel [1932: 680–682].

91. *Spring Pits.*—Quirke (1930: 88–91) has described how many small pits can be produced on a sandy beach by ascending waters.   The pits are characterized by concentration of coarser sediment in the central part and finer around the periphery (Fig. 97).   They are described as follows (page 91):

These pits or craters are usually less than 2 feet in diameter, their walls are

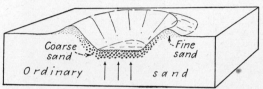

about 2 inches above the level of the surrounding sand, and probably 4 inches below, having a total depth of 6 inches.   They were characterized by a gradation of size of grain from a maximum coarseness in the central deep part to a minimum at the outside edge.

FIG. 97.—Spring pit developed in a sandy beach by ascending currents of water.   Typical pits have the form of a crater. They range in diameter from 0.3 to 0.6 m. (1 to 2 ft.) and have a total depth of about 15 cm. (6 in.), 5 cm. (2 in.) being a rim that rises above the level of the surrounding sand. There is a marked difference in the size of the sand grains on the rim and in the bottom of the crater.   The maximum coarseness is in the deepest central part of the pit, whereas the finest is at the outside edge.   A surface with many pits has a dimpled appearance.   Spring pits should be expected in rocks along with wave and rill marks, trails, and other beach-side markings.   (Art. 91.)   (*Sketch based on description and photograph by Quirke, 1930, Jour. Geology, 38: 88–91, Fig. 3.*)

Spring pits are ephemeral features limited to a narrow site along the beach and probably are rarely preserved;[1] yet they deserve mention along with their associated structures (raindrop imprints, rill marks, etc.).

92. *Gas Pits.*—Certain distinctive pitlike depressions (Fig. 98) may be formed at the surface of a fetid mud that is giving off gas produced by decomposition of the included organic matter.   Maxson (1940: 142–145)

---

[1] Hart and Hawley (1934: 85) have described peculiar cylindrical structures, in the Cambrian sandstone near Kingston, Ont., which they called "fossil quicksands." These structures ". . . have diameters ranging from two to ten feet and rise vertically through horizontal strata from an unexposed horizon, attaining a visible height of twenty feet.   They are composed of sand grains similar in character, size, assortment, and heavy residual content, to those of the contiguous beds."   The authors conclude that they ". . . were formed by currents of water rising through the strata and destroying original bedding" before the sand was finally cemented.   The currents, according to the authors, ". . . possibly created quicksands and issued at the surface as submarine springs.   Alignment of the structures suggests such springs may have risen from a buried fault."

Simpson (1936: 106) has described a somewhat similar cylindrical structure from the Paleocene of Argentina but rejects ". . . the explanations advanced to explain somewhat similar structures elsewhere."

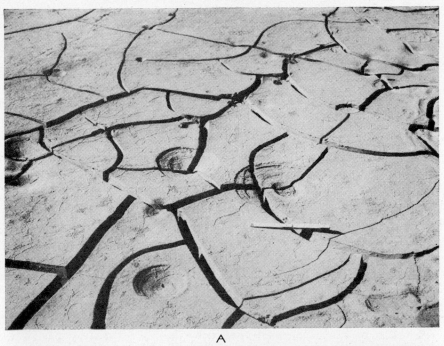

A

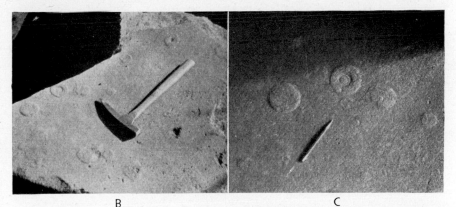

B   C

FIG. 98.—Gas pits. *A.* Gas pits in a mud bar showing different stages of obliteration. The rule is 30 cm. (12 in.) long. Depressions of this sort should be expected in ancient sandstones, siltstones, and shales. *B, C.* Supposed gas pits in Cambrian sandstone of Grand Canyon, Arizona. (Art. 92.) [*A after Maxson,* 1940, *Jour. Sedimentary Petrology,* **10**: 142, *Fig.* 5. *B* and *C after McKee,* 1945, *Carnegie Inst. Washington Pub.,* **563** (1), *Plate 7d.*]

has described such gas pits,[1] which, if preserved without too much erosional modification, could be used as a top and bottom criterion. They are present in mud-cracked sediments; and since shrinkage cracks are commonly preserved, it follows that gas pits of the type here described may be preserved and should be expected.   McKee (1945: 45, Plate 7*d*) reports pits possibly of this origin in the Grand Canyon Cambrian (Figs. 98*B, C*).

Gas pits range in diameter from a few millimeters (fractions of an inch) to several meters (6+ ft.) and in depth to slightly more than a meter (4 ft.).   They average about half a meter (1.5 ft.) in diameter and 20 cm. (8 in.) in depth.   They should be expected on the top surfaces of shales deposited as organic muds.   The smallest of them bear some resemblance to rainprints, for which they might well be mistaken.   Buckland (1842: 57) noted this resemblance in describing certain bubble-produced pits and commented as follows:

The origin of these holes appeared to have been the rise of bubbles of air through the bottom of little partial shallow ponds of water on the mud, the general surface of which, from its convex form, had allowed no water to rest upon it . . . a slab of new red sandstone . . . from near Birmingham, containing a few impressions of vegetables, was covered with small tubercles in close contact with one another, and apparently caused by the deposition of sand in holes formed by the rise of bubbles of air from a subjacent bed of clay . . . some of the cavities, and casts of cavities, . . . which have been attributed to rain-drops, may have been due to the extrication of air-bubbles; care would therefore be necessary to distinguish between these two causes of phaenomena, which have hitherto been exclusively attributed to rain.

93. FULGURITES.—When a bolt of lightning strikes and penetrates loose dry sand or soil, it may form a small tube of fused material along its path through the sediment.   Such tubes, known as *fulgurites*, are not uncommon in present-day sand deposits, and at least one possible example in an ancient sandstone (Raritan formation of New Jersey) has been reported [Barrows (1910: 294–319); see also Darwin (1860: 76–77), Merrill (1886: 83–91), Grabau (1924: 72–74), and Petty (1936: 188–201)].

Fulgurites show considerable range in dimensions.   Some are tiny tubes; others are as much as 62 mm. (2½ in.) across and nearly 20 m. (60 ft.) long.   They descend vertically or obliquely into the surficial

---

[1] The gas pits form as follows (Maxson 1940: 142):

The generation of the natural gas methane during the decomposition of organic debris is responsible for minor phenomena of sedimentation termed gas pits. Some of these are small circular pits with surrounding mud mounds formed by the escape of gas bubbles from the surface of mud bars. Larger crater-like pits are formed in submerged mud and silt bars as the result of erosion in the vicinity of active gas bubble agitation.

material, commonly branch or become contorted near their extremities, and diminish in size to a pointed thread. The wall of the tube, composed of fused grains of quartz sand, is thin (1 to 5 mm.). It has a smooth inner surface and a rough granular exterior, which is typically corrugated longitudinally. Some fulgurites have an imperfect lip of vitreous material.

Should fulgurites happen to be preserved, their presence would indicate a dry, terrestrial deposit and their position in the deposit, especially if bedding is present, should indicate which was the upper direction at the time of the discharge (Fig. 99). Although many articles have been written about fulgurites present in loose sands now at the surface, no unequivocal example of a penecontemporaneous one in an ancient sedimentary rock seems to have been cited [see Petty (1936: 188–201)].

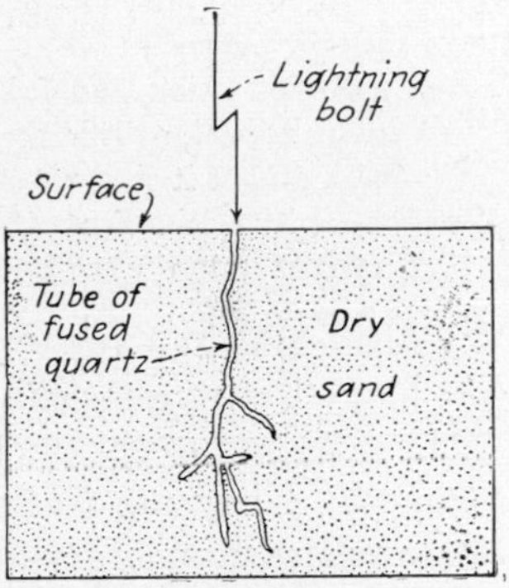

In a study of fulgurites, Julien (1901: 673–693) reported several examples of fused surface films produced in solid rock by lightning bolts. One example mentioned was a crevice with glazed walls. It seems highly unlikely that glazed surfaces of this origin would be preserved; if they were, however, they would indicate an ancient land surface.

94. IMPRESSIONS (IMPRINTS).—Imprints are made on the surface of soft muds and yielding sands by many objects of both organic and inorganic nature. These imprints exhibit almost limitless variety, and many of them, particularly in the older sedimentary rocks, have not been satisfactorily explained. Only a few will be considered here. Most of these may be seen in the process of formation at the present time, or they may be viewed shortly after formation. Some are excellent indicators of the top of a bed; others have limited use in this respect; and still others are of such rare occurrence or have so little chance of being preserved that they are of academic interest only.

FIG. 99.—Diagram showing the formation of a fulgurite. As the lightning bolt travels downward in the dry sand, it fuses the sand grains together along its path and forms a small glass-walled tube, smooth on the inside and rough on the outside, that terminates downward in several irregular branches. The tube is always small—a few millimeters—in diameter but may be several meters long. (Art. 93.)

Since imprints are negative or concave features on the top of the bed in which they were formed, it follows that their counterparts may be expected on the underside of the overlying stratum. These counterparts are commonly more useful and reliable than the imprints because they are more sharply outlined.

Geologic literature contains many descriptions and illustrations of tiny pitlike depressions, which usually are interpreted as imprints made by rain drops. Twenhofel (1921: 359–371) found experimentally that pits which are closely similar in general characteristics may be produced in soft sediments in at least eight different ways. They may be made by

1. Raindrops
2. Hailstones
3. Drip [Lyell (1851: 242) mentions waterdrops from bird's wings and from fish in their beaks]
4. Spray and splash
5. Bubbles floating in shallow water and becoming anchored to the bottom because of mud settling on their surfaces
6. Bubbles formed on the surface of a flooded area, the bubbles developing from the air pushed out of the earth and held to the bottom by the settling sediment
7. Bubbles rising and falling over very shallow water (*i.e.*, shallow water with bubbles will, as it lowers on a surface, finally let the bubble rest on the substratum and as it rises will lift the bubble off again)
8. Bubbles arising from the decay of organic matter contained in mud and making their way to the surface, where they either burst or remain attached

Although these depressions can be made in both sand[1] and mud, they are likely to be preserved only in argillaceous materials, for a sand surface is much more susceptible to change by slight erosion than is one composed of mud. They are to be expected along with mud cracks and similar features in sedimentary rocks that were deposited in environments where the bottom was always shallow and at times exposed to air.

Depressions produced by items 1 to 4 are formed only on surfaces exposed to the air; those formed by items 6 to 8 are not likely to be preserved as a rule, for they are made in shallow water and hence may easily be destroyed by movement of the water. Gas pits, which are described in Art. 92, require special conditions (*i.e.*, presence of decaying organic matter in the mud) and hence are to be expected only on the bedding surfaces of carbonaceous shales.

Pits formed by falling objects (items 1 to 4) have a raised and roughened rim not always well preserved in rocks; those formed by bubbles in the water (items 5 to 7) do not have such rims, being simple hemispherical depressions with smooth walls; and the pits formed by escaping gas are likely to have a tiny hole in the bottom, this hole being the top opening of the tube by which the gas rose to the surface of the mud.

Twenhofel (1921: 371) points out the value of these features as follows:

Impressions of the types described are made on the upper surfaces of strata and there occur as depressions. Their obverse is on the under side of the overlying strata, where they occur as wart-like mounds. It hence follows that where

[1] McKee (1945: 323) mentions raindrop impressions preserved on the foresets of dunes in the Coconino sandstone, but such impressions are probably rare.

impressions made by rain, bubbles, etcetera, are present, one is enabled to tell which is the top or younger side of a section, and this may give the key to the unraveling of a problem in complicated structure.

95. *Raindrop and Hailstone Imprints.*[1]—Raindrops and hailstones, falling on soft sediment such as that on muddy tidal flats, make small impact craters, which are circular if the object falls vertically downward and slightly elliptical if its path is oblique to the surface[2] (Figs. 100, 101,

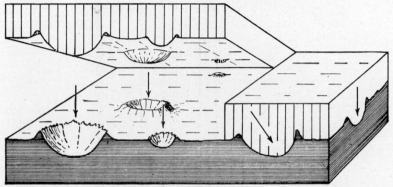

Fig. 100.—Diagram showing a shale layer pitted with large hailstone and small raindrop impressions and overlain by a later bed that has on its underside counterparts of the impressions. The arrows indicate the direction of fall of the stones and drops. Vertically directed objects make symmetrical pits, whereas slanting ones form pits that have the farther rim somewhat higher than the nearer. Compare with Figs. 101 to 103. Imprints made by hailstones and raindrops have a slightly raised rim, whereas bubble impressions lack such a rim (see Fig. 104). (Art. 95.)

102). The rim of the crater rises somewhat above the general surface and is likely to be rough, differing in these respects from the bubble-

[1] Many writers have called attention to the formation, occurrence, associations, and significance of imprints made in soft muds and yielding sands by falling raindrops and hailstones. Many of the recorded occurrences were published a hundred years ago at a time when geologists were being profoundly impressed by the discoveries of dinosaur tracks in many parts of the world. In more recent times, writers have considered the imprints as a possible top and bottom criterion. The following list of authors is merely representative of those who have written on the general subject of raindrop and hailstone impressions; it is by no means complete but will lead the interested reader well into the literature on the subject: Deane (1844: 73–77; 1845: 213–215; 1861: 1–61); Desor (1850: 200–202; 1852: 131–132); Lyell (1851: 238–247); Warren (1855: 187–188); Wyman (1855: 253–254); Dawson (1868: 27, 407); James (1884: 124–132, 151–166); Perry (1889: 326–336); Ransome and Calkins (1908: 30, 31, 42, 61); Barrell (1912); Cox and Dake (1916: 32); Kindle (1916: 542–547); Twenhofel (1921: 359–371; 1932: 490, 677–680); Leith (1923: 187); Collins (1925: 41); Madigan (1928: 210–216); Fenton and Fenton (1933: 491); Belyea (1935: 154–155); Black-welder (1941: 1944); Lahee (1941: 53, 54, 102, 103); McKee (1945: 323).

[2] *Science News Letter*, 1939, **35**: 18, reports that "fossil prints of slanting raindrops that marked the earth during a northeast gale in Colorado 250 million years ago are on exhibit at Chicago's Field Museum."

formed pits described in Art. 96. The rim of an elliptical pit tends to be higher on the side toward which the object was directed. Imprints of hailstones are likely to be larger, deeper, more irregular, and with more ragged rim than raindrop impressions [Lyell (1851: 243)].

Counterparts of the imprints adhere to the underside of the bed covering the pitted surface and appear as small blisters or wartlike protuber-

FIG. 101.—Recent raindrop imprints on tough clay that settled out of ditchwater from a placer operation. The specimen is about 10 cm. (4 in.) long. (Art. 95.) (*Specimen in Sedimentation Laboratory, Harvard University.*)

ances (Fig. 103). They are typically several times larger than the tiny, centrally pitted mounds described as pit and mound (Art. 90). They lie on the under- rather than on the upper surface of a bed and vary in size by a factor of 2 or 3, whereas the much smaller pitted mounds are fairly uniform in size (Figs. 93, 95).

Inasmuch as drops of water other than rain and objects other than hailstones can make impressions of the type just described, it may well be that some imprints preserved on pitted surfaces of sedimentary layers were formed by them, but if so it will probably be impossible to determine the source of the water or the nature of the falling object.

96. *Bubble Impressions.*—Bubbles may leave imprints of three types in soft muds. A bubble coming to rest on the surface of the substratum is likely to make a small hemispherical pit with a smooth wall and a rim that is flush with the surface (Fig. 104), as contrasted to the rough and raised rim of a raindrop or hailstone crater (Fig. 100). If such a stranded bubble were coated with sediment and then flattened somewhat, the impression formed by it would be slightly hemiellipsoidal.

A bubble of gas or liquid originating in the mud[1] and rising through it to the surface may form a pit with a tiny hole in the bottom leading into the tube below, but such pits would differ slightly from those described in Arts. 90 and 91 in having a somewhat elevated rim [Hughes (1884: 178–186)].

Finally, bubbles drifting over a surface of soft mud may touch bottom momentarily to leave a shallow depression similar to that described in the second paragraph above, except that it would not be so deep; or they may drag along over the bottom for some distance, leaving behind a shallow, straight or sinuous round-bottomed groove. This

Fig. 102.—Hailstone impressions (reduced about one-half) in the shale film at the top of a layer of red sandstone from the Triassic beds of the Connecticut Valley. The hailstones, coming from the lower right, struck the mud surface at an angle, so that a prominent impact rim was formed on the upper left side of the tiny craters. The obverse of this imprinted surface, constituting the underside of the covering layer, has a papillose surface. (Art. 95.)

groove, if filled with sand or mud later, might well have a counterpart that would be interpreted as a "worm trail" or "fucoid."

[1] Lyell (1851: 241), one of the first to study imprints in rock layers, stated:

Being desirous of ascertaining whether air-bubbles, rising through mud and bursting as they reached the surface, could give rise to cavities similar to those caused by the fall of rain, I poured some pounded mud . . . on a small quantity of water, and shook the basin containing it, upon which numerous bubbles of entangled air rose through the mud, and, on bursting at the surface, left cavities resembling in size the ordinary rain-prints from Nova Scotia, but very different in character. Nearly all of them were perfectly circular, with a very sharp edge, and without any rim projecting above the general surface. In a few cases, however, there was a slight, narrow rim, sharper and more even than that of a rain-print. In no instance was this rim connected with a greater depression at one end of an oval concave depression. Most of the pits produced by these air-bubbles were different also from rain-prints, in being deeper than they were wide. Their sides were very steep, and often over-arching, the cavity below the surface being wider than the opening at the top. The axis of some few of these deeper cavities was oblique to the surface of the mud. Where two bubbles had touched, a vertical thin parting wall of mud was left between them.

Fig. 103.—Simulated raindrop imprints made by drops of water falling on soft plaster of Paris (*B*), and obverse (*A*) of same surface, showing the appearance of the tiny domes that fit into the imprints. Compare *B* with Fig. 101, which is a naturally imprinted surface in tough clay. The two specimens are 13.5 cm. (5.4 in.) long. (Art. 95.) (*Specimens, numbered 1895, in the Sedimentation Laboratory, Harvard University.*)

James (1884: 124–132, 151–166) has called attention to certain "mud bubbles" in the Cincinnati rocks. These bubbles had been considered of organic origin and had been given binomial designations. Eight species and one variety had thus been created; yet the objects to which they referred were formed inorganically. Thirty years previously, Lyell (1851: 241) had described similar bubbles in muds from the Bay of Fundy.

All these imprints probably are preserved only under unusual conditions, but they may prove useful as top and bottom criteria if they are sufficiently distinct in outline and obvious in nature.

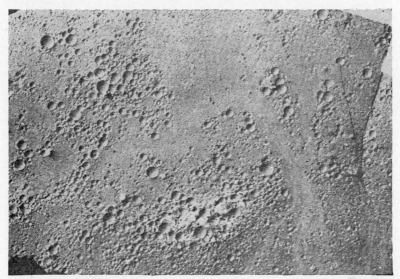

Fig. 104.—Impressions made by stranded bubbles, somewhat reduced. These bear close resemblance to raindrop impressions but differ in lacking the typical rim.   (Art. 96.)   (*After Twenhofel*, 1921, *Bull. Geol. Soc. Am.*, **32**: 365, *Fig.* 5.)

97. *Impressions Made by Drifting or Floating Objects.*—Careful and prolonged observation on the bottoms of shallow bodies of fresh and saline water and on the beaches and tidal flats bordering them would undoubtedly show many kinds of impressions made by various inorganic objects temporarily grounded or swept along in water so shallow that they dragged on the bottom, leaving behind a characteristic marking of some sort. Pieces of pumice and other rocks that will float might make such markings; blocks and fragments of an ice pack might be driven ashore and in the process leave a series of essentially parallel angular grooves that would yield sharp-crested rectilinear ridges similar to those commonly observed on the underside of some sedimentary strata [Hall (1843: 235)]. A slight shift in wind direction might cause the observed change in a second or third set of crossing grooves. Since the grooves are not deep, it would be necessary to postulate a rather uniformly thin mass of pack ice (see Art. 104).

98. *Imprints, Casts, and Pseudomorphs of Crystals.*—Under favorable conditions crystals of ice, salt, and certain other substances grow in soft surficial sediment, forming a distinctive system of tiny reticulated grooves (ice) or pyramidal ridges made by protruding corners of crystals (salt, pyrite, etc.). If now the ice crystals melt, or the others disappear through solution, imprints of the original crystals remain and, if the sediment is sufficiently indurated to retain them, may be filled with mud

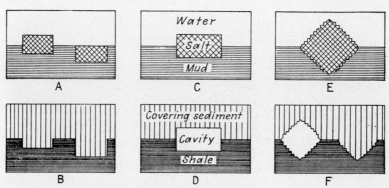

Fig. 105.—Impressions, molds, and pseudomorphs of salt crystals. *A.* Two salt crystals growing in mud; one is only partly embedded, whereas the other lies completely embedded. *B.* Diagram showing same bottom as in *A*, after crystals have been dissolved and the cavities left by them filled with sediment. The left projection into the shale is an incomplete pseudomorph of the original crystal; the right, a complete pseudomorph. Compare with Fig. 107. *C.* A large salt crystal partly embedded in mud. *D.* The bottom shown in *C* was covered by sediment, which temporarily preserved the crystal. Later the crystal was removed by solution, leaving a cavity, or complete mold. Under some conditions this cavity may be filled with introduced substances. This kind of mold, or cavity, filling is of no use for determining tops and bottoms. *E.* A large salt crystal growing in mud. *F.* Two possible kinds of preservation resulting from the burial of the bottom shown in *E*. The left cavity is a complete mold of the original crystal. At the right is an incomplete pseudomorph made by the filling of the hopper-shaped cavity left by predepositional solution of the original crystal. (Art. 98.)

or sand and thus preserved (Fig. 105). Counterparts in the form of tiny ridges and pseudomorphs would be present on the underside of the covering bed and would be composed of the same material as that of the bed (Fig. 106). Kindle (1929*a*: 180) and Raymond (1930: 291) have reported such pseudomorphs of salt crystals from the Upper Cambrian Roche Miette formation of Alberta, but neither states whether the pseudomorphs lie on the surface or are attached to the underside of the overlying bed.[1]

[1] Kindle (1929: 23) reports from the Roche Miette ". . . beds of impure limestone crowded with moulds of large salt crystals showing very plainly the cubes and concave hopper-shaped crystals in which common salt crystallizes" and in the same year (1929*a*: 180) reports many beds ". . . with salt crystal pseudomorphs, ripple marks (rare) and mud cracks," and Raymond (1930: 291) states that "the pseudomorphs after salt crystals in the red layer," which he calls "hoppers," ". . . are attached to the surfaces of thin layers of yellow dolomite interbedded with red shale,

A specimen of the Roche Miette collected by Dr. Raymond is illustrated in Fig. 107, and it seems that the pseudomorphs of sand are counterparts of original salt crystal impressions formed when the mineral dissolved.

Daly (1912: 82), in describing the Pre-Cambrian Kintla formation, stated:

A special feature of the argillites is the great abundance of casts of salt-crystals. . . . The casts represent both complete cubes and the hopper shape

Fig. 106.—Top surface of a fine-grained limestone bed showing calcite pseudomorphs of salt (halite) crystals *in situ* (white polygons) and polygonal imprints from which crystals have been removed. (Art. 98.)

of skeleton crystals. . . . The cubes are of all sizes up to those 4 cm. or more in diameter. Ripple-marks and sun-cracks, especially the latter, are likewise very abundant.

Miller (1937: 55–57) reports casts of halite crystals from the Beekman-town limestone of Pennsylvania, and other Paleozoic examples have been described by Vanuxem (1842: 108) and Logan (1863: 632).

Another example is described by Dunbar (1924: 177) from the famous Permian Insect Hill locality in Kansas.

The molds of great salt hoppers . . . rise from the surface of the lowest limestone band into the succeeding shales. They appear as low blunt pyramids

into which the pseudomorphs project. The cubes vary from three-eighths of an inch to one inch along a side."

with their sides striated in a direction normal to their axes, which in most cases stand vertical but in some are more or less inclined.   They thus resemble the tops of half submerged octahedrons but they never display more than this one set of faces.   However, since they rise above the layer of muddy limestone, of which they are lithologically a part, they cannot be considered pseudomorphs of crystals but must be regarded rather as primary structures.[1]   I am indebted to Dr. George P. Merrill, of the United States National Museum, for the suggestion that they may be the fillings of the hollow bases of large hopper-shaped crystals of halite.   According to this interpretation the salt hoppers grew upon and partly

Fig. 107.—Salt crystal pseudomorphs from the Cambrian Roche Miette formation of Alberta.   It appears that the view shows the *underside* of a sandstone layer, in which case the square prominences represent fillings of cavities left by solution of original salt crystals, as illustrated in Figs. 105 *A*, *B*. (Art. 98.)   (*Specimen in Sedimentation Laboratory, Harvard University.*)

embedded in the limy mud bottom of a body of water surcharged with sodium chloride, and the basal hopper of the crystal gave shape to the limy pyramids, which remained even after the subsequent incursion of fresher waters had redissolved the salt.   The size of the crystals was notable since the pyramids range from 2 to 10 inches across.

[1] A query was sent to Dr. Dunbar with reference to the possible top and bottom significance of the molds he described, and he replied as follows (Apr. 12, 1946):

I have just looked at the material I brought back and I suspect I have the molds of crystals that were embedded in the surface of the sea floor.   If so, the crystals formed and then were dissolved, leaving depressions in the sediment which were filled with the next layer of mud.   In that case, the molds would be on the under side of the layer facing down and all would be incomplete on one side.   It really would take field observations in each case to determine whether this was true.   I recall very well the impressions of crystals in the Camillus shale in New York, and there the sediment had solidified around crystals which were later dissolved away, perhaps even during the present erosion cycle, so that we have complete molds of crystals.   In such a case they would not indicate the orientation of the beds.

Apparently salt crystals grow just under the surface of the mud, possibly with some of the crystal protruding, so that while they exist they form tiny pyramidal ridges and other angular projections, which rise above the general surface of the substratum. If such a crystal is not destroyed before burial, its counterpart on the underside of the overlying bed will be a "hopperlike" imprint[1] (Fig. 105). If the crystal is destroyed soon after burial, the resulting cavity may persist and may be filled later with material introduced by ground waters. If the covering sediment is very thin, however, which is likely, it will collapse into the cavity and ultimately harden to form a more or less perfect pseudomorph of the original crystal. Crystals formed secondarily along or near a contact between two beds would have no significance as to top or bottom.

Under favorable conditions, ice crystals form from the film of water covering a clay bottom or from the water present in the upper few millimeters of the mud. The acicular crystals, impinging on the bottom mud or growing in the superficial layer of clay, produce characteristic markings or clefts that commonly show the 30° and 60° angles peculiar to ice. Subsequent desiccation of the clay warps the surface and slightly distorts the curved and rectilinear clefts (Fig. 108). If these ice-crystal impressions are well enough preserved, they should be useful as a top and bottom criterion (Fig. 109).

Allan (1926: 494–500) made many artificial ice crystals and reported at length on their characteristic features. His article is an excellent guide for the investigator who wishes to study suspected ice-crystal markings in ancient rocks. Both recent and ancient ice-crystal impressions have been reported, and several cases in point are worth brief notice here.

Shaler, Woodworth, and Marbut (1896: 992, Fig. 39) described and illustrated recent ice-crystal impressions observed in the clay pits of Cambridge, Mass. (Fig. 108), and Clarke later (1918: 206–207) accepted the suggestion of J. B. Woodworth that certain fucoidal markings (*Fucoides graphica*) in the Devonian Portage beds were best interpreted as the imprints of ice crystals (Fig. 110) [see Schuchert (1927: 123–131) for a discussion of Upper Devonian winters.] Udden (1918: 8) reported "fossil ice crystals" from Upper Cretaceous formations in Texas; and though he gave no information which might indicate whether or not they

---

[1] Lyell (1851: 241) reported a case in point, in describing certain small protuberances on a slab of recently hardened mud:

. . . the protuberances were seen to be irregular in form, and beneath them were found small pellets of shale and crystals of salt, which had evidently lain on the beach, and then been covered with a film of sediment. This solid matter not having shrunk when the muddy layer dried in the sun, a small projection was caused. Small cracks were usually visible round the base of each of these protuberances.

Courtesy of J. A. Allan

Fig. 108.—Imprints of ice crystals. *A.* Imprints formed in mud containing a small amount of moisture. The specimen is about 20 cm. (8 in.) long. The counterpart of such an imprinted surface, which would

could be used as a top and bottom criterion, he did use them to locate a definite zone on both sides of a fault, thereby determining the amount and direction of movement.

FIG. 109.—Fasciculate markings in the Carboniferous Cambridge slate of eastern Massachusetts. These may be ancient ice-crystal impressions (*cf.* Fig. 108). The specimen is about 15 cm. (6 in.) long. (Art. 98.) (*Specimen on display in the Geological Museum of Harvard University.*)

Several years ago Twenhofel (1932: 675–677) summarized much of the literature on ancient and recent ice-crystal impressions. Since this summary, Mark (1932: 171–176) has reported impressions in the Lake

be the underside of the covering stratum, would consist of numerous single and fasciculate ridges. Some so-called "fucoids" in ancient rocks may have been formed in this manner (see Art. 114 and Fig. 110). The specimen, which is on exhibit in the Geological Museum of Harvard University, is the same one illustrated by Shaler, Woodworth, and Marbut, 1896, *U.S. Geol. Survey Ann. Rept.*, **17** (1): 992, Fig. 39. *B*. The ridged counterpart of an imprinted surface. The crystal grooves were definite and pronounced when produced artificially. The imprints were made in fine sand, and the counterpart was obtained by pouring plaster of Paris over the imprinted surface. The specimen is reduced to about one-fourth natural size. It should be noted that sandstone layers showing small ridges possibly of this origin have those ridges on the undersurface. (Art. 98.) [*B is after Allan, 1926, Am. Jour. Sci.*, **11** (5) : 499, *Fig. 8. The print was kindly furnished by Dr. Allan.*]

Bonneville beds, and Lamont (1938: 3) has suggested that *Oldhamia antiqua* and *O. radiata* are due to "a kind of frost-stencilling" possibly like that shown in Fig. 109.

99. Features Produced by Objects Dropping into or Material Loaded onto Soft Unconsolidated Sediment.—Extraneous objects dropping from

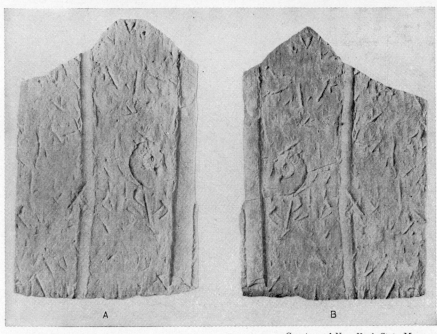

A   B

Courtesy of New York State Museum

FIG. 110.—Furrowed and imprinted sandstone layer from the Devonian Portage beds of New York (much reduced). *A.* The specimen (a plaster replica of the original surface) shows numerous supposed ice-crystal impressions (small fusiform depressions) lying on a sand surface that is imprinted by a goniatite shell and grooved by two prominent rectilinear furrows that are longitudinally striated. Since the fusiform imprints are superimposed on the furrows, they must have formed later. *B.* The counterpart of the original surface *A* preserved on the underside of a sandstone stratum. The smaller impressions (and ridges) lie at various angles with reference to the bedding plane and to each other, suggesting the radiate arrangement of typical ice-crystal impressions (*cf.* Fig. 108) [See Clarke (1918: 206.] (Arts. 98, 104, 114.) (*After Clarke*, 1918, *Bull. N.Y. State Mus.*, **196**: 227, *Plates* 22, 23.)

air or water onto *hydroplastic*[1] sediments that can yield by compaction or flowage sink into the sediment for some distance and when buried show

[1] The author is indebted to his colleague, Prof. Walter L. Whitehead, for the term *hydroplastic*, which the latter would qualify as follows (May 20, 1946):

Fine-grained fragmental sediments with high water content undergo homogeneous change of shape by positional shifting between their constituent grains or particles. Adsorbed water films and interstitial liquids facilitate this movement on an infinite number of minute surfaces. The materials possessing such intergranular characteristics may be designated *hydroplastic*. Upon loss of water and consolidation they lose this kind of plasticity.

structural relations to the mud penetrated and to the covering sediment that are useful in determining the top of the sequence containing them.

The distance the object penetrates and the deformation it produces depend upon the physical condition of the sediment. Thus ice-rafted and plant-rafted boulders may drop into soft sands and muds, producing deformation like that shown in Fig. 111, and bombs and blocks of lava, expelled from a volcano, may sink into readily yielding ash, as shown in Fig. 292.

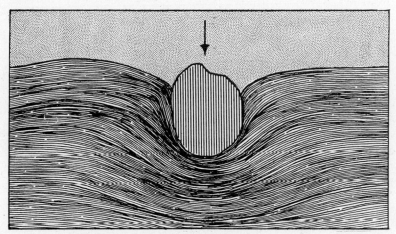

Fig. 111.—Shale-sandstone sequence overlying the Squantum tillite on Squantum Head, Massachusetts, showing a large pebble that sank deeply into the hydroplastic mud, compressing the laminae directly beneath, causing them to be somewhat thickened alongside, and dragging the upper laminae downward. The sand was deposited later and fills the triangular moat around the embedded pebble. The pebble is about 35 mm. (1.5 in.) long. (Art. 99.)

A thin layer of sand, deposited on water-filled mud or soft organic debris, may, because of slight differential loading, cause the plastic sediment to flow, and the flowage in turn may produce characteristic structures in the sand (Art. 102) or in the organic material (Art. 99).

100. Boulders Embedded in Sand and Mud Deposits.—A boulder, released from an iceberg or from some plant[1] that has transported it, upon dropping onto a bottom covered with soft clay and silt or with silt and

[1] Darwin (1860: 497 *ff.*) describes how boulders may become entangled in the roots of trees and later, when the tree is washed into the sea, may be transported great distances from its source. He points out that such floating trees may not be seen because, being weighted down, they float beneath the surface. According to Darwin (1860: 498), "these facts may possibly throw light on single stones, whether angular or rounded, occasionally found embedded in fine sedimentary masses."

It is highly probable that certain marine algae of the *Fucus* type transport pebbles and small boulders great distances, and when it is realized that such plants have been in existence for many geologic periods it seems altogether possible that sporadic

sand tends to sink into the soft sediments. It compacts the material directly beneath and may produce some deformation of the sediment around its periphery (Fig. 113). The sediment may even flow out from under the object and form a circumferential ridge rising slightly above the bottom (Fig. 114).

Relations similar to those just described can be seen around ice-rafted boulders lying in the varved shales associated with the Squantum tillite on Squantum Head, near Boston. The laminae of the shale covering a

Courtesy of American Association of Petroleum Geologists

FIG. 112.—A quartzite boulder showing deformation of laminae produced by pebbles falling into water-filled sand. The boulder is about 12.5 cm. (5 in.) long. (Art. 100.) (*Slightly modified after Rettger, 1935, Bull. Am. Assoc. Petroleum Geologists, 19: 274, Fig. 1.*)

boulder end abruptly against it around the base and sides and arch only slightly as they pass over. The arching laminae thin slightly over some of the boulders. It usually should be possible to determine the top of a formation containing an erratic boulder by noting the relations of the laminae around the boulder (Fig. 113).

In addition to the example just cited, Collins (1925: 66) reports scattered boulders in the Pre-Cambrian Gowganda formation, and Fig. 115 shows the relations of the surrounding laminae to such boulders.

---

pebbles and boulders in ancient formations may have been distributed by them [see also Emery (1941: 92–93) and Emery and Tschudy (1941: 855–862)].

Rettger (1925: 274) illustrates a quartzite pebble showing two stones which fell into the original sand when it was in such physical condition that a pebble could sink into it some distance (Fig. 112).

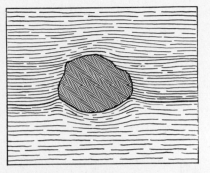

Fig. 113.　　　　　　　　Fig. 114.

Fig. 113.—A limestone boulder embedded in thin-bedded Upper Cambrian limestone at the gorge east of St. Albans, Vt. The boulder lying directly above the hammer sank into the soft layers in coming to rest, dragging them downward in the process. The larger part of the boulder remained above the soft bottom and was buried later by thin layers that first end abruptly against it and higher up arch gently over it. (Art. 100.)

Fig. 114.—Diagram illustrating how a boulder, coming to rest on a soft mud bottom, slightly deforms the upper laminae and is subsequently covered by laminae the lower of which end abruptly against it, whereas the later arch gently over it. The depth to which the boulder sinks into the soft sediment is determined largely by the condition of the bottom material. Compare this diagram with Fig. 111. Boulders showing these relations occur in the laminated shales associated with the Squantum tillite of eastern Massachusetts. The boulders range in size from a few centimeters to half a meter in greatest dimension. (Art. 100.)

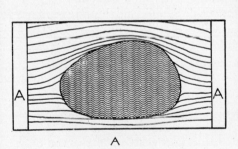

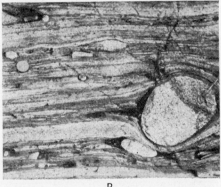

A　　　　　　　　　　B

Courtesy of Geological Survey of Canada

Fig. 115.—Buried boulders. (Art. 100.) *A.* Sketch of a pebble in laminated graywacke of the Pre-Cambrian Gowganda formation of Ontario, showing that the pebble punched through some of the underlying laminae before coming to rest. Laminae above the line *AA'* were deposited later; the first of these end abruptly against the pebble, whereas the later ones arch gently over it. The pebble is slightly less than natural size. (*Modified after Collins, 1925, Geol. Survey Canada Mem.,* **143**: 66, *Fig.* 6.) *B.* Photograph showing buried boulders similar to the one in *A.* The rock is Canadian Pre-Cambrian. (*Photograph, 46433, furnished by the Geological Survey of Canada.*)

They lie in the midst of graywacke characterized by graded bedding, and the lamination around them, according to Collins (1925: 66–67),

. . . seems to show that the pebbles dropped into the originally soft, finely stratified mud with enough force to punch through several laminae and partly bury themselves. The laminae near the base of a pebble inclusion terminate abruptly against it as if pinched out by the sinking pebble, whereas the upper part of the pebble is arched over by laminae which only thin out somewhat toward the apex.

101. Bombs and Lava Fragments Embedded in Ash and Tuff Deposits.—Bombs and large lava fragments falling into soft, unconsolidated, fine-grained pyroclastics are embedded with characteristic structural relations to the surrounding materials. Burial in water-deposited and water-covered volcanic sediments probably produces structural relations essentially like those which can be observed in fine-grained pyroclastics recently deposited on land. In either subaqueous or subaerial deposits the relations of the body to the enclosing sediment should indicate the direction of fall and hence the bottom of the deposit in which the object lies (Fig. 292). Wentworth and Williams (1932: 34, Fig. 3) reproduce a fine photograph of an embedded block showing structural relations similar to those illustrated in Fig. 292.

Ancient water-laid and subaerial ash and tuff deposits should contain occasional extraneous blocks and bombs, particularly if the locality is near the original site of the volcano, and these objects should be expected in terranes of volcanically derived rocks (Art. 188).

102. Flow Casts.—Soft hydroplastic sediments, if unequally loaded with sand or gravel, yield to the weight of the superincumbent load by flowing. The resulting structure is a layer of coal or shale with the upper surface thrown into asymmetrical drawn-out folds and broad, rounded depressions. The overlying sand, which can flow because of its large water content, molds itself to the undulating surface of the mud or organic sediment, so that on compaction the sand layer shows a counterpart of the surface on its *underside* (Figs. 116, 117). The "rolls," lobate ridges, and other raised features thus produced and preserved in the overlying sandstone are here given the designation *flow cast*[1] because they represent the filling of the negative features produced by the flowage of the soft underlying sediment. It is to be noted that flow casts are preserved only on the underside of a sandstone layer. The underlying rock, typically coal or mudstone, preserves no diagnostic structure, presumably because it was essentially a highly viscous fluid at the time when it was deformed.

Flow cast is not uncommon in ancient sedimentary rocks and is a reliable top and bottom criterion. The author has used it successfully in determining the tops of steeply inclined and overturned Mississippian strata on Cape Breton Island, Nova Scotia,[2] and in folded Pennsylvanian

---

[1] This designation was suggested by Dr. Walter L. Whitehead, who has studied the structures with the author in the field.

[2] The following brief description of typical flow-cast structure is abstracted from field notes made by the author:

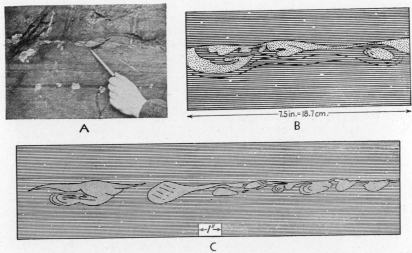

FIG. 116.—Sandstone flow cast in the Pennsylvanian Wamsutta red beds of the Narragansett Basin, Rhode Island. This feature, which is exposed along the edge of the Pawtucket Reservoir, is a thin discontinuous layer of fine sand lying in the midst of fairly steeply dipping silty red shale. The sand bodies are typically flat on the upper surface but irregularly lobate on the lower. Internally they exhibit a kind of cross-lamination together with lines of flowage. The general upper surface of the discontinuous layer is a bedding plane that truncates the structures in the sand bodies. The discontinuous layer is believed to have been formed by sand sinking into an essentially fluid mud (Art. 102), but antidune action may also have played a part (Art. 73 and Figs. 69, 70). *A.* Photograph of a part of the feature, showing some of the detailed structure. *B.* Diagram showing details of a small part of the feature. *C.* Diagram of several discrete masses of sand, showing internal structure. (Arts. 102, 148, 156.)

beds in the Narragansett Basin in Rhode Island (Figs. 116, 117). Sorby (1908: 197, Plate XIV) described and illustrated a somewhat similar

Certain thin sandstone beds in the Mississippian Horton sandstone-shale sequence of Cape Breton Island, Nova Scotia, have an unusual undersurface. The surface, at first glance, has the appearance of pahoehoe lava, and it is obvious that the fine sand of which the beds are composed must have flowed to develop the present configuration (Fig. 117). All beds with such undulatory undersurfaces rest on an unctuous and silty mudstone which is so closely jointed that all original sedimentary structures are obscured. In no exposures observed does a sand bed exhibit any evidence of flow on its upper surface. On the contrary, some of the beds have a flat upper surface, whereas others have that surface ripple-marked. Both features show the contemporaneity of the flow-cast structure. Intercalated mudstone layers contain knotty and gnarled masses of "rolled-up" or "balled-up" material, which are interpreted as mud-flowage structures. As a rule, however, these are not in direct contact with the undulatory undersurfaces of sand beds.

It appears that the muds and sands of a part of the Horton series were, at the time of deposition, so full of water that they could flow readily under slight differential pressure. As sand, probably in rippled layers, was deposited on the soft, plastic mud, the latter tended to flow out from under areas of greater load (*i.e.*, greater thickness of sand as under a ripple crest) with consequent deformation of its surface. Simultaneously the overlying sand adjusted itself to the irregularities of the mud surface. As the mud lost water during deformation, it developed sufficient strength to resist

Fig. 117.—Flow cast in a fine-grained sandstone from the Mississippian Horton formation of Cape Breton Island, Nova Scotia. The surface shown is on the underside of a thin sandstone layer. Such layers invariably rest upon mudstone, which, being quite susceptible to weathering, appears in all exposures as a minutely jointed mass that disintegrates readily and separates cleanly from the overlying sandstone. In some exposures the mudstone directly below the flow cast is intensely "balled up" and even fractured. Flow cast is believed to form when water-filled sand sinks into viscous hydroplastic mud. Deformation is started by uneven loading of the mud. The initial condition in the sand that started the deformation may well have been ripple ridges, for some of the sandstone layers have flow-cast structure on their undersurface and ripple marks on the upper. The numerous, roughly parallel curvilinear grooves in the sandstone surface are interpreted as shear fractures produced in the sand when it could no longer flow. The specimen is about ½ m. (18 in.) wide. (Arts. 102, 148, 156.)

feature many years ago;[1] and even he seems to have been antedated by Fuchs (1895: 371–374), who, according to Bucher (1919: 207), described a

---

further flow and the sand maintained its undersurface configuration. In some beds downfolds of sandstone show a series of tiny step faults produced by shearing of the sand body. Shearing took place when the sand could no longer flow because of loss of some of the contained water.

Sandstone beds in which flow-cast structure is well developed separate freely from the underlying mudstone with a clean lobate surface. The relief of the mudstone surface, on the other hand, is not preserved because of the extensive joints that divide the rock into tiny blocky fragments.

[1] Sorby (1908: 197) describes the structure, here reproduced in Fig. 118c, as

. . . a case where the current was so gentle that only very fine-grained green material was deposited in just the same creamy semi-liquid condition as recently-deposited clay in which

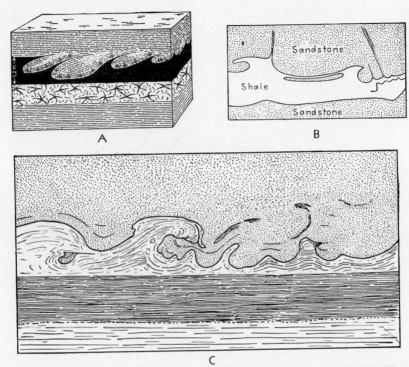

FIG. 118.—Flow-cast structures resting on coal, mudstone, and shale. All are ascribed to differential loading of a soft, viscous sediment by sand. The sand, being full of water at the beginning of the deformation, could flow readily. Later, upon losing some of the water, it became rigid and thereafter failed by shear. (Arts. 102, 156)

A. Sandstone flow cast resting on a German coal bed 1.2 m. thick. The first sand that was spread over the soft carbonaceous material sank into it, forming rolls in which some of the original stratification is still preserved. Later sand was deposited without disturbance. Compare this structure with that illustrated in Fig. 116. (*After Kukuk*, 1936, *Glückauf*, **41**: 1027, *Abb.* 17.)

B. Basal sandstone deformations from Ordovician rocks of central Victoria, Australia. The sketch is one-fourth natural size. Prominent fissures rise from reentrants in the base of the sandstone, and a thin sandstone lamina lies completely detached in the shale. This type of structure, which has also been found in Silurian rocks of the Melbourne district, is designated "basal sandstone deformations" by Hills (1941) and Hills and Thomas (1945: 57) and ascribed to penecontemporaneous deformation connected with compaction. (*Modified after Hills and Thomas*, 1945, *Econ. Geology*, **40**: 57, *Fig* 5.)

C. Sketch of flow cast in a fine-grained ash layer that was deposited on a clay while the latter was still in a semiliquid condition. About 25 to 35 mm. of the clay was affected by the sand, which appears to have been swept in by a current moving from left to right. Wisps of the clay were caught in the flowing sand, and their present position indicates the extent of flowage in the sand. (*Sketch based on a photograph of the Langdale slate by Sorby*, 1908, *Geol. Soc. London Quart. Jour.*, **64**: 197, *Plate* XIV. *Figure is reduced somewhat more than one-half.*)

" . . . peculiar variety of mudflow structure imitating ripples . . . from the lower surfaces of 'Flysch' sandstones. . . ." Bucher (1919: 207)

the amount of included water is about 80 per cent., so that it can be easily washed up by a gentle current. Then must have come a fresh volcanic disturbance and deposit of ashes, with a current moving from left to right, which broke up this semi-liquid material into what might be compared with breaking waves, some of which were permanently entangled in the ash, and others carried away. This not only shows the original character of the deposits, but also roughly the time that elapsed between the disturbances. Very fine-grained

goes on to say that the structure has been " . . . proven experimentally to form when a viscous mass (like plaster of Paris) flows over a yielding substratum (like sand)." The suggestion of Bucher (1919: 207) that the structure be referred to as *pseudo-ripple* does not seem to have been followed.

If, as Bucher states, the structures described by Fuchs were formed by plastic sediment flowing over yielding sand, they are not the same as flow cast, for the latter structure is formed by water-filled sand flowing over and sinking into highly viscous mud.

In recent years several writers have described structures that seem to have the same characteristics as flow cast.

Kukuk (1936: 1020–1029), in describing some structures peculiar to certain German coals, cited and illustrated a coal-sandstone sequence showing what appears to be flow-cast structure along the contact (Fig. 118). According to Kukuk, the irregular contact was formed shortly after the peat bog was covered and was caused by the unequal loading of sand on the soft, plastic organic material [see also Stutzer and Noé (1940: 348, Fig. 122)]. From the higher Silurian rocks of the Kerry district in Wales, Earp (1938: 141–148) has reported zones of contorted sandstone and shale (Fig. 234) that he ascribes to " . . . subaqueous gliding of soft mud and silt during deposition [page 147]." From rocks of the same period in the Melbourne district of Australia, Hills (1941) and Hills and Thomas (1945: 57–58) have described, as "basal sandstone deformations," structural features on the underside of sandstone layers that are believed to have been formed during the soft-rock stage, probably as a result of compaction (Fig. 234). Careful perusual of the more recent geological literature, both at home and abroad, would undoubtedly reveal scores of references like those just cited (Art. 152).

Several structures resembling flow casts in some particulars have been described and illustrated and deserve brief mention here for the sake of completeness.

Trail and underplight, discussed in Art. 103, resembles flow-cast structure in that it consists of a layer of contorted sand and gravel resting with uneven contact on soft mud. It forms in a different manner, however, and seems to be confined to surficial regolithic materials churned up by frost action.

---

material does not remain in this semi-fluid condition for more than a few weeks; and therefore we have permanent evidence that, in some cases, the volcanic disturbances were separated by only a short interval.

This structure, although apparently of somewhat different origin than typical flow cast, is nonetheless a reliable top and bottom feature and is of special interest because of its clearly outlined details.

Lamont (1938: 14; 1941: 150–151) has called attention to an unusual rippled structure (Fig. 70) in detrital limestone that he ascribed to antidune formation (Art. 73). A transverse section of the beds affected has some resemblance to flow cast, though Lamont's explanation is probably the more likely one. The Irish examples that Lamont (1941: 150–151) illustrates are quite similar to small lobate structures in the Wamsutta red beds of the Narragansett Basin in Rhode Island (Fig. 116).

Stutzer and Noé (1940: 402–403, Figs. 183, 184) describe and illustrate several eroded brown coal beds in Saxony covered by sand which bears to the coal a relation somewhat like that of flow cast to the underlying shale. In these examples, however, the abrupt contact between the two rocks and the nature of the overlying sediment point clearly to the unconformable relationship of coal and sand.

103. FROZEN GROUND STRUCTURES—HEAD, TRAIL AND UNDERPLIGHT, WARP, ETC.—Surficial materials—gravels, sands, and finer sediments—are churned and contorted, in some cases to an almost unbelievable degree, by alternate freezing and thawing. This action, reaching to depths of several meters in extreme cases, produces in the material affected a variety of contortions that Dines *et al.* (1940: 198–226) propose to include under the general term *head.*[1] Bryan (1946a: 622–642), analyzing the same problem, has just published a comprehensive nomenclature on the structural features of frozen ground, and the interested student is referred to this article as the latest word on the subject.

Another group of amazingly contorted glacial sediments has recently been described and illustrated by Carruthers (1939: 299–333) from the northern glacial drifts of Great Britain. This article deserves the scrutiny of any geologist who has occasion to study recent or ancient glacial deposits.

Trail and underplight has been proposed[2] as a designation for a peculiar bipartite structure present in certain Pleistocene deposits of England. It consists of a thin contorted sand or gravel layer, the *trail*, which rests with irregular contact on a substratum of what was once soft mud, the *underplight* (Fig. 119*B*). Deeley (1916: 2–5), in an attempt to

---

[1] Their proposal (p. 206) is to the effect that those features and structures in consolidated and unconsolidated soils which " . . . are clearly the result of slow flow, from higher to lower ground, while over-saturated with water from melting snow or ice, rain, or lines of springs or seepages" be classed together under the general term of head.

[2] SPURRELL, F. C. J., 1887, A sketch of the history of the rivers and denudation of West Kent, etc., *Geol. Mag.*, (3)**4**: 121–122. Spurrell accepted the term trail, which had been used earlier, and proposed the term underplight. See also Dines *et al.* (1940: 198–226).

explain how trail and underplight might be formed, experimented with tar, sealing wax, and sand.   He was able to produce a structure (Fig. 119*A*) closely resembling that of trail and underplight and concluded from his experiments that the essential features could be formed (page 4)

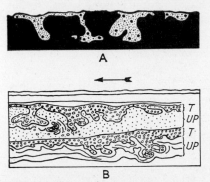

A

B

FIG. 119.—Trail and underplight. (Art. 103.) *A.* Diagram showing how wax-bound coarse and fine sand settled into a layer of pitch about 25 mm. (1 in.) thick when the whole was heated from above.   According to Deeley (1916: 5), who performed the experiment, the pitch was first poured into a shallow cardboard box and allowed to cool.   After it had cooled, a thin layer of sealing wax mixed with coarse and fine sand was run over it. When the whole was cold, a gas flame was applied to the surface and both wax and pitch were slowly heated from the surface downward, with consequent decrease in viscosity.   The wax-bound sand slowly sank into the yielding pitch.   After 10 hours the mass was allowed to cool, and when sectioned the structure shown in the diagram was revealed.   The coarse grains of sand stand in a vertical position, especially near the sides of the descending masses of sealing wax, as do the stones in trail-and-plight, a structure which Deeley was trying to explain. [*Modified after Deeley,* 1916, *Geol. Mag.,* (6) **3**: 5, *Fig.* 2.] *B.* A sketch of trail and underplight. [*Adapted from Spurrell's original diagram as illustrated by Deeley,* 1916, *Geol. Mag.,* (6) **3**: 3, *Fig.* 1.] The arrow indicates the general direction of motion in the mobile gravel layer.   The scale is considerably reduced.   Deeley (1916: 2–5) concluded from his experiment illustrated in *A* that trail and underplight was formed by slow sinking of heavy sands and gravels into plastic mud with properties like those of brittle tar.   Most present-day geologists consider the feature a frozen ground structure.

. . . if the clay were wet and were alternately frozen and thawed, then for a short time after each thaw the clay, brickearth, silt, loam, or soft chalk would be in a slightly fluid condition, and any beds of superior gravity which rested upon them would sink into the deposit below.

Trail and underplight has been reported from several British localities [Deeley (1916: 3)], and Wills (1938: 184) recently described and illustrated (Fig. 120) a similar structure in Pleistocene sands and gravel along the Severn River in England.   He ascribed it to " . . . solifluxion under glacial conditions. . . . "

In North America Bryan (1936: 222–228) and others have adopted the term *warp* for the contorted zone[1] near the surface produced by the churning action and solifluction resulting from alternate freezing and thawing (Art. 125).   In his latest article, Bryan (1946a: 621, 636) proposes *mollisol* for the surface layer, " . . . which thaws each summer and freezes each winter. . . . "

104. GROOVE CASTS.—Geologic literature contains scattered descriptions and illustrations of bedding surfaces with rounded or sharp-crested rectilinear ridges a few millimeters high and many centimeters long.

[1] Sand-blasted stones (ventifacts) are commonly incorporated in the churned-up material [Bryan and Nichols (1939: 434), Nichols (1941: 29), and Wills (1938: 184, Fig. 3) recently illustrated a cross section showing a layer of such stones resting unconformably on a contorted zone in the Pleistocene terrace deposits along the Severn River in England.

The ridges are striking because of their marked parallelism and constant size, and particularly because they are confined to the *undersurfaces* of sandstone layers lying on mudstone. Two or three sets, usually differing somewhat in size and transecting one another, may be present on the same surface (Figs. 121, 122).

These interesting and puzzling ridges, here designated *groove casts*, seem to represent sand fillings (casts) of rectilinear, V-shaped and U-shaped grooves existing in the upper few millimeters of the bottom sediment on which sand was deposited. They show the same general relations as the flow casts with which they are closely associated. They can hardly be the fillings of mud cracks because of the regularity of

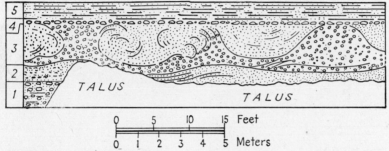

Fig. 120.—Deformed sand and gravel overlain by a layer of wind-etched pebbles in the Pleistocene deposits along the Severn River in England. The section consists of (1) horizontally bedded gravel and sharp sand; (2) sharp sand and seams of pebbles, horizontally bedded below, but somewhat festooned above; (3) very irregular and contorted gravel and clayey sand; (4) layer of wind-etched pebbles in the base of (5); (5) loamy red sand with slight horizontal bedding. The contortions in bed 3 are believed by Wills (1938: 184) possibly to have been formed by "solifluxion under glacial conditions either during or after the accumulation of 3 and 2." (Arts. 103, 108, 148.) (*Adapted from Wills, 1938, Geol. Soc. London Quart. Jour.*, **94**: 184, *Fig.* 3.)

pattern of any set of ridges. The original grooves appear to have been made by simultaneous rectilinear advance of a squad of objects propelled by a current, but it must be admitted that this suggestion is vague and indefinite.

Two possible agents come to mind. A thin sheet of pack ice composed of many broken blocks and propelled across a shallow bottom could leave many shallow, rectilinear and parallel grooves made by the very ends of some of the blocks as they plowed over the bottom.[1] Larger blocks would make large grooves—much larger than those under consideration here.[2] A wind shift would cause drift in some other direction, and thus a second set, or even a third, could be superimposed on existing grooves. Clarke (1918: 206) accepted this explanation as a result of suggestions made to him by J. B. Woodworth.

[1] More than a century ago Lyell (1845: 144) reported that a Doctor Harding had observed furrows formed in this way in mud along the estuaries near Wolfeville, N.S.

[2] See Williams (1881: 318–320), who ascribes certain channels in muds to icebergs

A second agent might be algal rafts with rock anchors. Upon coming into shallow water, such stones might be dragged across a tidal flat, either inland by a rising tide or seaward by undertow, plowing grooves in the bottom sediments as they advanced or retreated. It does not seem possible, however, that this agent could produce large systems of parallel and rectilinear grooves such as those shown in Fig. 121.

A   B

Courtesy of New York State Museum

FIG. 121.—Groove casts in the Devonian Portage sandstone of New York (much reduced). *A.* Original grooved surface showing numerous rectilinear furrows and striations thought to have been cut into the sediment of the strand by wave- or current-transported objects that were dragged across the bottom. It will be noted that not all the depressions are parallel, indicating that direction of movement changed. *B.* Counterpart of *A*, showing rectilinear sharp-angled ridges of sand that represent the backfillings of the grooves. (Art. 104.) (*After Clarke*, 1918, *Bull. N.Y. State Mus.*, **196**: 219, *Plate* 15.)

Hall (1843: 234–237; 1843a: 422–432; 1843b: 148–149) and Dawson (1855, 1868) were among the earliest North American geologists to describe and illustrate ridges similar to those here discussed. Many years later Clarke (1918: 204–206) described and illustrated well-preserved groove casts from the Devonian Portage beds of New York but was doubtful about the general explanation of that day, *viz.*, that they were formed by tidal currents or by the dragging of irregular objects such as algal anchor stones over wet sand. He was inclined to accept the suggestion of J. B. Woodworth that ice blocks plowed the grooves. Groove casts are especially characteristic of shallow-water clastic layers associated with coal-bearing sequences. The author has seen them in vertical Horton beds of the Nova Scotia Mississippian, in the Pennsylvanian of the Appalachian trough, and in beds of the same age in southwestern Indiana (Fig. 122). These are probably ascribable to some agent other than grounding ice packs or icebergs.

FIG. 122.—Groove casts on underside of Mississippian Horton sandstone layer from Cape Breton Island, Nova Scotia. This surface represents the counterpart of an original grooved mud bottom. The sandstone bed lay upon a mudstone. (Art. 104.)

Where observed *in situ* they lie on the underside of the layer. If this is always the case, then they constitute a reliable top and bottom criterion.[1] Since there are many kinds of surface ridges and ridgelike markings on the upper surface of some beds, care should always be taken that true groove casts are not being confused with such surficial ridges. The

[1] Hall (1843: 237, Fig. 103) illustrated a semicylindrical specimen with many fossils on the rounded side and considered it a filling of a mud furrow, the shells having been drifted into the furrow before deposition of the superincumbent mud.

marked parallelism of the former, together with the fact that they lie in contact with mudstone, should suffice to prevent such confusion.

105. Inorganic Objects between Layers.—Concretions, boulders, and ventifacts, lying along the separation plane between contiguous beds, may show, by their relation to the two bedding surfaces, that they lay upon one bed as they were buried by the sediment now constituting the other.

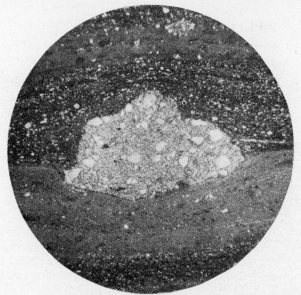

Courtesy of Geological Survey of Canada

Fig. 123.—Photomicrograph of laminated graywacke from the Pre-Cambrian Gowganda formation of Ontario, showing a cross section of two complete bipartite layers with a quartzite pebble between.   The pebble, coming to rest on the finer laminae of the lower layer, caused them to be bent downward to some extent.   The coarser basal laminae of the covering layer first abut against the pebble, but later laminae arch gently over it.   The gradation upward in each bipartite layer, from coarse to fine materials, furnishes a second means of distinguishing top and bottom and corroborates the interpretation of the relations shown by the pebble.   The individual graded layers range in thickness from about 0.5 to 3.0 mm.   (Arts. 51, 97, 105.)   (*After Collins*, 1925, *Geol. Survey Canada Mem.*, **143**: 66, 148, *Plate* XIB. *A print from Collins's original negative*, 35019, *was furnished by the Geological Survey of Canada.*)

These relations may be useful as top and bottom criteria.   Similar relations are also developed on a microscopic scale as shown in Fig. 123.

106. BURIED CONCRETIONS.—Only syngenetic concretions (*i.e.*, concretions formed just before or simultaneously with the deposition of the enclosing sediment) [see Tarr (1921: 373–384; 1935: 1493–1534)] are reliable for determining the top or bottom of beds (Fig. 124).   Twenhofel (1932: 713) states that " . . . thickening and bending upward of laminae toward concretions, with some laminae terminating against them, strongly suggest a syngenetic origin."   Even if the concretion can be proved syngenetic, its relations to the surrounding rock are not always definite enough to establish which direction was up or down at the time it was buried. Usually, as shown by Fig. 125, most of the concretion lies above the general surface on which it came to rest. Ellipsoidal concretions are consistently flatter on the bottom side and rest in a shallower depression, whereas the curvature of the top side is distinctly more convex upward.[1] Also, as pointed out in a preceding sentence, some of the laminae of the covering layer end abruptly against the concretion,

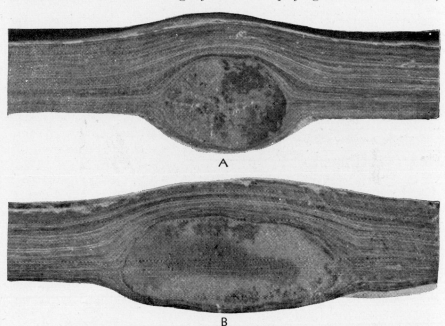

Fig. 124.—Syngenetic concretions in the Eocene Green River shale of Wyoming ($\times$ 5). *A*. A spheroidal concretion that sank into the bottom sediments about halfway and was later buried. The orientation of this concretion is uncertain. *B*. A concretion flattened in the plane of bedding. When it came to rest on the bottom materials, only a few of the uppermost laminae of the substratum were disturbed, for it did not sink into those materials to any extent. Later sedimentation surrounded the concretion with more thin laminae, the first of which were steepened peripherally by settling. The concretions may be of coprolitic origin. (Arts. 106, 113.)

whereas later laminae rise steeply toward it, either ending against it or passing over it in a gentle arch. Tarr (1921: 373–384) and Trefethen (1947: 56–58) mention that some concretions have slickensided surfaces on the upper side, but it is uncertain whether this slickensiding was caused by the surrounding beds slipping down around the concretions during their consolidation or by the upward growth of the concretions themselves.

The late Dr. W. A. Tarr[2] made two additional comments on concretions that are worth repeating here.

[1] W. A. Tarr, personal communication, Apr. 13, 1938.
[2] *Ibid.*

I have recalled another feature which I observed in the flint of the English chalk and in the chert of the Pennsylvanian in Kansas. When nodes develop on a nodule they are consistently on the upper portions and may in themselves, as they grow outward from the nodule, curve upwards. Of course where chert nodules occur in a formation containing stylolites these features consistently develop on the upper portion of the nodule.

Trefethen (1947: 56–57) also reports that some stylolites curve over chert lenses, his examples being in the Burlington limestone of Missouri. He notes another small feature in chert nodules themselves, which if found clearly developed, might be of use as a top and bottom criterion. This consists in V-shaped cracks reaching downward into the chert nodule from the *upper* surface. These cracks, according to Trefethen (1947: 58),

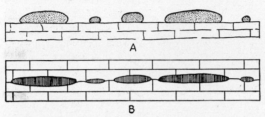

FIG. 125.—Syngenetic chert nodules and lenses in limestone. *A.* Diagram showing spheroidal and ellipsoidal masses of silica that have come to rest on the ocean floor where calcareous muds are being deposited. *B.* The probable appearance of the original silica masses of *A* after burial and alteration to chert. It is to be noted that, although the chert nodules and lenses are slightly convex downward, most of their mass lies above the general bedding surface. The chert nodules range in size from millimeters to centimeters. (Art. 106.) *(Sketches based on suggestions by the late Prof. W. A. Tarr.)*

. . . may be the result of dehydration and shrinkage, or they may be tension cracks formed by settling and slight deformation under load. In either event they probably developed before the chert had reached the rigidity of complete dehydration and crystallization.

Cracks of this sort should be looked for in chert nodules believed to be of primary or syngenetic origin.

Syngenetic concretions of material other than silica (*e.g.*, iron sulphide) tend to adhere to the bed in which they grew rather than to the covering layer if the contiguous layers are separated (Fig. 147).

If a syngenetic crystal forms and then becomes unstable, it will upon disappearing leave a cavity, which, if the surrounding material permits, will persist until filled with incoming sediment. Thus a sedimentary pseudomorph of the original crystal will stud the underside of the covering layer and will fit into the cavity once occupied by the original crystal. Raymond (1930: 29) has described such pseudomorphs in the Upper Cambrian Roche Miette formation of Alberta (Art. 98), and a specimen is illustrated in Fig. 197.

In summary, it may be said that syngenetic concretions are useful in top and bottom determination if their relations with surrounding rock are self-evident. Because these relations vary greatly however, it is always advisable to seek other criteria for purposes of corroboration.

107. BURIED BOULDERS.—Boulders coming to rest on a soft, hydroplastic substratum sink into the sediment some distance and exhibit diagnostic relations with both supporting and covering sediment, as discussed in Art. 100.

If the substratum is firm enough to support the boulder, however, the latter will deform the underlying material very little. Consequently, the first few laminae deposited usually end abruptly against the boulder (as they do against a syngenetic concretion), and under special conditions a thin capping of the first deposit remains on top of the boulder (Figs.

FIG. 126.—Sketch showing how shale laminae abut against and then arch over buried pebbles, with some sagging of the laminae between pebbles. This figure should be compared with Fig. 111 to determine how the relation of laminae around a buried pebble or boulder differs from that around a similar object which dropped into soft sediment and was then buried. Many examples of this sort of relation may be seen in the stratified shales, sandstones, and conglomerates associated with the Carboniferous Squantum tillite on Squantum Head, Massachusetts. (Art. 107.)

126, 127). Later laminae rise gently, as they approach the buried object, and either abut against it or pass over it in a gentle arch.

108. BURIED VENTIFACTS, LAG GRAVELS, AND SOLUTION-FACETED PEBBLES.—Ancient ventifacts (wind-etched and wind-faceted pebbles and boulders), lag gravels, and solution-faceted pebbles on sand plains and deserts may have been buried by advancing dunes or other aeolian deposits and never again uncovered. These buried stones should lie for the most part in the position they had when buried (*i.e.*, the faceted or etched side of the stone should be up). Such a ventifact (Fig. 128*A*) was discovered some years ago in the St. Peter sandstone, which has been widely interpreted as an aeolian deposit, and geologic literature contains several references to similar occurrences.[1]

[1] BATHER, F. A., 1900, Wind-worn pebbles in the British Isles, *Proc. Geol. Assoc. for 1900*, pp. 396–420 (article contains an excellent list of references); GRABAU, A. W., 1924, "Principles of Stratigraphy," pp. 54–55 and reference list on pp. 92–98, A. G Seiler, New York; BRYAN, KIRK, 1931, Wind-worn stones or ventifacts—a discussion and bibliography, *Nat. Research Council, Ann. Rept. 1929–1930, Rept. Comm. Sedimentation*, pp. 29–50.

Grabau (1924: 54) states that ventifacts have been found in the Pre-Cambrian Torridonian sandstone of Scotland, the basal Cambrian of Sweden, the Permian Rothliegendes of Germany, and the Triassic Bunter-sandstein of Thuringia, but he says nothing about the position and orientation of the individual stones.

Wills (1938: 184) found a layer of Pleistocene ventifacts in the base of a loamy red sand, which transects a much contorted bed of sand and gravel (Fig. 120); Schoewe (1938: 111) has reported ventifacts of Pennsylvanian age in the upper 5 ft. of the Fountain formation of Colorado

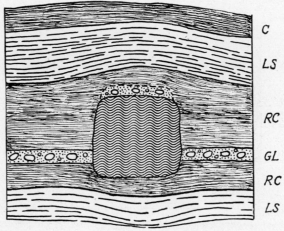

Fig. 127.—Pebble buried in Pleistocene silt and clay showing one prominent thin layer of coarser material obviously deposited soon after the pebble came to rest on the bottom silt. The sketch is slightly reduced. *C* = clay; *GL* = grit layer; *LS* = laminated silt; *RC* = red clay. (Art. 107.) (*Modified after Tarr*, 1935, *Bull. Geol. Soc. Am.*, **46**: 1499, *Fig.* 1.)

and states that they are found *in situ;* and more recently Barnes and Parkinson (1940: 665–670) have described dreikanter from the basal Cambrian Hickory sandstone of Texas. The latter occurrence is of special interest, and its description is worth quoting in part (page 669):

Many of the dreikanter of this locality are exceptionally large, some of which range up to 4 inches across. These . . . are mostly faceted on the surfaces which were upward during basal Cambrian time. . . . The dreikanters were not disturbed while finally being covered by sand as is attested by their present position with the faceted faces upward. The sand which incorporated them must have been wind blown rather than water borne, otherwise many of the pebbles would have been turned over onto their faceted faces. These dreikanter are found in place by turning over basal sandstone slabs.

An invading sea would, of course, disturb ventifacts and lag gravels; but if some dune sand were associated with the stones or if the incoming sediments were muds, the stratigraphic succession would be significant. The larger stones would tend to remain on the surface where they were etched, whereas smaller pebbles would probably lie at a slightly higher position in the overlying material because of minor transportation.

Some years ago Bryan (1929: 193–208) directed attention to the development of solution-faceted pebbles in dry regions, noting (page 208) that

. . . the pebbles may be considered as proof of the chemical breakdown of rocks in climates where such activity is ordinarily underrated [*i.e.*, in dry regions], and,

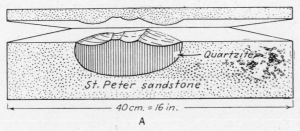

A

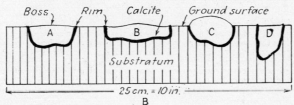

B

Fig. 128.—Ventifacts and solution-faceted pebbles. *A.* A wind-etched quartzite boulder in the Ordovician St. Peter sandstone about 1 mile north of Blue Mounds, Wis. The boulder was found *in situ.* *B.* Diagram showing solution-faceted pebbles of different shapes in relation to the ground surface and substratum. Each pebble has a coating of secondary calcite. (Art. 108.) [*B adapted from Bryan,* 1929, *Am. Jour. Sci.,* (5) **18**: 194, *Fig.* 2.]

if found in sedimentary rocks, as a record of land surfaces long exposed under conditions of moderate aridity.

Solution-faceted pebbles are quite likely to be embedded in the substratum with the etched surface upward (Fig. 128*B*), and if buried *in situ* they provide an unusual top and bottom criterion. Such buried pebbles have been reported from Pleistocene gravel deposits of New Mexico by Fiedler and Nye (1933: 34),[1] and Prof. Kirk Bryan tells the

[1] In discussing the geology of the Roswell artesian basin of New Mexico, Fiedler and Nye (1933: 34–35) report:

Solution-faceted limestone pebbles were found in gravel deposits partly cemented by caliche or calcium carbonate. . . . They have a concave upper surface, which in many of them has no definite relation to the original shape of the pebble but is roughly parallel to the land surface. The under sides of the pebbles are rounded. These pebbles occur chiefly in the upper 3 or 4 feet of the gravel deposit, where it is cemented by caliche.

author that he has observed several superposed layers of similar pebbles in other Pleistocene gravels of New Mexico.

Solution-faceted pebbles lying on a flat or gently sloping surface of denudation are thought to be dissolved by rain water and dew. Those formed on the surface of gravel layers are likely to be shaped to some extent by running water.

A second type of solution-sculptured limestone pebble was recently described by Scott (1947: 141–152). The pebbles are present in a Pleistocene gravel terrace in the semiarid Wind River Basin of Wyoming. They bear a system of solution-produced grooves, ridges, pinnacles, and other features on their upper surfaces and a caliche shell attached to their

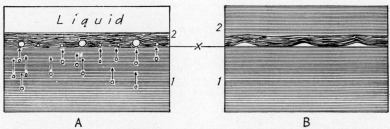

A   B

Fig. 129.—Intraformational cavities (slightly enlarged). *A.* Gas bubbles, generated by chemical action in the lower part (1) of a mud deposit, rise toward the surface, in some cases joining with others, but are trapped before they can get through the surface laminae (2). The larger bubbles cause arching of the restraining laminae. *B.* During consolidation the smaller bubbles may be squeezed laterally into the larger ones, and the latter tend to be flattened out considerably. The slightly arched laminae, however, remain and form a conspicuous structural feature breaking the homogeneous laminar stratification and indicating the top of the sequence. (Art. 109.) (*Diagrams based on suggestions by O. F. Tuttle.*)

bases. These pebbles, as those described in the preceding paragraph, would if buried *in situ* furnish a reliable top and bottom criterion.

109. OPEN OR FILLED CAVITIES.—Recently the attention of the author was called to a phenomenon produced during sedimentation that might provide a top and bottom criterion.[1]

As successive thin laminae of sediment are precipitated and covered, chemical reactions going on within the deposited layers cause the evolution of gas, which tends to rise toward the surface. At a level, or levels, determined by several physical factors the gas bubbles are arrested in their upward migration. At this level they are able only to arch the overlying few laminae slightly. If now these tiny domes, which have relief of only tenths of a millimeter to a millimeter or so, can be maintained until the sediment composing them has acquired some rigidity, they may be preserved along a bedding surface as a permanent feature— scattered tiny hemiellipsoidal protuberances convex upward and cracked

[1] Communicated to the author by O. F. Tuttle, Nov. 1, 1942.

if the sediment dries out before burial[1] (Fig. 129).   Air or water trapped in rapidly settling muds might produce the same effect.

This phenomenon is somewhat like that producing pit and mound structure (Art. 90), but it takes place during the early phases of compaction rather than during deposition, and the resulting bubbles do not reach the surface of the substratum and burst (see Art. 92).

The cavities thus produced may remain open indefinitely, or they may be filled by material precipitated from circulating solutions.   In the latter case they would appear as a line of eyelets along the bedding, each eyelet being somewhat flattened on the bottom and gently domed on the top (Fig. 129).   Features like these have been observed in ancient rocks, but they do not seem to have been mentioned very often since Lyell (1851: 241) first described them.   The mud bubbles described and illustrated by James (1884, Plate V) possibly had the same origin.

110. Organically Produced Ridges and Depressions.—Throughout geologic time, beginning soon after the appearance of life, plants and animals have been leaving on the soft substrata on which they dwelt or across which they moved an almost limitless variety of relics of their existence.   Plants leave many markings on sands and muds and when torn loose from the substratum may drift across bottoms so shallow that they or their anchorage stones plow furrows and gouge depressions in the soft sediments.[2]   Animals leave trails, tracks, and footprints in the sediments over which they move; coprolites and other excreta, composed of some of the materials they have eaten, are left in their wake; and hard parts of the animal itself (*e.g.*, the valve of a clamshell) may come to rest

[1] Lyell (1851: 241) has called attention to certain small convexities on the upper surface of a mud deposit apparently formed in the same manner.   His description follows:

Another set of small convexities, also protruding from the upper surface of the mud, proved to be crusts of small cavities, each cracked at the top, and were suspected by Mr. Faraday, to whom I showed them, to be bubbles of mud which had dried without bursting. He succeeded in producing similar convex protuberances experimentally, by pounding up the Kentville mud, moistening it with water, and then, by means of glass tubes, introducing air below, which rose to the top in bubbles.   Some of these being dried, consolidated without breaking, until finally the crust which covered the cavity where the air had been imprisoned, cracked at the top on shrinking, like the convex protuberances from the Bay of Fundy.

[2] Darwin (1860: 497) saw trees with stones enmeshed in their roots that had been torn loose from their moorings and drifted across hundreds of miles of ocean to become stranded on a distant island.   Marine algae with anchor stones of numerous kinds and dimensions are a common sight along many present beaches, and since algae are of ancient origin it may be assumed that their progenitors utilized stones for anchorage and occasionally marked soft bottoms with these stones when torn up and drifted into shallow water.   Brown (1912: 544–547) mentions such seaweeds with anchor-stones in Sandwich Bay, Labrador.

on bottom materials soft enough to receive a perfect imprint of the shell. Later, if the shell is dissolved, the convex or concave imprint remains as a fossil. Animal hard parts, released from their host by decomposition, are nothing more than bits of material subject to the waves and currents and other activities on any bottom, and they, like inorganic stones, may also leave markings as they are drifted or propelled across soft bottoms. Finally, both plants and animals make permanent structures on shallow bottoms; these may be so small that they are buried by the first few laminae of the covering bed or so large that they extend upward through several formations (*e.g.*, coral bioherms).

111. TRAILS, TRACKS, AND FOOTPRINTS.[1]—Animals make many kinds of trails, tracks, and footprints in unconsolidated sands and soft muds.[2] These are legion in number and variety—greater even than the kinds of animals that make them, for a single individual can make more than one type of trail or track. Only a very few, therefore, can be discussed here. They may be preserved in sand, though the nature of this material is such that markings made on its surface have relatively little chance of being preserved.[3] In soft mud (sandy silts, silty clays, organic muds, etc.), however, the probability of preservation is much greater.

---

[1] Trails, tracks, and footprints in ancient rocks have attracted world-wide attention, not only from geologists and paleontologists but also from naturalists and amateur scientists, and geologic literature contains many descriptions and illustrations, some of which first appeared more than two centuries ago.

The first geologists to carry on field work in America noted the now familiar trails of the Cambrian Potsdam *Climactichnites* [see Woodworth (1903: 959–966)], which somewhat resemble the impression left by a truck tire in soft, sandy mud; the peculiar three-toed tracks of the eastern Triassic, which were first ascribed to birds before it was realized that there had been dinosaurs with three-toed feet [see Lull (1904, 1915) for extensive bibliographies]; and the spectacular footprints of dinosaurs at many localities in western North America. Although these evidences of ancient and long extinct animals are now so familiar as to be commonplace, we should not lose sight of the fact that their discovery created a sensation only a short time ago because of the strong support they gave to scientists who were casting aside the concept of the Universal Flood and looking for fossil evidence to support the evolutionary hypotheses of Darwin and Wallace.

[2] On present beaches, tidal flats, and alluvial plains, where man has not settled, animals make myriads of tracks and trails that stand a good chance of preservation. On ancient beaches, undisturbed by man, animals left the same kind of record.

Brown (1912) describes such a modern beach on Sandwich Bay, Labrador, where the animals of the region, free to wander without man's interference, have left an amazing record of trails and tracks.

[3] McKee (1945: 323) mentions reptilian footprints headed uphill on dune foresets in the Coconino sandstone and states that these were preserved because the sand was damp at the time they were formed. Dampness is probably one of the prime prerequisites for preservation of imprints in sand.

Trails may be a straight or curved line of pimples or pits, short angular or rounded ridges or depressions, rounded or angular continuous ridges or furrows that may be simple or composed of several lobes, irregular ridges and depressions, and a great variety of other forms.[1] They may be striated or ribbed longitudinally, and some exhibit the same sculpture transversely.

The use of trails as criteria for determining the top surface of a bed is definitely limited by several important factors. It must first be established that the structure is a trail and of organic origin. Next, the relations of the trail to the contacting bedding surfaces should be examined

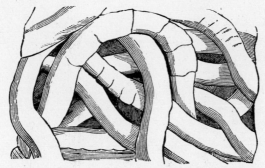

Geological Survey of Canada

Fig. 130.—Sketch of the undersurface of a sandstone layer from the Mississippian Horton series of Nova Scotia, showing sinuous interlaced ridges of sandstone that appear to have been made by the backfilling of worm trails left in a soft, plastic mud. The mud, later indurated to mudstone, has been weathered and eroded away, leaving the intertwined sand fillings in relief. Features like these are common on the undersurface of sandstone layers overlying mudstone. They do not occur on the upper surface of sandstone layers except under unusual conditions. (Art. 111.) (*After Dawson, 1868, "Acadian Geology,"* p. 256, *Fig.* 79.)

to determine whether the original was a ridge or a groove. Finally, satisfied as to the origin and nature of the marking, the investigator can proceed to establish the sequence of beds containing the fossil. The investigator should be forewarned, however, that more often than not structures which he thinks are trails give only inconclusive evidence.

Since trails may be either ridges or depressions on the substratum, it follows that they should have counterparts on the underside of the overlying bed. Some counterparts furnish a more faithful record than the original[2] (Fig. 130). An example is the well-known fossil *Arthrophycus*

[1] Hughes, T. M., 1884, On some tracks of terrestrial and fresh-water animals *Geol. Soc. London Quart. Jour.*, **40**: 178–186.

[2] Stauffer (1939: 500) describes an example of this relation as follows:

Trails and burrows may be observed commonly in the shale or in the limestone lenses [of the Middle Devonian Olentangy shale of Ontario]. The bottom layer of the Canadian Encrinal (probably Prout) limestone fills or fits into large furrows that were surface trails of this sort, and associated with these are the teeth of Polychaeta, conodonts, and fish, together with phosphatic coprolitic bodies of unknown origin.

(Fig. 131), usually regarded as a worm burrow [Sarle (1906: 203–210); Shimer and Shrock (1944: 719)]. Inasmuch as it always lies on the *underside* of sandstones resting on shale [Hall (1843: 46), Grabau (1913: 463), and others], it is difficult to understand how a worm could burrow through mud and yet excrete sand or how a worm could travel along the bedding plane between sand and mud and leave the kind of trail that is found.

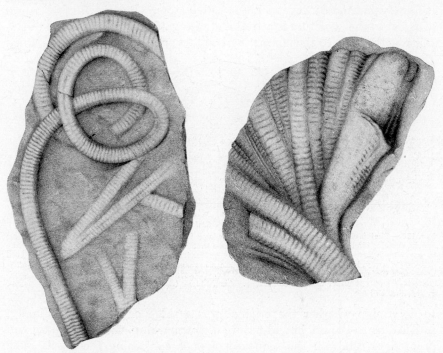

FIG. 131.—*Arthrophycus alleghaniensis* (Harlan), a Silurian trail commonly found on the underside of sandstone layers overlying shale. The fossil is believed to represent the sand filling of a trail made in soft mud by a crawling animal of some sort. Both figures are reduced about one-half. *A.* Fragment of a coiled specimen. If this illustration is correctly drawn, it is possible that the trail was not made by the same species of animal that made the fossil shown in *B. B.* Cluster of trails. (Art. 111.) (*After Hall, 1852, Pal. N.Y., Vol. 2, Plate 2, Figs. la, lc.*)

It is here suggested that typical *Arthrophycus* and many other *underside* "trails" of similar nature were formed as follows:[1] Some invertebrate animal (possibly a worm, mollusk, or arthropod) crawled over a soft mud

---

[1] Grabau (1913: 463) made essentially the same suggestion more than 35 years ago. The expression typical *Arthrophycus* has been used because certain fossils not properly belonging in this genus have been referred to it. There is some question, for example, as to whether the two types of fossils illustrated in Fig. 131 were made by the same species of organism. The mode of origin suggested here applies best to the type shown in Fig. 131*B*; some other explanation will probably have to be found for fossils such as that shown in Fig. 131*A*.

surface leaving behind a rounded, faintly transversely rippled furrow. This furrow or trail was later filled with sand. The counterpart thus formed had a perfect imprint of the "tracked-up" mud surface, and being an integral part of the sand layer it is always on the underside of that layer. It must be established, of course, that a certain "trail" really occurs on the underside; but if the relations are similar to those just described for *Arthrophycus*, then one should be on the alert for counterparts and use them accordingly. It is almost certain that many of the

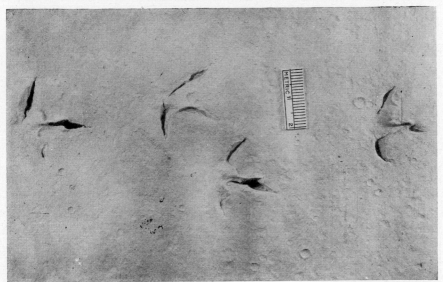

FIG. 132.—Recent bird tracks made in soft mud that is also pitted with imprints of raindrops. The mud was quite soft at the time when the tracks were made, as indicated by the depth to which the bird's toes sank. The specimen was obtained from hardened mud along the Bay of Fundy, Canada. (Art. 111.)

so-called "worm trails" and "fucoids" described and illustrated in geologic literature are actually sand fillings of small furrows made in soft substrata by invertebrate animals.

Walking animals often leave tracks or footprints on sandy and particularly on soft, muddy surfaces (Figs. 132, 133) of flood plains, tidal flats, and beaches. If the soft sand and mud can take and retain the impression, these imprints are buried without much modification and they and their counterparts are reliable top and bottom features (Fig. 133). Counterparts commonly record the details of a footprint much more faithfully than the shale beneath because of the latter's tendency to break up readily upon weathering. Consequently, plaster replicas of the original "tracked" surface, made by pouring plaster of Paris over the counterpart, may have to be prepared in order to study the footprints as they appeared originally.   A case in point is illustrated by Sternberg (1931; 1932: 59–85; 1933: 953–954, Plate 35) (Fig. 134).

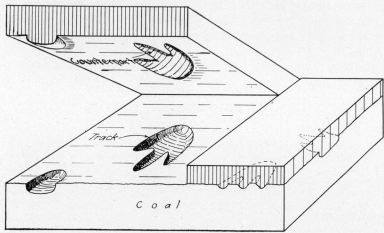

FIG. 133.—Track of a giant dinosaur in a Cretaceous coal bed in Wyoming.   The footprints were filled with mud, and the counterpart thus produced adheres to the undersurface of the overlying black shale. In underground mining these counterparts are commonly visible in the roof and are dangerous because they sometimes break loose and fall to the floor.   The tracks are about 1 m. long from the base to the tip of the central toe and were made by a giant dinosaur, which, as it walked across a coal swamp, sank nearly ⅓ m. (1 ft.) into the coaly material.   (Art. 111.)   (*Sketch based on verbal description by E. S. Shorey.*)

FIG. 134.—Slab of Pennsylvanian sandstone from Nova Scotia, showing the counterparts, or negatives, of footprints made by the amphibian *Pseudobradypus unguifer* (Dawson).   The scale is one-fifteenth natural size.   It should be noted that these counterparts are on the *underside* of the layer.   (Art. 111.) (*After Sternberg, 1933, Bull. Geol. Soc. Am.,* **44**: 962, *Plate 35, Fig. 3.*)

   Shuler (1917: 294–298) describes and illustrates some well-preserved tracks in Lower Cretaceous limestone of Texas that appear to have been made by a dinosaur wading in plastic calcareous mud (Fig. 135).   In this case the calcareous substratum faithfully preserved the track itself.

Probably the most widely known animal tracks or footprints are those made by the three-toed dinosaurs of the Mesozoic. These gigantic beasts, wandering over tidal flats, alluvial plains, and swamps, left their footprints deeply impressed on the soft sediments of the substratum. Burial of the imprints and formation of their counterparts resulted in a faithful record of the momentary passing of one of the mightiest of all creatures. Such footprints are abundant in the Triassic Newark series

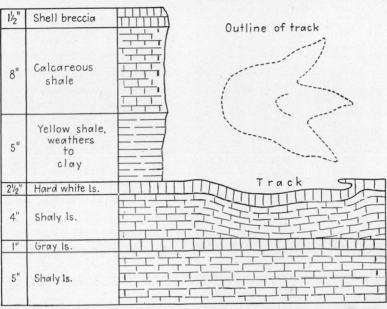

FIG. 135.—Cross section of a part of the Lower Cretaceous Glen Rose formation of Texas, showing one thin limestone bed that was tracked up by a passing dinosaur while still plastic enough to take and preserve the imprint of a foot. The outline of the track is one-twelfth natural size. The easily eroded shale overlying the tracked-up limestone has been removed, so that the track now appears as a three-toed depression in the limestone surface. (Art. 111.) [*Modified after Shuler*, 1917, *Am. Jour. Sci.*, (5) **44**: 297, *Fig.* 3.)

of the Atlantic seaboard[1] and in the Jurassic and Cretaceous formations of the western United States[2] and Canada. Elsewhere, the world over,

[1] Deane (1844: 73–77; 1845: 214–215; 1861: 1–61); Hitchcock (1844: 292–322; 1848: 129–256; 1858: 1–220); Lull (1904: 461–557; 1915: 1–285; etc.) (see also U.S. Geological Survey Bibliographies).

[2] In Wyoming, mighty *Brontosaurus* left its footprints in a coal swamp, and later, when the swamp was buried by carbonaceous mud and the organic matter solidified to coal, the counterparts of the footprints remained to show that the animal had passed that way. These counterparts, as much as 1 m. (3 ft.) long and ⅓ m. (1 ft.) thick, appear as large, downwardly projecting bumps on the underside of the black shale roof over the coal (Fig. 133). They are a constant danger to miners because they sometimes break along the bedding and fall to the floor of a tunnel or room. (The author is indebted to Prof. E. S. Shorey, University of Wisconsin, for this information.)

similar footprints have been found or are to be expected in Mesozoic

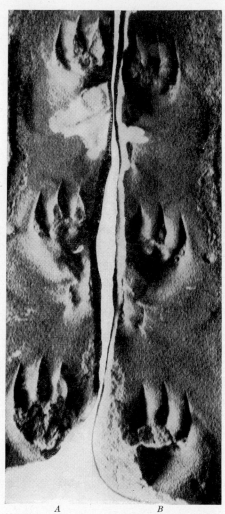

A   *B*

Courtesy of U.S. National Museum

FIG. 136.—Two sandstone slabs from the Permian Coconino sandstone of the Grand Canyon, considerably reduced, showing tracks (*B*) and negatives of the tracks (*A*) made by an extinct amphibian. It is to be noted that the two contiguous layers separated rather cleanly along the bedding surface, so that the negatives of the tracks are on the *underside* of the overlying bed. (Art. 111.) [*After Merriam, 1930, Carnegie Inst. Washington News Service Bull.*, **2** (11): 82. *Fig.*]

strata [see Albritton (1942: 161–181), Branson and Mehl (1932: 383–398), Carman (1927: 385–396), and Shuler (1917: 294–298)].

Quadrupeds other than reptiles, and of various ages, have also left footprint records (Fig. 136). Merriam (1930: 79–84) describes and illustrates many of these (Fig. 136) and states that, through the labors of the late Dr. Charles W. Gilmore, footprints of about 30 species of extinct amphibians and primitive mammals are now in the U.S. National Museum in Washington.

Inasmuch as the large and well-preserved footprints of quadrupeds occur in strata that are commonly folded into mountains, it follows that they may be quite useful in unraveling some complicated structures. Counterparts should always be sought in these rocks.[1]

Many kinds of systematic and symmetrical markings have been interpreted as the tracks of invertebrate animals.[2] Worms, certain

[1] Hughes (1844: 180) observed black grains of peat and broken, blackened vegetation in troughs of ripple-marked surfaces, and Stetson (1945) reported the concentration of vegetable debris in the troughs on the lee side of current ripples. If a heavy biped or quadruped should walk across a rippled surface where such concentrations of organic material were present and should compress the debris into the substratum, the ultimate counterpart of the footprint might have a thin carbonaceous film separating it from the original imprint.

[2] Raymond (1922: 108–114) suggests that many so-called "worm trails" on bed-

mollusks, and arthropods of the walking and crawling type usually are credited with having made the markings. If the tracks are sharply enough defined and well enough preserved for the original to be differentiated from the counterpart, they are usable as top and bottom criteria.

112. BURROWS AND BORINGS.[1]—Many animals burrow or bore tubular holes into the substratum, and if these excavations are so disposed

Courtesy of L. W. Stephenson, U.S. Geological Survey   *Courtesy of L. W. Stephenson, U.S. Geological Survey*

FIG. 137.   FIG. 138.

FIG. 137.—Problematical cavities (shown as white streaks) in cut of Illinois Central Railroad, 4.5 miles southeast of Corinth, Miss.

Stephenson and Monroe (1940: 169–170) describe these as follows: "Cavities ½ to 2 feet in diameter, some of which are branched, filled with leached gray sand, extend from the basal 2 or 3 feet of the surficial formation into the underlying glauconitic sand of the Coffee to a maximum depth of 6 or 7 feet. A few pebbles of quartz and quartzite are scattered through the gray sand, and in most of the cavities a number of pebbles are segregated at the bottom [see Fig. 138]. . . . The sand-filled cavities are believed to have been produced by the roots of pine trees and subsequently filled by sand and pebbles falling in from above as the roots decayed or were burned out by forest fires. The bleaching of the sand may have been effected by the organic acids resulting from decay of the wood." Cavities such as these may be expected along ancient unconformities. The segregation of boulders at the bottom of the cavity is noteworthy. (Art. 112.) (*After Stephenson and Monroe, 1940, Bull. Mississippi Geol. Survey,* **40**: 170, *Fig. 37.*)

FIG. 138.—Near view of a problematical cavity similar to those illustrated in Fig. 137. A dozen or more pebbles averaging about 25 mm. (1 in.) in longest dimension are segregated in the bottom of the cavity, which appears as a broad white zone. Several of the pebbles are outlined. Cut of the Illinois Central Railroad, 6 miles southeast of Corinth, Miss. (Art. 112.) (*After Stephenson and Monroe, 1940, Bull. Mississippi Geol. Survey,* **40**: 171, *Fig. 38.*)

as to bear a diagnostic relation to the surface of the material in which they lie they may serve on occasion as useful top and bottom criteria.

Clams and brachiopods that burrow in sand and mud may be entombed in the bottom of their tubes where they lived, and even if the shell is dissolved away the tubular excavation, open at the top and

---

ding surfaces of sandstone and shale layers were probably made by gastropods and other short-bodied invertebrates.

[1] Stephenson and Monroe (1940: 170) describe small, sand-filled, tubular cavities in the Upper Cretaceous deposits of Mississippi and conclude that they were "produced by the roots of pine trees and subsequently filled by sand and pebbles falling in from above as the roots decayed or were burned out by forest fires" (Figs. 137, 138).

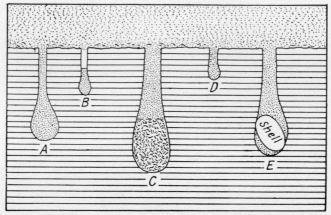

Fig. 139.—Diagram showing relation of burrows to substratum and of fillings to burrows. The organisms that excavated the tubular cavities burrowed downward into the soft sediment of the substratum. Usually the organism disappeared before the burrow was filled, but in some cases the shell was buried *in situ* at the rounded and expanded end of the burrow as shown in *E*. *A* and *D* show burrows of different sizes completely filled with sand like that in the covering layer. *B* is a small burrow that was only partly filled. The cavity above the incomplete filling might well become filled with calcite or some other mineral later. *C* is a large burrow that was partly filled with shell fragments and other debris before sand was washed in to complete the filling. *E* shows a burrow with the organism that made it buried *in situ* at the bottom of the excavation. This shell might be dissolved later and the resulting cavity filled with calcite or some other mineral as in *B*. Burrows usually are confined to the upper few centimeters or inches of a layer. This type of burrow, excavated into the soft sandy or silty substratum, should be compared with the boring drilled into solid rock as illustrated by Fig. 143. (Arts. 112, 169.)

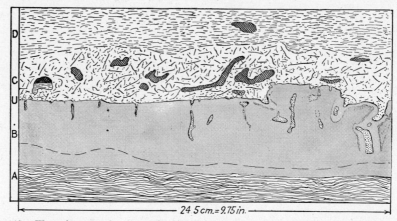

Fig. 140.—Worm burrows along unconformity between Black River and Trenton limestones near Elkin, Ky. *A.* Wavy laminated limestone with many small calcitic stringers, which may be fossils. *B.* Compact fine-grained limestone containing numerous vertical seams of calcareous sand representing the fillings of burrows dug into the soft calcareous mudstone. Around some of the larger burrows is a zone of lighter color that ends away from the burrow in a streak or band of darker color. *C.* Layer of platy shell fragments with random orientation mixed with more finely comminuted shell fragments similar to the material in the burrows. The layer also contains numerous calcite-filled cavities. One of these cavities—at the extreme left—was partly filled with sediment before calcite was deposited. *D.* Clastic layer composed of fine shell fragments strewn out essentially parallel to stratification. *U.* Unconformity between Black River (below) and Trenton limestones. (Art. 112.) (*The sketch is based on specimens* **90,354** *and* **90,354a** *in the U.S. National Museum.*)

rounded at the bottom, shows by its position below the bedding surface, which is the upper side of the layer (Fig. 139). The burrows may remain open, or they may be filled with material similar to that in the overlying bed (Fig. 140).

The ubiquitous *Scolithus*, however it may have been formed, appears to represent a burrow of some sort. It ends upward at the bedding surface and extends vertically or obliquely downward for many centimeters (several inches) into the bed. So far as observed, the tubes have never been seen to start at the base of a bed and extend upward into it

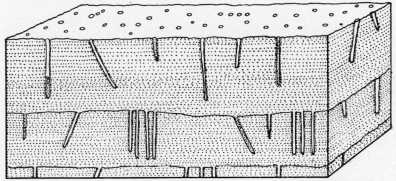

Fig. 141.—Vertical and steeply inclined burrows excavated by an unknown organism (*Scolithus*) in the sands of Cambrian sea bottoms. So far as observed these burrows always extend downward from the surface of a bed, never upward from the base. They may be open, partly filled, or completely filled. Commonly the filling makes a slender axial rod that can be removed. The tubes range in length from 1 to 10 or 15 cm. but maintain uniform diameter—about 3 to 4 mm.—regardless of length. In any typical specimen the majority of the burrows are essentially vertical; hence, if deformed beds show most of the tubes inclined strongly in one direction, it is possible to determine the direction and amount of differential movement between beds. (Arts. 112, 169.)

(Fig. 141). Since the tubes called *Scolithus* are usually vertically disposed in undisturbed beds—*i.e.*, essentially perpendicular to the bedding planes—their mass deviation from this position of perpendicularity to bedding in folded or faulted beds indicates the direction and amount of shear, as pointed out by Dale (1902: 12).[1]

The U-shaped burrows made by certain marine worms (*Arenicolites*)

[1] Dale (1902: 12) reports deformed *Scolithus* tubes from Cambrian quartzite near Arlington, Vt., as follows:

At a point a half mile southeast of East Arlington, on the eastern side of the brook and road, the quartzite crops out, filled with annelid borings and dipping about N.20°W. at an angle of 10°, the direction of the dip being probably due to the northerly pitch of a fold with a N.-S. axis. As borings made by annelids in sand are vertical, they should remain vertical to the bedding, which here dips 10°. This would give the borings an inclination of 10° from the vertical, or 80° from the horizontal in the opposite direction, which is S.20°E., but they actually dip at an angle of 45° about S.65°E. The amount of shear has thus deflected them 35°, and the direction of the shear has also deflected them 45° farther eastward.

always loop downward into the substratum, with the ends of the loop open to the surface, and one opening commonly has around it an annular ridge, which represents some of the sediment cast from the burrow (Fig. 142).

Under certain conditions sand hoppers, a type of amphipod, dig tubular burrows as much as 25 cm. (10 in.) deep by kicking out the sand first in one direction and then in the opposite, so that the excavated sand grains constitute two prominent rays radiating in opposite directions from the boring.   Emery (1944: 26) describes the boring and rays as follows: " . . . [The] hopper forms two rays of sand, each of which may have a

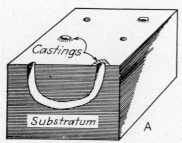 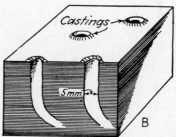

Fig. 142.—Worm burrows.   *A.* Diagram illustrating the U-shaped burrow excavated in mud and sand bottoms by the marine worm *Arenicola.*   The animal feeds at one end of the burrow and casts off excreta at the other.   The burrows may extend downward from the surface for half a meter or more (several feet).   *B.* A burrow like those in *A,* which is present in the Devonian Chemung formation of New York.   The burrow is 5 to 6 mm. in diameter, and the wall is about 2 mm. thick.   This burrow, to which the name *Arenicolites chemungensis* has been applied, is believed to have been excavated by a worm.   The curvature of the burrows, their relation to the surface, and the ring of castings about the opening provide means of determining the top surface of a bed.   (Arts. 112, 169.)   (*A diagrammatic. B modified after Whitfield,* 1904, *Bull. Am. Mus. Nat. History,* **20**: 473–474, *Plate* 14, *Figs.* 1, 2.)

length of 10 to 25 cm. and a width of 3 to 6 cm.   The hole is elliptical and 5 to 12 mm. in longest diameter.   The depth is commonly 10 to 25 cm."

There are many other borings and associated features that may be observed in the process of formation on existing beaches.   These furnish examples of the kind of inconspicuous feature that may be present on the surface and in the upper part of ancient sandstone beds.   Inorganic structures, which Emery (1944: 28) calls *sand domes,*[1] commonly form over the burrows just described as the rays of sand are being destroyed.

[1] Emery (1944: 28) describes the features as follows:

The domes are initiated by a wave which covers the top of the burrow with a plug of wet sand.   As the next wave washes over the beach, water percolates into the sides of the burrow, displacing the air of the hole.   Because the cover of wet sand over the hole is more or less air-tight, the air becomes slightly compressed.   The pressure is released either by blowing out part of the cover of sand or by lifting up a dome of sand, and forming an "air laccolith."   Domes formed in this manner commonly range from 1 to 12 cm. in diameter, and 2 to 30 mm. high with a roof thickness of 2 to 30 mm.   The next wave which washes over the dome usually destroys it, but by truncating it so that the upturned edges are bevelled.   Where the dome roof consists of several alternating laminae of light and dark

A few invertebrates (certain sponges, echinoderms, and mollusks) bore holes into solid rock, and if surfaces thus affected are buried the borings indicate which of the two facing surfaces is the original and which the obverse. Certain boring mollusks make a flask-shaped cavity,[1] which communicates with the surface by a small tubular neck (Fig. 143), and Buckland (1842*a*: 57) has discussed how deep, irregularly rounded holes were etched into limestone by the slime of the common garden snail *Helix*. Echinoids drill holes shaped like shallow bowls;[2] other organisms drill holes that have the shape of a downwardly pointed artillery shell[3] (Fig. 144); and certain invertebrates, possibly boring sponges, riddle the upper few millimeters of some rock surfaces with a system of ramifying tubes and grooves (Fig. 145). If such sculptured surfaces were ever encountered repeatedly in a sedimentary series, they should indicate the order of succession of the beds.

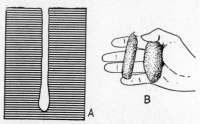

FIG. 143.—Molluscan boring and fillings of the cavity. *A.* Vertical tube in solid rock made by a boring mollusk. The boring enlarges somewhat in the basal part and has a rounded bottom. *B.* Two partial fillings of tubes like that in *A.* Since the boring has the characteristic shape shown in *A*, the top or bottom of a layer or of a rock mass containing such tubes can be determined with confidence from the enlarged basal part or from the rounded end of the partial filling if it has been preserved *in situ.* Borings excavated in solid rock prove that the rock was near enough sea level so that the shallow-water boring mollusks could attack it. For similar borings excavated in soft sediments essentially penecontemporaneously, see Fig. 139. (Arts. 112, **167,** 169.) [*Adapted from Cox and Dake, 1916, Bull. Univ. Missouri School Mining Metallurgy,* **2** (4): 34, *Figs.* 12, 13.]

113. COPROLITES AND CASTINGS.—Animals that eat the materials of a bottom excrete pellets of many kinds known as "coprolites," "castings,"

colored sand, the site of the dome is marked by concentric rings of alternating light and dark sand. Many such rings can be seen near the upper part of the beach reached by the tide. . . .

In answer to a query by the author, Dr. Emery wrote (Nov. 2, 1944):

I believe you are quite right in assuming that the bevelled edges of the sand domes might be used as indicators of the top and bottom of sedimentary rocks. On my trip . . . to the Caribbean and South America I had frequent opportunities to look at beaches and I was interested to find that sand domes were present on practically all beaches. Accordingly, I should think that they might be relatively common in consolidated sandstones of beach origin.

[1] Cox and Dake (1916: 34) state that A. C. Lawson " . . . has for years used the traces of the cavities made by boring mollusks to determine the structural positions of certain Tertiary formations. Such animals bore holes on a wave-cut rock surface which increase in diameter downward." When such tubes are preserved, either empty or partly or completely filled, they are reliable top and bottom criteria as shown in Fig. 143.

[2] These are common on rocky shores in many parts of the world.

[3] Borings of this nature may be observed on the desert floor of the Cul-de-Sac

"fecal pellets," etc.[1]   These excreta, being soft and more or less unconsolidated at the time of deposition, tend to become cemented to the substratum during consolidation.   When they are buried the layer covering

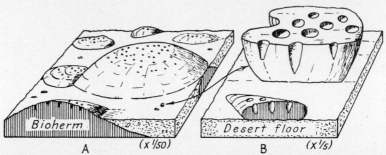

FIG. 144.—Vertical conoidal borings in calcareous bioherms and boulders on the desert floor of the
Cul-de-Sac graben in the Dominican Republic.   The symmetrical holes penetrate several centimeters
into solid rock and boulders and literally riddle the exposed surface of low biohermal mounds and knolls
made by corals and other lime-precipitating organisms.   During the late Tertiary, or possibly even more
recently, the present desert floor, now only a few tens of meters below sea level, was covered by marine
waters.   During this period of submergence numerous organisms built many low biohermal mounds.
Later, boring animals drilled conoidal holes into the bioherms and also riddled many of the calcareous
boulders scattered loosely over the bottom.   If the fixed bioherms and loose boulders were buried *in
situ*, as well they might be in this case, the downwardly directed holes, which probably would be filled
with sediment similar to that of the covering layer, would provide an excellent top and bottom feature.
A. A small area of the desert floor showing several biohermal mounds, pitted by borings, and a few
scattered boulders.   *B.* A boulder, considerably reduced, showing the typical appearance of a pitted
surface and incomplete longitudinal sections of three borings along a curved broken surface.   A smaller
coralline fragment is shown in the immediate foreground.   (Art. 112.)

them has groovelike counterparts (Fig. 146), and when the contacting
layers separate the coprolites adhere to the surface on which they came to
rest, thus indicating the top of the sequence (Fig. 147).

Sedimentary strata rich in
graben in the Dominican Republic,
about 2 km. south of Descubierta
along the trail around the western
end of Lago Enriquillo.   These
conical holes penetrate several
centimeters below the surface of
low mounds and irregular knolls of
algal and coralline limestone.   Inasmuch as these mounds are an
integral part of the solid rock floor,
now a few tens of meters below sea
level, it follows that, if the present

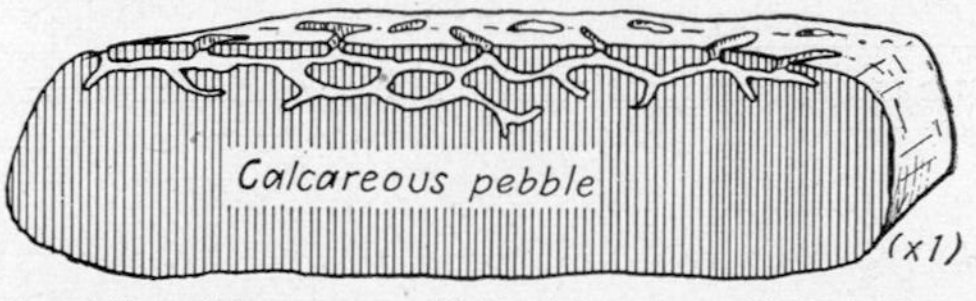

FIG. 145.—Calcareous pebble with upper third riddled
by ramifying borings.   The organism that made the
borings was able to excavate them in hard rock.   Many
calcareous pebbles and large molluscan shells show this
type of boring.   If the majority of such pebbles or shells
were so oriented that the riddled surfaces faced in the
same direction, the indication would be that they were
buried *in situ*, hence with the riddled side up.   (Art.
112.)   (*Sketch is based on specimens collected along the
Jamaican coast.*)

surface were submerged, the borings and their fillings would become criteria for determining the old erosion surface (Fig. 144).

[1] DAPPLES, E. C., 1938, The sedimentational effects of the work of marine scavengers, *Am. Jour. Sci.*, (5) **36**: 54–65; MOORE, H. B., 1939, Faecal pellets in relation to
marine deposits, "Recent Marine Sediments," Trask, ed., pp. 516–524, American
Association of Petroleum Geologists.

organic remains and carbonaceous matter, such as the Rhaetic of Europe (Fig. 147), the thinly laminated Kokomo limestone of Indiana, and the

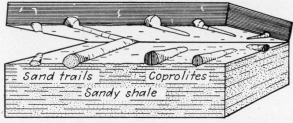

Fig. 146.—Diagram to show how coprolites and sand-filled burrows, sand trails, and similar features tend to adhere to the upper surface of a layer because of being cemented to the bottom materials during and after consolidation. If the overlying sediment is mud, the laminae may end abruptly against the small ridges or arch over them gently. The coprolites and sand trails here shown have diameters measurable in millimeters, but the same features commonly attain dimensions as great as 5 cm. (2 in.) or more. (Art. 113.)

Green River shale of the western United States, contain many coprolites and small concretionary pellets that may have had an excretal origin (Fig. 124). Some of these pellets may prove useful as top and bottom criteria.

Fig. 147.—Specimen of the Triassic Rhaetic "bone bed" from Westbury on Severn, England (reduced one-half). Coprolites and bone fragments are firmly attached to the upper surface of the layer. Pyrite crystals coat a part of the same surface. Features of this sort do not project downward from the undersurface of a layer. (Arts. 106, 113, 171.)

114. Fucoids.—During the past century, especially from about 1840 to 1910, it was common practice for paleontologists to apply the omnibus term *fucoid* to indefinite markings of many kinds that they could not refer to described genera.   The fossils were designated *fucoidal* because of their imagined resemblance to the straplike markings and ridges that the common marine alga *Fucus* might leave if buried under favorable conditions.   The same practice since about 1910 has differed only in terminology—now the structures are said to be *algal*.

Some of the so-called "fucoids" and "algal fossils" may have had a plant origin, but others were more probably made by animals.   A good many, however, are probably not organic at all.   Clarke (1918: 204) interprets *Fucoides graphica* from the Devonian Portage beds of New York as counterparts of ice-crystal impressions, and some fucoidal markings bear close resemblance to the fillings of incomplete mud cracks (Art. 119).

Regardless of their mode of origin, however, certain of these *incertae sedis* "fossils" may be useful as top and bottom criteria if they are studied *in situ*.   Whenever found they deserve to be scrutinized before being rejected.

115. Surficial Cracks in Sedimentary Layers and Rock Surfaces.— Under certain conditions surficial sediments and the solid rock surface itself become cracked or fissured.   The openings thus formed, if filled with sediment from above, provide an obvious means of determining the relative ages of the contacting layers.   Local sedimentary features associated in origin with the cracking phenomenon can also be used in some places as top and bottom criteria.

Cracks and fissures penetrating a layer or a series of layers from the surface downward may originate as follows:

1. Shrinkage cracks caused by desiccation and compaction—mud cracks are formed in this way.
2. Crevices produced in the soil by freezing and thawing—so-called "ice cracks" observed in cold regions.
3. Fissures produced dynamically during earthquakes or vulcanism[1]—these openings may or may not be filled immediately and may extend from some layer at depth upward, even to the surface, as well as from the surface downward. The fillings of such fissures are called "clastic dikes" and are discussed in Arts. 126 to 128.   Certain of the surficial cracks, however, are considered in this section.
4. Cracks, crevices, and fissures produced in the solid rock surface by local weathering and limited erosion along joints and other predetermined planes or zones of weakness.   Larger weathering and erosional features are described in Arts. 130 to 132.

[1] Dikes and sill-like bodies of mud are known to have been intruded into loose sands in the vicinity of mud volcanoes in Trinidad.

116. MUD-CRACK.[1]—Desiccation and compaction of water-filled argillaceous and calcareous muds produce a system of shrinkage cracks, which, in their typical development, form a network and divide the surface into irregular polygonal areas[2] (Figs. 148, 156, 158, 162). If these fissures remain open while the surface is being buried and persist after the surrounding sediment has hardened to rock, they constitute a trustworthy indicator of the top surface of the layer they penetrate (Fig. 160). On

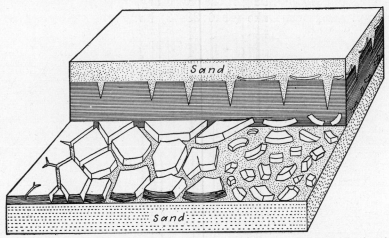

FIG. 148.—Diagram illustrating the formation and burial or destruction of mud cracks and mud-crack polygons. The lower part of the diagram shows a thin mud layer on sand, with mud cracks well developed on the left and curved polygonal plates and chips on the right. In the background, mud is shown overlying the mud-cracked surface. The buried fragments make an intraformational sharpstone conglomerate. In the upper shale layer, V-shaped mud cracks are filled with sand. Several mud laminae separated from the main body of mud to curl up along the edges. These may lie convex or concave upward. (Arts. 116, 117, 119 to 121.)

the other hand, if they are filled, which is usually the case, and the mud-cracked surface is then buried (generally by sediment like that in the fillings), the overlying layer when hardened into rock has on its underside a network of ridges, the fillings, which are counterparts, or negatives, of the original cracks (Figs. 148, 149). Not uncommonly the ridged undersurface, especially if the bed of which it is a part is sandstone,

[1] Also called *sun cracks*, particularly in the earlier geologic literature, *shrinkage cracks*, *desiccation cracks*, or *fissures*, etc. In this work mud-crack is used for the reticulate pattern produced by shrinkage cracks, and mud crack, unhyphenated, for a single crevice. The plural of the latter is mud cracks.

[2] If the layer of mud undergoing cracking lies as an irregular sheet on a rippled or otherwise ribbed and corrugated surface, the system of shrinkage cracks that comes into existence may reflect the network of ridges on the buried surface. Likewise, on clay surfaces recently sculptured by ice-crystal formation, subsequent mud cracks are likely to follow the lines of weakness determined by the course of the larger impressions [Shaler, Woodworth, and Marbut (1896: 992)].

is a better top and bottom feature than the original mud-cracked surface, which may through weathering and erosion be much broken up and the cracks, therefore, largely effaced.

Caution should be exercised in using fillings of mud cracks for top and bottom determination until the shape, depth, and other characteristics of the original cracks have been determined. A thin layer of mud, overlain and underlain by sand, is quite likely to be cracked entirely through, and the sand filling of the crack may, therefore, adhere to either sand bed. Cox and Dake (1916: 38–43) have called attention to the

FIG. 149.—Fillings of limited mud cracks adhering to the undersurface of the overlying (younger) sandstone. Primary and secondary cracks are clearly developed. The fillings are tabular because the original cracks had parallel walls. The relief of the fillings is the same as the thickness of the mud-cracked layer since the cracks were of the limited type. The specimen is from the Roubidoux sandstone of Missouri. (Arts. 116, 117; 119.) [*After Cox and Dake*, 1916, *Bull. Univ. Missouri School Mining Metallurgy*, **2** (4): *Plate* 1.]

indeterminate nature of such fillings for top and bottom determination, and Bradley (1930: 144) has commented in similar vein, as follows:

Sand-filled mud cracks have been considered a useful aid in determining the normal sequence of beds where they are steeply folded and overturned. The fact that the sandy casts may make ridges on either the upper or under surface of a bed does not exclude them from this use but it does necessitate a careful examination of the mud-cracked layer so as to discriminate between the two types of ridges.

See Figs. 148, 149.

Certain inconspicuous features associated with sand fillings in limited mud cracks are discussed in Art. 119.

Mud-cracked beds when viewed in transverse section are seen to be penetrated by digital extensions of the material constituting the overlying layer (Fig. 150). Viewed from above the layer appears to be smooth if the cracks are filled with an easily fractured mineral (such as calcite) or with thinly laminated shale; slightly grooved if the more easily removed fillings have been somewhat eroded (Fig. 151); or slightly ribbed by

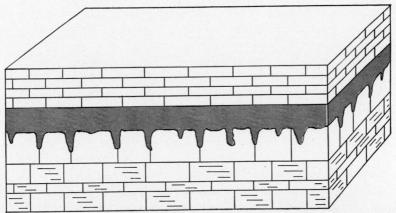

Fig. 150.—Digitate structure along stratification plane in Ordovician (Platteville) limestone near Kentland, Ind. The thin layers of dolomitic limestone are separated by shale films 10 to 15 mm. (about 0.5 in.) thick that are smooth on top but ridged on the underside. The tiny, flangelike ridges, which appear as digitate wedges in transverse section, represent the fillings of mud cracks in the lower lamina. This structure appears in strata that dip at steep angles and furnishes a reliable top and bottom criterion. (Arts. 116, 119.)

Fig. 151.—Top surface of a mud-cracked limestone bed, showing the polygons, somewhat rounded on the corners and edges, separated by mud-filled cracks. Both first- and second-order cracks are developed. The illustration is about one-half natural size. (Art. 119.)

resistant fillings that rise a few millimeters above the general bedding surface. In general the differences in lithology between fillings and polygons, together with the interrelation of the two, should suffice to indicate whether the surface being viewed is the top of the mud-cracked layer. The problem is not so easy, however, if the shale itself has been eroded away so that only a fretted surface remains. Such a surface must be carefully examined to determine the original relation of fretwork and shale (see footnote on page 205 and Art. 119).

Many investigators have cited mud-crack as a useful top and bottom criterion, but there seems to be no record of the first use of the feature for this purpose. As early as 1908 Ransome and Calkins (1908: 42, 61) pointed out how mud cracks in certain Pre-Cambrian clastic formations of the Coeur d'Alene district of Idaho could be used to determine that the beds were overturned:

The cracks are in the finer-grained dark layers and are filled in with the slightly coarser whitish sand. At this point the beds dip steeply to the south, but the cracks are on the northern or under side of the clayey layers, showing that the beds are overturned and illustrating a manner in which sun cracks may frequently be used to detect an overturn [page 42].

References to mud cracks in the better known textbooks are cited in the table in Chap. I, and additional references are listed in the Bibliography constituting Chap. VIII.

117. *Shape and Size.*—Mud cracks are straight or variously curved in plan, and the polygons bounded by them have rectilinear or curvilinear sides. The number of sides ranges from three or four to six or seven, and the polygons may be approximately equiradial, much elongated, or of some intermediate shape. Many differently shaped polygons commonly occur on the same surface within an area of a few square meters (Fig. 152).

Complete mud cracks are characterized by fissures of first, second, third, etc., magnitude that separate the surface of the affected layer into polygons of different sizes and shapes (Fig. 153). The negative of such a surface has a similar system of angular ridges of different magnitude that separate the undersurface of the covering bed into polygonal cells (Fig. 148).

If shrinkage is not carried to completion, incomplete mud cracks are formed. These are single, bifid, or trifid cracks, typically with lenticular cross section, marking the incipient contraction polygons. The negative surface of these has angular ridges, similarly disposed, which match the incomplete cracks (Fig. 154). Incomplete mud cracks and their counterparts are fully as useful for top and bottom determination as completely formed cracks. Fenton and Fenton (1937*b*: 1918–1923) have described and illustrated examples from the ancient Belt series of western North America and from the Silurian Medina of New York, the author has

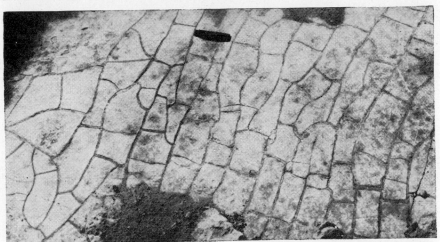

Fig. 152.—Mud-cracked surface of quarry floor in Silurian Byron dolomitic limestone a few miles south of Byron, Wis. Polygons show wide range in shape and size. Primary, secondary, and tertiary cracks are all well shown. The upper part of the fillings has been removed, so that the cracks have the surface appearance of shallow, parallel-sided grooves. The rule in upper center is 17.5 cm. (7 in.) long. (Art. 117.)

observed them in several Paleozoic formations (Fig. 149), and they are known to have the same wide distribution both areally and stratigraphically as complete forms.

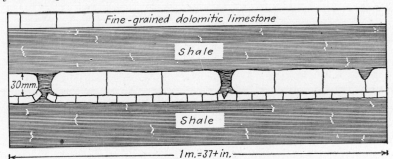

Fig. 153.—Shale-filled complete and incomplete mud cracks in two thin dolomitic limestone layers of the Upper Cambrian Gorge formation at Highgate Center, Vt. The thicker calcareous layer cracked completely through at the left and in the center, but at the extreme right the crack extends only halfway into the layer. The thinner underlayer also cracked through at the left, and the ends curled upward, but under the center crack only an incomplete crack formed, and at the right there is no indication of incipient cracking. Before burial the polygons of the thicker layer had their edges rounded slightly. The cracks are filled with shale similar to that above and below. The laminae in the fillings show prominent concavity. Note exaggeration of vertical over horizontal scale. (Arts. 117, 119.)

An unusual radiate type of mud-crack was discovered some years ago by Dr. I. M. Goldman and was described and illustrated by Kindle (1926: 73, Plate III). Dr. Goldman's photograph is shown in Fig. 154A.

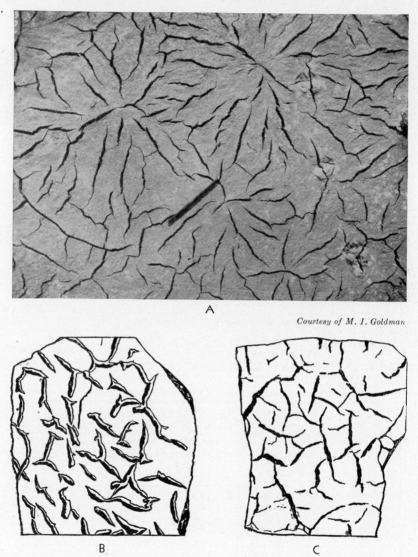

A

Courtesy of M. I. Goldman

B   C

Fig. 154.—Incomplete mud cracks. *A.* Radiate mud cracks in bottom sediment of Black Rock playa, northwestern Nevada. The pencil indicates the scale; it is about 15 cm. (6 in.) long. If preserved in a rock, these cracks might well be called incomplete mud cracks. *B, C.* Incomplete mud cracks in strata of the Belt series in the northwestern United States. *B.* Negatives of incomplete mud cracks ($\times$ 0.7). This is the undersurface of a bed, and the sharp-crested discontinuous ridges represent fillings of the original cracks. *C.* Incomplete mud cracks ($\times$ 0.6) appearing as ragged-walled discontinuous clefts in the upper surface of a layer (*cf.* with *A*). (Art. 117.) (*A after Goldman in Kindle, 1926, Royal Soc. Canada Trans.,* **20**: 71–75, *Plate* 3, *Fig.* 2. *B and C after Fenton and Fenton, 1937, Bull. Geol. Soc. Am.,* **48**: 1920, *Figs.* 6, 7.)

The author [Shrock (1940: 229–232)] has described well-developed rectangular mud cracks from the Byron dolostone of Wisconsin (Fig. 156). It is probable, however, that these two types of mud-crack are not common.

Typical mud cracks are rarely more than a few centimeters (1 to 2 in.) across but show considerable range in depth (Fig. 158). Cracks of microscopic size, possibly formed in the same way as typical mud cracks, have been described and illustrated from the Canadian Pre-Cambrian by Collins (1925: 70, Plate 13A) (Fig. 157), and gigantic cracks over 3 m. (10 ft.) deep have been reported from the Mesozoic Shinarump shale of Utah by Gilbert (1877, 1880) (Fig. 159). In their typical development, however, their average depth ranges from a few millimeters to a few centimeters.

In rare instances, where favorable conditions persisted for a considerable length of time, a system of mud cracks maintained itself through repeated sedimentary increments, so that a columnar structure developed in the bottom material. Kindle (1914: 35–44) reported columnar structure, supposedly of such origin, from a Silurian limestone in eastern Quebec, and Chadwick (1940: 1923) recently called attention to similar repeated cracking in New York limestones, referring to the rock as "ribbon-banded" and "straticulate." The columns so produced are as much as a meter long (2 to 3 ft.), showing that the polygonal network of cracks persisted throughout the time necessary for that thickness of calcareous mud to be deposited. The author has observed the same columnar structure in a laminated limestone (the so-called "Ribbon limestone") of the Mississippian Windsor series in Nova Scotia. It is clearly of mud-crack origin and persists for a depth of at least 20 cm. (4 in.).

The principal cracks, which form first and are the wider and deeper, commonly persist horizontally for several meters and may have rather marked parallelism with each other. Secondary and tertiary cracks usually extend only across the areas outlined by the larger crevices (Fig. 158).

Viewed in transverse section, some mud cracks are seen to have parallel sides and a horizontal bottom (Fig. 153), some have a V-shaped profile (Fig. 159), and a few have the cross section of a tiny stump (Figs. 148, 163). Although the cracks are typically confined to a single layer, they may transect many thin laminae of several distinct layers, thereby producing the columnar structure discussed in a preceding paragraph.

118. *Environment of Formation and Materials Affected.*—The commonest sites for mud-crack formation are the bottoms of recently dried-up ponds, abandoned river channels, and dried-out flood plains; temporarily

exposed playa bottoms, tidal flats, and marine beaches; and the desiccated tops of recent mudflows. The surfaces on which mud cracks form

A

Courtesy of C. R. Longwell

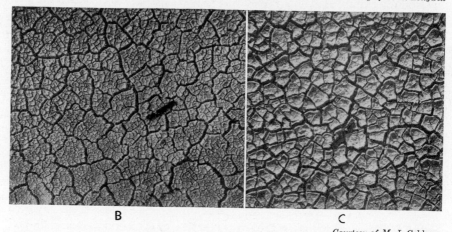

B   C

Courtesy of M. I. Goldman

Fig. 155.—Mud cracks. *A.* Unusually regular polygonal mud cracks in a playa bottom. Note that
large particles have collected in the cracks. *B.* Reticulated mud cracks from a playa in northwestern
Nevada. First-, second-, and third-order cracks are developed. The pencil is about 15 cm. (6 in.)
long. *C.* Concave mud-crack polygons in a playa bottom in northwestern Nevada. The pencil is
about 15 cm. (6 in.) long. As contrasted with *A* and *B*, first- and second-order cracks are well developed. (Art. 117.)

are generally flat or gently sloping, though MacCarthy (1922: 702)
observed well-developed cracks on a 38° slope of a mud flow. It is
obvious, therefore, that there is a chance for error in assuming that a

given mud-cracked surface was flat or nearly so at the time when the cracks formed.

Mud cracks most commonly develop subaerially,[1] but shrinkage cracks of essentially the same nature can form under water by freezing and thawing of the bottom sediments, as suggested by Moore (1914: 101 –102), or by substratal drainage and subsequent contraction, as pointed out by Twenhofel (1923: 64). It is doubtful, however, whether sub-aqueously formed mud cracks are common in ancient strata.

Willard (1925: 286–287) reports an unusual, and probably not often repeated, formation of incipient mud cracks *over* water. In the Bad

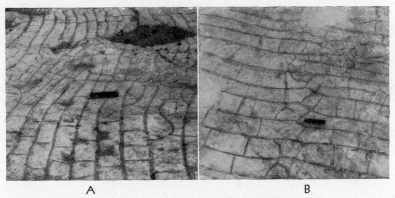

A   B

FIG. 156.—*A, B*. Rectangular mud cracks on the floor of a quarry in the Silurian Byron dolomitic limestone, a few miles south of Byron, Wis. The unusual parallelism of the primary cracks is interrupted here and there by areas of irregular polygons. These rectangular mud cracks occur on the same layer as those shown in Fig. 152 and appear to have developed under essentially the same conditions. The rule in the center of the photographs is 17.5 cm. (7 in.) long. (Art. 116.)

Lands of South Dakota, "water holes" become covered with a thick, scumlike deposit of fine mud. While still supported by a few centimeters of water, this scum develops a network of shrinkage cracks that outline polygonal areas and expose narrow lanes of the underlying water. The formation of the mud cracks is described by Willard (1925: 286) as follows:

As the water beneath the scum gradually sinks into the ground or evaporates, the cracking scum settles and becomes stranded upon the creek bed. Further desiccation results in the production of the actual cracks along the already established lines. Final drying out curls up the layers.

It is doubtful whether these mud cracks could be differentiated from those formed under normal subaerial conditions on a playa bottom.

[1] The polygons of mud-cracked surfaces, both in rock and on present-day mud flats, are commonly pitted by the imprints of raindrops and hailstones, impressed with the footprints, tracks, and trails of many kinds of animals, and pitted with the tiny impressions left by salt crystals that were dissolved before they could be buried. They may also bear a thin armor of sand grains.

Water-filled argillaceous and calcareous muds and silty sands are the present-day sediments most often seen with well-developed mud cracks. However, Swartz (1927: 70) calls attention to a type of shrinkage crack, to which he applies the term *subaerial*, that occurs commonly in areas " . . . wherever a damp soil dries or a loosely compacted soil becomes more tightly compacted (*e.g.* compacting of frozen soils after thawing, or of a newly filled ground)." Such cracks are not easily destroyed and may withstand repeated rains, snows, freezing, and thawing. If it were not

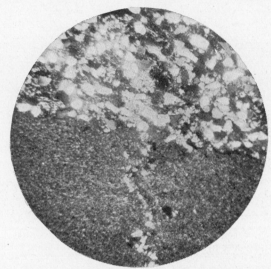

Courtesy of Geological Survey of Canada

Fig. 157.—Photomicrograph (× 20) of banded cherty quartzite from the Pre-Cambrian Cobalt series of Ontario. The section, cut normal to the bedding, shows the upper, very fine-grained silty part of one layer overlain by the coarser, sandy basal part of the next layer above. The vertical line of quartz grains in the silty layer is interpreted as the filling of a fine crack that was open when the overlying sand was being deposited. (Art. 117.) (*After Collins, 1925, Geol. Survey Canada Mem.,* **143**: 70, 150, *Plate* 13*A. A photographic print from Collins's original negative,* 46452, *was furnished by the Geological Survey of Canada.*)

for the fact that they are developed in materials likely to be removed by long-continued erosion, they would probably be of common occurrence in ancient rocks. So far, however, they do not seem to have been recognized, though there is a possibility that some irregular mud cracks in continental deposits are of this type.

Shales, argillaceous limestones, and silty sandstones are the most common mud-cracked rocks, but others have been reported. Cox and Dake (1916: 40, Plate 15) illustrated well-formed shrinkage cracks in California asphalt, and Stutzer and Noé (1940: 350) report sand- and clay-filled shrinkage cracks in coal. These latter, however, do not seem to be common; much more common are larger fissures cutting across entire coal seams (Arts. 126 to 128).

119. *Fillings of Mud Cracks.*—Mud cracks are filled in several ways and with almost any kind of sediment except coarse sand and gravel.

Courtesy of H. B. de Cerenville

Fig. 158.—*A, B.* Mud cracks of three ages in flood-deposited silt along the reservoir area of Macarao Dam near Caracas, Venezuela. The silt layer is about 10 cm. (4 in.) thick, and the widest primary cracks measure 12.5 cm. (5 in.). The cracks developed over a period of days. The rule in the center foreground is 1 m. long in both pictures. (Arts. 116, 117.)

Boulders and pebbles, however, may collect in the shallow grooves between adjoining polygons as described and illustrated by Longwell (1928: 142, Fig. 7). Fine sand, silt, and clay are the commonest mate-

Fig. 159.—Sketch showing great mud cracks in the Shinarump shale of Utah, backfilled with sand similar to that of the overlying Vermilion sandstone.
    Gilbert (1880: 9) describes this occurrence as follows: "On the northern flank of Mt. Ellsworth [Henry Mountains of Utah] are the vestiges of a system of mud-cracks, such as form where wet clays are dried in the sun. Where the under surface of the Vermilion sandstone is exposed to view, it is seen to be marked by a network of ridges which once occupied the sun-cracks of the Shinarump clay; and where the clay is seen in juxtaposition, tapering fillets of sand can be traced from the ridges downward ten feet into the clay." (Art. 117.) (*After Gilbert, 1877, U.S. Geol. and Geog. Survey Rocky Mtn. Region, Henry Mountains, Utah, p. 9, Fig. 1.*)

rials. If sedimentation is continuous through the period of filling and burial of the mud cracks, the fillings are likely to have the same lithology as the overlying bed and commonly remain as counterparts on the underside of the bed upon its separation from the mud-cracked layer.   This is particularly true of sandstone counterparts and beds (Fig. 149).   If fillings and overlying material are laminated shale, the separation plane between the mud-cracked and overlying layer may transect the filling where it joins the latter and cause it to remain with the former.   This usually occasions no difficulty, however, in recognizing which is the original mud-cracked surface, because of the difference in lithology shown by the fillings and polygons (Fig. 148).

If the mud-cracked surface is buried in such manner that some of the cracks are not filled, the incoming sediment arching over them instead, the cavity remaining may be filled later with a secondary mineral.   The Silurian Kokomo limestone of Indiana and Byron dolomitic limestone of Wisconsin contain such cracks filled with calcite (Fig. 160), and the tiny calcitic wedges, ending abruptly upward against the overlying lamina and pointing downward toward the base of the bed they penetrate, contrast sharply with the gray color of the adjacent, fine-grained argillaceous limestone.   It is probable that at the time when they were formed the mud cracks in the above-mentioned limestones were not nearly so wide as at present.   They seem to have been enlarged by introduction of the calcium carbonate, which not only filled the tiny clefts but to some extent also penetrated horizontally between the laminae, as shown in Fig. 160.

The Black River limestone near Kentland, Ind., consists of thin limestone beds separated by intercalated shale layers that exhibit digitate structure on their undersurface (Fig. 150).   The small ridges showing this relation are thought to be the fillings of mud cracks; hence the layer they penetrate is below them in original order of succession. Since some of the beds at this locality are vertical and others steeply inclined, these digitate structures have been useful in corroborating the conclusions about structure drawn from other top and bottom criteria.

Sand, silt, or clay may be washed or blown into mud cracks, finally filling them completely, and may then be succeeded by sediment of different nature.   The lithology of such a filling usually offers sufficient contrast to the surrounding polygons and overlying rock to indicate its origin and significance (Fig. 148).   These fillings, of course, indicate the top of the bed in which they lie unless they are tabular and transect the entire thickness of the mud-cracked layer (Fig. 161).   Should they appear as ridges on the surface of one of two contacting beds—a definite possibility—it should be obvious by their nature and relations that they are counterparts of the grooves in the opposing layer, hence that they lie on the underside of the layer to which they are attached.

Carnallite is reported by King (1946: 14) to fill mud-crack fissures in

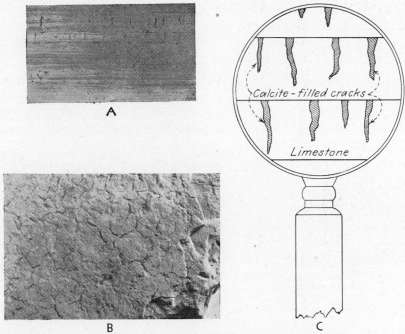

Fig. 160.—Mud cracks in the Silurian Byron dolomitic limestone of eastern Wisconsin. *A.* Transverse section of bed, showing calcite-filled incomplete mud cracks. It should be noted that the cracks do not always extend to the base of the layer containing them. *B.* Upper surface of same bed as shown in *A.* In this view the incomplete cracks appear as discontinous clefts. *C.* Magnified view of a small portion of *A*, showing the relations of the incomplete cracks to several contiguous layers. *A* and *B* are reduced (×0.65). (Arts. 116, 119.)

Fig. 161.—Typical filling of limited mud cracks, showing ridges representing primary and secondary cracks. Some of the mud-cracked shale still remains in the cell-like depressions between the sandstone ridges. The surface could be either the underside of the sandstone layer covering the mud-cracked shale or the upper side of the bed beneath the shale; hence this type of filling is indeterminate for top and bottom determination. The scale is 50 mm. (2 in.) long. (Art. 119.)

a salt clay bed of the Salado formation of New Mexico. The clay bed grades rapidly downward into clean solid halite and is succeeded by a 5-cm. (2-in.) layer of carnallite. King (1946: 14) describes the fissures and their unusual fillings as follows:

The fissures [5 cm. or less wide] are restricted to the clayey bed, not extending into the underlying halite, and they have the polygonal pattern of mud cracks. Carnallite was available for filling mud cracks during and immediately after deposition of the salt clay, but thereafter the sediment was halite. The carnallite

A   B

Courtesy of J. H. Maxson

Fig. 162,—Mud-cracked silt at the mouth of Kanab Creek, Grand Canyon of Arizona, showing flat, convex, and concave polygons. *A.* View showing two areas of mud cracking, the lower along the edge of the water, the upper on a rock ledge. *B.* View about at right angles to *A* (note position of hammer in the two views). The cracks appear to have developed almost simultaneously. The polygons on the lower level dried concave upward; those on the upper bench, convex upward. Some flat polygons appear in both areas. From this local variation it should be concluded that the direction of concavity of mud-crack polygons is not a sure indicator of top and bottom. (Art. 116.)

stringers are therefore interpreted as fillings in mud-cracks at the time of deposition.

Under special bottom conditions fragments of fossils and small complete specimens are sometimes washed into mud cracks and later buried to make an unusual filling. Such pockets of fossils would have unusual interest if no record of the fauna were preserved in the overlying strata.

The filling of a mud crack tends to have one of two fundamental forms, and each form has variations produced by special conditions.

By far the commonest form is a V-shaped ridge that fits into the crack with point downward and usually remains attached to the underside of the covering bed upon separation of the layers (Fig. 148). If the filling does split along the separation plane, thus remaining in the crack, its downward termination within the bed is sufficient to indicate that it is pointed toward the bottom of the layer it penetrates (Fig. 148). This feature has been described and illustrated by many authors—Gilbert (1880: 9), Thwaites (1912: 53), Tanton (1930: 74), and others.

If, in the formation of V-shaped mud cracks, the upper few laminae of sediment curl up[1] slightly at their edges, thus breaking free from the main body of the layer for a few millimeters away from the crack, the crack itself flares out at the bottom and the filling then has the profile of a dagger or of an I beam with the top flange cut off (Figs. 148, 163). Such fillings are immediately obvious and are reliable indicators of the top or bottom direction in a sequence. They are to be expected in series of alternating thin shale and sandstone layers.

If the V-shaped crack penetrates the mud layer to a considerable depth, without completely transecting it, still a different type of filling results, as described and illustrated by Cox and Dake (1916: 46–47). Such fillings are found well developed in the Wamsutta red-bed sequence of the Narragansett Basin, where they are closely associated with other types of fillings (Fig. 163).

A less common type of filling has a tabular shape and transects the shale completely. It is usually composed of sand and terminates both below and above against layers of sandstone. Since such fillings may remain with either the upper or lower sandstone layer, it is obvious that they are indeterminate for top and bottom determination, as pointed out by Cox and Dake (1916: 38–46), who based their conclusion on the field work of Radcliffe (1913). That tabular fillings can be misleading is well

---

[1] The formation and significance of flat, convex, and concave mud-crack polygons have been discussed by many writers, and a general survey of the literature on the subject indicates that many physical factors are involved [see Kindle (1917: 135–144; 1917c: 910–916; 1923: 138; 1926: 71–75), Fenton (1918: 113–115), Ward (1923: 308–309), Swartz (1927: 69–70), Longwell (1928: 136–145), Twenhofel (1932: 685–692), and Bradley (1933: 55–71)]. Barrell (1913: 459) cited concave polygons in the Mauch Chunk and Newark shales as evidence of deltaic conditions, but it was not until Kindle (1917: 135–144) published his conclusions, based on certain laboratory experiments, that geologists began to discriminate between flat and curved polygons. Kindle's experiments showed that mud-crack polygons formed in nonsaline water are typically concave upward, whereas those formed in saline water remain flat or become slightly convex upward. After publication of Kindle's conclusions, several geologists accepted them without comment and interpreted the mud-cracked formations they were studying accordingly. However, Twenhofel (1932: 686–690) showed that flat, concave, and convex polygons can all be formed essentially simultaneously on the same surface in the same mud and water, a phenomenon that Ward (1923: 308–309) had observed and reported several years before Twenhofel's contribution. Figure 162 shows the three types of polygons in a mud-cracked silty layer on a rock ledge at the mouth of Kanab Creek, Grand Canyon of Arizona.

established by the illustration (Fig. 164) of a slab of Roubidoux sandstone from Missouri. These should be compared with the fillings shown in Fig. 149.

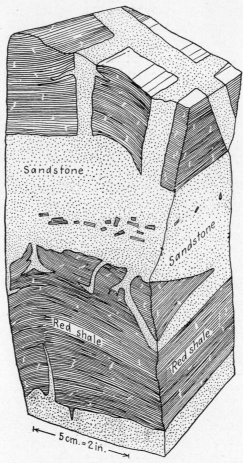

FIG. 163.—Complete and incomplete sand-filled mud cracks in the Pennsylvanian Wamsutta formation of the Norfolk Basin, Massachusetts. The complete cracks furnish no clue as to whether or not the beds are in normal position, but the several differently shaped incomplete cracks are reliable indicators of the top of a bed. The lateral and basal flanges of the sand fillings represent materials washed into lateral openings caused by slight upward curling of the shale laminae along the original crack. In the lower left-hand corner of the specimen is a thin sandstone dike that ends upward in the shale. The main sandstone layer has a thin zone of shale fragments, suggesting that during deposition of the sand a thin layer of mud was also deposited, then later cracked and disintegrated, and the fragments incorporated in the thickening sand. (Arts. 117, 119.)

If, however, the polygonal plates resulting from "limited mud cracking" [as Cox and Dake (1916: 38) designate cracks that extend completely through a mud layer] become concave upward and are then buried, the shape of the filling should be significant (Fig. 163) and the curvature of the concave polygons should be trustworthy.[1]

In cases where the polygons outlined by limited mud cracks remain flat rather than becoming concave, the upper few laminae of the shale

FIG. 164.—Fillings of limited mud cracks adhering to the lower (older) bed of sandstone (Roubidoux of Missouri). The shale of the original mud-cracked layer has been eroded away, leaving the fillings as reticulated tabular ridges. The relief of the present ridges is the same as the thickness of the original mud-cracked layer since the cracks were of the limited type. (Art. 119.) [*After Cox and Dake*, 1916, *Bull. Univ. Missouri School Mining Metallurgy*, **2** (4); 42, *Plate* 17.]

may curl a little around the edges so that tiny wedges of the filling

[1] Cox and Dake (1916: 48) state:

In studying the application of the above [*i.e.*, curvature of polygons] to the limited type of mud cracks, careful search was made by means of quarrying off slabs of sandstone in areas where such cracks were known to be abundant, but no print of the upper surface of the mud layer was found in place. A study of some 360 specimens, all of which were in place in undisturbed beds in localities separated by a number of miles, showed 250 cases in which the surfaces between the projecting mud crack fillings were flat or slightly concave, about 100 with well marked concavity, and 10 with a very slight but irregular convexity. These, of course, all represent the original upper surface of the older bed, and the lack of convex surfaces is corroborative of the view just presented. A large majority of the loose slabs, which probably came from the younger or originally overlying bed, showed convex inter-crack areas.

In further confirmation of this, a number of the slabs with convex inter-crack areas show minor narrow ridges, less prominent than the larger ones, which are believed to represent the fillings of small unlimited cracks which did not penetrate the entire thickness of the mud layer and which, therefore, mark the original bottom of the overlying younger layer. A further corroboration may sometimes be secured by considering the curvature of the thin septae which adhere to the fillings, and which probably themselves are the filling of the horizontal openings between successive laminae. Where enough of any septum is preserved to show curvature, the curvature has been found to conform to that of the inter-crack area.

penetrate the shale as downwardly slanting frills of the main filling (Fig. 163). An additional fact worth noting is that the uppermost part of a mud-cracked shale is typically of much finer grain than the remainder of the layer, a result of the finest sediment having been deposited last. These and other inconspicuous details show why it is so important to study transverse sections of contiguous layers as well as the bedding surfaces.

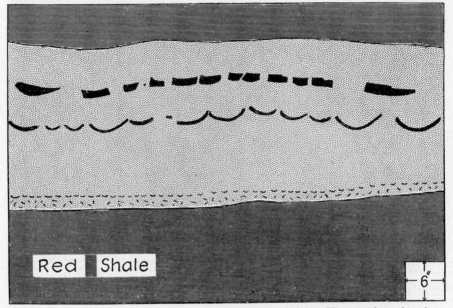

Red Shale

Fig. 165.—Curved shale plates in a sandstone layer of the Carboniferous Wamsutta formation, along Big Pond, Braintree, Mass. At the base of the sand layer one thin mud lamina was fragmented and disturbed; the second cracked into many tiny concave plates that were buried with little disturbance. In the upper half of the sand layer the lower, thinner mud layer cracked into prominently concave plates that were not greatly disturbed on being buried. The upper mud layer was divided into flat polygons by limited cracks. The polygons thus formed remained flat and were buried in that condition. (*Cf.* with Fig. 166.) (Arts. 120, 144.)

120. *Curved Shale Plates in Sandstones.*—If a few centimeters of mud or silt are deposited on a sand layer and then uncovered and exposed to the air so that the sediment can dry out and crack completely through, the polygonal plates are very likely to become concave by curling up around their peripheries. Since these concave plates are fairly strong, they are likely to be buried without much fragmentation or disturbance, for the incoming sediment can be deposited under the upturned edges to form a support.

Such concave shale plates are common in the Wamsutta red beds of the Narragansett Basin (Figs. 148, 165, 166), and the original mud layer from which they came is believed to have been broken up in the manner

just described.   In some beds the original mud layer was deposited on a
surface of wave-rippled sand, and the
crests of the ripples localized the
mud cracks so that the resulting polygons not only started with an initial
concavity but also had prismatic
shapes (Fig. 166). In vertical or
steeply inclined beds a zone or single
layer of curved shale plates, all concave in the same direction, can be a
very useful top and bottom indicator,
for the plates on the true surface are
disposed concavely upward. If, on
the other hand, a zone of such
curved plates shows much disturbance, with plates and their fragments
variously oriented, it is not likely
that the arrangement of the plates
has top and bottom significance. It
should be pointed out in this connection that, if the plates are convex
upward, and unsupported at the
time of burial, they are almost
certain to collapse because of the
weight of the overlying sediment
(Fig. 148).

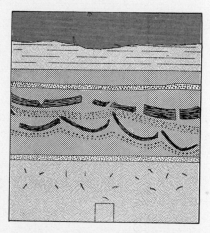

Fig. 166.—Curved and flat shale chips in
sandstone layers of the Carboniferous
Wamsutta formation along Big Pond,
Braintree, Mass. The prominent curved
plates are part of a thin mud layer originally
deposited on a gently rippled surface. The
primary cracks formed along the crests of the
ripples. The gently concave mud plates in
the troughs, turning up somewhat along their
edges, developed more pronounced concavity and were buried by fine sand with
little disturbance. The second mud layer,
which was somewhat thicker, developed only
slightly curved polygons. (Cf. with Fig. 165.)
The square outlined at the base is 50 mm.
(2 in) on each side. (Arts. 120, 144.)

A further refinement of the above-described feature has been observed

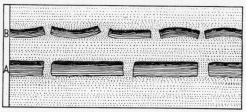

Fig. 167.—Textural gradation in shale chips resulting from mud cracking. In the two shale layers
shown the finer sediment is at the top and the coarser at the bottom regardless of whether the chips are flat
or curved.   A. A shale layer, which when cracked entirely through, was either too thick or too quickly
buried for the individual polygons to curl.   B. A thinner layer in which some polygons are flat, some
convex, and some concave (Cf. with Fig. 162).   This criterion must be used with caution, for cases have
been cited where polygons curved in a certain way have the finer material in the basal part. (Art. 120.)
[Sketch based on mud-cracked layers in the Wamsutta formation of Carboniferous age south of the Blue Hills
in eastern Massachusetts. The cracked layers are seldom more than 2 or 3 cm. (1 in. or so) thick.]

in some rocks. A sand surface, made gently rolling by eroded wave-
ripple ridges, was covered with the silt and clay deposited from a single

influx of mud.   The finest sediment, being deposited last, came to rest on the concave surface of the curved trough deposit (Fig. 167).   The argillaceous lamina thus deposited should have the coarsest material at the base and the finest at the top.   The same textural gradation should hold for curved shale plates deposited originally as mud on a sand surface. It does not matter in this regard whether the polygons are flat, convex, or concave, so long as they have not been disturbed.[1]

121. *Intraformational Sharpstone Layers (Breccias).*[2]—If the plates of a mud-cracked layer are subjected to fragmentation followed by some erosion and transportation before burial, they will be rounded to some extent.   If deposited with variable orientation, they constitute one type of intraformational sharpstone conglomerate, or breccia (Fig. 168). This kind of deposit is not likely to have any common characteristic indicating top or bottom.

If, however, the mud cracks do not extend to the base of the bed, so that only the upper laminae are disturbed, the rounded and angular platelets and chips are strewn over the source layer and may be embedded in the comminuted sediment derived from the underlayer or in the material brought in by the disrupting currents.   Such a deposit, if it can be proved to have originated in the manner just described, can be used as a top and bottom criterion.   It may, however, be indistinguishable from a similar-appearing breccia at the *base* of a shale layer.   Its use as a criterion, therefore, depends on whether or not its origin and sedimentational significance can be determined.

122. *Shale Disks and Plates in Sandstone.*—A thin mud-cracked layer may be so extensively disrupted and eroded that only a few plates escape disintegration, and these are rounded into flat discoidal pebbles.   Most of them are likely to be deposited with the plane of the two larger dimensions parallel to the bedding surface.   Many such flat shale and mudstone pebbles are present in shallow-water and continental sandstones, particularly those associated with coal beds.   They are not in themselves of any use as top and bottom criteria, although they do determine bedding in massive sandstone deposits (Art. 9).   However, if the rock in which they lie is folded intensely, the argillaceous plates develop cleavage showing the top or bottom of the bed (Fig. 388), where this could not have been determined otherwise.

---

[1] Seemingly this generalization does not always hold, for J. H. Maxson wrote the author as follows concerning photographs of curved polygons (May 16, 1946): "The concave mud crack chips of the other photograph showed increase in grain size from top to bottom, whereas the convex chips showed a reverse gradation."

[2] For further discussion of intraformational conglomerates see Walcott (1894: 191–198) and Hyde (1908: 400–408).

123. *Summary of Mud Cracks.*—V-shaped mud cracks and their fillings are reliable top and bottom features if used with discrimination and with an understanding of their limitations. Limited (parallel-sided) mud cracks and their fillings are indeterminate, but certain detailed structures associated with them may be useful. Curved plates of mud-cracked shale are likely to be fairly reliable indicators of top and bottom, especially if they are derived from a layer representing a single influx of mud.

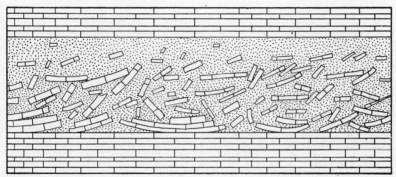

Fig. 168.—Intraformational sharpstone conglomerate in the Upper Cambrian limestone at the gorge east of St. Albans, Vt. The randomly oriented plates of limestone are embedded in a matrix of fairly coarse quartz sand that was washed and blown into the late Cambrian sea from the Adirondack land mass to the west. The fragments were clearly derived from the underlying thin-bedded limestone, as indicated by the relations along the base, where a few laminae are turned up as though from mud cracking. Current action probably was partly responsible for shingling some of the fragments and arranging others essentially parallel to the stratification. Strong currents, acting on a mud-cracked bottom, are thought to have torn up the top layers of the substratum and then mixed the fragments with the sand they were bringing into the sea. The layer is about 1.5 m. (4.9 ft.) thick. The individual laminae average slightly less than 25 mm. (1 in.) in thickness. (Art. 121.)

Mud-cracked layers have been reported from sedimentary rocks of all ages, but the literature describing them is much too voluminous to list here. The use of mud cracks as a top and bottom criterion is mentioned by all authors of textbooks on structural geology and sedimentation and by many others, but by far the most comprehensive discussion is that of Cox and Dake (1916: 37–50), to which every interested investigator will wish to turn [see also Fenton and Fenton (1937b: 1918–1923)]. Another body of literature deals with the formation of present-day mud cracks. This is summarized by Kindle (1917a: 135–144; 1917c: 905–916; 1926: 71–75), Kindle and Cole (1938: 278–283), and Twenhofel (1932: 685–692).

124. FALSE MUD CRACKS.—There are almost certainly a few systems of cracks in sedimentary rocks that normally would be mistaken for mud cracks if their origin were not known. A case in point is described by Bell (1921: 160) from the Horton formation of Nova Scotia as follows:

An extraordinary feature presented by these beds [Upper Horton] on their exposed bedding surfaces is a polygonal system of cracking that might readily be mistaken for true sun-cracking [= mud cracking].   Careful inspection, however, reveals the presence of carbonaceous traces of a dichotomously branching system of rootlets, and not uncommon association with casts of upright tree stems, denoting clearly that they are fossil soils. . . .

. . . the pseudo filling [of a crack] varies from 3 to 30 mm. in width and the intervening polygons are commonly about 25 cm. in diameter.

Another type of ridge that might be mistaken for the sand counterpart of a mud crack, except that it lies on the *upper* side of the layer, is

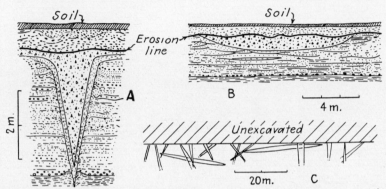

Fig. 169.—Frost cracks in surface sediments near Cambridge, England.   A. Transverse section of a fully developed crack, showing central unstratified filling, stratified lining layer, and horizontally stratified sands and gravels slightly distorted adjacent to the crack.   B. Longitudinal section of crack. C. Ground plan of frost cracks in partly excavated pit.   (Art. 125.)   (*Modified after Paterson*, 1940, *Geol. Soc. London Quart. Jour.*, **96**: 102–105, *Figs.* 4–6.)

described by Bell (1929: 34) from the same Horton formation mentioned in the preceding paragraph.

The surface of certain thin quartzite beds overlain by argillaceous beds have large, fucoidal-like, raised casts of organic origin resembling branching fucoids and from 10 to 15 mm. in diameter.   The branching is dichotomous, and it is possible that these may represent branching roots. . . .

125. FROST AND ICE CRACKS.—Soils and surficial rocks in certain cold regions of the earth are deformed and riven by frost action (Art. 103),[1] with formation of V-shaped fissures that are meters wide, deep, and long.   Later, the openings are backfilled by slumped material or by water- and wind-transported sediment.   Such fissures have been described by Paterson (1940: 99–130) from glacial drift in England and Baffin Bay, Canada, and they may be expected in ancient regoliths, particularly tillstones and lithified soil beds known to have been formed in cold environments (Fig. 169).

[1] See Bryan (1946: 168; 1946a) for a comprehensive treatment of frost action and the structural features of frozen ground; see also Art. 103.

Berkey and Hyde (1911: 226, Figs. 4, 5) describe and illustrate V-shaped cracks that developed during the arching of a frozen sand layer. The cracks are on the convex side of the arch and are filled with sand of coarser texture that slumped into the crevices.

Williams (1936: 129–132) has described an unusual complex of cracks developed by frost action in flat-lying, thin-bedded Ordovician limestones in Ontario. He calls these "frost circles" and points out that they form where major joints cross at right angles. A detailed description and explanation are given in the footnote[1] (Fig. 170).

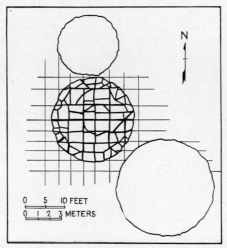

FIG. 170.—Sketch plan of frost circles on Cloche Peninsula, Lake Huron. The middle circle is shown complete with numerous major and minor cracks. These frost circles are developed in the uppermost 12.5 cm. (5 in.) layer of a thin-bedded Ordovician limestone. The circumferences consist of a low rim of limestone blocks that have been forced radially outward against and over the limestone outside the circle. (Art. 125.) (*Modified after Williams, 1936, Royal Soc. Canada Trans.*, **30**: 130, *Fig.* 1.)

Sharpe (1938: 35–39, Fig. 5) mentions the polygonal networks of stones that gather into cracks in the soils of polar regions, and Conrad (1946: 277–296) in a recent article gives an excellent description of the nature and mode of formation of these interesting features. The proba-

[1] The *frost circles* are developed in the upper layer of a thin-bedded limestone. The layer has a thickness of 75 to 125 mm. (3 to 5 in.) and in being separated from the underlying rock by frost action has been fragmented in roughly circular areas (Fig. 170). The circles, according to Williams (1936: 131–132), have an average diameter of

. . . about 20 feet, but some are as small as 15 feet in diameter, and some as large as 24 feet. The circumferences consist of blocks of limestone some 5 inches thick and varying in size and shape, but averaging from 5 to 14 inches to the side, which have been forced radially outward against and over the blocks outside the circle. Thus the rim is raised about 1 foot above the general level. Some of the circles touch, but we did not observe any that cut each other.

bility of their being preserved is essentially nil, but if found in an ancient formation they would no doubt be a puzzle to both sedimentationist and structural geologist.

126. CRACKS FILLED WITH CLASTIC DIKES.—Many sedimentary formations contain tabular bodies of clastic material transecting the bedding at various angles. These intruding bodies, usually referred to as *clastic dikes* by analogy with igneous dikes, represent extraneous materials that have invaded the containing formation along cracks either from below or from above. If the dike can be shown to have been intruded from one direction or another, its relationship to the containing

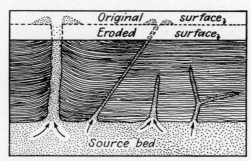

FIG. 171.—Diagram showing origin and stratigraphic relationships of clastic dikes composed of materials injected into superjacent beds from an underlying source bed. It should be noted that some of the fissures broke through to the surface so that the clastic materials were actually erupted onto the surface, a phenomenon often observed during earthquakes. Later erosion removed the surficially ejected sediment, and the dike itself was truncated and then covered by later beds. Some of the fissures developed only in the lower part of the overlying bed, so that the dikes did not reach the original surface and have not yet been exposed by erosion. If the dikes cannot actually be seen rising out of the source bed, several means are available for establishing that the clastic material did come from below rather than from above. The laminae around the largest of the dikes have been noticeably upthrust, showing clearly that the sand was forcibly injected from below. (Arts. 126, 127.)

rock provides a criterion for determining the top or bottom of that rock at the time when the crack formed.

There are two quite different types of clastic dikes if genesis be considered: (1) those formed by intrusion of clastic or fluid material derived from some underlying source layer and emplaced under abnormal pressure and (2) those formed by introduction of material from above, either under some pressure or by simple filling of a preexisting crack or crevice. The first type can usually be genetically related to some underlying source and commonly shows internal and marginal structures that indicate injection under pressure (Art. 127; Fig. 171). Dikes of the second type can usually be identified by the undisturbed wall of the crack, internal stratification, foreign nature of constituent materials, and other features discussed in Art. 128 (Fig. 171).

Clastic-dike materials consist of asphalt, bituminous sand, coal, gravel, sand, silt, clay, and calcareous materials. Under favorable conditions probably any unconsolidated or easily deformed material could invade a crack and solidify to form a clastic dike. Rocks containing dike materials intruded from below are usually of sedimentary origin but may be igneous if in the form of thin flows [Campbell (1904: 135–138)]. Cracks filled with dike materials introduced from overlying beds or from the surface may occur in any kind of rock and originate in many ways.

127. *Clastic Dikes Formed by Substratal Intrusion.*—Clastic materials, if they contain enough water or petroleum to have the property of a fluid, can be injected from below into a fractured formation if there is sufficient pressure.[1] The pressure necessary may arise from the load of

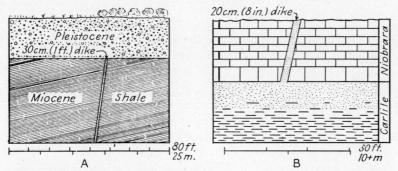

Fig. 172.—Ancient clastic dikes. *A.* Diagram of an exposure near Santa Cruz, Calif., showing Miocene shale cut by a thin sandstone dike that terminates abruptly at the erosion plane truncating the shale. The sand of the dike is totally unlike that in the overlying Pleistocene material and could not have been derived from it. Hence it represents a pregravel stage of sand emplacement. The walls of the crevice are straight and clean. (Arts. 127, 128.) (*Modified after Newsom*, 1903, *Bull. Geol. Soc. Am.*, **14**: 250, *Fig.* 18.) *B.* Sandstone dike cutting the Niobrara limestone of the Kansas Cretaceous. The dike appears to have formed when a crack opened in the limestone and sand from the underlying formation was injected into the opening. (Art. 127.) (*Modified after McMillan*, 1931, *Bull. Am. Assoc. Petroleum Geologists*, **15**: 843, *Fig.* 1.)

the overlying bed, it may be accumulated gas pressure, or it may be hydrostatic pressure. The fracture can result from shrinkage in the invaded materials, apparently a common phenomenon in coal and mud [Price and Lucke (1942: 601–616)]; from shear and tension during an earthquake shock;[2] or from fracturing associated with folding and

[1] An unusual clastic dike composed of sedimentary fragments in an igneous matrix has been reported from the Tintic district of Utah by Farmin (1934: 356–370), who called the features "pebble dikes" and concluded that [the fragments] "were broken from underlying formations by fluids of magmatic origin and were injected upward into the country rock." Fairbairn and Robson (1944: 33) consider certain of the Sudbury breccias to have had a similar origin.

Bloomer (1947: 48–51) recently described an unusual clastic dike formed during the folding of Ordovician rocks in Virginia. Younger Chazy shale was intruded into older Beekmantown limestone on the underside of an overturned fold. If the usual rule were followed in this example, *i.e.*, that the intruding material is older than the rock intruded, the conclusion that the beds are right side up would be wrong.

[2] Many writers, describing phenomena observed during an earthquake, mention

faulting or some similar earth movement such as landsliding.   When the crack forms, water or petroleum laden with clastic material is forced upward, and in some cases laterally, into the fractured material.   Later, when the water flows out or the petroleum becomes asphalt, the solid materials left behind constitute the tabular mass that is called a clastic dike (Fig. 172).

If strata transected by dikes of clastic materials should later be folded or faulted into steeply inclined attitudes, the bottom of the beds could be determined if it could first be demonstrated that the dike material came from below and from only one direction (Fig. 172).

Clastic dikes of the type just described have been reported from many formations in the geologic column and are known to exist the world over. A few examples will suffice to show the range in size, constituent materials, age, and distribution of this type of clastic dike.   References to many other occurrences will be found in the writings of the authors cited in the footnote.[1]

Clastic dikes of the kind being discussed are usually composed of sand, though Campbell (1904: 135–138) reported conglomerate dikes cutting a Cretaceous andesitic flow in Arizona, and many writers have described clay dikes in coal [Gresley (1898: 35–58); Ashley (1899); Price (1933: 1527–

---

how the ground was rent by fissures from which waters laden with sand and mud flowed or spouted forth.   Cases are recorded where the fissures later closed or were choked with sediment injected into them from below or washed and blown into them from above.   Landslips and avalanches commonly accompany earthquakes, forming gaping crevices on slopes and diverting drainage into newly formed cracks at lower levels.   Many of the clastic dikes so far described have been explained as materials injected into overlying beds during an earthquake (Art. 127).

Granular materials such as sand and gravel cannot flow within beds unless the particles are separated by liquid to such an extent that they no longer interlock, whereupon the mass behaves as a fluid rather than as a solid.   Inasmuch as many clastic dikes were clearly injected from below under high pressure, it follows that the material flowed as just described.   Prof. W. J. Mead has suggested to the author that conditions favorable for such flow are commonly produced during an earthquake. The successive S and P waves deform the sand, forcing it first into loose packing, then into close packing.   In the latter condition interstitial water is released under pressure and forced upward into any existing fractures, carrying sand and silt with it. If the source bed is then changed to a loosely packed condition or sheared, the water just ejected may be drawn back into the sand, but the material injected into the fracture will remain there, for under these conditions it cannot flow downward.

[1] Diller (1890: 411–442); Hay (1892: 50–55); Clarke (1900: 96–98); Grabau (1900: 357–361); Hartnagel (1903: 1138–1139); McCallie (1903: 199–202); Newsom (1903: 227–268); Glenn (1904: 522); Campbell (1904: 135–138); Eldridge (1906: 437–444); Jenkins (1925b: 244–245); Russell (1927: 402–408); Williams (1927: 153–174); Croneis (1930: 132–133); McMillan (1931: 843); Kelsey and Denton (1932: 139–148); Parker (1930: 131–136; 1933: 38–51); Kugler (1938: 297–299); Lahee (1941: 74–75).

1533); Roe (1934: 115); Stutzer and Noé (1940: 357–358)]. Eldridge (1906: 437–444) has described veins composed of asphalt that was forced into cracks at considerable depths, and Kugler (1938: 298) has reported oil-soaked sandstone dikes in Trinidad over 3 m. (10 ft.) thick that

. . . carry edge-worn pieces of fossiliferous rock derived from beds stratigraphically several hundred feet below. In other parts of Trinidad, *clay* and *silt* dykes are proved by their foraminiferal assemblages to be derived from beds which occur stratigraphically as much as 5,000 feet deeper.

Kugler thinks the materials in these dikes may have been intruded under great gas pressure.

An unusual kind of clastic dike was recently reported from the Pickaway member of the Mississippian Greenbrier limestone of West Virginia. This limestone has a widespread system of subparallel cracks normal to bedding that are filled with siliceous and argillaceous clastic sediment. The cracks are thought by Price and Lucke (1942: 601–616) to be the result of prelithification induced by compaction. The materials of the filling are supposed to have been intruded into the cracks from intercalated and underlying beds. The clastic bodies seem to be similar to the clay dikes that Eardley (1938: 1339–1340) has reported to be forming in 3-m.-deep cracks in the impure calcareous muds of Great Salt Lake in Utah.

Sandstone dikes were noticed by many of the earlier American geologists and have been found cutting many kinds of rock ranging in age from Pre-Cambrian to Pleistocene. Diller (1890: 411–442) was one of the first of the late nineteenth-century geologists to describe sandstone dikes, which cut Cretaceous shale in the Sacramento Valley of California, and he related them to Tertiary mountain building. His paper was followed, during the next 15 years, by a number of articles describing sandstone dikes in localities scattered widely over the United States. Hay (1892: 50–55) reported such dikes from the White River beds of Nebraska; Newsom (1903: 227–268) described dikes of bituminous sand in California Miocene shales (Fig. 173); McCallie (1903: 199–202) reported Cretaceous molluscan sandstone dikes cutting Cretaceous clays in Georgia; and Glenn (1904: 522) reported sandstone dikes in the basal Eocene clay of Tennessee. More recently Russell (1927: 402–408) pointed out that the material of sandstone dikes cutting the Mowry shale of South Dakota was injected from the underlying Fall River sandstone; Williams (1927: 153–174) found pre-Fox dikes cutting the Upper Cretaceous Belly River and Bearpaw formations in Alberta; Croneis (1930: 132–133) mentioned sandstone dikes that deformed the wall of shaly sandstone for more than a meter on both sides of the dike, in the Pennsylvanian Atoka sandstone of Arkansas; McMillan (1931: 842–843) reported a dike cutting the Cretaceous Ft. Hays limestone of Kansas (Fig. 172*B*); and Parker (1930: 131–136; 1933: 38–51) described clastic dikes and plugs injected into early Mesozoic sandstone in New Mexico. An unusual clastic dike intruded from younger into older rocks during folding was recently described by Bloomer (1947: 48–51). A fuller description will be found in the footnote on page 213.

Stainbrook (1945: 147–157) recently described an unusual type of substratal intrusion involving Devonian strata of Iowa. The Independence shale, normally underlying the Cedar Valley limestone, occurs as

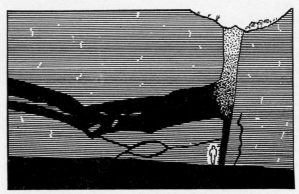

Fig. 173.—Clastic dikes of bituminous sand intruded into Miocene diatomaceous shale from below. The exposure, which is near Santa Cruz, Calif., is about 16 m. (50 ft.) high, and the man standing to the left of the vertical dike near its base gives the general scale of magnitude of the features.   (Art. 127.) (*Modified after Newsom, 1903, Bull. Geol. Soc. Am.,* **14**: 239, *Fig.* 9.)

much deformed fillings in joints, crevices, and solution chambers of the limestone. According to Stainbrook the shale was forced upward into the openings because of the pressure exerted on the plastic material by the weight of the overlying sedimentary rock.

Some of the dikes mentioned in preceding paragraphs are ascribed by the observers to injections caused by the weight of the superincumbent beds or by earthquake shocks. Others, however, seem to be genetically related to folds and faults, and the original fractures may have been contemporaneous with the regional deformation.

As evidence that the dike materials were forcibly injected from underlying formations, Campbell (1904: 135–138) identified dike boulders that came from an earlier conglomerate beneath the invaded andesite flow; Newsom (1904: 233 *ff*.), Williams (1927: 153–174), and Croneis (1930: 132–133) cited contorted wall materials as indicating injection under pressure; Stainbrook (1945, Fig. 6) showed "flow lines" in masses of injected shale; and Diller (1890: 425) reported that mica flakes and shale plates in the peripheral part of some dikes are oriented parallel to the wall.

Glen (1904: 522) and Kugler (1938: 297–299), among others, used fossils to determine the source of the dike material and to demonstrate that it had been injected from below. Meek (1928: 271–277), and later Kelsey and Denton (1932: 139–148), used heavy accessory minerals for the same purpose.

In summary, it may be stated that if the materials of a clastic dike can be proved to have been injected from an underlying source, the relations of dike and intruded rock should suffice for top and bottom determination of the latter.

128. *Clastic Dikes Formed by Filling of Surface Fissures.*—A second type of clastic dike results from the filling of a crevice or fissure open to the surface. The material washed, blown, or otherwise brought into the opening is likely to exhibit considerable range in composition and texture. The walls of such dikes do not exhibit the deformation commonly observed along dike materials injected from below, and the fissures themselves may end downward in a formation rather than transect several formations as is common with injected dikes (Art. 127). If the dike ends upward against an unconformity, it may be the only sedimentary record of a certain interval of geologic time (Figs. 171, 172), inasmuch as the surface deposit from which its materials were derived was swept away before the overlying sediment was deposited.

Surface cracks, crevices, and fissures originate in many ways. Here we shall consider only a few in which the filling has the general shape and relations of the familiar igneous dikes. Most of these seem to have had an origin related to some sort of earth movement. Crevices and fillings of other types common along unconformities are discussed in Arts. 130 and 132.

Geologic literature contains many references to clastic dikes formed by subaerial or subaqueous filling of surface openings. Cross (1894: 225–230) was one of the first American geologists to report dikes of this sort. He described sandstone dikes as much as 300 m. wide filling crevices in granite in the Pikes Peak region and concluded (page 225) that " . . . the sand was forced into the fissures under great pressure." Collins (1925: 35) found apophyses of arkose and argillite extending downward into granite, filling depressions that probably represent cracks in the pre-Huronian surface. Newsom (1903: 253, Fig. 19), many years before, had described and illustrated a somewhat similar example where sandstone dikes penetrate a basalt basement along joints that were enlarged by solution (Fig. 174).

Case (1895: 248–254) ascribed mud and sand dikes of the Oligocene White River formation to injection from below under hydrostatic pressure, but Lawler (1923: 160–172) more recently showed that the dike materials came from the surrounding and higher formations and represent fillings made in crevices open to the surface. Clarke (1900: 95–98) described and illustrated an unusual sandstone dike in the Silurian

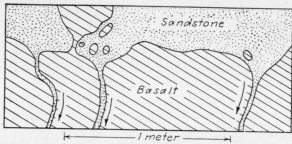

FIG. 174.—Sand-filled crevice in basalt. Diagram of sandstone crevice fillings in basalt near Stanford University, California. The dikes, or fillings, which are only a few millimeters thick as a rule, extend downward into the basalt as much as 8 m. (25 ft.). The sand constituting them is similar to the material of the overlying layer and was introduced from the surface. The crevices may represent joints formed by cooling of the basalt (see Fig. 348). It is probable that the original openings were widened to some extent by subsequent weathering and erosion. (Art. 128.) (*Modified after Newsom*, 1903, *Bull. Geol. Soc. Am.*, **14**: 253, *Fig.* 19.)

Manlius formation of New York that extends downward into but not through that limestone from the unconformity between it and the overlying Devonian Onondaga limestone (Fig. 175). Grabau (1900: 357–361) concluded that the formation of the fissure and violent injection of

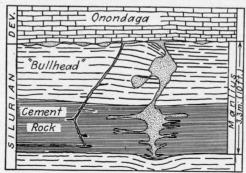

FIG. 175.—Unusual clastic sand dikes in the Silurian Manlius limestone of New York. The diagram shows the irregular nature of the fissure walls and the lateral apophyses in the lower part of the larger dike. The apophyses are essentially parallel to the bedding. The dikes ramify through the cement rock but do not seem to transect it. The sand is supposed to have been forced into the fissures from above, and it is to be noted that small pockets of sand lie along the unconformity between the Devonian and Silurian formations. The sand of the dikes and of the disconnected pockets is identical and is considered to represent Oriskany (Devonian) time, for elsewhere that formation intervenes between the Onondaga limestone of the Devonian and the Manlius of the Silurian. (Art. 128.) (*Adapted from sketches by Clarke*, 1900, *N.Y. State Mus. Mem.*, **3**: 97, *and Grabau*, 1901, *Bull. N.Y. State Mus.*, **45**: 119, *Fig.* 24.)

sand from above took place almost simultaneously, possibly as a result of an earthquake shock. Sand similar to that in the dike lies in scattered pits along the unconformity, showing that the dike was formed while the

Manlius was covered with quartz sand, most of which was later swept away before deposition of the overlying Onondaga limestone (Fig. 175). Clarke (1907: 293–294) described another sandstone dike associated with the Silurian-Devonian unconformity in eastern Quebec. During the erosion of the Silurian limestone, which now stands vertically in Port Daniel Bay, some of the sand being swept across the surface sifted into calcite-lined cavities in the limestone, which evidently were not there when the limestone was deposited. The sand is different from the overlying Bonaventure clastics (Devonian-Carboniferous) and seemingly represents all that remains in the region of an ephemeral precursor of the Bonaventure. The sand itself shows pronounced stratification in the hourglass-shaped cavity.

Jenkins (1925: 202; 1925a: 12; 1925b: 234–246) has described clastic dikes from eastern Washington that fill cracks in both sediments and basalt. The dike materials are gravel, sand, silt, clay, and dust. Some of the cracks they fill are thought to be the effect of earthquake shocks. Kramer (1934: 193–196) reports dolomite dikes in the Texas Permian Merkel formation and points out that the dike material was introduced into a crack from the surface. Ashley (1899: 58) described and illustrated a thin irregular layer of detrital coal along an erosion surface with a joint in the underlying shale filled with an extension of the layer (Fig. 176). Kruger (1938: 305–307) much later reported a clastic dike of glacial debris cutting granite, and Fackler (1941: 550–556) found clastic materials filling deep crevices in Keweenawan lavas of Minnesota.

One of the more unusual examples of surface cracks was reported from Mississippi by Monroe (1932: 214–215), who stated that the cracks formed in surficial exposures of the Jacksonian Yazoo clay and persisted for more than 5 years. Some observers have suggested that the cracks were formed during an earthquake, but inasmuch as no such disturbance has occurred in the region within recent times Monroe rejects this explanation and suggests that they were formed by subsoil creep.

The cracks are as much as 15 cm. (6 in.) wide, 2 m. (6 ft.) deep, and 50 m. (160 ft.) long. There is always a low ridge 30 to 45 cm. (1 to 1½ ft.) high and 60 cm. to 1 m. (2 to 3 ft.) wide on the downslope side of the crack. This ridge, which has the appearance of a tiny fault scarp, is much steeper on the side next to the crack. In time the ridge will probably disappear, but the crack might well be filled with foreign sediment. The filling would then become a permanent feature of the rock.

These and many other examples that could be cited [see Newsom (1903: 252–268), Jenkins (1925b: 244–245), and Williams (1927: 164–174) for bibliographies on clastic dikes] show how great is the variation in the nature of clastic dikes and the fillings of surface cracks and fissures.

In summarizing the general subject of clastic dikes, we can hardly improve on Jenkins (1925*b*: 246), who states:

It appears, then, that in every case fissures are first formed and then fragmented materials are dropped, washed, or pressed into them, from above, below, or from the sides. This action has taken place at the surface in open fissures; under water in fissures on the bed of the sea or other bodies of water; and also far below the surface of the earth in consolidated rocks. The filling from below has come about by pressure of some sort, in some cases undoubtedly hydrostatic.

After severe earthquakes, mud-craters are not infrequent near active faults, and this filling of mud in the neck of the miniature crater is nothing more or less than a clastic dike. Some of the most extensive sandstone dikes are located near faults. Earthquakes caused by faulting, or the slipping of consolidated rocks, crack the surface rocks and then the cracks are filled with clastic materials.

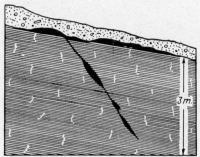

FIG. 176.—Clastic dike of detrital coal in Pennsylvanian shale, southwestern Indiana. The diagram shows a thin, irregular layer of coaly detritus along an old erosion surface, with a joint in the underlying shale filled with similar carbonaceous material. The original crevice in the shale appears to have closed before it was completely filled. (Art. 128.) (*Modified after Ashley, 1899, Indiana Dept. Geol. Nat. Resources Ann. Rept.,* **23**: 58, *Plate* 3, *Fig.* 14.)

Two general statements can be made concerning the use of clastic dikes as top and bottom criteria. If the material of the dike can be shown to have been introduced from some buried source, direction of movement within the dike points toward the surface, and downward the dike material connects with the source bed. If, on the other hand, the material came from the surface and filled crevices and fissures open to the surface, its composition and relations to the intruded rock as well as its relations to the unconformity between the intruded rock and the overlying beds should indicate the direction toward the surface whence the original dike materials came.

129. CYLINDRICAL STRUCTURES TRANSECTING SANDSTONES.—Peculiar cylindrical and funnel-shaped masses of sandstone, vertically transecting strata of essentially contemporaneous age and similar lithology, have been described from widely scattered areas. Their origin seems to be in doubt, and it is not known whether any of them have internal structures or external relations with the containing rocks that would make them useful top and bottom criteria. Certainly, however, they deserve further investigation with this question in mind.

Greenly (1900: 20–24) has described sandstone pipes transecting Carboniferous limestones in England, and Hobbs (1907: 128–140), in discussing sand vents and craterlets associated with earthquakes, ascribes the origin of these pipes to earthquake shock. Simpson (1936: 106) has described cylindrical masses from Patagonia that may have been formed as a result of a seismic shock, and the somewhat similar structures reported by Hawley and Hart (1934: 1017–1034) from Ontario (Fig. 177) may have originated in the same way. However, in reply to a query by the author, Dr. Hawley wrote that he had found no evidence to support the suggestion that the Ontario structures were a result of an ancient earthquake.[1]

A   B

Fig. 177.—Cylindrical structures in Upper Cambrian sandstone near Kingston, Ont. *A*. Sketch showing relations of cylinders to general bedding. *B*. Photograph showing details of cylinder I of *A*. There is no marked re-sorting of sand in the cylinders, but stratification planes and cross-lamination are lacking. The cylinders are believed by Hawley and Hart (1934: 1034) to mark paths of ascending currents of water that destroyed bedding and made cylindrical zones of quicksand. (Art. 129.) *(From Hawley and Hart, 1934, Bull. Geol. Soc. Am., 45: 1024, Fig. 3 and Plate 123. Sketch drawn by W. C. Güssow. Photograph by J. E. Hyde.)*

130. Features of Relief on Surfaces of Weathering and Erosion.—

Crevices, fissures, chimneys, wells, troughs, sinkholes, and other negative features are etched and eroded into solid bedrock where conditions are

[1] Hawley and Hart (1934: 1034) summarize their discussion of the cylindrical, trunklike structures in the Ontario Cambrian sandstone as follows:

From an unexposed horizon these rise vertically through nearly horizontal strata. They are shown to be composed of sand grains similar in characteristics and in general size and assortment to those of the enclosing beds, and are considered to have formed during, or after, deposition of the sand, but before final cementation. The concentric, cylindrical color banding is believed to be concretionary in nature, localized by the presence of vertical cylinders of uncemented and not excessively disturbed sand. The formation of these is attributed to the action of currents of water, rising vertically through the strata from, possibly, a buried fault line or other controlling structure, destroying the original bedding throughout the cylinders, forming quicksands therein, and appearing at the surface as submarine springs. Structures under this hypothesis, might conveniently be referred to as "quicksands enclosed by concretions."

[Also see Hart and Hawley (1933–1934: 85–86).]

favorable. Weathering follows joints, cracks, and bedding planes in localizing solution and modifies the shape and size of preexisting features. Postdepositional weathering below the surface produces openings that in time stope their way to the surface, becoming backfilled with overlying rock in the process. All these features may be filled with material derived from the surface or from superincumbent formations, and filling and cavity are in many cases useful as top and bottom criteria (Fig. 178).

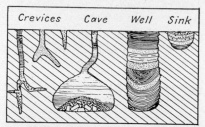

FIG. 178.—Diagram showing several different features to be expected on ancient karst surfaces. Crevices may be narrow and shallow with a simple wedge-shaped filling, or they may be deep and of complex nature. Deep crevices may have more than one kind of sediment in them, indicating that the first material washed or blown in was different from later sediment. Caves and subterranean tunnels are connected with the surface by means of crevices and cylindrical shafts. Surficial detritus is introduced into the subterranean cavities through these openings and may ultimately fill both cave and shaft. Not uncommonly the earliest deposit on a cave floor is the accumulation of blocks that dropped from the walls and roof of the cavity while its domal shape was being stabilized. Wells and cylindrical shafts, frequently reaching great depths and attaining meters in diameter, are common on both ancient and recent karst surfaces. Straight shafts 0.3 m. (1 ft.) in diameter and filled with ferro-aluminous earth have been observed in Jamaica, extending downward into Oligocene limestone as much as 5 or 6 m. They seem to have been formed slowly by downward solution, so that as fast as they were deepened red earth was washed in to keep the opening filled. Similar shafts, developed on a greater scale and containing a diversity of sediments, have been reported from the Silurian limestone of northeastern Illinois (see Fig. 185). The diagram shows one of these shafts or wells with an earlier sequence of sediments deformed by differential settling and soft-rock deformation before the later materials were brought in. Sinks are perhaps the commonest feature on karst surfaces, and filled sinks are to be expected, therefore, along ancient buried karst unconformities. They may be filled with clay, carbonaceous sediments, or residual iron and aluminum ores. (Arts. 130, 131.)

Erosion of bedrock surfaces and also of unconsolidated surficial materials produces localized scour and fill, narrow tortuous channels commonly called "dalles," rectilinear troughs or grooves, potholes, and many other negative features, all owing their origin to the erosive action of running water (Figs. 179, 180). Wind and ice may also erode and sculpture bedrock surfaces, producing on them certain features, which, if buried and viewed in cross section, would be helpful in determining top and bottom in the beds.

Relations of contiguous formations along major and regional unconformities are discussed at length in Arts. 25 to 27. The features and relations discussed in the following paragraphs are chiefly local in extent and small in size. Those produced dominantly by weathering are included in Art. 131; those formed mainly by erosion are discussed in Art. 132.

131. SURFICIAL OPENINGS AND DEPRESSIONS PRODUCED BY WEATHERING.—Solution sinks (sinkholes), shafts, wells, crevices, enlarged joints, and other less obvious depressions produced by the solvent action of ground water are common features on a present-day karst surface (Fig. 181). Similar features have been reported from numerous ancient rocks in which they lie below prominent unconformities. Some of the depressions were filled during the development of the karst surface;

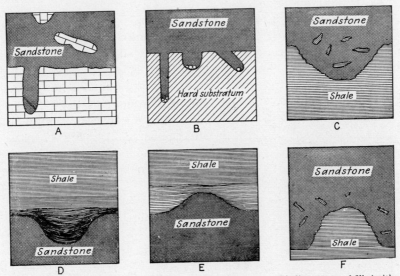

FIG. 179.—Erosive features on an unconformity. *A.* A crevice eroded in limestone and filled with sand. Further evidence of erosional unconformity is furnished by the boulders of limestone included in the sandstone. *B.* Potholes eroded into quartzite, then later filled with and buried by sand. The boulders that were used to cut the potholes were buried *in situ.* *C.* Sand-filled erosional channel in shale. Fragments of shale in the sandstone prove the sandstone to be the younger deposit. *D.* Shale-filled erosional channel in sandstone. The shale laminae sag slightly in the axial part and rise gently toward the sides of the channel—deformation due in part to compaction. *E.* Sandstone prominence buried by shale. The shale laminae rise slightly toward the mound before terminating against it. Some laminae may be thinner where they arch gently over the prominence. *F.* An erosional remnant of shale buried by sandstone. Fragments of shale in the sandstone prove the latter to be the younger. The scale of development of the features shown in *C* to *E* ranges widely in magnitude from microscopic on the one hand to many meters of height or depth on the other. *A* is reduced to about one-third, *B* to about one-hundredth, natural size. (Art. 130.)

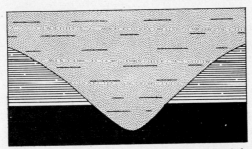

FIG. 180.—Sand-filled channel that was eroded through mud into coal and then backfilled with sand Features of this sort are common in coal-bearing sequences and are known as "rolls." (Arts. 130, 132.) (*Modified slightly after Ashley,* 1899, *Indiana Dept. Geol. Nat. Resources Ann. Rept.,* **23**: 51, *Fig.* 12.)

some were filled later when the cavernous surface was submerged; and some, filled with material from the overlying formation, did not come into existence until after the unconformable surface was covered by sediment.

These latter openings are filled with materials let down into them as they were dissolved downward into the rock. A few typical examples are worth brief description.

Crevices, shafts, and fissures are a common sight in karst areas and many are filled with soil derived from solution of the limestone. Soil-filled pipes and crevices, and many other similar openings that lack a filling of any sort, are characteristic of the spectacular karst developed in the Tertiary limestones of Puerto Rico, Hispaniola, and Jamaica (Figs. 178, 181) and have been reported from many parts of the world.

Crevices, cracks, and saucerlike depressions, developed on a minor

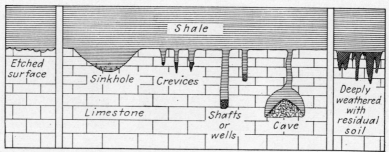

Fig. 181.—Weathering features along a buried karst topography. The etched surface at the left is produced by both quiet and flowing water. See Fig. 183. Fragments of residual chert and slickensided red residual clay are to be expected at the bottoms of sinkholes, crevices, and shafts. Likewise, ancient residual soil layers may be preserved on an irregular surface of crevices and pinnacles, as shown at the extreme right. Caves are likely to have debris fallen from the roof piled on the floor, and such piles are commonly covered with flowstone. The diagram shows shale as the covering sediment, implying that the karst surface was submerged. Under certain conditions a karst surface might also be buried by terrestrial deposits. In fact, some depressions on existing karst surfaces have been completely filled by sediment washed and blown in from the surrounding region. (Art. 131.)

scale on limestone surfaces undergoing solutional weathering, are likely to be present along unconformities separating two limestone formations (Fig. 182). Some years ago Dr. E. O. Ulrich showed the author a specimen of unusual interest in this connection. The specimen consists of a coarse-grained detrital limestone in welded contact with a semilithographic limestone. A conspicuous digitate mass of the former extends downward several centimeters into the latter, filling a crevice in the fine-grained limestone that had been formed before the detrital material was washed in (Fig. 182). Lowenstam and DuBois (1946: 15–23) describe and illustrate clay- and sand-filled fissures that extend from the unconformity between the Devonian Cedar Valley and Wapsipinicon limestones downward into and through the latter into detrital Silurian beds. The material filling the cracks was introduced before the Cedar Valley was deposited and came from an unknown source.

Solution-etched limestone surfaces, such as may be observed on rock surfaces that are covered by water for long periods, have a characteristic topography composed of many shallow bowls and conical depressions with thin, serrated rims. Hudson (1910: 161–196) describes and illustrates such etched surfaces in the Ordovician dolomitic limestones of Valcour Island, New York. The pits on the upper surface are conical, with steep sides; those on the lower, basin-shaped and shallow (Fig. 183). If such a surface were buried, it should if viewed in cross section present a profile that could be used to determine the top or bottom of the contacting beds (Fig. 183).

Pits, facets, and furrows, all showing considerable range in magnitude and detail of surface configuration, develop on limestone surfaces as a result of the solution action of standing and running water. Smith and Albritton (1941: 61–78) have called attention to the development of these features in the jointed Cretaceous limestone of Texas,

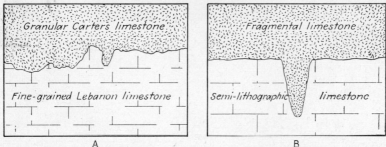

A   B

FIG. 182.—Weathering and erosional features along contacts between limestones. *A.* Uneven contact between two Ordovician limestones differing widely in texture. Reduced about one-half. (*Sketch adapted from Bassler, 1932, Bull. Tennessee Div. Geology,* **38**: 244, *Plate* 32*A.*) *B.* A welded contact between limestones of different texture with some of the granular material filling a crevice several centimeters deep in the surface of the dense semilithographic limestone. Reduced about one-half. (Art. 131.)

where, according to the authors, "corrosive effects . . . . are primarily a function of the degree of slope on which meteoric water falls." Features similar to those described by Smith and Albritton are characteristic of chemically etched limestone surfaces; hence they may possibly be present along karst unconformities.

Filled sinkholes and caves along ancient unconformities are common and have been reported from many localities and from several different geological periods. Just as present-day karst surfaces commonly have local accumulations of residual chert and silicified fossils, particularly in the depressions, so also did ancient surfaces [Leith (1925: 513–523)]. Such material may be incorporated in the base of the formation covering an ancient surface of weathering as pointed out by Bassler (1932: 74), who cites a case in point.

. . . the Hermitage as exposed along Dixon Creek near Dixon Springs, Smith County [Tennessee], commences with a 3 to 6 inch layer of ferruginous conglomerate, which contains *Dalmanella fertilis* and in places includes silicified fossils of the underlying Lowville limestone, indicating subareal weathering at the end of the Lowville to form the silicified fossils and the red soil that contains them.

Purdue (1907: 251–256) reports sand-filled caves and sinkholes in the Ordovician Everton limestone of the Ozark region along an ancient karst unconformity between that limestone and the overlying St. Peter sandstone. Depressions in the old surface seem to have been

Courtesy of New York State Museum

FIG. 183.—Surface etching of a New York Ordovician dolomitic limestone. (Art. 131.) *A.* Under-surface of block shown in *B* and *C*. The light is from the upper left; hence the surface must not have a botryoidal appearance. The depressions are relatively small, broad, and quite shallow as compared with those on the upper surface shown in *B* and *C*. *B.* Side view of block showing deep conical nature of surface pits. Note profile of gently pitted undersurface. *C.* Top view of slab shown in *A* and *B*. Note polygonal rim of confluent cupholes. (*After Hudson*, 1910, *Bull. N.Y. St. Mus.*, **140**: 161–196, Plates 7–9.)

filled with water- or wind-borne sand during the deposition of the St. Peter sand. A somewhat similar condition exists in southwestern Wisconsin, where the St. Peter sandstone fills depressions in the surface of the underlying Oneonta formation. Sinkholes along the top of the Silurian Kokomo limestone of Indiana are filled with travertine-cemented breccia of that formation mixed with the cherty beds of the overlying Kenneth formation (Fig. 184). Meyerhoff and Collins (1935: 94–95) report sinkholes in the Madison limestone that are filled with breccia and red soil and overlain by the Pennsylvanian Minnelusa formation.

An unusually instructive case of an ancient buried karst surface was described recently by Walters (1946: 660–710). Drilling in central Kansas has revealed a pre-Pennsylvanian erosion surface developed on Cambro-Ordovician limestones around Pre-Cambrian monadnocks. This ancient land surface is pitted with sinkholes and solution valleys that contain *in situ* leached residuum derived from the underlying limestone and transported material derived from neighboring residual deposits. Some of the solution valleys form circular moats around Pre-Cambrian hills. The karst surface now lies beneath more than 1,100 m. (3,300 ft.) of Pennsylvanian and later sediments.

Cooke (1926: 261; 1943: 42) reports sinkholes in the Paleocene Clayton limestone that are filled with fine micaceous sand like that in the overlying Nanafalia (Wilcox) formation. These are exposed along the Chattahoochee River near Ft. Gaines on the Alabama side.

An unusual type of sink-hole is described by Dane and Pierce (1934:1493–1505) from the Cretaceous of Colorado. Masses of brecciated Hays and Smoky Hill limestones (Niobrara) are in contact with the underlying Carlile shale, with relations indicating that

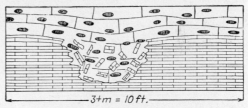

Fig. 184.—Cherty Kenneth limestone filling an ancient sinkhole in the thinly laminated Kokomo limestone. Many Kokomo fragments are included in the sink filling of impure Kenneth. This unconformity between two Silurian limestones may be seen in the Markland Avenue quarry in Kokomo, Ind. (Art. 131.)

they are fillings of collapsed caverns that started in lower limestones and stoped their way upward, probably during the Pleistocene. Bretz (1940: 337–384) has described several filled solution cavities in the Silurian Joliet limestone of northeastern Illinois. These are of particular interest in that they are filled with deformed Pennsylvanian sediments which apparently subsided into the cavities as solution deepened and enlarged them (Fig. 185). The features support Bretz's (1940: 337) conclusion

. . . [that] not all buried "sink holes" at the contact of a limestone and an overlying shale formation are relicts of a former karst topography, that some such "sinks" may develop *de novo* or may become greatly enlarged by solutional removal of limestone after the shale was deposited.

They should not be confused with other shale-filled solution cavities described by Weller (1899: 483–488) from a different part of northern Illinois. These deposits, supposed by Weller (1899) to be of Devonian age but more recently referred to the Mississippian by Croneis and Scott (1933: 207–208), fill solution cavities in the Silurian limestone (Fig. 186).

Weller (1899: 486–487) referred to the relation between filling and wall rock as a "subterranean unconformity" and described the formation of the feature as follows:

The waters which collected upon this land surface in part percolated through the underlying rock strata and by solution increased the size of many joint cracks. At a later period, near the close of the Devonian, when the sea again occupied the region, sand was sifted down into these open joints, and with it the teeth of fishes which inhabited the sea thereabout. It is perhaps possible that the opening which has in recent time been uncovered at Elmhurst, was during this late Devonian time large enough for the entrance of some of these fishes, and that they sought this opening for shelter, much as fishes, at the present time enter similar openings.

Courtesy of J. H. Bretz

Fig. 185.—Solution cavity in Silurian limestone of northeastern Illinois. This cavity was filled with downward-sagging Pennsylvania sands, shales, and a coal seam. It is believed to have been formed slowly after the shale had been deposited upon the old limestone surface. As circulating ground water dissolved the limestone along the contact with the overlying shale, the cavity gradually deepened and the soft overlying sediments, adjusting to the deepening cavity, came to have a synclinal structure. This cavity cannot be interpreted as an ancient sinkhole on a buried karst surface. It is, on the contrary, a postshale feature that came into existence after deposition of the Pennsylvanian sediments. (Art. 131.) (*After Bretz, 1940, Jour. Geology,* **48**: *338, Fig. 1. Print made from the original negative kindly loaned by Dr. Bretz.*)

Cave fillings always present an interesting stratigraphic anomaly in that they are bodies of foreign material within an otherwise homogeneous formation. The material filling a cave may, in rare cases, be introduced from below, as Stainbrook (1945: 152–153) has shown for bodies of Devonian Independence shale squeezed upward into the Cedar Valley limestone of Iowa (Art. 127).

Day (1928: 412–415) has described and illustrated certain unusual solution "pipes" in the coast sandstone of Syria. These are vertical holes, 25 to 50 cm. (10 to 20 in.) across and 1.5 to 5 m. (5 to 15 ft.) deep, that spread out funnellike at the surface and taper like a cigar at the bottom. They are found in a calcareous dune sand of Quaternary age and are filled with red sand from the overlying formation. Day (1928: 413) ascribes the features to weathering, stating: "It seems certain that they are due to the solvent action of water making its way down through the rock."

Westgate and Fischer (1933: 1161–1172) have described small local pockets of fish remains in depressions along the unconformity between the Devonian Columbus and Delaware limestones. They are not certain how the surface relief was produced, but their illustration (Fig. 187) shows clearly that the irregular surface was in existence when the bone deposits were collected in the depressions. Read (1940: 1975) recently

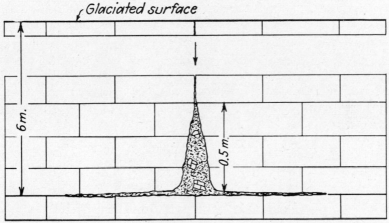

Fig. 186.—Subterranean unconformity in Silurian limestone at Elmhurst, Ill. During a post-Silurian weathering period, surface waters enlarged joints and dissolved out small cavities for many meters below the surface. At a later date (Devonian or Mississippian), when the sea submerged the region, sand, mud, fish teeth, and brachiopod shells sifted downward into the cavities and filled them. All post-Silurian formations had been eroded away before the coming of Pleistocene glaciers or were scraped off by that ice, so that today the cavity fillings are the only record of post-Silurian sediments in the region (Art. 131.) (*Sketch based on description and illustration by Weller*, 1899, *Jour. Geology*, 7: 483–488, *Fig.* 1.)

reported bone pockets from the lower Permian Lueders formation of Texas, and Stutzer and Noé (1940: 350–355, Fig. 127) describe and illustrate a fissure filling of unusual interest in that it contained (page 352) "numerous specimens of *Iguanodon*, a gigantic dinosaur which was 3–4 meters high. . . . "

There are undoubtedly many other cases in the geologic column where locally the record of a long interval of time is now represented by nothing more than the filling of a fissure, crevice, or sinkhole. These fillings, if properly related to the containing rock, can be used as top and bottom criteria. Certain of these surface fillings have been called "clastic dikes" and are discussed in Arts. 126 and 128. Wedges of sediment filling enlarged joints in igneous rocks are typical examples of this sort of clastic dike.

132. EROSIONAL FEATURES—SCOUR AND FILL,[1] CHANNELS, POT-HOLES, ETC.—Under certain local conditions the erosive power of streams and water currents becomes great enough so that shallow depressions are scoured out of the loose, unconsolidated bottom sediments or out of the solid rock over which the water is flowing. Some excavations so produced are asymmetrical pits and troughs. Usually they have the upstream slope

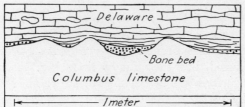

FIG. 187.—Diagram showing the unconformable contact between the Columbus and Delaware limestones, both Devonian, of Ohio. Channels eroded into the Columbus limestone were backfilled with bone fragments and other detritus before the calcareous muds of the Delaware were deposited. This is an example of how fossils may be preserved along unconformities. (Arts. 131, 177.) (*Modified slightly after Westgate and Fischer, 1933, Bull. Geol. Soc. Am.,* **44**: 1169, *Fig.* 3.)

much steeper than the downstream and are disposed transverse to the general current direction (Fig. 188). When the current ceases

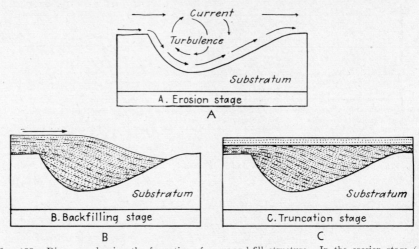

FIG. 188.—Diagrams showing the formation of scour-and-fill structure. In the erosion stage (*A*) strong bottom currents start excavating at certain places and produce a canoe-shaped depression that has an asymmetrical profile, the steeper slope being on the up-current side. During the backfilling stage (*B*) granular sediments (silts, sand, and gravel) are transported along the bottom and washed into the scoured-out depression, becoming cross-laminated in the deposition. If there is a short renewal of erosion after the depression has been filled, the upper part of the cross-laminated layer is partly eroded away and the foreset laminae are truncated (*C*). Later horizontally deposited sediments then transect the inclined laminae of the fill material. (Art. 132.)

excavating and starts depositing sediment, the depression is backfilled,

[1] In an article by Black (1928: 301–307), British scour-and-fill structures are excellently described and illustrated as "washouts." Black interprets them as follows (p. 302): " . . . these masses of sandstone are lenticular in section, and may readily be shown to fill channels eroded in the level-bedded strata below."

Courtesy of U.S. Geological Survey

Fig. 189.—Cross-bedded conglomerate in the Chadron formation on the east slope of the Black Hills south of Fairburn, S.D. The scour-and-fill structure exhibited by the conglomerate was produced by the scouring out and backfilling of prominent channels cut into the underlying shale by strong currents. The man in the center of the picture indicates the magnitude of the individual units. (Art. 132.) (*After Darton, 1905, U.S. Geol. Survey Prof. Paper,* **32**: 68, *Plate 25B.*)

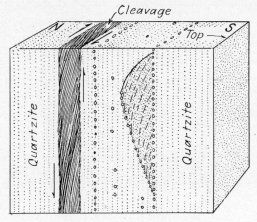

Fig. 190.—Scour-and-fill structure in the Pre-Cambrian Baraboo quartzite in Ableman's Gorge west of Baraboo, Wis. The beds dip vertically and face southward. They lie in the north limb of a syncline. The asymmetric form of the scour-and-fill structure and the layer of coarse particles along the bottom of the channel provide reliable top and bottom criteria, and the conclusions based on these criteria can be corroborated by noting the relations of the well-developed cleavage present in a 10-cm. (4-in.) layer of argillaceous material. The outcrop lies in the northwestern part of an east-west-trending canoe-shaped syncline. (Arts. 132, 276.)

often with more coarsely textured material than that in the substratum (Fig. 189). As the current sweeps detritus along the bottom, some is washed into the depression, the coarser grains rolling down the steep slope as the deposit advances across the excavation, and the filling thus made is an asymmetrical lens of cross-laminated detritus fairly flat along its upper boundary and rounded along its lower contact with the substratum.   Not uncommonly there is a thin layer of coarser grains or pebbles at the bottom of the filling along its contact with the underlying material (Fig. 190).   If erosion is temporarily renewed after the depression has been filled, the upper parts of the inclined laminae may be truncated and afterward buried beneath horizontal laminae with some-

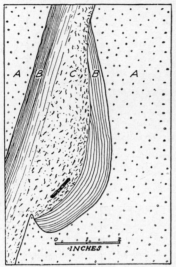

what coarser grains at the base (Figs. 188, 190).   If the current that did the excavating suddenly loses its erosive power and the water covering the depression thus becomes relatively quiet, some time may elapse before the depression is filled up to the general bottom.   If this happens, the sediment making the filling is almost certain to be of finer texture than the surrounding material and it is also likely to have essentially horizontal laminae that sag downward somewhat to conform with the original surface of the depression.   The partly filled pits (Fig. 191) reported by Stearn (1934: 152) in the top surface of a sandstone layer, although interpreted by him as connected with an intraformational conglomerate, seem to be better explained as scour-and-fill structure of the type just described.

FIG. 191.—An unusual type of scour-and-fill structure in the Pennsylvanian Stanley sandstone of Arkansas.   The top of the steeply inclined beds is to the left.   The erosion channel was back-filled with laminated mud, which was later covered by sand. *A*, sandstone; *B*, argillaceous shale; *C*, arenaceous shale with plant fragments and a specimen of *Calamites stanleyensis*. (Art. 132.) (*After Stearn*, 1934, *Econ. Geology*, **29**: 152, *Fig. 3.*)

Certain structural details of scour and fill should be noted so that the feature is not confused with ripple-mark or buried mounds.   (1) If the filling has its typical cross-laminated structure, the laminae are truncated on the upper side and tend to be tangent with the gentler slope of the original depression, as shown in Figs. 188 and 190.   This structural detail should suffice to differentiate a filling from an incomplete ripple ridge, which, if cross-laminated, shows the laminae truncated along the gentler slope and also lacks coarse grains on the same slope (Figs. 59, 192).   (2) In fillings that are not cross-laminated (the absence of this feature being an indication that the filling was not made by currents), the horizontal laminae that are likely to be present sag downward so as to conform in a general way with the asymmetrical surface of the original excavation (Figs. 191, 193).   As pointed out by Cox and Dake (1916: 30–31), the texture and lithology of such fillings are likely to differ rather conspicu-ously from those of the surrounding rock.

Scour and fill is a common and widespread feature in detrital sedi-mentary rocks of all kinds, and it has been described and illustrated by many writers, some of whom have mentioned its use as a top and bottom

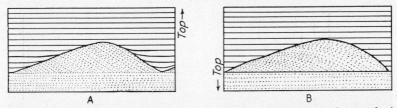

Fig. 192.—Diagrams showing the difference between a scour-and-fill structure and a cross-laminated ripple ridge. The ripple ridge (*A*) has flat foreset laminae parallel to the steeper slope and sharply truncated along the gentler slope. In the scour-and-fill structure (*B*) the inclined laminae are curved, asymptotic along the gentler slope, not parallel to the steeper slope, and sharply truncated along the upper boundary. Diagram *B*, therefore, shows an inverted structure. If the channel were excavated in clearly stratified sediment, the bedding would end abruptly at the edge of the feature. By contrast, if a ripple ridge is buried by laminated mud, the individual laminae rise slightly as they approach the ridge and in some cases they may arch gently over the prominence. Ripple ridges and scour-and-fill structures range in dimensions from a few centimeters to as much as a meter in a transverse direction. Compare these diagrams with Fig. 59. (Arts. 68, 132.)

criterion.[1] It may be developed on a microscopic scale, or it may have such grand development that the fillings are several meters thick, many meters wide, and tens of meters long.

Although scour and fill is most commonly found in conglomerates, sandstones, and finer clastics (Fig. 194), it may also be present in calcar-eous rocks and in glacial deposits. Shallow depressions scoured out in

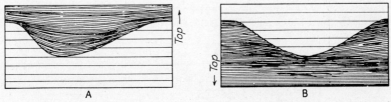

Fig. 193.—Diagrams showing differences between mud-filled scour-and-fill structures and ridges buried by mud. In the scoured-out excavation the laminae of mud bend downward in adjusting to the asym-metrical shape of the excavation, and the contact of the laminae with the wall of the substratum is asymptotic (*A*). In *B*, which shows a ridge buried by laminated mud, the laminae slope gently away from the ridge, showing that they were deposited around and over it. *B*, therefore, is inverted. The features shown in *A* and *B* usually are measurable in centimeters or inches. (Art. 132.)

unconsolidated calcareous muds may be filled later with comminuted shell material, and the fragments of the filling tend to be imbricated as a result of current action (Fig. 274). It does not seem likely that an asym-metrical mass of shell fragments such as that just described would be mistaken for an incomplete ripple ridge, especially if there are only a few

[1] Cox and Dake (1916: 30–31), Leith (1923: 208), and Lahee (1932: 86).

scattered deposits. If, on the other hand, there are many such asymmetrical ridges lying at regular intervals along definite bedding surfaces, their origin by scour and fill should be questioned (see Art. 70 and Figs.

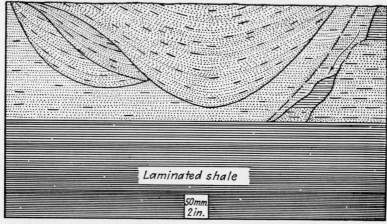

Laminated shale

50mm.
2in.

FIG. 194.—Multiple scour-and-fill in the Carboniferous Cambridge formation near Commonwealth Pier, Boston Harbor. The beds have an east-west strike and a northerly dip of 20°. The sketch shows early penecontemporaneous slumping, followed by almost complete removal of slumped material. Then came normal deposition of fine sand, followed by a second episode of slight faulting. This period of sedimentation ended with the cutting of three successive channels, the last being much the deepest. The scour-and-fill structures are composed of fine, strongly laminated sandstone. The underlying laminated shale was not affected by either the early deformation or the subsequent erosion. The small square at the base of the diagram is 50 mm. (2 in.) on each edge and gives the scale of the sedimentary features. (Art. 132.)

65, 85). Glacial till and outwash deposits may contain pseudo scour-and-fill structures. These appear to represent deposits made in a depression produced by erosion, but collapse due to the melting of a partly or completely buried block of ice seems a more likely explanation (Fig. 195).

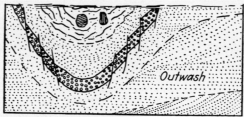

Outwash

FIG. 195.—Faulted syncline in a Pleistocene outwash deposit near Wellesley, Mass. The feature probably owes its origin to the melting of a block of ice buried in the sand. The layers of gravel, sand, and silt gradually sank as the ice melted, the gravel layer most conspicuously adjusting by a series of small normal faults. The syncline has a maximum width of about a meter. Features such as this may be expected in sandstones and conglomerates believed to represent ancient outwash deposits. (Arts. 132, 146.)

The initial dip of the laminae is commonly steepened along the walls of the original depression by slump, and in some deposits small, parallel normal faults cut the filling. The entire profile of the filling must be observed to establish its identity. Either half of the structure might well be mistaken for a faulted glacial delta deposit like that illustrated by Leith (1932: 209).

In addition to the scour-and-fill structures discussed in preceding paragraphs, many other channels, troughs, and depressions along unconformities have been eroded into sediments and rock surfaces and later backfilled with sediment when the erosion surface was buried. Some of these have been discussed at length in the section on unconformities (Arts. 25 to 29). A few special examples deserve consideration here [see also Sheldon (1928: 243–252)].

Strong bottom currents may scour out linear troughs of more or less symmetrical cross section trending in the same direction as the flow.

FIG. 196.—An erosional unconformity between two limestones. The surface of the lower Silurian Manlius limestone was channeled; then limestone gravel derived from the Manlius and quartz sand brought in from a distance were deposited in the bottom of the channel to a depth of about 17.5 cm. (7 in.). Next followed the deposition of about 15 cm. (6 in.) of argillaceous and calcareous mud, followed by the purer calcareous sediments constituting the Onondaga limestone. The width of the channel is about 6 m. (18 ft.) and its depth slightly more than 1 m. (3½ ft.). (Art. 132.) (*Modified after Grabau, 1900, Bull. Geol. Soc. Am.,* **11**: 357, *Fig.* 5.)

Twenhofel (1932: 668) mentions such channels in certain formations on Anticosti Island and states that " . . . the channel fillings in some instances resemble casts of logs." Grabau (1900: 357) described and illustrated a broad, shallow channel eroded into the Silurian Manlius limestone of New York and then backfilled with Devonian clastics and later Onondaga limestone (Fig. 196). In other places the Onondaga rests directly on the irregular surface of the Manlius with a clean contact (Fig. 197). Many years ago Williams (1881: 318–320) described sand-filled channels in the Upper Devonian Portage shales of New York and ascribed them to icebergs dragging across the soft muddy bottom [see also Cox and Dake (1916: 28–31), Clarke (1918: 199–238), and Schuchert (1927: 123–131)].

Thin lenticular coal seams commonly lie in eroded channels and shallow basins (Figs. 38, 198) and in some cases have rather unusual structural relations (Fig. 199). Coal seams are commonly thinned or completely cut out by erosion channels backfilled with clastic materials that may be cross-laminated [see Ashley (1899), Bell (1929), and Stutzer and Noé (1940)] (Figs. 180, 200). The sand of such channel fillings may sink into the coaly matter if it is plastic, thus producing flowage structure (Fig. 201).

Stutzer and Noé (1940: 405, Fig. 186) report potholes in Carboniferous coal of the Waldenburg Basin of Germany that are backfilled with

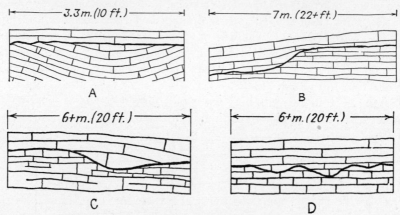

Fig. 197.—Erosional unconformity between the Silurian Manlius limestone and Devonian Onondaga of New York. *A.* Sagging layers of Manlius are truncated by the erosion surface, giving the contact the appearance of an angular unconformity. *B.* One side of a probable erosion channel in the Manlius filled with gently dipping Onondaga beds. *C, D.* Uneven contact caused by pre-Onondaga channeling of the Manlius limestone. In all the above cases the limestones are either in direct contact or separated by a thin layer of decomposed shale that represents the intervening Devonian Oriskany formation. (Art. 132.)　(*Modified after Grabau*, 1900, *Bull. Geol. Soc. Am.*, **11**: 356, *Figs.* 1–4.)

conglomeratic sandstone containing fragments of the coal itself. No other ancient potholes along unconformities have come to the attention of the author, but it is highly probable that they do exist because of their

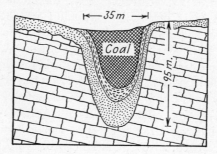

Fig. 198.—Ancient, sediment-filled sinkhole in Ordovician dolomitic limestone near Stanton, Mo. The coal, which is low-grade bituminous, is massive and is separated from the basal Pennsylvanian sandstone by a bed of flinty fire clay. The syncline of sandstone, clay, and coal apparently was formed slowly as the sinkhole deepened. (Art. 132.)　(*Based on an original sketch by L. C. Raymond.*)

rather common occurrence in present-day stream channels cut in rock [see Elston (1917: 554–567; 1918: 37–51)].

133. Secondary Features.—Certain features and structures existing along or directly adjacent to the surface of contact between contiguous

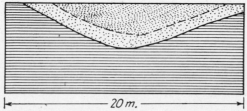

Fig. 199.—Diagram showing a channel eroded into shale and then backfilled with sand, a relation commonly present in coal-bearing sequences. The first sand brought in was deposited in the channel without much classification; the later was deposited with well-developed cross-lamination. (Art. 132.) (*Modified after Kindle in Ashley*, 1899, *Indiana Dept. Geol. Nat. Resources Ann. Rept.*, **23**: 1093, *Fig.* 749.)

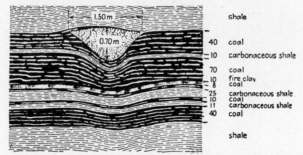

Fig. 200.—Diagram showing deformation of strata beneath a mass of sandstone deposited in a channel that had been eroded into fairly soft and plastic sediments. The sand body sank into the underlying materials to some extent, so that its gently convex upper surface did not rise far above the general bottom. (Art. 132.) (*After Kukuk*, 1920, *Glückauf*, **41**: 807, *Abb.* 7.)

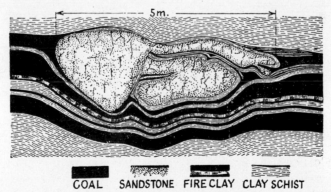

Fig. 201.—Diagram showing deformation of coal seams and intercalated shale layers by an irregular mass of sandstone. The sand was presumably deposited on the soft coaly material and hydroplastic muds when they could still flow to some extent. The laminae of the overlying shale arch gently over the billowy upper surface of the sand mass. There may have been some scouring out of the coaly material before the channel was backfilled with the sand that caused the deformation of the underlying strata. (Art. 132.) (*After Kukuk*, 1920, *Glückauf*, **41**: 805-810, *Abb.* 8.)

layers are obviously of secondary origin (*i.e.*, they were formed after the beds were lithified). Two of these are mentioned here because of their possible significance as criteria for top and bottom determination.

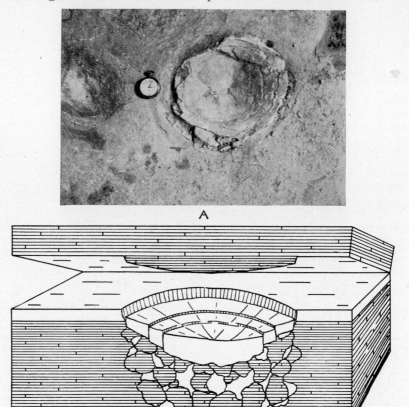

A

B

Fig. 202.—Collapse features in the thinly laminated Byron dolomitic limestone (Middle Silurian) of eastern Wisconsin. *A.* View looking directly downward on two of the features. To the left of the watch is a depression that once seated one of the curved discoids; to the right is a typical discoid in place. Note the several concentric fractures. The large discoid is all that remains of the thin layer that originally covered the surface. *B.* Diagram showing a cross section of one of the discoids and the porous nature of the semilithographic limestone directly beneath. The circular disk appears to have sagged downward, fracturing concentrically in the process. The projection from the overlying layer into the shallow cavity is usually smoothly rounded. The collapse may possibly have been caused by decomposition of buried organic matter originally trapped in the soft calcareous muds. (Art. 134.)

134. Collapse Features.—Certain layers in the fine-grained, thin-bedded Byron dolomitic limestone (Silurian) of eastern Wisconsin contain peculiar collapse features of uncertain origin (Fig. 202). The feature consists of a roughly circular concave plate sharply separated by one or more circular cracks from the layer of which it was obviously once a part. There may be other incomplete concentric cracks in the plate itself; in addition to these, there are well-developed radial cracks that are largest near the center of the plate and typically die out before reaching the periphery (Fig. 202). If the structure can be viewed in transverse section, there is nearly always a cavity or a spongy mass directly beneath the depressed plate, suggesting that cavity and downwarped plate are parts of a single structure.

It may be that calcareous mud locally charged with organic matter developed shrinkage cracks and the associated collapse features when the organic matter disappeared through decomposition. The formation of the feature apparently took place while the beds were somewhat lithified, as shown by the numerous cracks.

Regardless of origin, however, these collapsed plates clearly indicate the top of the layer in which they occur and by their relation with the overlying bed show that they lie beneath that bed (Fig. 202).

135. STYLOLITES.[1]—Many soluble rocks, especially limestones and marbles and to a limited extent relatively insoluble sandstones and quartzites [Tarr (1916: 819–820)], exhibit in cross section zones of com-- plicated zigzag structure referred to as *stylolites*. When separated the juxtaposed surfaces of contiguous beds appear very rough, the vertically fluted irregularities of one surface fitting into their counterparts on the other. These structures, whose origin has for a long time been a matter of debate, have been fully described and illustrated in a large number of articles (see the footnote below).

Stockdale (1922, etc.) proposed that they were formed by differential solution of hard rocks under pressure ("solution-pressure theory"), whereas Shaub (1939: 47: 61), raising numerous objections to this theory, concluded that they were formed in unconsolidated sediments as a result of contraction and pressure ("contraction-pressure theory"). Evidence can be found to support and refute both theories; hence it seems probable

[1] See BASTIN, E. S., 1933, Relations of cherts to stylolites at Carthage, Missouri, *Jour. Geology*, **41**: 371–381; 1940, A note on pressure stylolites, *Jour. Geology*, **48**: 214–216. GOLDMAN, M. I., 1940, Stylolites, *Jour. Sedimentary Petrology*, **10**: 146–147. PRICE, P. H., 1934, Stylolites in sandstone, *Jour. Geology*, **42**: 188–192. SHAUB, B. M., 1939, The origin of stylolites, *Jour. Sedimentary Petrology*, **9**: 47–61. STOCK-DALE, P. B., 1922, Stylolites; their nature and origin, *Indiana Univ. Studies*, **9**: (55): 1–97; 1923, Solutive genesis of stylolitic structures, *Pan-Am. Geologist*, **39**: 353–364; 1936, Rare stylolites, *Am. Jour. Sci.*, (5) **32**: 129–133; 1939, Stylolites, Abstract, *Bull. Geol. Soc. Am.*, **50**: 1989; 1941, Stylolites, primary or secondary? Abstract, *Ohio Jour. Sci.*, **41**: 415–416; 1943, Stylolites: primary or secondary, *Jour. Sedimentary Petrology*, **13**: 3–12; 1945, Stylolites with films of coal, *Jour. Geology*, **53**: 133–136. TARR, W. H., 1916, Stylolites in quartzite, *Science*, **43**: 819–820. TREFETHEN, J. M., 1947, Some features of the cherts in the vicinity of Columbia, Missouri, *Am. Jour., Sci.*, **245**: 56–58. YOUNG, R. B., 1945, Stylolitic solution in Witwatersrand quartzites, *Geol. Soc. South Africa Trans.*, **47**: 137–142.

that structures generally called stylolites had multiple origin.   Here we shall consider them as secondary features, though the author believes with Shaub that certain stylolitic structures may well be of essentially penecontemporaneous origin.

There seems to have been no mention of any characteristic of stylolites which might make them useful in determining the top or bottom of the

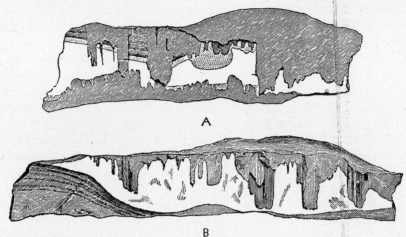

A

B

FIG. 203—Specimens of stylolitic Devonian limestone from Port Dover, Canada.   The stylolitic columns penetrate a mass of chert embedded in the limestone and are best developed on the upper side in *B*.   In *A*, however, the relation of stylolites to chert is confused by the presence of fragmental chert (stippled) in a thin layer above and below.   Even in this specimen the larger columns penetrate the chert from above.   (Art. 135.)   (*After Logan*, 1863, *"Geology of Canada," p.* 633, *Figs.* 437, 438.)

sequence in which they occur.   In fact, in a reply to a question on this point, Stockdale (letter dated June 13, 1938) wrote negatively as follows:

I have thought a great deal of the relationships of stylolites to this problem [*i.e.*, their use as a top and bottom criterion] and have been unable to come to any convincing conclusion.   As a matter of fact as things now stand I doubt if stylolites by themselves, at least in normal limestone beds, are a criterion.

On the other hand, Tarr (letter dated Apr. 13, 1938) wrote as follows concerning concretions and stylolites: "Of course where chert nodules occur in a formation containing stylolites these features consistently develop on the upper portion of the nodule."   Logan (1863: 532–533) long ago called attention to this relation of stylolite and chert nodule, using the accompanying illustration (Fig. 203), and only a few months ago Trefethen (1947: 57) reported the same relation as follows: "Stylolite seams are extremely common in the Burlington [limestone of Missouri]. They may pass through the limestone, undeflected above and below a pinch and swell in the chert, or they may curve over a chert lens." Though this relation seems plausible for syngenetic chert nodules, it needs to be tested fully in the field.   It is worth recording that Bastin

(1931: 371–381) found the relations between stylolites and secondary chert nodules quite variable at Carthage, Mo.

Stylolites seem to develop in a position such that the bisectrices of the angular zigzags and the axes of the grooved columns are always oriented vertically. If the strata are horizontal, the stylolite zone is likewise horizontal (Fig. 204). If the beds have an initial dip, the stylolite zone parallels the bedding but the bisectrices and axes are vertical. This relationship is well exhibited by the gently inclined strata around some of the Niagaran bioherms of northern Indiana [Stockdale (1922)]. This

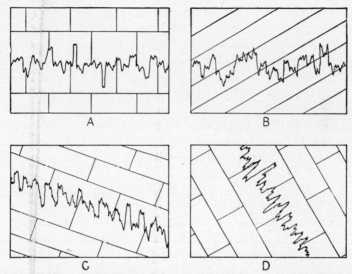

Fig. 204.—Stylolites. *A.* The common stylolitic structure with columns vertical and essentially perpendicular to bedding. *B.* Stylolite seam in tilted sandstone. Since stylolite columns are generally formed with vertical orientation, it is obvious that in this rock they formed secondarily after tilting [see Stockdale (1945: 133–136)]. *C.* Primary stylolites in reef-encircling beds with initial dip. It is to be noted that although the seam itself is parallel to bedding the columns are vertical rather than perpendicular to bedding. *D.* Primary stylolite seam in a series of steeply inclined limestone beds. Stylolites appear to be useless for top and bottom determination. (Art. 135.)

relation is shown in Fig. 204. Beds folded after stylolites have been formed in them show the bisectrices and axes in an inclined position (Fig. 204). Finally, stylolites that develop in steeply folded beds maintain a position as near horizontality as the features in the rock permit (Fig. 204). Although all these relations are interesting structurally, they have no usefulness for top and bottom determination, for they indicate only verticality, not direction of gravity, at the time of formation.

In view of the fact that stylolites are so abundant, however, especially in some marbles that have lost nearly every vestige of original structure, there is good reason to investigate them critically in order to determine whether or not they display any relation or characteristic that might be used as a top and bottom criterion.

CHAPTER V

FEATURES OF SEDIMENTARY ROCKS (III)

III INTERNAL FEATURES.

136. Introduction.—Certain structures and features lying within individual sedimentary layers or within a sequence of such layers have proved useful and reliable as criteria for top and bottom determination. Probably the most useful of all sedimentary structures is cross-lamination; others are penecontemporaneous structures, buried organic hard parts and gross structures built by organisms, primary and secondary cavities, and landscape marble.

Although it is true that most of these features were closely related to the surface at the time they were formed, they have been grouped together for discussion because they are found within a layer or in a series of layers rather than on a bedding surface.

137. Cross-Lamination.[1]—Cross-lamination is the designation now generally used for that structure, commonly present in granular sedimentary rocks, which consists of tabular, irregularly lenticular, or wedge-shaped bodies[2] lying essentially parallel to the general stratification which themselves show a pronounced laminated structure in which the laminae are steeply inclined (as much as 33°) to the general bedding (Figs. 208, 213).

The one outstanding feature of cross-lamination that makes it so useful and reliable a criterion for top and bottom determination is the angular relation of the laminae to the underlying and overlying strata or boundary surfaces. Although it is true that some cross-lamination is indefinite for one reason or another,[3] if the structure of the cross-lami-

---

[1] Variously called "cross-bedding," "foreset bedding," "false bedding," "oblique bedding," "diagonal bedding," "inclined bedding," "current bedding," "torrential bedding," "flow-and-plunge structure," etc.

[2] In an article that deserves careful study by all serious students of sedimentary structures, McKee (1940: 811–824) describes the three fundamental types of cross-lamination as they are displayed in the Paleozoic rocks of the Grand Canyon region [see also McKee (1945a: 1–168)]. Thompson (1937: 723–751) in another important article describes and illustrates the several kinds of cross-lamination made on beaches, bars, and dunes. Finally, the interested student is referred to the excellent discussion by Bagnold (1942: 1–265) of the physics of blown sand and desert dunes.

[3] During discussion of a report by Allison (1933: 144),

242

nated unit is apparent, then the top of that unit, and hence the top of the sequence in which it lies, should be determinable, for the angle between the laminae and the overlying layer is greater than the alternate angle between the laminae and the underlying bed (Figs. 205 to 208).   In fact, the most common type of cross-lamination is that in which the laminae are sharply transected at the top of the unit (Fig. 211) and tangent or nearly so (asymptotic) at the base[1].   Even when the angular relations

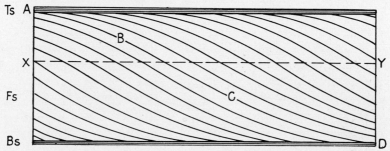

FIG. 205.—A complete cross-laminated bed with topset (*Ts*), foreset (*Fs*), and bottomset (*Bs*) laminae. The curve *ABCD* is a complete profile of the front of an advancing layer that is internally cross-laminated.   The upper part of the curve at *B* is concave downward; that at *C*, concave upward.   The complete form, therefore, does not have top and bottom significance.   Fortunately, however, the upper part of cross-laminated units is usually removed by penecontemporaneous erosion, producing truncation as shown along the line *XY*.   This truncation, together with the upward concavity and basal asymptotic relation of the laminae, provides an almost unfailing top and bottom criterion.   (Arts. 137, 138.)   (*Sketch based on Davis, 1890, Bull. Geol. Soc. Am.*, **1**: 198, *Fig. 2, and Bailey, 1930, Geol. Mag.*, **67**: 78, *Fig. 1.*)

appear to be similar above and below, a thin zone of larger or heavier grains may mark the lower part of the unit[2] (Fig. 209).

Prof. P. G. H. Boswell remarked that experiments on the deposition of sand from water-currents, carried out in glass-sided troughs some years ago by Prof. T. R. Wilton and himself, appeared to indicate that (1) a moderate velocity (up to 1.5 feet per second) produced ripples of a wave-length of about three inches in sand of average diameter $\frac{1}{100}$ inch, and current-bedding of the inflected form, asymptotic at top and base; (2) with increased velocity (up to 1.78 feet per second), the tops of the ripples were eroded to a plane surface that abruptly truncated the bedding; and (3) with a still higher velocity, much larger "whale-back" ripples or moulds were produced (of wave-length about 10 inches), on the lee side of which the bedding, although asymptotic at the top of the mounds, abutted abruptly on to the floor of the underlying material. . . . Some of the examples of current-bedding that appeared to give contradictory results might be due to exceptionally high velocities.

[1] Twenhofel (1932: 619) states that " . . . cross-lamination is important in structural geology, as the truncation at the top of the foresets gives a nearly unfailing means for the determination of the tops of beds."   Even with such a reliable criterion as this, there are the exceptional cases where the laminae show a sharp angle at the base and an asymptotic relation at the top.   Hills (1940: 6–7, Plate II*A*) describes and illustrates aeolian cross-lamination of this nature in Pleistocene dune sand at Barwon Head, Victoria, Australia.   (See also preceding footnote.)

[2] This type of cross-lamination has been called "torrential" [Hobbs (1906: 291)] and "compound oblique" [Grabau (1913: 402)] and has been ascribed to rapid

Many writers have stated that the concave portion of cross laminae face upward, but as Bailey (1930: 78) points out this is true only if the upper part of the complete foreset layer has been removed before deposition of the next layer (Fig. 205). The steepest angle of repose for cross-laminated sand is about 33°; hence laminae showing inclination in appreciable excess of this amount (Fig. 210) have been deformed.

138. MODE OF FORMATION.—Cross-lamination is made in bodies of granular sediment by currents of wind and water that build the deposit forward by successive additions of sediment on the down-current side (Figs. 205, 206). The body itself at the time of formation may be a terracelike layer or bank with linear or lobate front, a current-ripple ridge, a small delta or fan, a backfilling of a scoured-out channel, or a

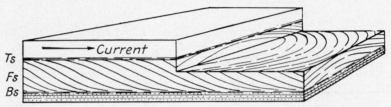

FIG. 206.—Diagram illustrating how a current of water constructs a cross-laminated deposit. The original layer, as shown in the left half of the diagram, consists of thin topset (*Ts*) and bottomset (*Bs*) layers bounding a thick middle layer in which the foreset (*Fs*) laminae are uniformly inclined in the direction in which the current flowed. The right half of the diagram shows the appearance of the bed after the upper part of the cross-laminated layer has been eroded away. Subsequent deposits would rest upon the truncated foreset laminae. (Arts. 137 to 139.)

sand dune of some sort[1] (Fig. 207). Subsequent surface erosion usually modifies the original shape of the cross-laminated deposit to some extent, so that upon burial it has one of the three common forms, layer, irregular lens, or wedge (Fig. 208). The erosion that produces this modification also strips away the so-called "topset laminae," if they were ever made

---

deposition by temporary streams in desert environments [Lahee (1941: 83)], though it is probable that the same structure can be formed under other environmental conditions. Read (1936: 469), in using cross-lamination for structural work on the Dalradian rocks of Scotland, states: "Asymptotic bottoms and truncated tops are everywhere observed, and the dark bands form always the bottom plane of a truncating bed." The normal white quartzite contains only a few grains other than quartz, whereas the dark bands are composed of biotite, zircon, garnet, epidote, and iron ore.

If any coarser than average grains are present in the cross-laminated unit, they will lie along the base and, as pointed out by Twenhofel (1932: 210), " . . . zones of cross-bedding in conglomerates locally may show a row of pebbles at the base of the cross-bedding, to which they were rolled as the foreset beds advanced."

[1] Twenhofel (1932: 619) states:

Cross-lamination develops under four general conditions or environments not sharply separated from one another: building of deltas and alluvial fans, outward building of the bottom in seas and lakes to the position of the profile of equilibrium, movement of sandbars and dunes, and formation of ripple marks.

at all, and bevels the foreset laminae, thus producing the sharp transection that marks the top side of the cross-laminated unit (Figs. 205, 211).

The unidirectional cross-lamination in current-ripple ridges and the chevron lamination in wave ripples are discussed fully in Arts. 68 and 77 in connection with ripple-mark.

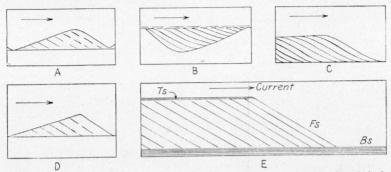

Fig. 207.—Diagrams illustrating different kinds of cross-lamination. *A.* Cross-laminated ripple ridge made by a wind or water current. *B.* Scour-and-fill structure with well-developed cross-lamination in the backfilled sediment. *C.* Cross-lamination in an advancing terrace constructed by a stream or shallow water current. The front of such a terrace is commonly lobate, with the lobes convex in the direction of flow. *D.* A sand dune with inclined laminae dipping as much as 33°. Dune cross-lamination may be developed on a grand scale (see Fig. 19). *E.* Cross section of a delta showing topset (*Ts*), foreset (*Fs*), and bottomset (*Bs*) beds. Delta foresets may be of such magnitude as to be mistaken for tilted beds. (Arts. 137 to 139.)

139. SHAPE OF CROSS-LAMINATED UNITS.—The complete form of a tabular cross-laminated unit is essentially that of an ideal delta composed of bottomset, foreset, and topset laminae (Fig. 206). Such perfect units, however, are almost never formed under the conditions best suited for extensive development of cross-lamination. Bottomset laminae usually are poorly represented and topset laminae are nearly always eroded off

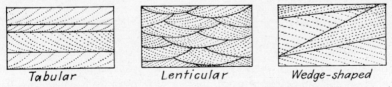

Fig. 208.—Diagrams showing the common shapes of cross-laminated units. Tabular and lenticular units are typical of water-laid sediments, whereas wedge-shaped units are characteristic of wind deposits. Under certain conditions, however, tabular units may also be formed by the wind, as illustrated in Fig. 219. (Arts. 138 to 139.)

before the unit is buried, so that in the majority of cases tabular crosslaminated units consist only of the foreset laminae sharply truncated at the top and tangential or nearly so at the base[1] (Figs. 212, 213).

Under conditions of frequently shifting current direction, as along the littoral zone, thin layers of sand are cross-laminated in opposite directions

[1] McKee (1940: 821; see also 1945a: 1–168), in describing the three fundamental

in alternating layers, giving rise to a "herringbone structure" if viewed in transverse section (Fig. 214). There usually is sufficient difference in the angle of contact at the top and bottom of some of the layers to determine the general order of succession. If this relation is indefinite, however, the cross-lamination cannot be used as a criterion of top and bottom unless associated features such as the coarse or heavy grains mentioned in Art. 131 and illustrated in Fig. 209 are discovered.

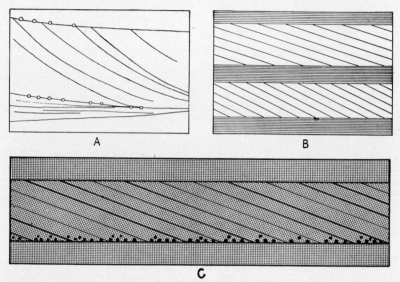

Fig. 209.—Cross-lamination. *A*. Sketch of cross-lamination in the Cambrian Appin quartzite at Loch Leven, Scotland, showing layers of quartz pebbles along the bases of curved foreset laminae. The scale is about one-tenth natural size. (*Modified after Vogt*, 1930, *Geol. Mag.*, **67**: 71, *Fig.* 5.)   *B*. Torrential cross-lamination in recent deposits in Calabria, southern Italy. Thick horizontal layers alternate with still thicker beds in which the laminae incline consistently in the same direction. (*After Hobbs*, 1906, *Bull. Geol. Soc. Am.*, **17**: 291, *Fig.* 2.)   *C*. Torrential cross-lamination with heavier and larger particles concentrated at the bases of the inclined laminae. The particles rolled down the steep slope of the advancing terrace and were buried by the successive foreset laminae. (Art. 137.)

According to Cox and Dake (1916: 29), "Cross bedding as developed in limestone generally has a lower angle of dip and shows less curvature than in sandstone, and is often indeterminate because it cannot be traced to its points of contact with the true overlying and underlying bedding

types of cross-lamination displayed in the Paleozoic rocks of northern Arizona, gives a typical characterization of this type as follows:

[It] consists essentially of single beds or layers, a few to many feet in thickness, each composed of a series of sloping, even, lamination surfaces which dip uniformly from top almost to bottom of the layer. Near the base the degree of slope gradually lessens until the lower surface of the bed becomes tangent to the curve formed by the lamination. This type of simple structure pattern has in many places been developed so extensively that successions of identically sloping laminae may be traced for as much as six hundred yards within single beds or layers.

planes." In many limestones, however, the cross-lamination shows no essential difference from that in sandstones and is fully as clearly developed (Figs. 213, 215).

Formations of granular sedimentary materials deposited under conditions of rapid scouring and filling have a characteristic "choppy" structure composed of successively overlapping, irregularly lenticular units that are strongly cross-laminated. In these units, which commonly represent only the lower parts of the original complete form, the laminae have pronounced concavity, a well-developed

FIG. 210.—Deformed cross-lamination in the Pre-Cambrian Seine series on the north side of Shoal Lake, Canada. Some of the foresets are inclined as much as 60°. Since primary foresets do not exceed 33 or 34°, that inclination being the angle of repose for sand in air and slightly in excess of the figure for water, it follows that those shown in the diagram have been deformed. In spite of the deformation, however, the concavity of the laminae and the top-side truncation provide reliable criteria for determining the top of the cross-laminated layer. The pocket knife indicates the scale. (Arts. 137, 139.) (*Adapted from Merritt, 1934, Bull. Geol. Soc. Am.,* **45**: 365, *Plate 40A.*)

tangency with the lower surface on which they rest, and a sharp transection at the top (Figs. 210, 216, 217).

Lahee (1941: 82) describes and illustrates a type of cross-lamination much like that just

Courtesy of J. D. Allan

FIG. 211.—Cross-lamination in the Lower Cretaceous McMurray tar sands of northern Alberta. The tops of the foreset laminae are sharply truncated by the overlying horizontally stratified layer. The width of the area shown is about 75 cm. (30 in.). (Arts. 137, 139.)

FIG. 212.—Cross-laminated glauconitic sandstone in the Upper Cambrian Franconia formation of western Wisconsin. The foreset layer is about 55 mm. (2.2 in.) thick. The foreset laminae themselves are sharply truncated at the top but asymptotic at the base. Cross-lamination is common in glauconitic sandstones the world over. (Art. 139.)

discussed which he calls "compound foreset bedding" and ascribes to construction on a delta where " . . . adjacent lobes interfere in such a way as to cause the building of foresets dipping now in one direction and now in another." [See also Davis (1890: 195–202), Smith 1909: 437), and Twenhofel (1932: 443).] Similar cross-lamination has been reported from the Parting quartzite by Singewald (1931: 404–413) and from the Coconino sandstone by McKee (1940: 821–822; 1945). It has also been observed in the Horton-Windsor clastics of Cape Breton Island and in Pleistocene sand-plain deposits (Figs. 216, 217).

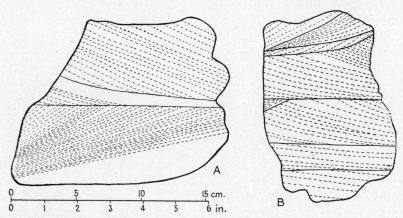

FIG. 213.—Cross-lamination in limestone. Limestones exhibiting cross-lamination are clearly of detrital origin since granular sediments are required for development of the structure. Recrystallization of the rock has obliterated the outlines of individual detrital particles, but weathered surfaces of the specimens show strongly inclined foreset laminae. In specimen A two prominent layers are without lamination. Specimen B shows foresets dipping at different angles and in several directions. Individual laminae in the two specimens range in thickness from 0.1 to 5 mm. and are fairly consistent as to thickness in any individual bed. (Arts. 137, 139.) (*Sketches based on specimens in the Sedimentation Collection of Harvard University.*)

The cross-lamination of aeolian deposits is characterized by interlocking units of wedge or polyhedral shape and is likely to be complex, with the laminae dipping in every direction[1] (Figs. 207, 218). Under certain

[1] McKee (1940: 823) describes this type of cross-lamination, as displayed in the Coconino sandstone (Permian of Arizona), and, in a pertinent discussion (quoted below), compares it with the two types of aqueous cross-lamination developed in associated strata.

A comparison between the cross-lamination in the Tapeats, Supai, and Coconino sandstones brings out differences that apparently are significant. In the first place, the Coconino structure consists entirely of sloping surfaces that form a pattern on each cliff face resembling many truncated wedges and it is devoid of flat-lying or horizontal layers that contain sloping laminae between top and bottom such as characterize both Supai and Tapeats cross-lamination in most localities. In the second place, the maximum dip found in the laminae of the Coconino sandstone is about 33°, whereas no clearly established examples in either of the other deposits are known to exceed 27° or 28°. Finally some of the low-angle slopes in the Coconino show a direction reverse to the normal. This probably means that they represent either depositional or erosional surfaces on the windward sides of the dunes, whereas in the two water-deposited types of sediment discussed, both deposi-

A   B

Fig. 214.—Herringbone cross-lamination in basal Potsdam sandstone of eastern New York. The sketch at the right of the photograph indicates the cross-lamination that can be observed in the sandstone. The penknife indicates the scale of the bedding. Under conditions of frequently shifting bottom currents, thin layers of sand are cross-laminated in opposite directions in contiguous beds. Such a succession if cut transversely presents a herringbone appearance. The foreset laminae in successive layers show angular or asymptotic contact at the base; they always exhibit marked truncation along the upper boundary. (Art. 139.)

conditions, however, water-deposited sands may locally show typical "aeolian" cross-lamination, as pointed out by Twenhofel (1932: 84), and wind-deposited sands may have tabular cross-laminated units as illustrated in Fig. 219.   However, it should not be difficult to determine the top of the cross-laminated formation by observing the angles of contact of the inclined laminae (See footnote, page 243).

An unusual type of cross-lamination designated "festoon cross-lamination" has been reported by Knight (1929: 56–74; 1930: 86) from the Casper and Fountain sandstones of Wyoming. Its formation is closely related to the scouring and filling actions of marine currents and is stated to be the result of " . . . (1) the erosion of plunging troughs having

Fig. 215.—Cross-lamination in a fine-grained Paleozoic limestone. The weathered joint surface shown is essentially perpendicular to bedding. It is not noticeable that the curved foreset laminae are predominantly concave upward. The specimen is about three-fourths natural size. (Art. 139.)

the shape of a quadrant of an elongate ellipsoid; (2) the filling of

---

tional and erosional surfaces appear only as horizontal planes when not developed on foreset slopes.

Students wishing to analyze statistically the cross-lamination of a given formation will find an excellent guide in a paper by Reiche (1938: 905–932).

the troughs by sets of thin laminae conforming in general to the shape of the trough floors; (3) the partial destruction of the filling laminae by subsequent erosion, producing younger troughs" (1930: 86).

140. Magnitude.—Cross-lamination ranges in magnitude from tiny units in silts and fine sands, visible only under the microscope, to single units several tens of meters thick in coarse sands and gravels.[1] The larger units are usually either of aeolian origin or the foresets of deltaic

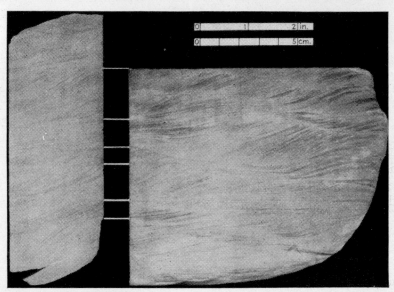

Fig. 216.—"Choppy" cross-lamination in a sandstone of the Mississippian Horton series of Nova Scotia, showing curved wedge-shaped units produced by scour-and-fill action. The current flowed consistently from right to left. The section at the left is perpendicular to that at the right. In this type of cross-lamination most of the curved laminae are concave upward. (Art. 139.)

deposits. Their steeply dipping laminae must be carefully distinguished from folded beds if they are seen only in limited exposures.[2] In general,

[1] Belyea and Scott (1935: 228) describe and illustrate microscopic cross-lamination from the 10,000-m.- (30,000-ft.-) thick Pre-Cambrian Halifax formation of Nova Scotia, and Tarr (1935: 1488) reports similar structure in the Pleistocene concretionary shales of the Connecticut Valley. On the megascopic side Twenhofel (1932: 622, Fig. 75) reproduces a photograph by E. L. Estabrook showing giant aeolian cross-laminated units as much as 10 m. thick in Mesozoic sandstone of the northern Shensi Province, China (Fig. 19).

[2] If cross-lamination is mistaken for normal bedding, as it might well be in large, isolated segments of a delta, the thickness estimates will be greatly in error and the orientation of the strata incorrect, as pointed out by Corbett (1937: 89–94). It might well be further noted that inasmuch as there is a variety of cross-lamination and bedding in recent deltas such as the delta of Fraser River, as pointed out by Johnston (1922: 115–129), large bodies of sandstone showing confusion of bedding may well be parts of ancient deltas.

however, cross-laminated units are rarely more than a meter or two thick and hence can be viewed in their entirety.

141. USE AS A TOP AND BOTTOM CRITERION.—There seems to be no certainty as to when or where geologists first recognized the true significance of cross-lamination and that it could be used to determine the top or bottom of a stratified succession.

Cox and Dake (1916: 26) state: "About 1910 Professor Smythe in a conversation mentioned the fact that Professor Davis had used this criterion for many years with classes in the field. This is the earliest account of its use the writers have been able to find." Lamont (1940: 1016–1017), however, in an article entitled "First Use of Current-bedding to Determine Orientation of Strata," discusses the revision by Shackleton (1940: 1–12) of the structure of Silurian and Devonian rocks in Eire pointing out how that investigator, using the truncated tops and asymptotic bases of current-deposited laminae, determined the correct order of succession, which, while at variance with currently held interpretations, clearly vindicated the conclusions reached some 80 years earlier by geologists who had insisted that certain beds were upside down. It seems that some geologists of that earlier day were well aware of the significance

FIG. 217.—Current-bedded or cross-laminated sand and gravel in a Pleistocene delta plain, showing characteristic lenticular units composed of laminae that are dominantly concave upward. This type of cross-lamination is produced by rapidly shifting currents that scour out channels and then backfill them with coarse sediments. This illustration should be compared with Fig. 216. (Art. 139.) (*After Mills*, 1903, *Am. Geologist*, **32**: 162–170, *Plate 23A.*)

and use of cross-lamination, for as early as 1864 Kelly (1864: 156–158, 161–163, Figs. 1–2, Plate 9) described and published illustrations of the structure. Kelly was certainly one of the first to recognize and use the feature, and he concluded that, by using it, " . . . it may be known where steep dips or complex contortions present themselves, whether the original upper side of a bed is still uppermost, or whether a group of beds has been overthrown and turned upside down, as is sometimes the case." That the significance of cross-lamination was known at the same time by other geologists is clearly shown by an additional statement of Kelly (1864): "these facts were known by Mr. Patrick Ganley, who made numerous drawings of this kind of lamination about Slea Head for Sir Richard Griffith."

As a matter of further historical record, there is the fact that, although cross-lamination was used in structural work in Ireland long before North American geologists were aware of its significance in this respect, geologists from our side of the Atlantic very recently discovered an inverted

Courtesy of U.S. Geological Survey

FIG. 218.—Cross-laminated units of lenticular shape in the Navajo sandstone of Glen Canyon, Utah. The laminae begin as "highly inclined arcs of small radii" and "decrease in curvature until they merge into contact with the underlying strata." The units range in length from 3 to 100 m. (10 to 325 ft.). (Art. 139.) (*After Gregory, 1917, U.S. Geol. Survey Prof. Paper*, **93**: 58, *Plate* 12A.)

FIG. 219.—Aeolian cross-lamination in a beach-dune deposit along Lake Michigan at Muskegon, Mich. The tabular units were formed by the wind transporting sand along the beach. (Art. 139.)

succession of strata in Scotland which had been assumed by Scottish geologists to be right side up until they were shown the significance and use of cross-lamination in structural investigations [Vogt (1930: 68–73); Tanton (1930: 73–76); Bailey (1930: 77–92)].

Cross-lamination is one of the most widespread and best developed, and fortunately one of the most reliable, of all top and bottom structures; and because it occurs in all kinds of detrital rocks, ranging in age from early Pre-Cambrian to latest Pleistocene (Fig. 220), it has been used by geologists everywhere and is described and illustrated in all modern

textbooks of structural geology, stratigraphy, and sedimentation. No attempt is made here to list a complete bibliography, but the few references given will serve as an adequate beginning list for any student who desires to pursue the subject seriously[1].

142. False Cross-lamination.
Spurr (1894; 43–47) has described a type of apparent cross-lamination associated with current ripples that seems to have been formed by deposition (Fig. 61). Woodworth (1901: 281–283) has described how mica flakes, settling on the forward or lee slopes of current-ripple ridges, may, as successive sand layers accumulate, give rise to cross-banding inclined to the true stratification (Fig. 60); (Art. 68). Davis (1918: 284–285) describes and illustrates a type of false bedding, resembling cross-lamination, in the Franciscan chert of California and believes it may be due to scouring by currents that deposited the original siliceous material of the chert. It

FIG. 220.—Cross-lamination in a drill core. The rock, composed of fine-grained sand with laminae and plates of carbonaceous matter, is typical of upper Paleozoic sedimentation throughout North America. The core is 57 mm. (2¼ in.) in diameter. (Art. 141.)

is possible that this peculiar bedding was made in radiolarian debris that later was redissolved and redeposited to become chert, though this seems unlikely. There is also the possibility that the structure was formed by

[1] Spurr (1894: 43–47); Jaggar (1894: 199–201); Gilbert (1899: 135–140); Woodworth (1901: 281–283); Grabau (1907: 296); Sorby (1908); Bailey (1930: 77–92); Vogt (1930: 68–73); Twenhofel (1932: 618–623); Allison (1933: 125–144); Merritt (1934: 333–374); Thompson (1937: 723–751); McKee (1938a: 77–83; 1939: 64–81; 1940: 811–824; 1945a: 38–51); Reiche (1938: 905–932).

penecontemporaneous deformation. In any event the structure does not seem to be one that can be used for top and bottom determination. McKee (1938: 81) recently described and illustrated a similar structure from Colorado River flood deposits of the Grand Canyon (Fig. 221).

All these structures, though resembling cross-lamination, were formed in entirely different ways and cannot be used in the same way as cross-lamination for top and bottom determination.

Although true cross-lamination is limited to detrital sedimentary rocks, it is possible that a thick formation of mudstone composed of successively overlapping mudflows might have a crude type of lamination or bedding transverse to the true stratification.

Courtesy of E. D. McKee

Fig. 221.—Ripple laminae in a recent deposit along the Colorado River showing lee-side concentration of sediment and consequent development of a type of false cross-lamination. Compare with Fig. 52B. (Arts. 68, 142.) (*After McKee*, 1938, *Jour. Sedimentary Petrology*, **8**: 81, *Figs*. 4c, 4d.)

Fuller (1931a: 282–286) and Hoffman (1933: 189) have reported an unusual type of "cross-bedding" in flow breccias produced when basic lavas flowed into water (Art. 231).

143. Imbricate Structure within Conglomerates.—Imbricate arrangement of tabular pebbles is a common structure in river-laid rubble and gravel deposits, both ancient (Fig. 222) and modern, and may also occur, though probably rarely, in beach deposits. In this structure made by platy fragments and pebbles that are considerably longer and broader than thick, the long axis of the pebble dips upstream since in that position the fragment offers least resistance to the current. Hence in stream gravels the pebbles are shingled upstream, whereas in beach deposits they are imbricated seaward and down the slope of the deposit [Barrell (1916: 357); Lahee (1931: 93–94); Twenhofel (1932: 210)].

Becker (1893: 53–54) fully explained the formation of imbrication as follows:

If a flattened pebble is dropped into a running stream, the water will exert a pressure upon the stone until its inertia is overcome, and during this time the pebble will tend to swing across the current so as to present its greatest area to the pressure. As soon as the resistance due to its inertia is overcome, the pebble will sink through the water as if the fluid were at rest till its edge touches the bottom, and it will then tip down stream till it meets support. . . . Many pebbles thus deposited will, with few exceptions, be inclined down stream [*i.e., they will dip upstream*][1] and will rest against one another, like overlapping tiles.

This relation explains the fact that both in modern streams and in the ancient river channels containing . . . gravels, many of which have been tilted since their deposition, the pebbles . . . "shingle up stream," or . . . "imbricate" toward the source. . . .

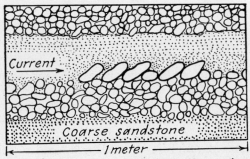

Fig. 222.—Imbricate structure in conglomerates. Diagram showing prominent imbrication of platy fragments along the top of a gravel layer in Pennsylvanian Wamsutta clastics near Attleboro, eastern Massachusetts. It is to be noted that the bases of the gravel layers are relatively even because the first pebbles to be rolled into place traveled over the smooth surface made by the underlying sand. Flat pebbles like those showing the conspicuous imbrication can be rolled along the bottom easily if turned so as to behave as upright disks in the current. When they fall over, they are likely to assume an imbricate relationship: for this is the most stable under conditions of strong bottom currents. Compare with Fig. 223. (Art. 143.)

On beaches pebbles are sometimes imbricated for a few feet in one or another direction and sometimes lie nearly flat. The constant reversal of the currents due to breaking and retreating waves prevents any extensive methodical arrangement, and this fact is of assistance in discriminating marine gravels from river deposits.

Imbricate structure in conglomerates has been reported from Pre-Cambrian rocks in Canada [Pettijohn (1930: 586–573) and Grout (1932: 278)], from Cambrian beds of the Rocky Mountains, from Devonian sandstone of England [Barrell (1916: 357, 371)], and from Tertiary deposits in British Columbia [Johnston (1922: 387–390)], to cite a few typical examples. Many other examples could undoubtedly be found if geologic literature were examined thoroughly.

The importance of imbricate structure as an indication of bedding is

[1] Becker undoubtedly meant that the pebbles would dip upstream when they came to rest.

discussed in Art. 7. It may also have a use in structural work, as pointed out by Pettijohn (1930: 571), who found that

. . . strike readings obtained from the arkosite and boulder beds differed from readings obtained from the common orientation of the elongate pebbles, particularly the flat pebbles of green schist, within the conglomerate beds. A careful study proved this to be due to an overlapping arrangement of the pebbles at the time of the deposition of the fragments. The line of common orientation clearly

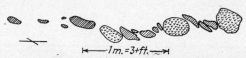

FIG. 223.—Imbricate arrangement of pebbles in a Pre-Cambrian conglomerate. The sketch shows the arrangement of particles in a single pebble band. The crosslined pebbles are composed of greenstone and green schist; the others are granite. The mapping of imbricate pebbles is illustrated in Fig. 224. (Art. 143.) (*Modified after Pettijohn, 1930, Jour. Geology,* **38**: *572, Fig. 4.*)

makes an angle with the top and bottom of the boulder bed as determined by the contact with the arkosite bands above and below. This angle varies, in many cases attaining from 35° to 40°. The relations between the two were represented on the structure maps by a symbol devised for the purpose: ⤙. The long line represents the true strike; the short line represents the apparent or false strike. This relationship proved useful in determining the major geologic structures, for it is clear that if the positions of the top and bottom were reversed by folding,

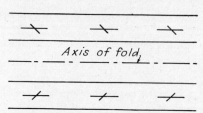

FIG. 224.—Diagram showing two outcropping bands of the same conglomerate, one on each limb of an isoclinal fold, with imbricate structure of the pebbles plotted on each. Compare this sketch with Fig. 223. Imbricate arrangement of pebbles must be used with caution in structural field work, as pointed out by Pettijohn (1930: 568–573). It can be used in determining major structural features but is not reliable for top and bottom determination. (Art. 143.) (*Modified after Pettijohn,* 1930, *Jour. Geology,* **38**: *571, Fig. 3.*)

the strike of the pebbles must show a different relation to the strike of the beds, even if the folding were isoclinal and the limbs remain parallel. . . .

(See Figs. 223, 224.)

It should be pointed out that the imbricate arrangement just described can be used to determine repetition of beds in folding and the trend of the folds but cannot be used to determine the top or bottom of the bed in which it occurs. This must be established by other criteria.

There are also other limitations to the use of pebble imbrication. The direction of imbrication must be constant to prove that the containing bed has structural unity; the layer showing the imbrication must be cut in such a way that the inclined pebbles are viewed from the side[1];

[1] Pettijohn (1930: 572) states in this connection:

It is to be noted . . . that no imbricate structure would be seen on the planed edges of vertical beds if the currents producing such structures had flowed in a direction approxi-

and there must be clear evidence that the alignment was produced by stream deposition rather than by dynamic pressure.

144. Shale Chips Overlying Sandstone.—If a sand bottom covered by a thin layer of silt and clay is exposed to air, the mud dries and shrinkage cracks (mud cracks; "sun cracks") develop. If the layer is relatively thin (a few centimeters), the polygonal plates outlined by the cracks usually curl up somewhat at the edges so that they are concave upward, pulling away from the underlying sand as desiccation proceeds. There are also conditions under which the plates may become arched, hence convex upward, so that the concavity or convexity of the plates cannot

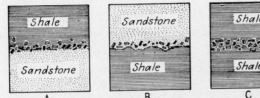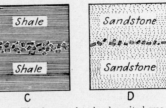

Fig. 225.—Sharpstone layers in shales and sandstones. *A.* The first mud to be deposited was broken up shortly after consolidation, by mud cracking or storm waves, and the fragments were incorporated in the base of the shale. If the fragments lay at the top of the shale, their relation would be like that in *B.* *B.* The upper few laminae of the shale were ripped up and fragmented and the fragments incorporated in the base of the sandstone. *C.* A thin shale sharpstone layer in the midst of shale. Minute details of bedding around the fragments and the relations of the fragments to the contiguous shale laminae *may* indicate which is the top or bottom; on the other hand, top and bottom determination may be impossible. *C.* A shale sharpstone layer in the midst of sandstone formed from the fragmentation of an original thin layer of consolidated mud. Unless the shale fragments are so oriented as to suggest original ripple marks in the sand, or mud cracking in the mud, they probably will prove useless for top and bottom determination. Compare with Figs. 165, 166. (Art. 144.)

be relied upon to determine the top of a bed containing them (see Art. 120).

Induration may be intense enough to give the dried mud considerable coherent strength, so that the original plates may be fragmented and the fragments ultimately incorporated in the base of the next deposit as a fine sharpstone conglomerate. Such a deposit would be abruptly separated from the underlying sand but would form an integral part of the bed containing it (Figs. 165, 166). Wind or water might also move these fragments, eroding them during transport, so that when finally buried (perhaps some distance from their source) they would all be rounded to a greater or lesser extent [see Cox and Dake (1916: 37–50); Lahee (1931: 52 –53); Twenhofel (1932: 685–692)]. (Fig. 225.)

A thin sharpstone conglomerate such as that just described would not be found at the top of a shale bed, for the plates would probably not separate from the mud bottom. If they did, they would be incorporated

mately normal to the present fold. The use of this structure in mapping . . . then, depends on the fact that the currents ran obliquely across the present structures or even parallel to the fold axes.

in the base of the overlying bed. If the incoming sediment were sand, the shale chips would mark the base of the sandstone. On the other hand, if the incoming sediment were mud, the plates might or might not be conspicuous, but in any case they would not have top and bottom significance if they lay within a bed of shale rather than near the top or bottom. Plates not buried by some type of sediment immediately after submergence would quickly lose their identity by slaking to mud (Fig. 225).

145. Features Produced by Penecontemporaneous Deformation.[1]— Many sandstones, shales, and limestones contain anomalous structural features—faults, contorted layers, and brecciated beds. From their internal structure and external relations, these fall into two types: (1) those formed prior to consolidation and induration of the sedimentary

---

[1] Many examples of penecontemporaneously deformed bodies and layers of sedimentary material have been described and illustrated in geologic literature. In most of them the areas over which particular structures can be studied are restricted, so that the full development of the feature and the shape and size of the deformed mass cannot be determined. Only a few of the more recent articles dealing with these structures are listed here; excellent bibliographies are given in some of the references cited.

BAILEY, E. B., L. W. COLLET, and R. M. FIELD, 1928, Paleozoic submarine landslips near Quebec City, *Jour. Geology*, **36**: 577–614; BAILEY, E. B., and J. WEIR, 1933, Submarine faulting in Kimmeridgian time: East Sutherland, *Royal Soc. Edinburgh Trans.*, **57**(2): 429–467; CARRUTHERS, R. G., 1939, On northern glacial drifts: some peculiarities and their significance, *Geol. Soc. London Quart. Jour.*, **95**: 299–333; EARP, J. R., 1938, The higher Silurian rocks of the Kerry district, Montgomeryshire, *ibid.*, **94**: 125–160; FAIRBRIDGE, R. W., 1946, Submarine slumping and location of oil bodies, *Bull. Am. Assoc. Petroleum Geologists*, **30**: 84–92; HADDING, A., 1931, On subaqueous slides, *Lunds Geol. Min. Inst.*, Medd. No. **47**: 377–393 [*Geol. fören. Stockholm Förh.*, **53**(4), No. 387: 377–393]; HENDERSON, S. M. K., 1935, Ordovician submarine disturbances in the Girvan district, *Roy. Soc. Edinburgh Trans.*, **58**(2): 487–509; JONES, O. T., 1940, The geology of the Colwyn Bay district: a study of submarine slumping during the Salopian Period, *Geol. Soc. London Quart. Jour.*, **95**: 335–382; KENT, P. E., 1945, Contemporaneous disturbance in lacustrine beds in Kenya, *Geol. Mag.*, **82**: 130–135; LEITH, C. K., 1923, "Structural Geology," pp. 223–233, Henry Holt and Company, Inc., New York; LIPPERT, H., 1938, Gleit-Faltung in subaquatischen und subaerischen Gestein, *Senckenbergiana*, **19**: 355–374; MILLER, W. J., 1922, Intraformational corrugated rocks, *Jour. Geology*, **30**: 587–610; NEVIN, N. M., 1942, "Principles of Structural Geology," pp. 186–204, John Wiley & Sons, Inc., New York; REIS, O. M., 1910, Beobachtung ueber Schichtenfolge, *Geog. Jahresber. Muenchen*, **22**: 1–285; RETTGER, R. E., 1935, Experiments on soft-rock deformation, *Bull. Am. Assoc. Petroleum Geologists*, **19**: 271–292; RICE, R. C., 1939, Contorted bedding in the Trias of N.W. Wirral, *Liverpool Geol. Soc. Proc.*, **17** (iv): 361–370; TWENHOFEL, W. H., *et al.*, 1932, Treatise on Sedimentation, pp. 739–752, The Williams & Wilkins Company, Baltimore (see also table of textbooks, Chap. I, pp. 22–23, and Index to References, Chap. VIII).

material (*i.e.*, by penecontemporaneous deformation); (2) those formed after lithification, hence of secondary origin.

It is of the greatest importance that these two types of structural feature be recognized in the field to avoid errors caused by confusing one with the other. Leith (1923: 228–233), Rettger (1935: 291), Lamont (1938), Lahee (1941: 188–194), and Nevin (1942: 186–189), among others, have discussed the characteristics useful in differentiating the two types and have pointed out some of the difficulties involved. Features of the first type are considered here; those of the second are discussed in Arts. 266 to 278.

146. Time and Mechanics of Formation.—Structural features ascribed to penecontemporaneous deformation show by their internal structure and peripheral relations that they could have been formed only by dislocation of loose, incoherent sands and silts, by flowage and folding of hydroplastic[1] sediments, or by fragmentation of partly consolidated sediments.[2] It is because the disturbances which produced these features took place during or shortly after deposition of the sediments involved that the features are here classified as *penecontemporaneous deformation*.

Penecontemporaneous faulting is a widespread phenomenon in loose sands and silts and is likewise commonly preserved in sedimentary rocks. Since the dislocation dies out downward and since the disturbed blocks are usually truncated above by an erosion plane separating the mass from the overlying horizontal layer, it is not difficult to determine the top or bottom of the disturbed formation (Figs. 195, 226, 227).

Flowage and intense folding mark the early part of the deformation when the sediments are hydroplastic—soft and so full of water that they fail almost entirely as a viscous fluid or plastic solid. Fracturing and faulting follow after the materials have been greatly compacted and much of the water has been expelled and when, as a consequence, the materials fail intergranularly by shear. The earlier type of failure commonly gives way to the later in the same rock, showing that deformation was essentially continuous.

Intraformational corrugation may run the complete gamut from only faint wrinkling to intense overfolding and overthrusting, all within a

[1] The term hydroplastic will again be employed, as defined in the footnote on p. 152 and used in Arts. 99 to 103—*i.e.*, for those clastic sediments (sands, silts, clays, and muds of all sorts) made plastic or highly viscous by their interstitial water.

[2] Leith (1923: 227) points out that during experimental deformation of soft sediments, such as that carried out by Rettger (1935: 271–295), " . . . there is more or less interpenetration of the materials of the different layers,—suggesting a criterion for the identification of such structures in the field."

single contorted layer. In such deformation the intensity of folding reflects the extent of movement and physical state of the sediment involved. Hydroplastic muds and muddy sands can flow readily; consequently they can be amazingly contorted. On the other hand, viscous muds and sands although flowing readily do not take on such intense plication,[1] whereas stiff muds tend to resist intricate folding and sands are likely to shear. Therefore, in a sliding mass, starting its movement as a semiliquid substance, loss of water and attendant increase of viscosity stiffen the sediment, giving it increased strength to resist movement, and the mass as a consequence builds up rigidity as it slides until it comes finally to rest as a solid and rigid mass even though intricately folded and faulted.

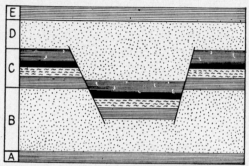

Fig. 226.—Diagram illustrating penecontemporaneous faulting of a coal sequence *C*. The faulting did not involve shale *A* and took place before the deposition of shale *E*. Both sandstones *B* by and *D* were involved. Such faulting could be the result of near-by channel cutting in sandstone *B*, by which support of the coal sequence was locally removed, causing a block of the sediments to slide downward and laterally. (Arts. 146, 148, 152.)

Since penecontemporaneous deformation, as considered here, is essentially a surface phenomenon affecting sediments at or immediately below the land surface or subaqueous bottom, it is highly probable that the structures produced will be eroded to some extent before burial. As a consequence, such eroded features die out downward, passing into normally stratified undisturbed beds, and are truncated and buried by similar overlying strata (Fig. 229).

Except for large landslides, subaqueous slides, and similar mass movements, it is probable that most cases of penecontemporaneous deforma-

───────

[1] Smith (1916: 146–156) reported a peculiar structure in sandstones that is confined to distinct layers. It consists of spheroidal and ellipsoidal or pillowlike masses of shale and shaly sandstone in the midst of sandstone layers. The observer believed that they " . . . are primarily due to internal readjustments of freshly and unevenly deposited sediments, acting mainly under gravitation. These readjustments may be aided, or started, by the action of strong currents" (p. 154). The structure as described and illustrated seems to be too much "balled up" to be of any use for top and bottom determination.

tion on the scale here considered do not affect sediments to depths exceeding a few meters. Movements of surficial materials in subaerial environments have been discussed thoroughly in a work by Sharpe (1938: 1–137), but no similar discussion of subaqueous environments seems to have been published.[1]

147. NATURE, OCCURRENCE, AND USE OF FEATURES.—Penecontemporaneously deformed bodies of sedimentary materials vary greatly in

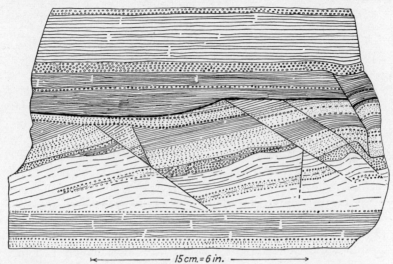

↦——————— *15cm.= 6 in.* ————————→

Fig. 227.—Penecontemporaneous faulting in sands and silts composing the Carboniferous Cambridge formation of eastern Massachusetts. The heavy horizontal line indicates an erosional unconformity of major importance so far as the sequence shown in the sketch is concerned. Other less important unconformities are also present, indicating that the faulting took place at several different times. It should be noted that there is extensive transection of laminae and layers along one border of the faulted zone—*i.e.*, along the top—whereas faulting dies out toward the other border, or downward. The slight arching of the shale laminae in the left-hand block may represent original depositional structure to a large extent. (Arts. 146, 148, 152.)

size, shape, internal structure, and external relations. They range from microscopic faults, folds, and brecciated zones to disturbed and contorted masses several meters in thickness and hundreds of square meters in area. In shape they are tabular, planoellipsoidal, irregularly domal, ridgelike, or lobate. Internally they are contorted or composed of laminar fragments with random orientation. In their typical development they lie in the midst of or alternate with undisturbed sediments. They are much

---

[1] Features produced by penecontemporaneous deformation on subaqueous bottoms are especially typical of shallow-water deposits, both fresh-water and marine, but there seems no important reason why similar features might not, under certain conditions, be produced at great oceanic depths (*e.g.*, by seaquakes and tsunamis). For experimental work on soft-rock deformation, see Rettger (1935: 271–292), Heim (1908: 136–157), Hahn (1913: 1–41), Lippert (1938: 355–374), Jones (1940: 335–382, and Fairbridge (1946: 90).

more common and widespread than is generally appreciated and are present in all common sedimentary rocks—conglomerates, sandstones, shales, limestones, coals, salinastones, and silicastones.

Features in conglomerates are likely to be the result of faulting. Both faulted and folded structures are represented in sandstones; the former indicate that the sand failed by shear, whereas the latter show that the sand contained so much water at the time of deformation that it flowed. The flow casts described in Art. 102 are thought to have formed in the latter fashion. Shear took place in the flow casts only near the end of deformation when the sand, having lost much of its water through closer packing, failed intergranularly. The features in siltstones, claystones, and limestones are likely to be greatly contorted layers, irregular planoconvex masses, and brecciated layers or irregular bodies (intraformational sharpstone conglomerates). This type of structure is common in recent and ancient stream and shallow-water deposits [Knight (1929); McKee (1938a: 81–83)], in Pleistocene and more ancient varved shales [Lahee (1914: 786–790); Sayles (1919); Tarr (1935: 1500–1501); Thiesmeyer (1939, Plate 17); Pettijohn (1943: 953–954)], and in clastic beds of almost every age widespread over the earth. Coal beds and associated layers exhibit certain structural features, both faulted and folded, that appear to be essentially contemporaneous with deposition (Fig. 39). Some of these are described and illustrated by Stutzer and Noé (1940: 323–426). Anhydrite salinastones are commonly characterized by thin, localized, intensely plicated layers, which unfortunately seem to have no use for determining top and bottom (Fig. 228), and the same kind of rock in salt domes is often amazingly contorted from flowage. Cherty bands in a few cases show internal corrugations and folds that appear to be original structures apparently formed before the gelatinous sediment hardened perceptibly. If the chert was hard, it fragmented and a brecciated chert layer was then formed. Such a brecciated rock was reported by Fenneman, who, in discussing a paper on intraformational corrugation by Clarke (1914: 37), stated: "A thick bed of cherty limestone in the St. Louis formation is brecciated, though included between undeformed beds. Here the chert is so broken as to show sharp corners almost splinters, as though the chert was formed before the deformation of the bed."

148. CLASSIFICATION OF FEATURES.—Three general categories of penecontemporaneous structural features may be recognized if position in the affected layer is used as a basis of classification (Fig. 229).

1. Those developed on or just below the *top* surface and not affecting the overlying stratum. Such features usually are reliable indicators of the top side of a bed (Fig. 229A).

2. Those lying within a single stratum or affecting a successsion of laminae in a general zone. These internal structures typically die out downward into undisturbed rock and have their plication and faults truncated on the upper side by an undisturbed layer (Figs. 229B, 232). This type of structure provides a reliable top and bottom criterion. However, the entire disturbed mass may be discordant with the surrounding undisturbed strata; hence care must be exercised in using such bodies for top and bottom determination (Fig. 236).

3. Those limited to the *undersurface* of a layer and affecting the underlying stratum (Figs. 116, 117, 229C). These are usually composed of

Fig. 228.—Localized laminar corrugation in a salinastone specimen about 30 cm. (12 in) long. Corrugations of this kind are characteristic of rocks composed of anhydrite and gypsum and usually are ascribed to forces produced by recrystallization. It should be noted that the individual zones of corrugation die out laterally and when viewed in cross section are arranged *en échelon* rather than in vertical succession. Folds of this sort cannot be used to determine tops and bottoms of beds. (Arts. 147, 152. (*Specimen in Mineralogical Museum of Harvard University.*)

sand and show by their internal structure, configuration, and relations to the underlying rock—always mudstone or shale—that they formed from a layer of water-filled sand which adjusted itself to the corrugations produced by flowage in the differentially loaded underlying hydroplastic mud. Careful study of this type of contemporaneously formed structure usually reveals characteristics that can be relied upon for top and bottom determination (Arts. 99, 102).

The commonest structural features of the three foregoing categories may be classified under the following types for purposes of description and illustration:

1. Linear surface folds and fault scarps obviously formed before the overlying undisturbed bed was deposited (Art. 150; Figs. 229A, 230)
2. Faulted layers in which the faulting dies out downward and the adjacent blocks are transected above by an erosion plane overlain by an undisturbed stratum (Art. 151; Figs. 226, 227)

3. Contorted and brecciated layers of essentially uniform thickness between parallel undisturbed beds (Art. 152)

4. Contorted and brecciated, planoconvex or irregular masses of variable thickness and local extent lying between and surrounded by undisturbed beds (Art. 153; Figs. 229A, 236)

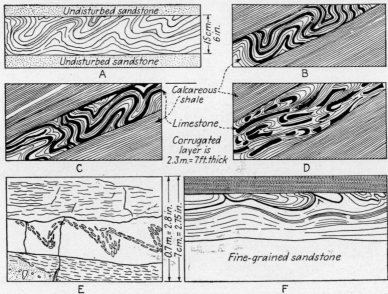

FIG. 229.—Comparative diagrams showing examples of intraformational corrugation produced by penecontemporaneous deformation. *A.* Corrugated shale-sandstone bed between undisturbed sandstone layers in the rocks directly overlying the Squantum tillite on Squantum Head, eastern Massachusetts. The folds were truncated before the overlying sand was deposited. Downward the folds die out without involving the underlying sandstone. *B–D.* Diagrams showing nature of intraformational corrugation in three different parts of a 7-ft. (2.3-m.) bed of alternating limestone and shale laminae in a Devonian formation at Cape Gaspé, Quebec. It is possible that this deformed bed was produced by postdepositional faulting rather than by penecontemporaneous sliding. *E.* Diagram showing a folded layer of Ordovician limestone pebbles embedded in fine-grained sandstone. The limestone beds above and below the folded layer are undisturbed. The pebbles are algal biscuits that originally lay flat on the bottom in the midst of calcareous mud. They were thrown into the folds shown when the enclosing mud slid downslope [see Brown (1913: 241–244)]. *F.* Corrugated layer of black-streaked siltstone lying between undisturbed layers of sandstone. The folds are truncated above and die out downward before involving the sandstone. (Arts. 148, 152, 153.) (*A diagrammatic. B–D modified after Logan, 1863, "Geology of Canada," pp. 391–392, Fig. 425. E modified after Brown, 1913, Jour. Geology, **21**: 241–244, Fig. 4. F diagrammatic and based on a specimen in the Sedimentation Collection of Harvard University.*)

5. Landscape marble and similarly churned-up structure, thought by some investigators to have been formed penecontemporaneously by gases rising through somewhat viscous mud (Art. 154; Fig. 239)

6. Flow casts confined to the undersurface of layers and formed by sand sinking into soft plastic mud (Arts. 102, 156)

7. Structures in frozen ground—head, warp, trail and underplight, etc. (Art. 103; Fig. 120)

149. TOP-SURFACE AND INTERNAL FEATURES.—Under certain conditions, masses of subaerial and subaqueous sediments suddenly lose their stability and slide down slopes for some distance, becoming folded and faulted in the process.[1]   Such movements have been given many different names (creep, landslide, mudflow, slump, subaqueous gliding, solifluction, etc.) and have been recognized by many investigators.   Sharpe (1938: 1–137) has discussed in considerable detail how the mechanism operates and what features it produces on the present surface.   A host of others, both in North America and abroad, have described and illustrated examples now preserved in formations as old as Pre-Cambrian and as recent as yesteryear (see Chap. VIII, Bibliography).

Bodies of sediment disturbed by creep and subaerial landslide have little chance of burial and are not considered further here.   On the other hand, bodies that originated through subaqueous sliding are commonly preserved, and a careful study of their internal structure and external relations to the enclosing rocks usually reveals characteristic features which can be used to determine not only the top of the deformed mass but also the direction in which it slid.   It should be noted in passing that muddy sediments, sliding subaqueously on gently sloping bottoms, provide a possible mechanism for transporting large blocks considerable distances from sea cliffs, subaqueous fault scarps, etc. [see Moore (1934: 432 –453)].   Ancient mudflows[2] and sandflows are preserved in rocks as old as Pre-Cambrian and should be expected in certain kinds of sedimentary rocks—deltaic and alluvial fan deposits, among others—of all ages.

150. *Linear Top-surface Folds and Faults.*—Some sedimentary layers contain features on the top surface or affecting the upper few centimeters or meters which show, by their relations to the stratum directly overlying, that they were formed while the sediment was still soft and before the overlying layer was deposited.

Linear folds and tiny fault scarps of a few centimeters in height and several meters in length are common in the Silurian Kokomo limestone at certain places along the Wabash River below Peru, Ind.   These are disposed parallel to the strike of thinly laminated argillaceous and dolomitic limestone layers, which dip from 2 to 5° with what appears to be the original inclination (Fig. 230).

They are believed to have been formed as a result of slight down-dip

---

[1] If hydroplastic sediments lying on a slope of a few degrees are suddenly jarred, as they would be during an earthquake, the internal cohesion of some parts is reduced and masses of the sediment slide down the slope, usually only a short distance.   Partly inundated sediments soaked with water, as after prolonged or intense rainfall, may respond in similar manner.   There is high probability that subaqueous sediments on bottoms sloping more than 2 or 3° will undergo some slipping and sliding before or soon after burial.

[2] BLACKWELDER, E., 1938, Mudflow as a geologic agent in semiarid mountains, *Bull. Geol. Soc. Am.*, **39**: 465–484.

thrusting of a few of the upper laminae. The thrusting may have been induced by a shock such as an earthquake might produce, with deformation possibly localized along a preexisting fracture, shrinkage crack, or a similar line of weakness. The folds commonly exhibit overturning and overthrusting down the dip and appear to have formed so soon after deposition that the calcareous muds had undergone little consolidation. They were formed at the surface, as evidenced by the fact that covering laminae end against their flanks or arch gently over them. The folds themselves do not extend downward into the underlying laminae more

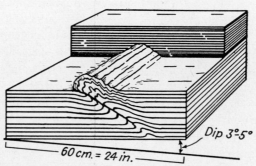

Fig. 230.—Small linear fold in the Silurian Kokomo limestone near Peru, Ind. The fold was formed while the laminated calcareous muds of the bottom were still soft enough to yield readily. It was later covered by the succeeding laminae, which abut against and pass over it without appreciable deformation. The down-dip thrusting may have been induced by an earthquake shock. Large masses of contorted and brecciated laminae, thought to represent slumped bottom materials, are present in the same formation at Kokomo, some 18 miles away [see Cumings and Shrock (1928: 118–120, *Fig.* 29)]. (Arts. 148, 150.)

than 6 or 7 cm., and the total width of the fold seldom exceeds 30 cm. (12 in.).

Linear ridges of this sort should furnish a reliable clue to the top surface of steeply folded layers and should be looked for in laminated shales and argillaceous limestones. Care should be taken, however, not to confuse them with secondary drag folds (Art. 268).

151. *Deformation by Glacial Overriding.*—Glaciers riding over till, soft alluvium, lacustrine clays, and similar sediments greatly disturb the surficial part of a deposit, producing intense folding and faulting in the material (Fig. 231).

Stutzer and Noé (1940: 375–379, 409–411) describe and illustrate numerous cases in which Pleistocene ice sheets in northern Germany greatly deformed the brown coal beds and associated strata which were near enough the surface to be disturbed by the weight or shove of the ice. Although there seem to be no reported cases of glacial disturbance of ancient coals in the geologic column, many glacial sediments of Pleistocene age or older appear to have undergone such deformation. For example,

Johnston (1915: 43, Plate 8) describes a case of deformation by glacial overriding near Ft. Frances, Ont., where a much contorted zone of sand directly underlies a till deposit, and the author has observed many contorted beds in both the Pleistocene clays of Wisconsin and Carboniferous Squantum tillite complex, which may be traced at least in part to the same cause (Fig. 231).

The Squantum tillite complex of Massachusetts, contains many highly disturbed beds of shale and sandstone that show effects of glacial overriding. Some of these represent disturbed sediments that were exposed to erosion long enough for many of the plications to be truncated,

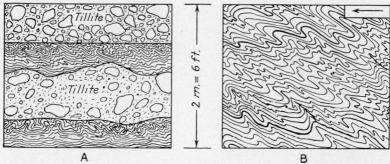

Fig. 231.—Deformation of glacial clays by overriding ice. *A*. Vertical beds of the Carboniferous Squantum tillite of eastern Massachusetts, showing two layers of highly contorted shale between layers of till. It is to be noted that deformation in the shale beds is most intense in the upper part and dies out downward. *B*. Highly folded Pleistocene varved clay as seen in the 2-m. (6-ft.) wall of a pit on the top of Bascom Hill on the campus of the University of Wisconsin at Madison, Wis. The ice moved from right to left (north to south). The folding of individual varves is much more intricate than can be shown on a diagram of this scale. (Art. 151.)

so that normally bedded strata or irregular beds of till now rest unconformably upon the old erosion surface. No difficulty arises in determining the top side of such a deformed zone. Many of the contorted layers, however, show no truncation or show it along both margins. These are shale and sandy shale layers, a few centimeters thick, that show an intricately contorted structure apparently formed by flowage of hydroplastic sandy mud that was unequally loaded. Slight differences in the weight of the overlying material, in this case bouldery till or glacial ice charged with debris, were sufficient to cause flowage of the easily deformed mud. The deformed masses themselves range in thickness from less than a centimeter to half a meter, and some show truncation of the plications along both upper and lower surfaces. Other contorted layers are intermixed along their margins with the contiguous sediments in such a manner that no sharp separation between contraposed materials is apparent. Lacking the characteristic top truncation, these contorted layers cannot be relied upon for top and bottom determination.

A provocative paper by Carruthers (1939: 299–333) on the mechanics of deposition in a melting glacier suggests an alternate method by which certain of the foregoing structures might have been produced and deserves serious consideration.

152. *Faulted and Contorted Layers.*—Many sandstone, shale, and limestone formations and many more sequences of sands, muds, and cal-

Fig. 232.—Penecontemporaneous deformation in clastics associated with the Carboniferous Squantum tillite of eastern Massachusetts. The specimen, taken from vertically dipping strata on Squantum Head, shows a 50-mm. (2-in.) layer of deformed sandy shale between undisturbed sandy layers. The deformation, which took place while the sediments were soft, did not affect the lowest part of the layer. The tops of the folds were eroded off before sand deposition was resumed. The truncated side of the disturbed layer is the top. (Arts. 148, 152.)

careous sediments contain thin, faulted, and contorted layers, which are unusually conspicuous because they lie between essentially parallel and undisturbed layers. As a rule such disturbed beds do not differ greatly in lithology from the contiguous strata.

The general nature and practical use of penecontemporaneous faulting is discussed in Art. 146; hence it is sufficient here merely to note that if the faulting dies out in one direction across the beds and is cut by an unconformity in the opposite direction, it provides a reliable top and bottom criterion (Figs. 226, 227). It is the author's conclusion that features caused by penecontemporaneous faulting do not provide so reliable a top and bottom criterion as certain of the contorted layers next to be discussed.

Four general types of contorted layers, not all of penecontemporaneous origin, are now widely recognized and may be characterized briefly as follows:

1. Thin layers showing truncation of the internal plications and faults along the top side and a gradual downward decrease in the intensity of disturbance to basal undisturbed beds (Fig. 229B). This type is clearly penecontemporaneous in origin and is the result of deformation that took place before the overlying stratum was deposited. Layers of this type are reliable for top and bottom determination and are discussed more fully in a later paragraph.

2. Thin, intensely plicated and faulted layers that are bounded both above and below by slip planes and are characterized by unoriented structural features that could have been formed only by deformation of soft sediments caught between oppositely moving horizontal strata. Layers of this kind, which have no reliable top and bottom significance, are, like type 1, also penecontemporaneous in origin, but they were deformed at a somewhat later time and after some superincumbent strata had been deposited on the layer that is now contorted (Fig. 229F).

3. Localized contortions, involving only a few laminations and dying out laterally in every direction from the area of most intense deformation, are characteristic of many laminated salinastones (Fig. 228). They are generally explained as the result of laterally directed forces caused by recrystallization. Such contorted zones have no top and bottom significance.

4. In certain sedimentary rocks that have been folded or faulted, thin contorted beds have been formed from relatively incompetent materials caught between oppositely moving beds. The folds that were formed are secondary in origin, of the drag-fold type, and have a genetic relation with regional structure. They were formed in rock and possess features that are lacking in the folds and faults of type 2. Their use as a top and bottom criterion is discussed in Arts. 267 to 273.

The most common and widespread penecontemporaneously contorted layers are those of varved clays, silts, shales, and slates. These are found in formations of all ages from Pre-Cambrian to Pleistocene and are reliable top and bottom criteria if the structural details are clear and the containing sediment or rock is well exposed. In typical development the contorted layers alternate with parallel undisturbed layers of similar material. Within the disturbed bed the contorted laminae show greatest deformation toward the top, where they are truncated, and die out downward into an undisturbed lamina (Figs. 229*C*, 232). This difference in structure at the top and base makes it possible to determine at once which is the top side of the bed and which the base.

Examples of the foregoing contorted beds are common and widespread not only in varved sediments and sedimentary rocks of glacial origin from Pre-Cambrian to Pleistocene but also in ancient formations of other origins. A few examples of both types are worth brief mention to give fuller information on their general characteristics.

Fig. 233.—Penecontemporaneous deformation and incomplete ripple marks in a sandstone-shale sequence directly overlying the Squantum tillite on Squantum Head, Massachusetts. The division in each scale is 10 cm. (4 in.). Layers 1, 2, and 3 contain incomplete ripple ridges; bed 4 contains a prominent layer of sand with a sharply defined, smooth base and an uneven top. At one place, sand and overlying silty clay seemingly were interfolded while both were soft. Bed 5 is distinguished by conspicuous folds that die out downward but are truncated on top by an almost plane surface. The once-continuous laminae of sand appear to have been severed in some instances during the deformation. Deformation obviously took place before deposition of bed 6, which has essentially the same stratigraphy as that in the upper part of 5. In this section, the strata of which are nearly vertical, both incomplete ripples and truncated penecontemporaneous folds provide reliable top and bottom criteria. (Arts. 70, 79, 152.)

Six or eight contorted layers, ranging in thickness from 7 to 30 cm., interrupt the orderly succession of varved layers directly overlying the Carboniferous Squantum tillite on Squantum Head in Massachusetts (Figs. 232, 233). Thiesmeyer (1939, Plate 17) has illustrated similarly deformed varved layers from the Loudon formation (late Pre-Cambrian or early Cambrian) of Virginia, Pettijohn (1943: 953–954) found deformed layers in Pre-Cambrian varved sedimentary rocks at several places in Canada, and the author has seen similar beds in the rocks at Kirkland Lake, Ont.; Lahee (1914: 786–790) and Sayles (1919; 1929), in their detailed studies of the Carboniferous Cambridge slate (closely associated with the Squantum tillite mentioned earlier), describe and illustrate deformed layers in that seasonally banded formation; and a host of writers have discussed the widespread occurrence of contorted beds in Pleistocene lacustrine clay deposits the world over. The deformation of these layers has commonly been ascribed to floating icebergs or lake ice, which, in running aground, thrust against and plowed up the soft hydro-plastic muds [Salisbury and Atwood (1897: 143, Fig. 6); Lahee (1914: 789); Sayles (1914: 156); Tarr (1935: 1500–1501)].   In view of the fact that the same type of contorted bed appears repeatedly in a particular section, each layer having about the same thickness, it seems that some explanation other than that just given should be sought.   Shaler (1888: 419) long ago suggested that an earthquake shock might disturb the upper part of the soft bottom deposits in a sea or lake, and such an explanation seems worthy of serious consideration.   There must have been myriads of miniature earthquakes during the periods of glacial advance, when the ice cracked upon surmounting prominences or sheared for other reasons, and the vibrations transmitted through the surficial and subaqueous sediments might well have caused the less stable upper part of a deposit to be deformed by folding or faulting, particularly if the sediments lay on a 2 or 3° slope.   Subsequent wave action would erode the tops of the plications and miniature horsts so that the sediment deposited imme-diately after the shock formed a layer on the surface of truncation. Undoubtedly other explanations are possible for some of the contorted layers, for they differ in their structure and relations from the typical layer that we are here considering.   Miller (1922: 597), for example, rejects the suggestion that the corrugations were caused by grounded icebergs or bottom erosion[1] and ascribes them to differential movement between beds in the mass, aided by gravity and possibly also by sub-aqueous slipping.   This explanation seems plausible for the contorted layer Salisbury and Atwood (1897: 143, Fig. 6) described and illustrated, for their photograph shows definite movement between horizontal layers with little displacement along the boundaries of the contorted layer.

Intraformational corrugation was long ago reported in the folded Devonian limestones at Cape Gaspé, Quebec, by Logan (1863: 391–392), who described a 2.5-m. bed to be

. . . made up of several thin layers of limestone and limestone shale, and present-ing a singularly wrinkled structure, from which the beds above and below are free. It would appear as if the layers, after their deposit, had been contorted by lateral pressure, the underlying stratum remaining undisturbed, and had been worn smooth, before the deposition of the next bed.   Where the inverted arches of the flexures occur, some of the lower layers are wanting; as if the corrugated bed had been worn on the under as well as the upper side.   The corrugations are precisely

---

[1] Kindle (1917*b*; 323–334) suggests that certain contorted sediments in Nova Scotia and southern Ontario were deformed as a result of channel cutting.   Where the cutting of a channel relieved the lateral pressure on a bed, the weight of the over-load forced the soft muds to flow laterally toward the channel.

in the direction of the dip and the peculiarity is not confined to a small part of the deposit. . . .

Clarke,[1] through personal communication with Miller (1922: 591–592), expressed approval of Logan's explanation and also commented on the corrugations before a meeting of the Geological Society of America in 1913 [Clarke (1914: 37)]. Miller (1922: 590–592), however, disagreed with Logan and Clarke and proposed that the corrugation had been produced *after* the sediments were buried by "differential movement within the mass" induced by local thrust faulting. He reached the same conclusion for the well-known contorted beds in the Trenton limestone at Trenton Falls, New York. At this locality two highly corrugated layers of argillaceous limestone, 1.5 m. (5 ft.) and 3.2 m. (10 ft.) thick, respectively, lie between undisturbed parallel limestone layers in a sequence that is near a thrust fault (Fig. 382). Many investigators have written about the Trenton Falls occurrence, and it has come to be a sort of type locality for intraformational corrugation. For many years the explanation offered by Hahn (1913: 1–41) was widely accepted. He ascribed the deformation to *subaqueous gliding*—a movement of soft hydroplastic sediment down a slightly inclined subaqueous slope—during which the laminae at and near the surface of the mass were folded and faulted. The deformed mass was then eroded to a nearly plane surface before the overlying stratum was deposited. Hahn's explanation presupposes that the sediment was at the subaqueous surface when it was deformed and that the deformation, therefore, was penecontemporaneous. Miller (1908: 428–433; 1915: 135–143; 1922: 587–590), on the other hand, contended that the corrugation was produced by slight tectonic differential slipping within the mass as a whole during the regional faulting. His explanation requires that the deformation was much later than deposition. He cites an analogous case of intraformational corrugation associated with

---

[1] Clarke [Miller (1922: 591–592)] described the Gaspé occurrence vividly in the following communication to Miller:

Crinkled strata lying between strata which show no evidence of dislocation are not of infrequent observation but, in most of the recorded instances, the crinkled layer is of softer stuff (that is, a highly aluminous mud rock) than the rigid beds above and below. The brilliant exhibition of this phenomenon on the cliffs of Cape Gaspé, first sketched by Sir William Logan, is not of this character. Here the middle deformed beds are of thin limestone leaves like those which bound them. They are crumpled into sharp, much involved and overlapping curves in which the limestone plates are broken sharply across. It seems very doubtful if any other explanation can be brought forward for this exceptional occurrence than that generally adopted for those of the first named category; a sliding of soft sea bottom deposits on a sloping surface under gravity, helped forward perhaps, if on a large scale, by earthquake shock or some other jolt-like impulse. . . . It follows from the conception of these structures that the deformation was contemporaneous, and preceded the deposition of the overlying beds.

faulting in the Frank area of Alberta, and reproduces the figure by Brock (1904) of the local structure to support his contention (Fig. 382). Miller's explanation, expressed in the following statement, is essentially the conclusion Nason (1894: 465) had previously reached in trying to explain such structure in certain blue clays near Albany, N.Y.:[1] "In the opinion of the writer [Miller (1922: 590)], differential movement (not always as an accompaniment of thrust faulting) is involved in many, if not most, cases, of intraformational corrugations."

The Trenton Falls case has been described in some detail for the purpose of showing how competent observers can reach radically different interpretations of the same structure. More careful field work than that of the earlier observers should demonstrate whether the corrugation is penecontemporaneous or tectonic.

Some examples of intraformational corrugation are so clear as to occasion no controversy. As a case in point, Brown (1913: 241–243) described a folded gravel layer in which the upper crests of the folds were truncated before the disturbed layer was buried; hence no doubt exists regarding contemporaneity of the folding (Fig. 229E). Miller (1922: 602–603) described and illustrated an unusual type of intraformational corrugation called to his attention by D. W. Johnson. Layers of corrugated sandstone are intercalated with the foreset beds of a cross-laminated sandstone and were formed contemporaneously with the forward advance of the foresets. Rice (1939: 361–371) recently described somewhat similar deformation in a Triassic sandstone of Cheshire, which shows overfolding and buckling of the deposition planes or foresets of current bedding. Not so obvious, however, is the corrugated bedding that interrupts the rhythmic lamination of the Green River oil shale of Wyoming; this lamination Bradley (1929a: 87–110) interpreted as seasonal banding or varving. Bradley (1931: 26, 28) ascribed the corrugation to: "the differential movements and readjustments within and between beds after burial and during compaction of the sediments . . . " and concluded (page 27) that " . . . it seems likely that contorted bedding due to differential stresses during compaction would be most commonly localized in beds that contained an abundance of organic matter, a relatively large proportion of micaceous clay minerals, and an unusually fine grained mineral aggregate." At an earlier date David White, in discussing a paper presented to the Washington Academy of Science by Winchester (1919: 295), had suggested that the Green River corrugations were developed in the original organic muds as a result of " . . . differ-

---

[1] Nason (1894: 465) concluded that an intraformational corrugated layer in blue clay near Albany, N.Y., was caused by one bed sliding over another down a slope too steep for the clay mass to maintain its equilibrium.

ential movements between somewhat more competent beds above and below" [Bradley (1931: 28)]. However, as noted above, this explanation was not acceptable to Bradley.

Several important papers on intraformational corrugation have been published in recent years. These deserve brief mention here to emphasize the need for a better understanding of penecontemporaneous deformation involving sedimentary materials.

From the coal-bearing sequences of Germany, Kukuk (1920: 805–810; 1924: 1167–1175; 1936: 1021–1029) and his associates have described and illustrated many features ascribed to penecontemporaneous origin [Stutzer and Noé (1940)]. Earp (1938: 125–160) cited an excellent example (Fig. 234) in the Silurian clastics of Wales and concluded that the

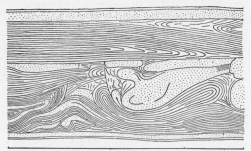

7 feet

FIG. 234.—Penecontemporaneous deformation of soft muds and water-filled sands. The diagram shows a contorted zone of shale and coarse sandstone between undisturbed layers in the Upper Silurian of Montgomeryshire, Wales. (Arts. 102, 152.) (*After Earp*, 1938, *Geol. Soc. London Quart. Jour.*, **94**: 142, *Fig.* 6.)

disturbances were caused by submarine sliding of hydroplastic mud and silt during deposition.[1]   Hills (1941) and Hills and Thomas (1945: 57–58) describe "basal sandstone deformations" of probable penecontemporaneous nature in Silurian clastics from near Melbourne, Australia (Art. 102).

The fold shown in Fig. 235, formed by an unusual distribution of iron oxide, occurs in flat-lying Pennsylvanian sandstone in southern Indiana. The stratification passes through all parts of the "fold" without regard for its structure. Such a fold as this, clearly of secondary and superficial origin, need not be confused with a true penecontemporaneous fold, for the stratification of the containing layers is in no way affected by the feature. This type of concretionary structure is apparently not uncom-

[1] In discussing the paper by Earp (1938: 158), W. J. Pugh pointed out that

A tectonic explanation of these disturbed beds was at variance with the simple structure revealed by mapping. The disturbed beds occupied their present position in the succession before the folding and faulting of the area took place. They appeared to be due to subaqueous sliding during the deposition of the sediments, sliding repeated over and over again through a maximum thickness of some 2500 feet.

mon in porous and permeable formations long subjected to weathering. Stephenson and Monroe (1940: 178, Fig. 42) describe and illustrate corrugated McNairy sand in the Upper Cretaceous of Mississippi, and Wanless (1946: 33, Plate 7, Fig. 2) reports similar structure in the Newton sandstone of the Pennsylvanian in Tennessee and Kentucky.

153. *Contorted, Faulted, and Brecciated Bodies of Irregular Shape.*— Irregular, roughly planoconvex masses of folded and faulted shales and limestones are present in some formations. They are lithologically similar to the enclosing rock and differ only in having greatly contorted internal structure. Such bodies, typically flat-based with an irregularly

Fig. 235.—False drag folds caused by ferruginous cementation of Pennsylvanian sandstone in a road-cut near St. Croix, Perry County, Indiana. The true bedding is horizontal but is obscured by the contorted bands of concentrated ferruginous cement. (Art. 152.)

domed or arched upper surface, have generally been explained as the result of subaqueous slumping and gliding. The shape of the mass and its relations to the enclosing rock are usually sufficient to indicate which is the top of the contorted mass. The structural details in some cases are well enough preserved to indicate the direction in which the sliding mass moved.

The deformed body is characteristically wedge-shaped in transverse section, with the thicker part of the wedge in the direction of movement (Figs. 229*B*, 236). The plan view would probably have a lobate outline down the slope, though the shape might be otherwise, depending on the nature of the bottom. Internally, the laminae or beds are crumpled, overfolded, overthrust, faulted, and in general mashed together in a confused structure. The basal part of the deformed body usually shows less contortion than the upper portion, and the folds tend to lose their identity downward, whereas upward they are transected and covered by horizontal strata. Peripherally the undisturbed enclosing strata abut against the deformed mass.

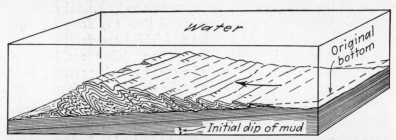

FIG. 236.—Diagram illustrating subaqueous flowage and attendant deformation of hydroplastic mud on a gently inclined bottom. Sliding may occur on slopes of less than 6° and probably is commonly initiated by earthquake shocks. At the right is shown a shallow excavation of the bottom materials. This depression, which furnished the sediments of the deformed mass, would deepen to the right for some distance if the diagram were extended. The diagram is based on structures observed in the Silurian Kokomo limestone of Indiana and the Carboniferous Cambridge slate of eastern Massachusetts. (Arts. 148, 153.)

The shape and relations to enclosing sediment, the little-deformed basal part and much-deformed and transected upper part, and the confused internal structure usually suffice to identify this type of deformed structure and to indicate the top of the succession in which it lies.

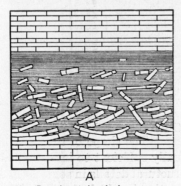
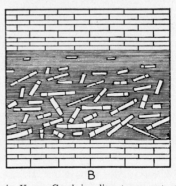

FIG. 237.—Intraformational sharpstone conglomerates in Upper Cambrian limestones east of St. Albans, Vt. Limestone slabs were torn loose from the bottom and left embedded with random orientation in the calcareous muds swept in during the disturbance. *A*. Part of a layer, about 1.5 m. (4.9 ft.) thick, showing the relation of slabs to bottom laminae. Mud cracks in the bottom laminae may have aided the currents that ripped up the bottom materials. *B*. Another part of the same layer as *A*, showing the fragments somewhat more strewn out by current action. In both cases it is to be noted that the disturbed layer has a rather sharp base and that the fragments become smaller and less numerous near the top. Compare these diagrams with Figs. 168 and 238. The individual laminae average somewhat less than 25 mm. (1 in.) in thickness. (Arts. 148, 153.)

Some thin-bedded shallow-water deposits have tabular or irregular bodies of fragmented laminae, the fragments having random orientation. These brecciated deposits have been designated by several names—

edgewise conglomerate [Walcott (1894; 1896: 34–40)]; intraformational breccia, etc. [Field (1916)].

If the laminae show such orientation and relation that no question arises regarding their derivation from one of the bounding formations (as shown in Figs. 237 and 238), the brecciated mass can be used as a top and bottom criterion. If, however, the laminae are scattered through a zone without clear relations to either bounding layer, the structure is without top and bottom significance.

Several explanations have been proposed to account for intraformational brecciation, but there is no need to dwell on these here other than to mention that storm waves, tsunamis, tidal currents, and subaqueous slides have been suggested.[1]

Courtesy of W. D. Michell

Fig. 238.—Intraformational sharpstone conglomerate ("edgewise conglomerate") about 6 ft. (2 m.) above the base of the Upper Cambrian Lodi shale near Cashton, Wis. As is typical of this kind of layer, the base is sharply defined and parallel with the general bedding, whereas the top is uneven. Base and top are indicated by ink lines. The fragments of the disturbed layer have the same lithology as that of the underlying strata and exhibit random orientation. (Arts. 121, 153.)

Intraformational breccias are known to be present in rocks ranging in age from Pre-Cambrian to Pleistocene; and since they are common and widespread, they deserve scrutiny to determine whether or not they show relations that can be relied upon for top and bottom determination.

154. *Landscape Marble.*—Certain types of argillaceous limestones contain thin layers and concretionary masses characterized by dendritic, frondlike, or bushlike structures that rise from a common base and in transverse section present somewhat the appearance of a forest on a dis-

[1] Collins (1925: 53) suggests that the intraformational brecciation in the Pre-Cambrian Espanola formation may have been penecontemporaneous and in citing similar brecciation in the Gowganda formation states that it " . . . appears to have been formed during deposition of the greywacke. It has been suggested that the Gowganda greywacke was frozen solid at the time of brecciation." Fairbridge (1946: 84–87) suggests several other modes of origin for intraformational brecciation.

tant horizon. It is from this imagined resemblance that the designation "landscape marble" comes (Fig. 239).

In these unusual layers and concretions the base is a fairly smooth plane that separates the structure sharply from the underlying layer. Upward, however, the individual structures rise to different heights above the base; hence the top side of the layer containing them is always obvious.

Landscape-marble structure has generally been ascribed to gases rising through soft muds and to shrinkage attending the consolidation of those muds [Woodward (1892: 110–114); Thompson (1894: 393–410)], but North (1930: 174) ascribes the crumpled surfaces " . . . to shrinkage

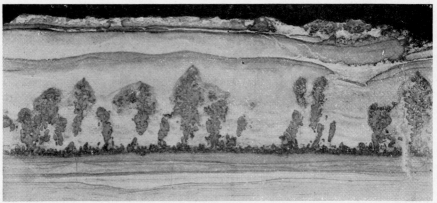

Fig. 239.—Landscape marble in argillaceous limestone from the River Avon, England, reduced about one-half. The individual dendritic masses rise from a common plane and extend upward into the dense limestone. The original plastic calcareous mud appears to have been arched over the dendritic masses. (Arts. 148, 154.)

of the original calcareous mud from which the nodules were formed . . . " On the other hand, Twenhofel (1932: 682) points out that, "whatever the origin of landscape marble, it seems very probable that pit and mound phenomena [Art. 90] can give rise to an almost identical feature" and Rettger (1935: 288), on the basis of observations made while conducting experiments on contemporaneous deformation of soft sediments, suggests " . . . that landscape marble may be produced when water levels are changed so as to cause movement of water and the formation of a hydrostatic head."

Still another possible explanation is that the characteristic arborescent structure formed as the result of a fluid mud of greater density sinking into one of less, as demonstrated experimentally by Nettleton (1936: 92–97, Figs. 4–8).

Whatever its origin, however, the characteristic arborescent profile constitutes a reliable criterion of the original up or down direction in the disturbed layer.

155. FROZEN GROUND STRUCTURES.—It is pointed out in Art. 103 that many closely related structural features exist in the zone of frost action and that certain of these are of possible use in determining top and bottom in ancient regoliths known or suspected to have been formed in cold climates.

Since most of the features that fall in the general category of *head* [Dines *et al.* (1940: 198–226)], *warp* [Bryan (1936: 222–228)], *trail and underplight* [Spurrell (1887)], and similar terms [see Bryan (1946a)] are penecontemporaneous with reference to existing regolithic materials, brief reference is made to them here but it is suggested that the student interested in the structures of frozen ground start his investigations with the articles cited.   These will lead directly to the heart of the problem.

Attention should also be called to the penecontemporaneous structural features formed during the melting of glacial ice.   The article on this subject by Carruthers (1939: 299–333) should stimulate field geologists to examine with greater care the more delicately preserved features of glacial and supposed glaciofluviatile deposits, which so often in the past have been completely overlooked.

The present discussion should not end without brief reference to those unusual networks of pebbles and boulders which gather in the frost and ice cracks of cold regions [Sharpe (1938: 33–46); Paterson (1940: 107–110)] and the conspicuous cracks themselves, which become filled with surficial debris [Berkey and Hyde (1911: 223–231), Patterson (1940: 99–130), and Conrad (1946: 277–296)] (Art. 125).

156. FEATURES ON UNDERSURFACES OF LAYERS.—If soft sediments such as plastic muds or "gelatinous" organic matter be covered by sand or gravel, the unequal pressure of overlying sediment may cause the soft underlying material to flow laterally.   In such manner sand and the underlying sediment may flow together, the water-filled sand adjusting itself to the billowy surface of the substratum.   This is believed to be the way in which the peculiar lobate structures, described in Art. 102 as flow casts, were formed.   Stutzer and Noé (1940: 348, Fig. 122), using a drawing of Kukuk (another of whose sketches is here reproduced as Fig. 118A), illustrate a disturbance of this kind in the Geitling coal bed in Westphalia.   The author has seen the same type of structure in the Wamsutta red beds of the Narragansett Basin in Rhode Island (Fig. 116) and in the Horton clastics of Cape Breton Island, Nova Scotia (Fig. 117).

It should be emphasized that the significant feature—the peculiar lobate structure—appears on the *underside* of sandstone layers, not on top. Since the shale underlying such layers is always much jointed, it shows no significant relict structure. It is quite likely that there are other features on the undersurfaces of sandstone beds formed in like manner, and the field geologist should always be on the lookout for them. Two recently described cases—one from the Silurian limestones of Wales [Earp (1938: 125–160)] and the other from rocks of the same age in the Melbourne district, Australia [Hills (1941: 167–191) and Hills and Thomas (1945: 51–61)]—are cases in point (Art. 152).

157. FEATURES PRODUCED BY DIFFERENTIAL COMPACTION AND OTHER SECONDARY PHENOMENA.—Much attention has been given in recent years to features produced by differential compaction because of their possible importance as oil-bearing structures [Mehl (1920: 520), Powers (1922: 233–259; 1926: 422–442); Hedberg (1926: 1035–1072; 1936: 241–287), Nevin and Sherrill (1929: 1–22), Trask (1931: 271–276), Terzaghi (1940: 78–90), Nevin (1942: 193–204), and others]. However, most such structures are obviously right side up and so large that the oversteepened dips and other associated structural features are not needed to determine top and bottom. Additional discussions of this important problem can be found in all modern textbooks of structural geology (see table in Chap. I, pages 22–23).

In addition to differential compaction, certain chemical changes that take place in sediments soon after deposition may produce characteristic structures of possible use as top and bottom criteria. The reliability of these is largely determined by whether they were truncated by erosion before burial. Woolnough (1910: 334–340; 1933: 1098–1106) and Croneis (1930) have described examples of these features that are ascribed to the swelling action of wetted bentonite. Woolnough (1933: 1098) points out that "anomalous folds" may be due to contemporaneous deformation produced by

(1) swelling of argillaceous members,
(2) plastic flow of bentonitic beds, and
(3) concretionary development on an unprecedented scale.

He describes and illustrates how a swelling shale seam deformed an overlying coal bed and its covering shale (Fig. 240).

In Art. 152 attention is called to the interpretation by Bradley (1931: 26–28) of the contorted beds of the Eocene Green River oil shale as due to readjustments and differential movements within and between layers of sediment after burial and during compaction.

Coal layers and associated strata exhibit a great range of structural relationships, many of which are probably to be explained as results of differential compaction [see Moore (1940) and Stutzer and Noé (1940)].

158. Partly Filled Primary and Secondary Cavities.—Many sedimentary rocks contain cavities which appear to have been present almost from the time consolidation began,[1] whereas in others the cavities are obviously of secondary origin. In still other cases it is difficult or even impossible to determine whether the cavity is primary or secondary.

In partly filled cavities the flat surface of the incomplete filling—*i.e.*, the plane of composition—acts as a spirit level, indicating horizontality

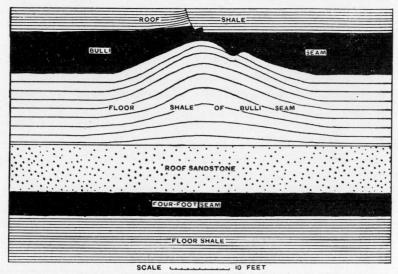

FIG. 240.—"Stone rolls" in the Illawara coal measures of New South Wales, Australia. Woolnough (1910: 338) rejects the possibility that the rolls were formed by slipping of the unconsolidated muds of a coal swamp as a result of local overloading with sediment. He suggests as an alternative that the compression which formed the folds in the floor shale and associated thinning of the overlying coal came long after the coal and covering sediments had been deposited. The localized folds are ascribed to "the swelling up of the shale as a result of hydration or oxidation or both." In only unusual cases are the coal and roof shale faulted. (Art. 157.) (*After Garlick in Woolnough, 1910, Royal Soc. New South Wales Jour. and Proc.*, **44**: 336, *Fig.* 6.)

and verticality at the time when the cavity was being filled. If the plane of composition is parallel to the stratification, the incomplete filling is a reliable top and bottom feature, for it obviously lies in the bottom part of the cavity (Figs. 1, 242). It matters not if the cavity be primary or secondary, provided that the plane of composition is parallel to stratification. An obvious exception to this rule is a postdeformational cavity

---

[1] The origin of primary or penecontemporaneous cavities is commonly obscure. The cavity may be a result of the way in which the sedimentary materials accumulated—*e.g.*, in some of the eastern Wisconsin Silurian bioherms, large and small cavities appear to be the result of the arching effect of felted masses of fossil fragments that constitute the roof of the cavities (Fig. 241). It may have resulted from solution of an entombed fossil shell or mineral mass; it may have originated during dolomitization; or it may have come into existence in still other ways (Art. 163).

in an overturned layer facing vertically downward, but such an occurrence seems highly unlikely.   If the plane of composition makes with stratification an angle greater than can be explained as initial dip, the filling was made after tilting of the containing bed.   Such a cavity

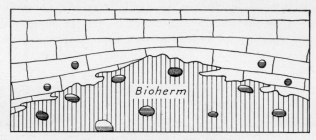

Fig. 241.—Original cavities in bioherms and their flanking strata.   The plane of composition in partly filled cavities may be used as a spirit level to determine original horizontality and which direction is up in steeply tilted biohermal complexes.   Stratified complete fillings are useful indicators of original horizontality but do not indicate which direction is up or down (see Figs. 1 and 2).   (Art. 158.)

filling may or may not have top and bottom significance but does have structural significance, as fully discussed in Art. 1 and illustrated in Fig. 1.

Primary cavities with incomplete penecontemporaneous fillings are common in some detrital algal limestones.   The Eocene Wasatch limestone of Utah has composite fillings, the lower part consisting of primary, fine-grained calcareous mud and the upper of clear secondary calcite

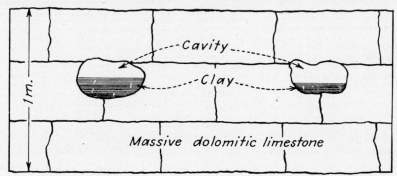

Fig. 242.—Partly filled cavities in the massively bedded Silurian Mayville dolomitic limestone of eastern Wisconsin.   These appear to be primary, for the clay in them is not found in the contiguous rock or in any of the joints.   The mud is believed to have been swept into the essentially contemporaneous cavities during a storm and to have settled out later.   The original cavity was probably completely filled with muddy water.   When the clear water drained away, the partial clay filling remained in the cavity.   (Art. 158.)

precipitated later (Fig. 243).   The author has observed similar incomplete and composite fillings in one of the algal layers of the Mississippian Windsor succession on Cape Breton Island, Nova Scotia.

Some ancient strata contain original cavities partly filled with essentially contemporaneous sediment not represented as a distinct layer in the geologic section. Cavities of this sort are common in the Wisconsin Silurian Mayville formation and in some of the bioherms of slightly later age. The cavities are irregular in shape and usually are about half full of laminated clay and silt (Figs. 241, 242). Certain cavities near the present surface may have been filled during the Pleistocene with fine sediment carried downward along fractures and crevices, but there is no sediment in the joints and cracks to suggest this, and cavities unearthed in quarries at depths of 15 to 30 m. (45 to 95 ft.) below the surface could hardly have been filled in this manner.

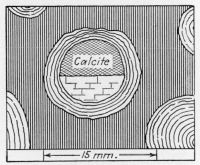

Hollow shells and the slightly larger cavities remaining after the shells themselves are dissolved away provide places where contemporaneous sediments can accumulate to form incomplete fillings. The several types of features that might form under these conditions—the incomplete and composite internal molds of Cullison (1938: 981–988)—are discussed and illustrated in Art. 182. Other primary and secondary cavities formed by buried organic remains are considered in Arts. 180 to 183.

Fig. 243.—Algal spheroid with composite filling of calcareous mud below and clear calcite above. Other spheroids are concentrically laminated to the center. Composite fillings of this sort provide a means of determining not only the plane of bedding but also the top of the bed in which they are present since the calcite marks the upper part of the filling. In some spheroids the calcite has been removed, and a hemispheroidal cavity marks its place. The interstitial sediment may be calcareous shale or argillaceous limestone. Algal spheroids of this kind are present in certain layers of the Mississippian Windsor formation of Nova Scotia and in the Eocene Wasatch limestone of Utah. Compare with Fig. 287. (Arts. 158, 181.)

Wherry (1915: 153–156) has described and illustrated an unusual oölitic rock from the Upper Cambrian Allentown formation of Northampton County, Pennsylvania. These ooids are unusual in that many have a bipartite structure, in appearance somewhat like a "half moon," with the dividing plane parallel to the bedding (Fig. 244). The conspicuous lower part of the ooids is quite dark in color and contains the residue which dropped down when the original oölite was dissolved away; the upper part is much lighter in color and contains almost no impurities. The ooid itself, other than the impurities just mentioned, is composed of secondary dolomite that was precipitated in the cavities left by dissolution of the original aragonitic oölites. The history of these "oölites," as outlined by Wherry (1915: 155–156), is given in the following footnote.[1]

[1] Wherry (1915: 155–156) states:

When the ooids were first formed they no doubt consisted of aragonite, whereas the matrix was dolomite-mud. Mixed with the aragonite, in varying amounts in the different

In flat-lying or gently dipping beds, secondarily developed cavities, such as those which ultimately are geodized, may have crystals in only the lower half or larger ones there than above. This feature, however, needs to be tested in the field to determine whether or not it has any value for top and bottom determination. Such crystals might develop in the same way in which stalactites grow in a cave. In caverns and similar underground openings it should be possible to differentiate the roof stalactites from the floor stalagmites, for the former are like icicles, whereas the latter resemble rounded stumps. Since their orientation determines the direction of gravity at the time when they were formed, stalactites and stalagmites must be essentially perpendicular to bedding to have top and bottom significance. In steeply inclined beds, therefore, predeformational stalactites and stalagmites formed while the beds were horizontal will be disposed at right angles to bedding, whereas post-deformational ones will be vertical, hence will make an angle with the bedding.

As a general rule, partly filled and crystal-studded cavities are useful top and bottom features only when it can be demonstrated that the incomplete filling or the crystals and other features were made before the containing beds were deformed.

159. Buried Organic Structures and Fossils.—Plants and animals may live, die, and be destroyed or buried in the same place; they may live and die in the place where they originated and grew but be buried else-

---

concentric layers, was the carbonaceous pigment. After the solidification of the sediment into rock and the development of joint cracks (but before the uptilting of the beds) waters penetrated along these cracks and along the bedding planes. Since aragonite is more soluble than the dolomite of the matrix, it dissolved away, leaving behind the carbon and the nuclei—sand grains and bits of kaolin—in some cases stripped of all concentrically deposited aragonite, in others still retaining a few layers. These settled to the bottom of the cavities in heaps, the shapes of which varied with the sizes of the nuclei and the stage in the solution process at which they fell into the masses of carbon powder.

At some later period water again traversed the rock, but this time conditions were favorable to deposition instead of solution, and secondary dolomite filled up all openings in the rock, tension and joint cracks as well as the holes left by the removal of the ooids. As is usual in the recrystallization of carbonate rocks this secondary material tended to approach the normal dolomite ratio, although as the analysis shows, a slight isomorphous admixture of calcium and ferrous carbonates still remained. The secondary crystallization took place so slowly and quietly that the heaps of carbonaceous dust were not disturbed, but merely enclosed by the crystal grains, and their shapes preserved.

The deposition of pyrite took place at still a later time. Migrating solutions brought in ferrous sulphate, which was reduced to sulphide by the carbon near the surface of the normal ooids, and around the black part of the divided ones. Apparently the rearrangement of the carbon particles in the latter rendered them more readily attacked, for both microscopic examination and the analysis show them to be the higher in limonite, which now takes the place of the pyrite. This last change, which represents the latest chapter in the history of the rock, was evidently brought about by the action of oxygen-bearing rain water.

where or destroyed in transit; or they may live in one spot or general environment, die in a different one, and be buried in still a third.[1] If, therefore, a fossil or the structure or feature made by an ancient organism is to be used for top and bottom determination, it is important to ascer-

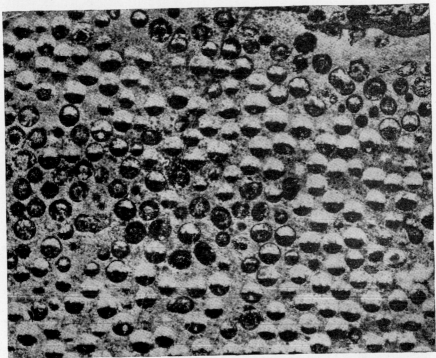

Fig. 244.—Cross section of an unusual oölitic rock from the Upper Cambrian Allentown formation of Pennsylvania, enlarged about 4.5 times. The unaltered oölites have the nucleus in a central position; those which show bipartite structure have nuclear and other insoluble material concentrated in the bottom part, where they dropped when the primary aragonitic oölite dissolved. The contact between dark and light portions is variable but tends to be slightly convex upward, giving the half-moon effect that is so obvious. Bedding is across the figure from left to right, with slight inclination to the right, and the top of the bed is toward the top of the figure. The dark portion of each ooid lies below, and the light portion above, the plane of composition. (Art. 158.) (*After Wherry, 1915, U.S. Nat. Mus. Proc.*, **49**: 156, *Plate* 40.)

tain as much as possible about the history of the fossil structure in order to determine its reliability as a criterion.

160. Fossils and Organically Produced Features and Structures Buried without Disturbance.—If bottom-dwelling organisms

[1] Wasmund (1926: 11–116) has proposed the term *thanatocoenose* for the relations and associations of a collection of dead organisms, as a companion term for *biocoenose*, which has long been used for a congregation of living organisms. Twenhofel (1931: 407–424; 1932: 147–152) has pointed out how the environments of life, death, the interval between death and burial, and burial differ and how these environmental conditions affect organisms and organic remains.

are buried in the position and with the orientation they maintained while living and if the hard portion of the organism has retained its entity[1] as a skeleton or other supporting structure, it should be possible, the living habits of the plant or animal being known, to determine the top of the sequence in which the fossils lie.

Little attention has been paid to this use of the living position of organisms in determining the top and bottom of inclined strata. Paleontologists have cited and illustrated many examples of organisms (both plant and animal) buried in the position of growth, but probably few have had occasion to utilize such fossils in structural work [see Kindle (1895: 349, 353), Cox and Dake (1916: 34–35), Grabau (1921: 665), Twenhofel (1919: 339–352; 1932: 355–356), Blackwelder (1926: 650), and Cloud (1942: 363–374)].

Algal bioherms, trees, attached sponges, coral and stromatoporoid heads and coelenterate bioherms, attached bryozoans, brachiopods, mollusks and arthropods, attached echinoderms and the roots or stumps of crinoids, and the tubes, borings, and trails of many animals, if buried without disturbance, constitute reliable criteria for determining top and bottom. Examples are cited in following paragraphs.

161. *Algal Structures.*—Certain characteristic structures in calcareous rocks, ranging in age from Pre-Cambrian to Recent, have long been referred to by a multitude of investigators as "algal" growths or more rarely designated by the preferable term *stromatolite*.[2] These structures, ranging in size from a few millimeters across and as much in height to gigantic masses measured in tens of meters and varying in form from irregular domal growths to columnar or hemispheroidal masses, have an internal structure composed of successive arched laminae that are usually convex upward (Figs. 245, 246). Inasmuch as the shape of the algal head and convexity of the internal laminae indicate the top of the containing layer, colonies buried *in situ* are reliable top and bottom features and have been used successfully for that purpose.

[1] For excellent discussions of the destruction of organic hard parts by marine scavengers and other macroorganisms, see Dapples (1938: 54–65; 1942: 118–126).

[2] Goldring (1938: 1–75) gives an instructive discussion of the well-known cryptozoan reefs of New York and supplements it with a valuable chapter on coralline algae as reef builders through the ages. Cloud (1942: 363–379), in a recent discussion of stromatolites ("structures commonly called fossil calcareous algae"), gives an extensive bibliography of 50 references. For additional data see Johnson (1940: 571–596) and Clarke and Teichert (1946: 271–276). The latter describe a type of wrinkled calcareous surface produced on the floor of a salt lake in western Australia by hollow sausage- and mound-shaped algal growths. The surface resembles wrinkling in Tertiary sandstone, which Richter (1937) ascribed to the alga *Chorellopsis bavarica.*

As early as 1913, according to Cox and Dake (1916: 35), Joseph Barrell, by using algal structures in Cambro-Ordovician strata of eastern

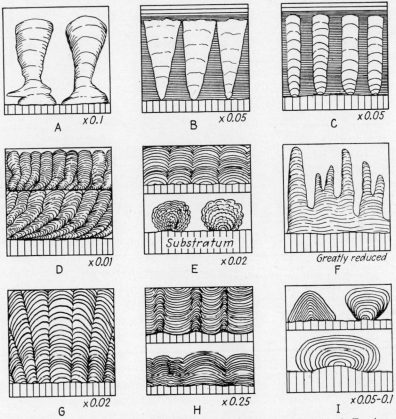

FIG. 245.—Diagrams showing variation in shape of stromatolites (algal masses). *A.* Two irregularly conoidal stromatolites of *Collenia* from the Belt series of Waterton-Glacier parks, Canada. (*Modified after Fenton and Fenton*, 1937, *Bull. Geol. Soc. Am.*, **48**: 1942–1943, *Fig.* 15.) *B.* Conoidal algal masses in a thin limestone member of the Mississippian Windsor formation of Nova Scotia (*cf.* with Figs. 253 and 254). *C.* Slender columnar stromatolites closely associated with *B.* Somewhat similar forms have been reported from South Africa (see Figs. 248 and 249). *D.* Biostromal layers of *Collenia* from the Belt series of Glacier National Park, showing varied inclinations of colonies in successive strata. (*Modified after Fenton and Fenton*, 1937, *Bull. Geol. Soc. Am.*, **48**: 1942, *Fig.* 14A.) *E.* Tabular stromatolite with many thin, symmetrically curved laminae and two spheroidal colonies with crinkled laminae that are more or less concentric. *F.* *Gymnosolen* stromatolite with branches. Since the forks of such forms always open upward, they provide a means of determining tops of beds. (*Modified after Cloud*, 1942, *Am. Jour. Sci.*, **240**: 367, *Fig.* 1e.) *G.* Typical structure in a large algal bioherm in the Pre-Cambrian Kona dolostone of Michigan. Compare this diagram with Fig. 247. *H.* Stromatolites with strongly laminated structure. *I.* Diagram showing the shapes of three common stromatolites, all more or less concentrically laminated. (Art. 161.)

Pennsylvania, " . . . was able to work out an overturned section of limestone which was not evident by any other means." Geologists investigating the Lake Superior Pre-Cambrian have used the convexity of algal laminae in the Kona dolomitic limestone for structural purposes

(Fig. 247), and Blackwelder (1915: 650) has called attention to the top and bottom significance of the hemispheroidal shape of stromatolites in

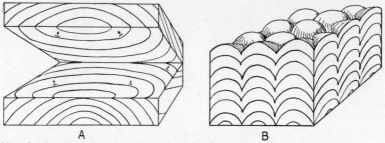

A   B

FIG. 246.—Sectioned stromatolites. *A.* Diagram of part of a large strongly laminated stromatolite, showing how the laminae dip away from the center of the hemispheroidal mass if viewed from above and toward the center if viewed from beneath. If a stromatolitic layer were vertical, the top or bottom could be determined by noting the inclination of the laminae with reference to the center of the mass. Stromatolites with this kind of structure are common. Excellent specimens are present in the Ordovician Oneota dolostone of the upper Mississippi Valley. These latter range in diameter from a few centimeters to as much as a meter. *B.* A small stromatolite (×0.5) from the Lower Ordovician of western Wisconsin. It consists of many closely packed cylindrical columns with highly arched laminae. (Art. 161.)

the Cambrian of Wyoming (see footnote on page 290 and Fig. 251). Many subsequent writers have mentioned how certain algal structures

Courtesy of W. J. Mead

FIG. 247.—Algal structure in the Pre-Cambrian Kona dolostone near Marquette, Mich. The successive laminae are consistently convex upward in each vertical band of arched layers. This feature has been proved a reliable top and bottom criterion in the Lake Superior region. (Art. 161.)

can be used in top and bottom determination, and in a recent article Cloud (1942: 363) reemphasizes " . . . that the laminae of many stromatolites [structures commonly called 'fossil calcareous algae'] which grow fast to the substratum are convex upwards, and that the forks of the branching forms are open toward the top; suggesting their use in determining tops of beds."

Nearly every geologic period saw the formation of stromatolites, algal bioherms, and similar structures, and a few typical examples deserve mention.

The Huronian[1] Kona dolomitic limestone of the Marquette range has great biohermal masses in which the concentric laminae are uniformly convex upward (Fig. 247). Some years ago, similar forms in Australia were explained as a special kind of asymmetrical folding.

[1] TWENHOFEL, W. H., 1919, Pre-Cambrian and Carboniferous algal deposits, *Am. Jour. Sci.* (4) **48**: 339–352.

The algal structures of the Pre-Cambrian Belt series of western North America should be cited here because of their intensive study by Walcott (1914: 77–156) and C. L. and M. A. Fenton (1931: 670–686; 1933a: 1135–1142; 1936: 609–620; 1937a: 497–508; 1937b: 1941–1950; 1939: 89–126). One of the growths, described by C. L. and M. A. Fenton (1939: 101–103) as *Collenia spissa*, consists of convexly laminated columnar colonies that may fuse to make bioherms and biostromes (Fig. 248). Balls of calcite that lie in the sediment between separate colonies call to mind calcareous oölites occupying a similar position in Ordovician algal biostromes (Fig. 252).

Fossil algae of unusual interest are reported from the Otavi system (late Pre-Cambrian or Cambrian) of Southwest Africa by Schwellnus and Roex (1945: 93–106). These writers differentiate three general shapes of growths—*conical* (pages 97, 99), *dentate* (page 100), and *bun-shaped* (page 101) (Figs. 249, 250).

The conical type

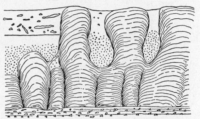

Fig. 248.—An algal biostrome of *Collenia spissa* in the Cambrian Snowy Mountain formation of Wyoming, much reduced. The algal colonies fuse and divide, being separated here and there by sediment containing balls of calcite crystals. The laminae in each colony are typically convex upward, and the colonies themselves tend to enlarge upward. The biostrome rests on thin dolomitic beds containing another genus of algae. (Art. 161.) (*After Fenton and Fenton, 1939, Bull. Geol. Soc. Am.,* **50**: 103, *Fig. 4.*)

. . . is represented by cones consisting of alternating concentric shells of dolomitic limestone and chert. The shells show up on the surface as round or oval rings which range in diameter from a few inches to 3 feet and also vary correspondingly in height from a few inches to roughly 3 feet . . . ; they are confined to a bed which can be followed for many miles along the strike. . . .

The axes of these conical structures are vertically disposed with regard to the bedding planes and the apices of the cones invariably point downwards. . . . Their spacing varies considerably; in places they are so closely packed as to occupy half the total area of the surface exposed.

These conical forms seem from the above description to be similar to Mississippian conoidal growths in the Windsor series of Nova Scotia mentioned in a later paragraph.

. . . The type of structure referred to as dentate is found in thin layers, from three inches to a foot in thickness, of chertified material which, in section, display a row of tooth-like projections [Fig. 249]. When exposed by weathering, these look like warts or rounded protrusions; in section they are seen to rest on a flat surface. The growths themselves show a faint, closely-spaced lamination which is more or less parallel to the base of the growth at the lower end, whereas farther upwards the laminae are slightly bent so as to be approximately parallel to the domical surface.   At the outer surface of the structures the laminae are usually bent more sharply downwards.   Dolomitic limestone rests horizontally on these growths, which are usually closely packed, and also fills the depressions between them.   In places as many as five superimposed layers of dentate structures are present in close succession separated by intercalations of dolomitic limestone a foot or more thick [page 100].

Fig. 249.—Columnar and bun-shaped algal structures in massively bedded dolomitic limestone of the Otavi system of South Africa.   The layers containing the columns range in thickness from 7.5 to 30 cm. (3 to 12 in.) and are persistent over large areas.   It should be noted that the columns start at a stratification plane and extend upward a variable distance in the layer.   Dolomitic limestone fills the depressions between the columns and rests horizontally on them.   Under conditions of weathering the columns are less resistant than the surrounding rock, and the surface of the weathered rock as a consequence has the dentate appearance shown in Fig. 250.   (Art. 161.)   (After Schwellnus and Roex, 1945, Geol. Soc. South Africa Trans., 47: 100, Fig. 5.)

Weathering of these less resistant dentate forms brings out prominent fossae that are bounded by narrow, vertically-walled partitions (Fig. 250).

Bun-shaped algal heads up to a foot in diameter were seen on precisely the same horizons as those on which the dentate forms are found.   In a few instances they are situated between the dentate structures, but more often lie isolated from them [Fig. 249].   The initial stage of formation is represented by flat, slightly

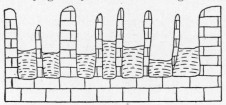

domed and finely laminated growths having, in section, the appearance of crescent moons.   Where fully developed they display in section the outline of a horseshoe.   The interior of the body consists of alternating fine and coarse laminations subparallel to its lower and upper surfaces.   Some of the laminations are siliceous [page 101].

Fig. 250.—Section illustrating how the algal columns shown in Fig. 249 weather into depressions so that the surface has a dentate appearance.   (Art. 161.)   (After Schwellnus and Roex, 1945, Geol. Soc. South Africa Trans., 47: 101, Fig. 6.)

Cambrian strata in many parts of the world contain algal structures. Blackwelder (1915: 646–650) found Middle Cambrian stromatolites shaped like an overturned kettle (Fig. 251) and used the shape for top and bottom determination.[1]   Cloud (1942: 368) illustrated a similar

[1] Blackwelder (1926: 650) describes the structural use of algal domes as follows:

biostrome from lower Paleozoic rocks of the Northwest Territories, Canada, and C. L. and M. A. Fenton (1937: 435–441; 1937a: 498) illustrated similar algal heads from the Canadian Rockies and from Pennsylvania.

The Ordovician cryptozoan domes, biostromes, and occasional bioherms have been known for over a century and have been described and illustrated in many reports. The most recent publication is by Goldring (1938: 1–75), who gives an excellent description of the biostromes and adds an instructive chapter on coralline algae as reef builders. The usual structure is that of a group of coalesced spheroidal masses with

Courtesy of U.S. Geological Survey

FIG. 251.—Denuded biostrome of algal stromatolites on a dip slope of Middle Cambrian strata in the Teton Mountains of Wyoming. The original interstitial and covering sediments have been swept away, leaving the biostrome with much the same appearance it must have had when buried. The prominent domal shape of the individual stromatolites indicates that the biostrome is only gently tilted. (Art. 161.) [*After Blackwelder*, 1915, *Am. Jour. Sci.* (4) **39**: 646, *Fig.* 1.)

strongly arched laminae (Fig. 252). Many colonies grew side by side to form a discontinuous or continuous layer. In such beds the spaces between adjacent colonies may be filled with sediment having a lithology

In beds devoid of fossils, of unknown stratigraphy and in vertical attitude, the true order of deposition is not always easily determined. In this instance it was found necessary to search very carefully for original sedimentary structures, and to weigh their evidence separately from that of the secondary structures, such as cleavage and drag-folds, that are due to deformation. In this instance the former consisted of clearly preserved ripple-marks in some of the metaquartzite formations, cross-bedding and variation of texture in sandy and dolomitic members, and the dome-shaped growths, supposedly of algal origin, in the marbles. A close study of the ripple-marks, cross-bedding, and change of grain showed that the top of the stratum in each case faced southeastward. Likewise the algoid domes are all convex toward the southeast, are attached to flat bases which have every resemblance to a contemporaneous sea-floor, and are surrounded with detrital dolomite (or calcarenite) resembling reef debris. All of these criteria, therefore, indicate that the southeast sides of the various formations were originally their tops, and that the sequence as it stands is not overturned.

different from that of the colony. Oölites commonly fill the spaces, and their presence indicates current action between the colonies at the time when they were formed (Fig. 252).

Fig. 252.—Cryptozoan structure in the Lower Magnesian dolostone (Ordovician) of western Wisconsin. Oölites are common in the depressions between adjacent masses. Successive layers are characteristically convex upward. The sketch is two-thirds natural size. (Art. 161.)

The Mississippian upper Windsor of Cape Breton Island, Nova Scotia, has four algal biostromes, each distinct in its structure from the other three. The third of the series in ascending order is a prominent biostrome consisting of upwardly expanding conical columns of gray porous limestone separated by yellow argillaceous rock (Fig. 253). This

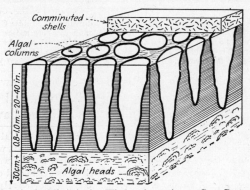

Fig. 253.—Algal columns in the Mississippian Windsor formation on Cape Breton Island, Nova Scotia. The columns are bluntly pointed at the lower end and expand upward to diameters of 15 to 20 cm. (6 to 8 in.). They are composed of tough, gray, slightly porous limestone and are separated interstitially by weak, yellow calcareous shale, which is commonly eroded out. (Art. 161.)

biostrome can be viewed in horizontal position along the shore just south of Mabou Harbor, on the east side of Northumberland Strait. Out in the strait at the northern end of Hood Island the same biostrome is vertical, with north-south strike, and the conical columns expand to the northwest,[1] indicating the top of the section in that direction. A further significant fact in this exposure is that the columns are not perpendicular to the two boundary bedding surfaces, as they were at the time of growth and burial. On the contrary, all have been rotated 35° away from their original growth position by the differential movement between the lower and upper beds during folding (Fig. 254). The biostromal layer has a vertical dip and a north-south strike, whereas the axes of the columns are essentially horizontal and strike N.35°W.

Johnson (1940: 571–596) describes algal limestones from the Pennsylvanian of Colorado; Bradley (1929: 203–223) reports algal reefs from the well-known Green River shale of the western United States; and many

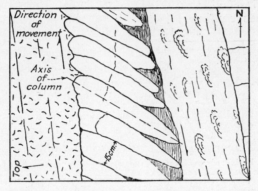

Fig. 254.—Vertical beds of Mississippian Windsor formation of Hood Island, Nova Scotia, showing deformation of algal columns and heads. The columns have been rotated about 35° from their original vertical position in the bed as shown in Fig. 253. (Art. 161.)

other occurrences from widely separated regions have been described and illustrated.

Algal structures of many kinds are to be expected in sedimentary rocks of all ages, and the ones useful as top and bottom criteria usually can be identified without great difficulty.

162. *Trees Buried in Growth Position.*—The stumps and root systems of ancient ferns, cycads, and other trees have been found buried *in situ* in many parts of the world and in deposits ranging in age from Devonian to Recent.[2] These are excellent indicators of the top or bottom of the for-

[1] Norman (1935: 38–41) compares these conical structures with columnar ones that Kindle (1914: 35–44) described and attributed to desiccation and concludes (p. 40): "It is probable, therefore, that the columnar structure was produced by the desiccation of calcareous muds deposited in shallow water."

[2] No attempt has been made to compile an extensive bibliography on the subject of buried stumps, trees, and similar structures, but the following references contain the essential literature: Lyell (1843: 353–356); Brown (1846: 393–396; 1848: 46–50; 1849: 354–360); Dawson (1851: 194–196; 1855: 116–188; 1861: 522–524; 1868: 150–

mation in which they lie and can be used where the strata are steeply inclined, as in the Joggins section of Nova Scotia, or overturned, as in some anthracite areas. In deltaic deposits, however, uprooted tree stumps, carried downstream to the marine part of the delta, may " . . . assume an upright position when they come to rest and give the appearance of being in place" in beds of marine deposition [Johnston (1921: 38)].

Stumps of ancient trees, uncovered by mining operations or natural denudation, excited the curiosity of many geologists of a century ago, and some of the best and most graphically described occurrences are to be found among the writings of such early observers as Lyell (1843: 353–356), Brown (1846: 393–396; 1848: 46–50; 1849: 354–360), and Dawson (1851: 194–196; 1855: 116–188; 1861: 522–524; 1868: 150–212). That this interest has continued is shown by the observations of Barrell

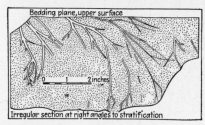

FIG. 255.—Root marks in red argillaceous sandstone of Upper Devonian age near Frostburg, Md. The surface on which the marks are shown is essentially perpendicular to the bedding plane. (Art. 162.) [*After Barrell*, 1913, *Am. Jour. Sci.* (4) **36**: 462, *Fig. 4.*]

(1913: 462), who described and illustrated root marks preserved in red argillaceous sandstone of Upper Devonian age (Fig. 255), and Jenkins (1925b: 241), who found rootlet tubes with calcareous linings in a lacustrine sand of the Pend Oreille River in Washington. The limy sheaths around the rootlets form hardened concretionary masses that ramify the sand deposit. Black (1929: 222–223) found rooted land plants in a Jurassic limestone, and Stutzer and Noé (1940) describe and illustrate many examples in coal-bearing sequences from all over the world.

Trees have been overwhelmed and buried by lava and ash, as illustrated by the famous "petrified forests" of the western United States [Holmes (1882: 125–132)] (Fig. 293); they have been overridden by continental glaciers, as in the well-known interglacial "forest beds" of northeastern Wisconsin[1] [Wilson (1932: 31–46); Thwaites (1937: 83–84)]; they may be buried by advancing sand dunes and by sand- and silt-laden

---

212); Lyell and Dawson (1853: 58–63); Kindle (1895: 349–353); Ward (1896: 488–495); Bell (1912: 328–333; 1914: 360–371); Grabau (1921: 504, 665; 1924: 516); Twenhofel (1932: 355–357); Stutzer and Noé (1940: 88–151, 167–168, 214); Lahee (1941: 96).

[1] Wilson (1932: 32, 36–37) states:

The forest bed is found on top of the varved clays, and above that are several inches of silty sediment. . . .

The logs occur most frequently in the layer of sediment above the forest bed, where they evidently fell after being broken from their stumps by the glacial ice. Most of the

streams;[1] and they seem to have been buried rather rapidly[2] in coal-forming swamps and on deltas (Figs. 257, 258).

Fig. 256.—A willow tree partly buried by sediment [1.3 m. (4 ft.) thick] on a flood plain where deposition was unusually rapid for a time because of local damming of a small stream channel.   Compare with Figs. 257 and 258.   (Art. 162.)   (*After Rittenhouse in Happ, 1945, Am. Jour. Sci.,* **243**: 120, *Plate* 1, *Fig.* 2.)

It is not uncommon to find stumps with the roots embedded in a

logs are found pointing toward the southwest . . . , and it is thought that here the last ice moved in that direction.

One stump was found *in situ* . . . , with the butt of the broken-off log almost attached. The roots of this stump extend along the forest bed peat. . . .

[1] Kindle (1895: 349) long ago reported an upright *Lepidodendron* surrounded by strikingly laminated whetstone rock, but with its interior filled with nonstratified sand like that in the surrounding rock, and Happ (1945: 114–126), in a recent article, described and illustrated (Fig. 256) a tree in the process of being buried by alluvium, probably in somewhat the same manner as the case Kindle described.

[2] Barrell (1917: 798), in discussing geologic rhythms and the rapidity of sedimentation under certain conditions, points out that

A fundamental conception connected with composite rhythms is that a long time interval may be represented by a short columnar section, and yet the individual beds may be deposited rapidly.   In coal measures, tree trunks may be preserved in erect attitude, showing burial before decay.   In marine deposits, sponges and coral colonies are in certain beds found smothered in mud.   Ammonite shells were partially or wholly buried before they could be destroyed.   Such burials may have been due to single unusual storms, recurrently scouring sediment from one locality to deposit it in another.   At the most, but a few years could have been occupied in the burial.   These features show rates of accumulation so rapid that even the advocates of very short geological time would have to admit for such instances recurrent deposition with lost intervals between.

lithified soil bed and the basal part of the trunk extending upward for several meters through successive layers of the overlying sediment. Twenhofel (1932: 355) states that near Madison, Mo., " . . . the stumps of a forest of great trees stand silicified in place of growth in the underclay" and further that " . . . in some of the younger coal beds of the western United States petrified stumps and roots are present *in situ* in the top of the coal."

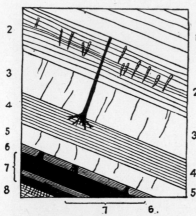

Fig. 257.—An erect tree and numerous *Calamites* in the Pennsylvanian sequence at Joggins, Nova Scotia. 1. Shale and sandstone containing plants with *Spirorbis* attached. 2. Sandstone and shale, 8 ft. (2.5 m.) thick, with many erect *Calamites*. 3. Gray sandstone. 4. Gray shale. The erect tree, rooted in this shale, passes up through 15 ft. (5 m.) of sandstone and shale. 5. Gray sandstone. 6. Gray shale, 6 in. (15 cm.) thick, containing prostrate and erect trees with rootlets; *Spirorbis* on plants. 7, 8. Double coal seam and underclay. (Art. 162.) (*After Dawson*, 1868, "*Acadian Geology*," *p.* 198, *Fig.* 40.)

163. *Invertebrate Animals Buried Alive by Sedimentary Materials.*—Certain invertebrate animals are firmly attached to the substratum and are known as "sessile benthos"; others live on the bottom in a position fixed with reference to that bottom. These are the boring and burrowing forms. Still others wander over the bottom and are called "vagrant benthos."

If these organisms build stony structures above the substratum and continue to construct until buried or if they are buried alive in their burrows or as they travel over the bottom materials, the orientation of structures and hard parts with reference to stratification and to the bottom on which the organisms lived usually is obvious, and makes easy the determination of top and bottom.[1]

[1] Hall (1852: 8, Plate 4, Fig. 2e) describes and illustrates linguloid brachiopod shells stranded on a layer of Silurian Medina sandstone, and the author has observed similarly stranded shells in the Silurian Kokomo limestone of Indiana. In the latter rock the shells lie at the end of a shallow groove made in the soft calcareous mud as they were pushed along by waves or currents. The larger pedicle valve is not uncommonly pushed on slightly beyond the brachial.

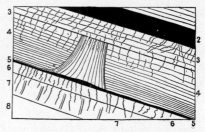

Fig. 258.—Tree stump buried *in situ* in Pennsylvanian sequence at Joggins, Nova Scotia. 1. Shale. 2. Shaly coal, 1 ft. (0.3 m.). 3. Underclay with rootlets. 4. Sandstone passing downward into shale, 3 ft. (1 m.), with erect stump resting on thin coal (5). 6–8. Shale and standstone with rootlets and erect *Calamites* (7). (Art. 162.) (*After Dawson*, 1868, "*Acadian Geology*," *p.* 200, *Fig.* 41.)

These stranded shells clearly mark the top of the stratum on which they came to rest.

Siliceous and calcareous sponges build tubular and vaselike skeletons that could be buried in their upright growth position. Calcareous coelenterate heads frequently are buried while alive (Figs. 259, 260), and the bioherms they construct usually show by their shape or peripheral relations which part is the upper surface (Fig. 261).

The root systems of crinoids and blastoids may be buried in the position of life (Fig. 262); edrioasteroids, attached to the upper surface of a boulder or shell, may be buried without any disturbance of the object to which they are cemented; and asteroids and echinoids would obviously indicate the top of a bed if they were buried alive. In this connection, the boring habit of certain echinoids should be noted, for if the animals were buried alive in the depression that they excavated the top surface of the substratum would be immediately obvious.

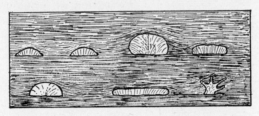

Fig. 259.—Coral and stromatoporoid heads buried in position of growth by fine coralline sand and mud. The laminae arch over the larger heads and if seen from above would exhibit quaquaversal dips. The heads vary from a few centimeters to a meter in diameter. (Arts. 163, 164.)

Bryozoans might well be buried alive under certain conditions, and the ramose or hemispheroidal zoaria should clearly indicate the top of the enclosing sediments in such cases.

Brachiopods are attached or related to the substratum in several ways. Some are attached by a threadlike muscular peduncle; some are cemented directly to the bottom or to some object lying on the bottom; and some live in holes that they have excavated into the soft materials of the substratum. If the habits of the individuals of a certain species are known, definite conclusions can be drawn by observing the relation of the majority of the shells to the substratum (Figs. 263, 264).

Inasmuch as the mollusks have evolved a great variety of relations to bottom materials, many of them if buried alive show the top of the deposit by their orientation or relation with reference to the stratification plane marking the original bottom. Pelecypods, being both sessile and vagrant benthos, as well as boring and burrowing individuals, are especially likely to be useful in this respect. Chitons, if buried alive, would have a significant orientation much like that of trilobites (Art. 168).

Among the arthropods, barnacles of the balanid type cement their shells to anything on the bottom; if they were buried alive, their position of growth would indicate the top of the enclosing deposit. Trilobites and crabs, buried while crawling over bottom sediments, clearly indicate which is the upward direction by their orientation along the separation plane (Figs. 265, 266).

This incomplete survey of the Invertebrata suffices to emphasize the importance of observing the orientation of undisturbed fossils and organically produced structures and features in sedimentary rocks. A few specific examples will now be discussed.

164. *Coelenterate Coralla and Bioherms.*—Coral and stromatoporoid heads typically have a ramose, pyriform, or domal shape; hence, if

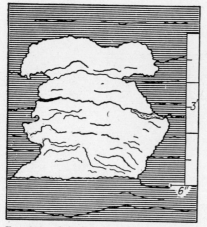

attached to the substratum or if the overwhelming majority of coralla at a definite horizon have the same orientation, it would be safe to conclude that they were buried in the position of growth and to use them as a criterion of top and bottom (Fig. 259).

Stromatoporoid genera such as *Clathrodictyon, Stromatocerium* (Fig. 260), *Beatricia,*[1] and *Cryptophragmus* might be found in the position of growth, and some coralline genera such as *Columnaria, Favosites, Halysites* and *Flabellum*, to mention only a few, commonly lie buried *in situ* in the enclosing rock.

Fig. 260.—Colonial *Stromatocerium* in massively bedded Ordovician Lamotte limestone of Vermont. The top of the mass and the several separation surfaces marking earlier tops are consistently convex upward. (Arts. 163, 164.)

Hemispheroidal, columnar, and conical bioherms, such as those described by Grabau (1903: 337–352), Cumings and Shrock (1928: 579–620, 1928a: 1–226), Fenton (1931: 203–212), Stockdale (1931a: 707–718), Cumings (1932: 331–352), Smith (1935: 48–49), Shrock (1938: 529–562), Butler (1940: 37–74), Laudon and Bowsher (1941: 2107–2160), and Parkinson (1945: 155–168), bear relations with the enclosing strata that clearly indicate the top or base of the mass (Fig. 261). Quaquaversal dips, oversteepening of the enclosing strata next to the bioherm by differential compaction, interwedging of biohermal and interbiohermal lithological facies, and other less obvious relations are important in determining the top or bottom of a biohermal complex.

[1] Twenhofel (1927: 105), in discussing *Beatricia*, states that " . . . an occasional rare specimen occurs in vertical position with the smaller end directed upward, and this appears to have been the position during life."

165. *Crinoid Root Systems.*—If one is fortunate enough to find well-preserved root structures of crinoids (or other pelmatozoans—cystoids and blastoids), it should be possible to determine whether or not the root system was buried in the position of growth. If this can be established, then the fossil provides a reliable criterion for determining the top of the bed on or in which it lies (Fig. 262). Buried root systems are common, especially in middle and upper Paleozoic strata, and should be looked for in calcareous and argillaceous rocks of those ages.

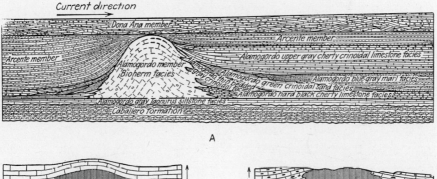

Fig. 261.—Bioherms. *A.* Bioherm in Mississippian sequence of New Mexico. The peripheral relations shown in this bioherm are similar to those present around Silurian and Devonian bioherms of the Michigan Basin. (*After Laudon and Bowsher, 1941, Bull. Am. Assoc. Petroleum Geologists, 25: 2128–2129, Fig. 10.*) *B.* A small stumplike mass of cavernous dolostone in the midst of thin-bedded dolomitic limestone of middle Silurian age near Lomira, Wis. There has been prominent steepening of the initial dip around the periphery of the structure because of differential compaction in the surrounding calcareous muds. Dozens of these features are present in an area of about 15 acres [see Shrock (1938)]. *C.* Coelenterate bioherm lying in the midst of shale and thin-bedded cherty limestone of middle Silurian age at Wabash, Ind. [see Cumings and Shrock (1928)]. (Art. 164.)

166. *Brachiopods Buried in Position of Growth.*—A few paleontologists have mentioned or described (and in rare cases illustrated) brachiopods that were buried in living position [Öpik (1930: 44), Twenhofel and Shrock (1935: 259–260, Fig. 93), and Cooper (1936–1937: 26–53)], but only a few genera have the kind of attachment to the substratum, which, if preserved, could be used for top and bottom determination (Fig. 263).

Burrowing brachiopods such as the living *Lingula* may be entombed in the sediment at the bottom of their burrows. Thus buried they indicate their burrowing habit and provide a means of determining the top of the layer in which they lie, as discussed in Art. 112. If in a shell bed the

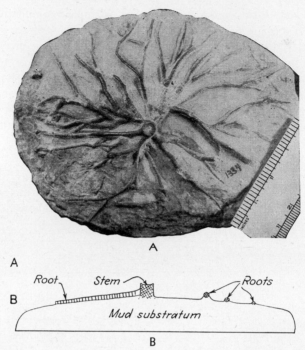

FIG. 262.—Root system of a Mississippian crinoid. *A.* View looking directly downward on the radial system. *B.* Diagrammatic sketch showing side view of *A.* (Art. 165.)

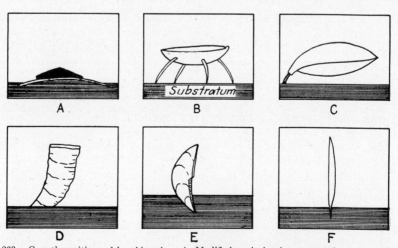

FIG. 263.—Growth positions of brachiopods. *A.* Modified conical valve cemented to a curved shell fragment partly embedded in the substratum. *B.* Shell elevated above the bottom by spines. *C.* Shell attached to substratum by fleshy pedicle. *D.* Cornucopialike shell cemented to the substratum. *E.* Shell with long pedicle beak partly buried in the bottom mud. *F.* Thin shell attached to the bottom by means of hingeline spines. Any of these shells if buried in growth position would provide a means of determining the top of the bed containing them. (Arts. 163, 166.)

great majority of cemented neotremates (*e.g.*, *Orbiculoidea*) lie on one side of the fragments to which they are attached, it is probable that this side represents the upper surface of the deposit. The flat and conical valves of a neotremate may also be buried essentially *in situ*, with the latter convex upward as illustrated in Fig. 264.

167. Mollusks Buried in Living Position.—Gastropods and pelecypods usually maintain a rather definite orientation as they move across the bottom, and if they were buried alive while active the orientation of the shell with reference to the substratum would have top and bottom significance. It is probable, however, that this kind of burial is relatively rare. However, a specimen of Middle Cambrian Burgess shale from

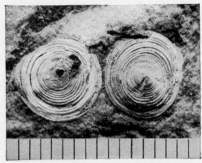

Fig. 264.—Flat (left) and convex (right) valves of an orbiculoid brachiopod in typical burial position. The conical valve usually is buried with the apex of the cone pointed upward. The scale is in millimeters. (Arts. 163, 166.)

near Field, B.C., displayed in the Geology Hall of the U.S. National Museum, shows hundreds of the tiny conical shells of the gastropod *Scenella varians* Walcott; the animals apparently were buried alive, for nearly all the cones point upward and rise above the bedding surface.

Certain clams excavate burrows in soft bottom materials, living in them at various depths beneath the surface and maintaining circulation with the overlying water by means of a tubular siphon or siphons. Individuals buried alive under these conditions would furnish a clue to the top of the enclosing bed. Such burials have been reported from ancient rocks, but are not common.

Cox and Dake (1916: 34, Figs. 12, 13) describe and illustrate an interesting case of the structural use of molluscan borings in California Tertiary rocks. They state that A. C. Lawson

. . . used the traces of the cavities made by boring mollusks to determine the structural positions of certain Tertiary formations. Such animals bore holes on a wave-cut rock surface which increase in diameter downward [see Fig. 143]. [The borings are preserved by fillings of material different from the enclosing sediment.] The containing rock offers absolute evidence as to the side of the unconformity on which the older formations lie, the direction of the base of the hole being determined either by a variation in size or by the rounded end of the filling.

Mollusks that cement their shell to a rock substratum or to objects lying on the bottom would, if buried alive, show the top or bottom direction in the deposit. Fossil "oysters," entombed in the position of growth, are to be expected in strata younger than the Paleozoic and should show relations similar to those they maintain in existing seas.

168. *Arthropods Buried Alive.*—Among the arthropods the Crustacea are the bottom dwellers most likely to be buried alive in present seas; in ancient seas, however, they shared this likelihood with the arachnid

FIG. 265.—Positive impressions of two specimens of *Calymene* from the Silurian Racine formation at Milwaukee. (Light is from the lower right.) Hundreds of specimens have been found, and in the majority of cases the carapaces were buried in living position. Compare with Fig. 266. (Arts. 163, 168.)

Merostomata (merostomes and eurypterids).

Permanently attached barnacles like *Balanus* should if buried alive offer a reliable criterion for determining the top of the enclosing rock (Art. 163).

Trilobites, merostomes, and eurypterids were vagrant benthos just as modern lobsters and crabs are. Like all vagrant benthonic animals, they were likely to be buried alive by sudden influxes of mud. Such burial seems to have occurred often, for many early and middle Paleozoic shales and limestones contain carapaces so completely preserved that live burial seems the only logical explanation (Figs. 265, 266). The well-known and often exquisitely preserved trilobites from the Cambrian Burgess shale, Ordovician Utica shale, and Silurian Racine dolomitic

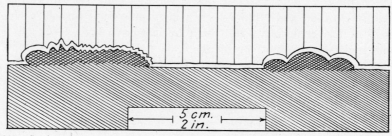

FIG. 266.—Section of two contiguous layers of Racine dolostone (Silurian) of eastern Wisconsin, showing longitudinal and transverse sections of specimens of the trilobite *Calymene* buried in crawling position. Dozens of similar specimens commonly occur in an area of a few square meters. Some of the carapaces may have been molts. Compare with Fig. 265. (Arts. 163, 168.)

limestone; the delicate merostomes from the Cambrian Lodi shale; the widely illustrated eurypterids from the Silurian water limes; and the crabs from more recent rocks are all examples of arthropods buried alive (see also Art. 178 and footnote 2 on page 318).

It is recognized that complete carapaces[1] of the arthropods just men-

---

[1] Some complete or nearly complete carapaces may represent molts buried so

tioned might be preserved even if the animal had died before burial, but such burials are probably not common.

169. *Borings, Burrows, and Tubes.*—The top and bottom significance of borings and burrows made by certain invertebrates is discussed fully in Arts. 110 and 112. Suffice it to state here that those borings and burrows which can be proved to have been excavated downward into the soft sediment or hard rock of the substratum are reliable top and bottom indicators.[1]

A few invertebrates secrete calcareous tubes, which are cemented to the hard rock bottom or to boulders, shells, and other objects on the bottom. One of the best known and of greatest antiquity is the tiny coiled tube of the worm *Spirorbis*. If many of the shell fragments on only one surface of a fossiliferous layer were covered with these tubes or others of similar nature, whereas the fragments of the opposite surface lacked them, it would be logical to conclude that the former surface was the top side of the layer.

170. *Trails, Tracks, Footprints, and Other Impressions Made by Sedentary or Moving Organisms.*—Sandstones, shales, limestones, and coals are full of raised and depressed features made in soft sediments by animals and plants. If the mode[2] and conditions of formation of the feature can be established or if its top and bottom significance can be observed in undisturbed rocks, the feature can then be employed with reasonable satisfaction in determining the attitude of steeply inclined beds.

The literature of trails, tracks, and footprints is voluminous and in many languages, and no attempt is made in this work to list more than a few of the more recent or well-known references (see Art. 111). The features are discussed at length in Art. 111, and little further comment is necessary here. Suffice it to state that both raised and depressed features

---

soon after being shed that they did not disintegrate. Since these would tend to retain the same relative position as that of the animal itself, they are fully as reliable as carapaces of animals buried alive if a few can be found with the same orientation on a single bedding surface or within a thin layer.

[1] An additional structural use to which the borings of marine animals may be put is in determining whether uplift or subsidence occurred after the boring was made. In this connection, Barrows (1913: 130) states

The remains of marine animals which are known to habitually bore into rock is evidence of an unconformity, because it presupposes the existence of a firm bed in an earlier formation, hard enough to attract the borers, before the overlying beds were laid down. Subsequent crustal movements were upward if the holes are found to have been eroded or filled with terrestrial deposits, or downward if filled with marine deposits.

[See also Cox and Dake (1916: 34), Barrows (1917: 965–972), and Art. 167.]

[2] A case in point is that of the well-known Upper Cambrian trail *Climactichnites*

made by active sedentary organisms and by moving animals may be useful top and bottom indicators if their mode of formation can first be established.

171. *Coprolites and Other Animal Excreta.*—Various benthonic and swimming animals deposit excretal pellets on bottoms over which they

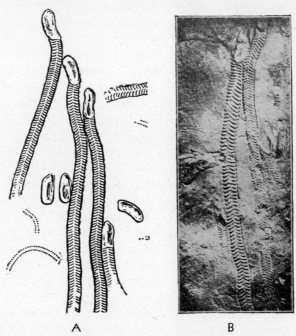

A   B

FIG. 267.—Upper Cambrian trails—*Climactichnites wilsoni* (Logan)—made in loose sand by a creeping animal that left a broad transversely ribbed trail resembling the track of an automobile tire. The transverse ridges are sharp-crested, whereas the separating grooves are round-bottomed; together they furnish a means of identifying the upper side of the trail. The trails, which reach 10 cm. (4 in.) in width, commonly terminate at one end in an oval body that is believed to mark an impression made by the animal as it came to rest on the bottom. (Art. 170.) [*A, reduced to one-fiftieth natural size, is after Clarke in Burling, 1917, Am. Jour. Sci., (4) 44: 394, Fig. 4. B, same reduction, also after Burling, ibid, Fig. 5.*]

pass, and if these do not disintegrate before burial they form characteristic spheroidal, ellipsoidal, rodlike, and irregular particles which are

(Fig. 267), which consists of a transversely corrugated band with a wider, oval-shaped impression at one end. Earlier geologists assumed that the trail was made by an animal which crawled on the bottom toward the oval impression, which was considered its last resting place. If this were true, the fossil, at least in some instances, would represent the burial of the trailmaking animal while it was alive. Burling (1917: 396), however, states that on one slab which he studied the trailmaking animal " . . . certainly started from the oval body end to crawl away," but he concludes that " . . . those in the Albany slab may have come to rest in the manner described by the early observers. Naturally, however, the conclusion that the oval body end was made last has called forth attempts to explain the disappearance of the animal."

likely to become cemented to the materials of the substratum. After the excreted masses have been buried and the covering sediment has been lithified, the contiguous layers are likely to separate in such a way that the coprolites, pellets, and other excreted forms remain attached to the top of the bed composed of the organic detritus on which they came to rest. Many such coprolitic layers are found in the Triassic Rhaetic bone beds of England (Fig. 147). For additional comments on coprolites and castings see Art. 113.

172. BURIAL POSITION OF DISTURBED AND DISINTEGRATED ORGANIC HARD PARTS.—The orientation of fossils within and upon the top or bottom surface of the containing bed and the relations they have with associated specimens furnish considerable information about the bottom conditions at the time of burial. These same relations commonly have top and bottom significance, as pointed out in following paragraphs.

When an animal dies and its flesh decomposes and disappears, the hard parts, released by the decomposition, become a part of the substratum, subject to the forces of destruction present there. On land the hard parts of animals and the more resistant parts of plants have little chance of preservation under normal conditions. In the case of aqueous organisms, however, the hard parts sink toward the bottom and if not destroyed in their descent finally come to rest with the bottom sediments.

173. *Fossils with Random Orientation.*—On quiet bottoms, over which the waters are full of organisms, the hard parts released from animal and plant tissue by decomposition accumulate in chaotic fashion as they sink to a resting place in the animal and plant debris of the substratum. Diatom frustules, foraminiferal tests, sponge spicules, fragmental corals, broken and disarticulated bryozoan zoaria, complete and disarticulated brachiopod and pelecypod shells, cephalopod and gastropod shells, crushed and disintegrated echinodermal tests, arthropod exoskeletal fragments, and the many different kinds of vertebrate hard parts (bones, scales, teeth, spines, ear bones, etc.)—all mingle in a tangled and jumbled accumulation in which the individual hard part has random orientation.

As such accumulations grow in thickness and extent, fine sediment sifts down into the highly permeable deposit, filling any shells that are partly open and gradually filling up the interstitial space. Earthquake shocks may jar the fossiliferous conglomeration enough to cause slight settling and reorientation of some of the fragments, and occasional unusually severe storms may create waves powerful enough to stir up the bottom materials. These same storm waves may rip loose from their substrata cemented or attached animals such as sponge coenostea, coralline coralla, and bryozoan zoaria. These stony masses will be rolled down slopes toward deeper water or along the bottom until they come to rest, quite probably in some position other than that of growth. The final deposit is a layer of fossils with a calcareous or shale matrix in which the individual fossils are oriented at random. In nature it is quite common to find this kind of fossiliferous bed succeeded by shale representing mud washed in after a flood on land or a storm at sea (see Art. 166).

174. *Reorientation by Penecontemporaneous Deformation of Enclosing Sediment.*—If, in accumulations like the one just described, shells and other fossils are not numerous enough to make a continuous layer, so that soft sediment constitutes most of the bottom deposit, the heavy

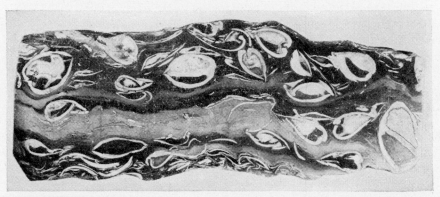

FIG. 268.—Reorientation of buried shells by penecontemporaneous deformation of enclosing sediment. Some of the shells are completely filled with black carbonaceous shale; others have a composite filling —the lower part of black sediment, the upper of gray calcite. The plane of composition of the partial shale fillings was horizontal at the time sediment entered the shells, but most of the shells containing the incomplete fillings were reoriented during flowage of the enclosing mud. In general, however, the shells have been rotated not over 45° from their original position so that the top of the bed can be determined by noting the relation of the incomplete filling and its plane of composition to the general bedding in the rock. Reduced (× ⅜). (Art. 174.)

articulated shells may sink into the soft mud. As the latter flows, already buried or partly buried shells are rotated from their original position. Inasmuch as many of the shells in this kind of deposit are likely to be only partly filled with mud, it is possible to determine the top of the fossiliferous layer by noting on which side of the flat plane[1] marking the upper surface of the partial filling the cavity or its secondary filling lies. It is necessary, of course, to select for this purpose only those shells which have the plane essentially parallel to the bedding. Partly filled shells that have been rotated far from their original position by mud flowage should be ignored (see Arts. 1, 180 to 183, and Figs. 1, 268).

---

[1] Cullison (1938: 987) has proposed calling this surface the "plane of composition," defining it as the horizontal plane of an incomplete filling formed at the time when the material is introduced into the shell (see Art. 182). The designation has been adopted here as applied to incomplete fillings in all sorts of cavities.

Cullison (1938: 986) credits Walter H. Bucher for the information that in certain beds of Upper Ordovician age partly filled shells, reworked after the filling had hardened, now lie in the rock with the planes of composition having random orientation. This situation should be compared with Fig. 268.

175. *Smothered Bottoms.*—The upper surfaces of many thin marine limestone beds alternating with shale layers have an unusual assemblage of fossils composed of complete, well-preserved, and commonly very fragile and delicate specimens associated with the comminuted organic debris remaining after scavenger action. Upon separation from the

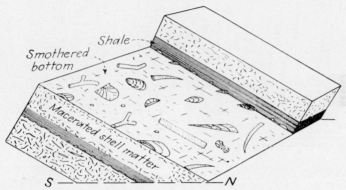

Fig. 269.—Smothered bottoms. Diagram showing thin-bedded Ordovician limestones near Kentland, Ind., with well-preserved fossils on the upper surface of the beds and macerated shell material scattered throughout. The intercalated shale layers are interpreted as representing sudden influxes of mud that buried the bottom-dwelling organisms. After the water had cleared, the fauna from neighboring bottoms unaffected by the mud moved in and established itself. The strata dip north at an angle of 30°. See Fig. 270. (Art. 175.)

contiguous shale the bottom of the limestone layer shows few if any recognizable fossils, whereas the top surface, from which some of the adhering shale may have to be removed, reveals the assemblage just described. A transverse section, especially if viewed under a microscope, shows that the bulk of the limestone layer is composed of comminuted fossils (Figs. 269, 270.)

This feature was helpful to Shrock and Malott (1933: 347) in determining the correct order of succession of steeply tilted and vertical Ordovician limestones near Kentland, Ind. Their discussion follows:

The numerous fossils which were collected from this quarry came mainly from the upper side of the layers [which dip northward from 51° to 70°]. The fossils themselves are firmly imbedded in the limestone, and are separated from the overlying layer of limestone by a very thin shale layer. The shale layer produces a zone of weakness along which the beds separate easily.

It may be suggested that the change from calcium carbonate precipitation to an influx of mud buried the organisms living on the bottom before the scavengers could chew them up, because the remainder of the limestone bed is to a large extent composed of pulverized shell fragments. Hence the side of the limestone layer having the fossils imbedded in it and in turn covered by shale would represent the top of the bed.

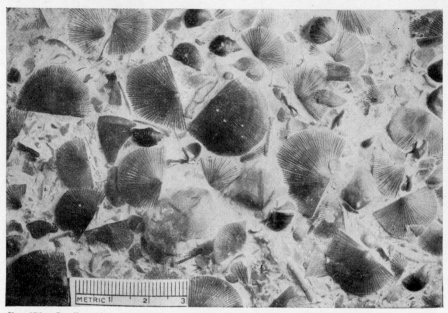

Fig. 270.—Small portion of a smothered bottom showing complete and fragmented shells as they lay when overwhelmed by a sudden influx of mud. Some of the gray calcareous mud can be seen between the larger shells. It is to be noted that most of the shells are convex upward. An assemblage like this would not be found on the lower surface of a bed. The rock is Upper Ordovician limestone from Anticosti Island, Canada. (Arts. 175, 178.)

In a later discussion of the Kentland area, Shrock (1937: 514) states that the faunal assemblage of one of the stratigraphic divisions consists of smaller than normal bryozoans, brachiopods, and ostracods which

. . . are especially abundant on the upper sides of the layers but often are not visible because of the argillaceous films which separate the layers. The layers themselves are composed largely of comminuted shell matter. Apparently the comminuted materials represent shells macerated by scavengers and fragmented by waves, whereas the well preserved fossils on the upper sides of the layers were saved by an influx of mud which buried them instantly.

Smothered bottoms, an expression here introduced for fossiliferous surfaces similar to those just described, are common and widespread in sequences composed of alternating marine limestone and shale layers (Fig. 270).

Many years ago Shaler (1888: 412–415), in discussing the origin of the divisions between layers of sedimentary rock, pointed out that

. . . the upper part of a layer of a limestone abounds in well preserved fossils which project slightly from its surface, while the lower layer of the overlying limestone stratum exhibits no such distinct fossils. Those which it contains are more or less commingled with the clay matter.

He went on to say that the argillaceous material of the barren shale partings between the limestone layers has the same nature as the matrix of the fossiliferous beds, and he ascribed the death and burial of the organisms in such sequences to earthquake shocks which killed the animals and affected their burial through stirring up the bottom materials. Although this explanation may be satisfactory in some cases, there are many others in which the organic debris obviously was not disturbed immediately before burial, for the most delicate structures of the assemblage remained intact on burial. More satisfactory for examples such as the latter is the explanation offered by Barrell (1917: 833), who accounted for fossiliferous layers intercalated with barren shale layers as follows:

. . . shells of living or recently dead mollusks were buried rapidly, perhaps in a single culminating storm, by a blanket of wave-stirred mud. During times of slow accumulation the successive generations of shells would be completely destroyed by boring animals, by solution, and by the recurrent wear of wave action. Thus it is characteristic of fossiliferous formations that the fossils occur in thin layers between much thicker unfossiliferous beds. Within the layer the shells are commonly well preserved, though often showing a disturbance by wave or current action. The preservation of fossils is, then, following this view, generally due to the recurrence of culminating storms at long intervals, which, stirring the bottom to unusual depths, suddenly bury a layer of organic debris beneath a protecting mantle of argillaceous or calcareous mud.

Twenhofel (1931: 422) has also pointed out that

Many marine limestones overlain by shales contain excellently preserved fossil shells on their upper surfaces, a preservation readily explained on the basis that the overlying shales were deposited sufficiently rapidly to bring about entombment before the shells had been seriously injured by scavenger organisms.

[See also Dapples (1938: 64)].

A second substance that can smother and penetrate the organisms and organic debris of a bottom is gelatinous silica. Figure 271 shows a layer of chert consisting of a fossiliferous lower part and a barren upper part. Chert layers of this kind are common in Middle Western Mississippian limestones and probably are widespread. They are believed to have been formed in the following manner: A bottom covered with myriads of echinodermal fragments was overwhelmed by an influx of gelatinous silica that, settling out of the overlying water, sank into and filled all the voids of the highly permeable and porous accumulation for a considerable distance below the surface. After the silica had completely covered the debris, it continued to be deposited as a layer free of fragments. It then hardened to chert, and the latter, when brought into the zone of weathering, was attacked along joints by ground water. The calcitic fragments were dissolved, and cavities were left to give the lower part of the chert layer a porous nature; the upper part, being largely unaffected, remained as dense, conchoidally fracturing chert.

FIG. 271.—Mississippian crinoidal fragments buried by silica. Gelatinous silica overwhelmed the crinoidal sand, filling the interstices and finally completely covering the bottom to a depth of several centimeters (5 cm. = 2 in.). Typical chert layers in exposures have a spongy basal part, caused by solution of fragments, and a dense, conchoidally fracturing upper part. Compare with Fig. 272. (Art. 175.)

176. *Random Burials.*—Spheroidal and ellipsoidal organic hard parts, if buried singly by muds or gelatinous silica, are likely to show the top of the entombing deposit by characterisitc relations to the surrounding sediments.

If a shell or other fossil lies partly or completely embedded in one surface of a chert nodule, its position is likely to be at the base of that nodule for several reasons. On the assumption that the object was overwhelmed by a descending mass of gelatinous silica, the latter would flow around and to some extent under it, as well as covering it, and upon hardening to a chert nodule, probably flat on the underside, would hold the entombed fossil in a firm grasp (Fig. 272). On the other hand, if the hard part dropped into a mass of gelatinous silica, it would if it had much weight sink into and through the soft silica, coming to rest at the bottom of the siliceous mass, where its relation to substratum and entombing material would be essentially the same as in the previous case (Fig. 271). In this kind of burial the organic hard part will probably retain its original composition, which is usually calcareous, for, as pointed out by Fowler *et al.* (1934: 50), " . . . if any fossils could sink into the gel they should collect at its base. Then in order that they be silicified, silica would have to diffuse through the silica gel"—a reaction that does not seem likely. The hard part may be removed later by solution, so that the only remaining record of its existence is a cavity on the walls of which are impressed the features of the external surface of the hard part. As a result of these modes of burial, cherty nodules may preserve the only

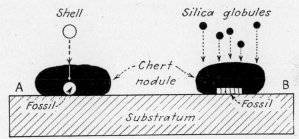

Fig. 272.—Burial of organic fragments by silica. *A.* A shell sinks into and through a discoidal mass of gelatinous silica, coming to rest on the substratum completely surrounded by silica. Later it becomes a fossil in a chert nodule. *B.* Small globules of gelatinous silica build up a discoidal mass around and above a fragment of a crinoid stem. Later this stem will be a fossil at the base of the chert nodule. (Art. 176.)

record of the life of a given bottom, for scavengers will have destroyed all the organic debris not protected by the silica.

Individual coral heads, massive bryozoan zoaria, complete brachiopod shells, and other organically produced hard parts, if buried singly by mud, are likely to show the same peripheral and top relations to the surrounding and covering laminae as buried boulders (see Fig. 259 and Art. 107). The surrounding laminae end abruptly against the object, generally rising sharply just at the contact, and later laminae arch gently over it. If the object is heavy enough to overcome the resistance of the supporting bottom materials, it sinks into them slightly and may produce visible disturbance; otherwise it merely rests on the surface of the substratum.

177. *Shell Heaps and Channel Deposits.*—On bottoms of strong current action, two significant features are occasionally formed. Under certain conditions the more resistant structures of plants and the hard parts of animals are heaped up on the bottom in windrows or mounds, between which the bottom is barren of organic remains. Mounds like these, consisting of finely comminuted corals, bryozoans, and brachiopods, rise as much as a meter above the top of the Silurian Byron dolomitic limestone of eastern Wisconsin (Fig. 273). They are especially significant because the fauna they preserve constitutes about the only record of the life of early Byron time.

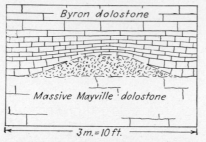

FIG. 273.—Shell heap along contact between Mayville and Byron formations of eastern Wisconsin Silurian. Shell fragments were heaped in low mounds and ridges on a shallow bottom and later buried by calcareous muds of the Byron. The material of the mounds consists of shell fragments, bryozoan shreds, small coral heads, and tiny mollusks. (Art. 177.)

Scott (1930: 53–56) describes heaps and ridges of shell fragments in the Cretaceous Fredericksburg limestone of Texas, pointing out that they have the form of large asymmetrical- and oscillation-ripple ridges (see Arts. 70, 79, and Figs. 65, 85). These ridges average about 85 mm. (3½ in.) in height and are spaced somewhat over 1 m. apart. They trend northeast-southwest, parallel with the old Cretaceous shore line. The profile of the two types of clastic ridges provides a reliable top and bottom criterion.

Strong bottom currents may cut longitudinal channels or excavate shallow basins in the bottom sediments, and these, if backfilled with organic debris and subsequently buried, constitute a useful top and bottom feature. In such depressions, as at Kentland, Ind. (Fig. 274), the fauna preserved in the channel fillings may be the only extant record of the life present in the general neighborhood at the time when the channels were cut, the other remains having been swept away by the currents that backfilled the depressions (see Art. 132.)

Hall (1843: 236, 237) describes and illustrates an interesting case of fossils preserved on the underside of the counterpart of a channel about 60 mm. across and several millimeters deep, and Westgate and Fischer (1933: 1161–1172) report bone beds filling channels on the upper surface of the Devonian Columbus limestone of Ohio (Fig. 187).

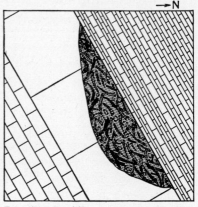

FIG. 274.—Fossiliferous scour-and-fill structure in thin-bedded dolomitic Ordovician limestone near Kentland, Ind. The channel was scoured cut by current action and then backfilled with comminuted material consisting of bryozoan shreds, brachiopod valves, and small ostracods. In the field this feature proved useful in corroborating the conclusions drawn from other data. The strata dip 60° to the north. The heavy middle stratum is about 5 cm. (2 in.) thick. (Arts. 132, 177.)

Both shell heaps and channel deposits of fossils, although somewhat similar in size and shape, can be useful in top and bottom determination if it is possible to determine their true nature.

178. *Separation and Burial of Plane, Convex, and Concave Hard Parts.* On bottoms where waves and currents are strong, the hard parts of organisms, released by decomposition of the flesh and tissue that once held them together, are subjected to the actions of the agitated water. As a result of the agitation some exoskeletal and skeletal structures are dismembered, many hard parts are broken, and all the organic debris is sorted out, transported, and ultimately deposited in conformity with the competency of the transporting agents, the nature of the constituent

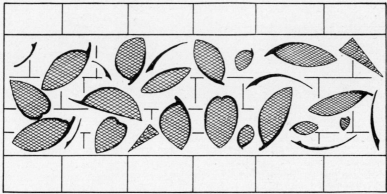

Fig. 275.—A fossiliferous limestone layer between barren layers in which the individual shells have random orientation because of little or no disturbance during or after burial. The diagram is based on a specimen of Ordovician Platteville limestone from Kentland, Ind. The shells are shown as about natural size. The material filling the shells is similar to the enclosing limestone but is crosshatched to make the fossils more conspicuous. (Arts. 176, 178.)

hard parts, and the environmental conditions prevailing at the sites of deposition.

Hard parts having top and bottom significance by virtue of their ultimate burial orientation include conoidal or semiellipsoidal coralline coralla, valves of brachiopod, pelecypod, ostracod, and conchostracod shells, and exoskeletal shields of trilobites, eurypterids, crabs, and other related crustaceans.

In relatively quiet waters these flat and curved hard parts merely collect where released from the animals upon their death and decomposition and assume random orientation dictated by bottom conditions. There is little about such a chaotic accumulation of shells and fragments to indicate which part of the deposit is younger. One feature previously mentioned (see also Art. 183) is the semilenticular cavity or cavity filling on the underside of certain curved fragments oriented with their convexity upward. Since a chaotic mass like the accumulation just described is almost certain to have curved fragments with almost every direction of orientation, the presence of the semilenticular cavities and their fillings under fossils with only a certain orientation gives a means whereby the top of the deposit, as well as original horizontality in the mass, can be determined (Fig. 275).

On bottoms where current action is appreciable, shells and exoskeletons may be buried quickly after being turned to a stable position on the bottom. This is particularly true of planoconvex and concavoconvex brachiopod and pelecypod shells. Planoconvex shells of *Hesperorthis* come to rest with the flat valve down and the highly curved valve convex upward (Figs. 276 to 279). The same is true of articulated pelecypod shells of the pecten type buried under similar bottom conditions. Resupinate and concavoconvex brachiopod shells, and both individual valves if they be separated, also come finally to rest with the valves convex upward (Fig. 278, 279).

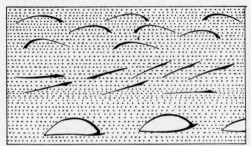

FIG. 276.—Granular argillaceous limestone containing separate valves and complete shells of a dorsi-biconvex brachiopod like *Atrypa*. In the upper zone the convex dorsal valves are disposed so as to rest convex upward. In the middle flat or slightly arched ventral valves are arranged with variable orientation but with a tendency to imbricate. In the lower zone complete shells lie with the flat valve parallel to bedding and the strongly arched valve convex upward. The diagram illustrates how shells are disarticulated and the separated valves selectively concentrated under strong current action. (Art. 178.)

On bottoms of moderate current action (*i.e.*, where the currents are strong enough to bring in and turn over convex valves but too weak to wash away the accumulating mud) the individual valves assume an imbricated relationship as they are buried. In a single layer, therefore, the valves on the bottom are concave with reference to the bedding surface; those within the bed are arched upward if viewed in transverse section; and those on the upper surface are convex with reference to the layer (Fig. 279). It is possible, therefore, to determine the top of such a bed by viewing a transverse section or one of the bedding surfaces.

On bottoms of strong current action, where fragmental and detrital sediments are the rule, coralla, bivalve shells, and crustacean exoskeletons and shells are carried over the substratum as far as the current can float, roll, drag, or slide them. During this transport the individual valves of the shells and the segments and shields of the exoskeletons are almost certain to be disarticulated or pulled apart and then separated spatially in conformity with their shape, size, and weight[1]. It is not uncommon to

[1] If the plane and convex valves of a given species of brachiopod or pelecypod or the cephalic and pygidial shields and thoracic segments of crustaceans are buried in

find contiguous layers with one showing mostly complete shells, the next full of convex valves, and still a higher one containing flat valves—all belonging to a single species. Such a succession merely shows that the

Fig. 277.—Section of a fossiliferous limestone from the Mississippian Windsor group of Nova Scotia, showing numerous current-strewn brachiopod valves that lie convex upward in the rock. The bulk of the rock consists of small concretionary calcareous pellets. Slightly reduced (×.8). (Art. 178.)

bottom currents in one specific locality varied in competency through the period of time represented by the deposits (Figs. 276, 278).

Usually the flat valves of bivalve shells and the flat plates of crus-

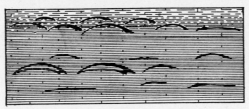

Fig. 278.—Current-strewn valves of *Sowerbyella* (XI), a concavo-convex Ordovician brachiopod. The enclosing sediment is argillaceous and finely granular limestone. The specimen from which the diagram was made came from Trenton Falls, New York. It is worth noting that the slightly curved dorsal valves tend to lie convex upward the same as the more strongly curved ventral valves. (Art. 178.)

tacean exoskeletons come finally to rest parallel to the bedding or in

close association, it would be reasonable to infer that the currents or waves which broke them up were gentle. If, on the other hand, pieces of a definite shape, size, or weight are selectively concentrated, it is obvious that the currents had sufficient competency and persisted long enough to effect a complete separation of the fragments involved.

shingled position, and their orientation has no structural significance (Figs. 276, 278).

Curved plates, on the other hand, are carried along until turned so as to be convex upward. Since this is the position of greatest stability for curved plates lying in the path of a current, as pointed out long ago by Sorby (1908: 189)[1] and reiterated by numerous textbook authors since

Fig. 279.—Three views of a thin fossiliferous limestone layer, showing preferred orientation of the two valves of the concavo-convex Ordovician brachiopod *Sowerbyella*. *A.* View of undersurface, showing both ventral and dorsal valves convex upward (concave with reference to the bedding surface on which they lie). *B.* View of upper surface of same specimen as *A*, showing both valves convex upward. *C.* Transverse section of same specimen as *A* and *B*, showing most of the valves convex upward. In this section it should be noted that two of the valves in the middle of the illustration have a calcite-filled cavity under them. (Arts. 178, 182.)

then, most of them are buried in this position, the direction of convexity indicating the top of the layer (Figs. 276 to 279).

Examples of selectively oriented fossil fragments are to be found in rocks of all ages from earliest Cambrian to coquinas on present-day beaches. Convex arthropod carapaces, *in toto* and as represented by individual shields and thoracic segments, are familiar to every paleontologist.[2] Upper Cambrian brachiopods, as illustrated by *Dicellomus* and

[1] Sorby (1908: 189) found that "separate valves of bivalve shells . . . easily turn over and lie with their convex side upwards, so as to offer much resistance to a current, and may thus be sorted by being left alone."

[2] As pointed out in Art. 167, the tiny conical shells of the gastropod *Scenella varians*

Westonia, to mention but two genera, are more often than not arrayed on bedding surfaces with convexity upward (Fig. 280). Similarly oriented brachiopod and pelecypod valves are abundant in Ordovician strata of North America, as illustrated in Figs. 270 and 279, and there is no reason to suppose that they do not also occur in strata of the same age in other

FIG. 280.—The top surface of a thin layer of Upper Cambrian sandstone from Wisconsin, showing both valves of the brachiopod *Westonia* lying convex upward, the preferred position of burial if there is appreciable bottom current. Contiguous layers commonly separate along a surface where shells are concentrated, and a few valves may cling to the undersurface of the overlying layer. (Art. 178.)

continents. The Ordovician Utica shale contains trilobite remains lying convex upward[1] on the top surfaces of beds and concave downward

---

Walcott lie with the cone pointed upward and rise above the general bedding surface. The position of entombment indicates that the animals were buried alive.

[1] An unusual mode of burial, in which the exoskeletons lie with their convex backs down, is illustrated by the well-known assemblage of *Triarthrus becki* individuals long ago described by Beecher (1894: 38–43). Exoskeletons complete with appendages and ranging in age from small larval forms to full-grown individuals lie with their backs down in the enclosing sediment. Since this position is presumably the opposite of that assumed in life and also since it is obvious, from the excellent state of preservation of the delicate ventral parts of the organism, that the environment of burial must have been one of quiet water, unusual conditions have to be postulated to explain the death position. Realizing this, Beecher (1894: 38–43) suggested that the trilobites, which could swim freely or crawl along the bottom, were killed by a sudden change in temperature brought about through a shift of currents and that (p. 40) " . . . on dying, they coiled themselves up in the same manner as the recent isopods. Then upon unrolling they would necessarily lie on their backs. Even if they did not coil up,

on the bottoms (Fig. 281). A similar assemblage has been observed in the Silurian Racine dolostone of eastern Wisconsin, where the highly convex cephalic and pygidial shields of *Bumastus ioxus* are stacked one on top the other, convex upward, like inverted evaporating dishes in a chemical supply room (Fig. 282). It is significant to note that a few meters above the Bumastus layer there is a veritable coquina of brachiopod, mollusk, and trilobite remains in which the individual fragments have random orientation.

Fig. 281.—Ordovician carbonaceous shale (Utica) from Collingwood, County of Grey, Ontario, containing trilobite remains. *A.* Top surface of a layer with two convex pygidia. *B.* Undersurface of covering layer with concave impression of *A.* *C.* Undersurface of layer *A*, showing concave impressions of two pygidia and one cranidium. All specimens reduced (×0.5). (Art. 178.)

Oriented brachiopod and pelecypod valves are common and widespread throughout strata of the later Paleozoic (Fig. 277), and the latter

any swimming animal having a boat-shaped form would settle downward through the water with the concave side up."

Laudon (1939: 211–213) has reported an unusual assemblage of carapaces of the Ordovician trilobite *Isotelus gigas* Dekay in the Bromide formation of southern Oklahoma. The assemblage is unusual for several reasons. Large congregations of excellently preserved specimens are present on the bedding surfaces of limestone layers, and the fossils commonly overlap because of being crowded closely together. Of special interest in our present discussion is the fact that (p. 213) "about half of the specimens are oriented in the ventral position so that the hypostoma is commonly exposed in position." This assemblage seems to be an excellent example of trilobites buried suddenly either while alive or almost immediately after death.

are characteristic of both Mesozoic and Cenozoic shell beds the world over.

If the actual curved valves that were deposited in the manner described in preceding paragraphs have been dissolved away, the containing bed tends to split through the cavity once occupied by the fossil. If the valve lay in complete contact with the underlying sediment, its original upward convexity is reflected by a small mound on the upper surface of the separation plane and a similarly shaped dome in the base of the overlying layer. On the other hand, if the valve was not pressed firmly into the substratum at the time of burial, so that a cavity remained under the highest part of the arched fragment, the surface of splitting will show the mound trun-

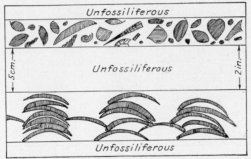

Fig. 282.—Massive Racine dolostone (Silurian) from eastern Wisconsin showing an upper fossiliferous layer in which the shells have random orientation and a lower in which cranidia and pygidia of the trilobite *Bumastus* are arranged convex upward. The two fossiliferous layers, which alternate with barren beds, illustrate how shells are oriented in conformity with environmental conditions on the bottoms where they accumulated. (Art. 178.)

cated by a horizontal plane—the plane of composition—but the dome will appear as before (Fig. 283).

179. *Differentially Eroded Fossils.*—Large organic structures, such as the trunks and limbs of trees, the shells of large cephalopods, the valves of large pelecypods, and the bones of animals, after coming to rest on the substratum where they are ultimately to be buried may be eroded on the upper surface before entombment. Since such an eroded surface, lacking the original features once present, would contrast sharply with the undersurface, which would retain those features, it constitutes a possible top and bottom criterion and has been used as such by Stearn (1934: 151, 154), who found differentially eroded stems of *Calamites* in tilted beds of Pennsylvanian age at the Parnell Hill quicksilver mine in Arkansas. He describes the fossil as follows (page 151): "In the shaly-sandstone a specimen of *Calamites stanleyensis* was found with the delicate reed flutings on its north side meticulously preserved and its south side smooth." He concludes: "It is considered probable that the preserved flutings were buried in mud, leaving the other side to be worn by wave wash. The smooth side would thus suggest the top of the beds. In each case the smooth side was found toward the south."

Doubtless other examples of differentially eroded fossils would be discovered if a more careful search of geologic literature were made with the matter in mind and more especially if the phenomenon were sought in the field.

180. PRIMARY AND SECONDARY FILLINGS OF HOLLOW ORGANIC STRUCTURES.—Sedimentary rocks contain certain kinds of organically produced cavities that if partly filled may serve as top and bottom criteria. In order to be useful these cavities must be partly filled, and the

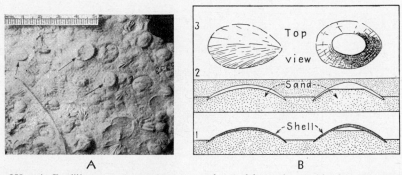

A   B

FIG. 283.—*A*. Fossiliferous sandstone showing complete and incomplete positive impressions left by brachiopod valves. The flat-topped incomplete impressions may have had their form originally, as illustrated in *B*, or may be the result of the top part adhering to the overlying layer. *B*. Diagrams showing how positive impressions are formed in sand. 1 shows two valves that have settled into the sandy substratum. The left one is fully supported, whereas the right one is not and will be buried with a cavity under the highest part of the arched valve. In 2 the valves have been buried and later dissolved away, but the underside of the covering layer preserves an impression of the original sandy bottom with the valves in place. 3 shows a top view of the complete and incomplete positive impressions as they would appear on a bedding surface. (Arts. 178, 182, 183.)

filling hardened, before the bed in which they lie is disturbed. Under these conditions the flat upper surface of the partial filling marks the horizontal plane at the time of formation and indicates the top of the deposit in which it lies.[1]

This flat upper surface, which Hadding (1929: 63–64) recognized as a geological spirit level and to which Cullison (1938: 983) applied the expression *plane of composition*, is of great significance in partly filled cavities. Since it defines horizontality at the time of formation, it is parallel to the bedding if there is no initial dip (Fig. 284). If there is a small acute angle between the plane and the bedding, that angle indicates

---

[1] The upper portion of the cavity may remain empty; it may be filled shortly after the shell is buried or long after by calcite or silica; and it may even become empty again by solution of the secondary filling. None of these conditions affects the use of the primary partial filling as a top and bottom criterion.

the amount of initial inclination[1] (Fig. 285).   In cases where both plane of composition and bedding surface are gently inclined to the present horizontal plane, the latter somewhat more than the former, either the bed has undergone steepening of dip by differential settling or has been folded, the actual amount of rotation being the angle between the horizontal plane and the plane of composition (Fig. 286).   Finally, if the plane of composition is parallel to bedding and the beds are folded, the angle of inclination is the total amount of rotation from the horizontal

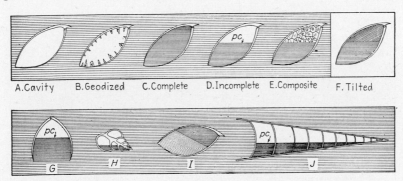

A.Cavity   B.Geodized   C.Complete   D.Incomplete   E.Composite   F.Tilted

Fig. 284.—Incomplete fillings. *A.* A brachiopod shell that remained empty after burial—a rather uncommon phenomenon. *B.* A shell that became geodized after burial by growth on the inner surface of radially directed calcite crystals. In some shells the crystals are confined to the lower part of the internal cavity (see Fig. 288). *C.* A shell that was completely filled at time of burial. *D.* Shell with an incomplete filling. The flat surface of the incomplete filling is the plane of composition *pc.* *E.* Shell with composite heterogeneous filling composed of an incomplete filling of mud separated by the plane of composition from the calcite-filled upper cavity. *F.* Shell with a composite homogeneous filling composed of two mud elements. After the shell had been about half filled and the mud slightly consolidated, it was tilted or rotated into a new position and the mud introduced later is differently stratified (see *I*). No enclosing sediment is shown since the shell has been reoriented to conform with *A* to *E.* Its true position is shown in *I.* *G.* A pelecypod with an incomplete filling. *H.* A gastropod with an incomplete filling. *I.* A brachiopod shell which was partly filled in another position and then rotated to the position shown in which the remaining cavity was filled. The complete filling, therefore, is composite and homogeneous. *J.* An incompletely filled cephalopod shell. (Arts. 180, 182.)

(Fig. 286).   This structural use of partly filled cavities is similar to that of inorganically produced cavities discussed in Arts. 1 and 158.

If at some time long after burial a fossiliferous bed is subjected to weathering, ground waters will deposit calcite, silica, and less commonly other substances in open spaces.   In this way the interstitial voids of highly fossiliferous layers are partly or completely filled.   Of more importance for the present purpose, however, is the fact that hollow shells, partly filled with bottom sediments during or soon after burial, are now

---

[1] Cullison (1938: 985–986) points out how initial inclination and subsequent steepening of dip by compaction, etc., might be determined in strata peripheral to buried and resurrected hills of the Ozark region, where Bridge and Dake (1923: 93–99) recognized dips as great as 30°.   Other possible uses of incomplete fillings are identification of tilted cross-laminated beds and recognition of reworked or disturbed fossils (see Arts. 1, 172).

completely filled with the introduced substances. Small cavities left under curved valves lying convex upward are likewise filled, and any other partly filled cavities in the rock are likely to be completely filled. Those cavities which were partly filled originally and later completely filled have a bipartite filling which might well be designated *composite*. It consists of two parts, a lower deposit of massive or laminated sediment, essentially like that of the enclosing rock, and an upper hemispheroidal part composed of calcite, silica, or some other introduced substance.

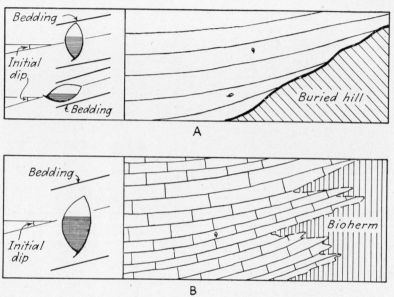

Fig. 285.—Incomplete fillings as indexes of initial dip. *A*. Diagram of gently inclined strata on the flank of a buried hill. Two shells with incomplete fillings, as shown at the left, indicate the initial dip of the strata. *B*. Inclined strata on the flank of a bioherm. Their initial dip is indicated by the brachiopod shell with an incomplete filling, as shown at left. (Arts. 180, 182.)

The two parts are separated by the flat and originally horizontal plane of composition.

The cavities under discussion are most common in oölitic and pisolitic algal limestones, in the hollow shells of brachiopods, gastropods, and cephalopods, and under single, curved brachiopod and pelecypod valves lying convex upward in the rock.

181. *Cavities in Algal Limestones.*—Those algal limestones composed dominantly of concentrically laminated spheroids and irregularly shaped concretions lying in a matrix of calcareous fragments and fine-grained sediment commonly have scattered spheroids and ellipsoids that were originally hollow. After formation of the hollow shell, openings developed, and finely divided sediment entered. Some of the shells were completely filled with this sediment, whereas others were left only partly filled.   The introduced material later shrank as it dried out and hardened, and a cavity was left in the upper part of the shell, even in those shells which had been completely filled.   In the final stage, calcium bicarbonate was brought into the cavity and, from the solution, calcite crystallized, so that in the lithified deposit the concentrically laminated spheroids and

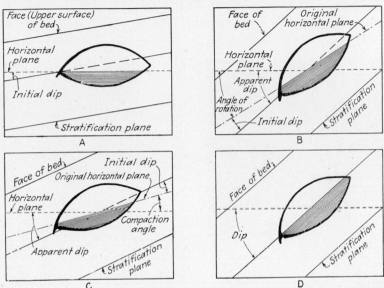

FIG. 286.—Incomplete fillings as indexes of initial and true dip. *A.* Incompletely filled brachiopod shell in a bed with about 9° of initial dip.   The horizontal plane coincides with the plane of composition of the incomplete filling but makes a slight angle with the bedding. *B.* Bed similar to *A* that has been tilted into a strongly inclined position.   The plane of composition of the incomplete filling can be used to determine both initial dip and angle of rotation. *C.* Incompletely filled brachiopod shell in a gently inclined bed that had an initial dip of about 9° and has been further steepened by compaction. *D.* Incompletely filled brachiopod shell in a fairly steeply inclined bed.   The angle between the horizontal plane and the plane of composition of the incomplete filling is the true dip since bedding and plane of composition are coincident. (Arts. 180, 182.)

ellipsoids now have a bipartite, or composite, filling.   This filling consists of a lower, stratified hemispheroid or hemiellipsoid of fine calcareous mud and an upper part of clear calcite.   The plane of separation marks horizontality at the time when the lower part of the filling was made (Figs. 242, 287).

There are many of these composite fillings in fresh-water algal limestones of the Eocene Wasatch formation of Utah (Fig. 287), and almost exactly similar ones have been collected from one of the thin algal limestone beds of the Mississippian Windsor formation of Cape Breton Island, Nova Scotia.

182. *Incomplete and Composite Internal Molds.*—Burial of hollow shells and other external organic structures (such as the calices of blastoids and crinoids, the bivalve shells of brachiopods and pelecypods, and the straight or coiled shells of gastropods and cephalopods) results in complete filling of some[1] with sediment, whereas others are only partly filled and many are so tightly sealed as to remain empty. Only the incompletely filled shells are of interest here, for they are the only ones of use for top and bottom determination.

If an incompletely filled shell is sectioned transversely to the bedding, the original internal cavity is seen to consist of two parts. The lower part of the cavity is occupied by a filling composed of sediment similar to

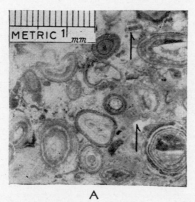
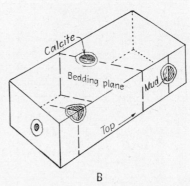

A   B

FIG. 287.—Cavities in spheroids made by the fresh-water alga *Chorellopsis coloniata* Reis. *A.* Polished surface of a piece of the fresh-water Eocene Wasatch algal limestone showing two hollow, concentrically laminated algal spheroids with composite fillings. In each the gray lower half of the filling is succeeded by a thin milky-white layer, the latter representing the last suspended sediment to be deposited. The upper half of the cavity was later filled with clear calcite, which appears dark in the photograph. The bedding in the rock is indicated by the flat upper surface of the milky-white layer, and the arrows indicate the top of the rock. Compare with Fig. 243. *B.* Diagram of a block of the limestone containing several composite fillings of algal spheroids, illustrating how the fillings can be used to determine the bedding plane and the top of the bed. The algal spheroids average about 10 mm. in diameter. (Arts. 158, 181.)

that in which the fossil is entombed. Cullison (1938: 982–983) proposes to call such a filling an *incomplete internal mould*, and its flat upper surface the *plane of composition*. This plane surface forms the floor of the upper portion of the original cavity. If this remaining cavity is then filled with

[1] Inasmuch as shells are sometimes buried in muds made unusually soft by high water content, it follows that the fluid sediment can enter the shell through the smallest openings. As a consequence, many of the shells are likely to be filled completely. It also follows, however, that the original mud filling will also decrease in volume as it dries out and hardens, just as the surrounding sediment is compacted; hence the internal cavity of the shell though filled completely soon after burial will have only a partial filling after the introduced mud has lithified. Later, mineral substances may be brought into the small cavity above the shrunken filling and there precipitated to form calcite, quartz, etc. The final result, therefore, may be a composite filling, the plane of composition separating the older mudstone filling from the younger one of mineral.

calcium carbonate, silica, or some other similar substance brought in by ground water, the original internal cavity of the shell has a bipartite filling—a primary lower part and a secondary upper part, the two separated by the plane of composition. Cullison (1938: 983) proposes that such a duplex filling be called a *composite internal mould*. From the above description, it is obvious that incomplete fillings are excellent top and bottom features, for the plane of composition and the underlying incomplete filling are made at the time when the shell is buried; hence they clearly indicate both horizontality and verticality at the time of formation (Figs. 284 to 286).

Partly filled shells are not uncommon in stratified sedimentary rocks, though Cullison (1938) seems to have been the only investigator who has published anything in North America on the subject.[1] However, in 1926, while a student at Indiana University, the author was shown and had explained to him several partly filled silicified spiriferoids from the Devonian of southern Indiana, and doubtless other students have studied similar specimens. It seems likely, therefore, that the phenomenon has been known for a long time, but this in no way detracts from the observations of Cullison (1938).

Incomplete and composite fillings have been observed in *Platystrophia* and *Rhynchotrema* from the Cincinnati Ordovician; in spiriferoids from the Silurian Racine of eastern Wisconsin; in completely silicified spiriferoids from the Devonian of southern Indiana; in brachiopod shells in the Mississippian Windsor formation of Nova Scotia; in silicified brachiopods, camerate crinoids, and blastoids from Mississippian boulders of Missouri [Cullison (1938, Plate 1)]; and in gastropod shells from the Maryland Cretaceous [Cullison (1938, Plate 1)] and from the Eocene Wasatch algal limestone of Utah. It is probable, therefore, that the phenomenon is much more common and widespread than has generally been supposed.

Brachiopod shells may be buried so rapidly or by material of such nature that none of the sediment enters the shell. At a much later date, circulating ground waters may seep into the shell or into the cavity left by the shell, if it has been dissolved meanwhile, and there deposit soluble substances that ultimately crystallize into small crystals covering the bottom of the cavity. Such partly geodized brachiopod shells (*e.g.*, *Platystrophia* and *Rhynchotrema*) are present in the upper Ordovician argillaceous limestones and shales of the Cincinnati region and occasionally in Devonian rocks of similar lithology at Milwaukee (Fig. 288).

183. *Cavities under Convex Plates.*—Ordinarily valves of bivalve shells come to rest convex upward on bottoms swept by currents. Upon burial they sink or are pressed into the soft bottom until the undersurface

[1] See Hadding (1929: 63–64).

touches the sediment at every point. If the valve later disappears through solution, its position is marked by a curved cavity bounded by a lower moundlike surface and an upper dome (Fig. 283 and Art. 178). Under some conditions, however, as in the case of rather firm sandy or muddy bottoms, the curved valve may enter the substratum only part way, so that a lenticular cavity remains directly under the highest part of the convex fragment. If, then, after burial, the valve is later removed by solution, its position is marked by a semilenticular cavity, bounded by the bedding surface on the bottom and by a dome on top. If the bed splits through the cavity, as it is likely to do, a truncated mound marks

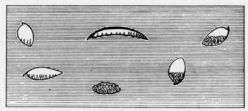

Fig. 288.—Brachiopod shells buried in mud and later geodized by the introduction of mineral matter. The crystals, usually calcite, grew upward from the floors of the hollow shells. Some of the shells are completely filled. Examples of this phenomenon have been seen in the Ordovician shales of the Cincinnati region and the Devonian shales at Milwaukee. (Art. 182.)

the site of the burial, the flat surface being on the upper side[1] (Fig. 283). If the valve persists, the cavity under it may be filled with calcite (Fig. 279) and the filling usually contrasts strikingly with the surrounding rock. In burials where curved valves are dominantly convex in one direction (*i.e.*, upward), such cavities are not needed to determine the top of the fossiliferous layer. In deposits showing curved valves with every orientation, however, they are present only under those valves which lie convex upward (Fig. 279), as pointed out in Art. 176.

[1] Truncated mounds of this sort are present in certain Devonian sandstones of New York and in the Mississippian Windsor formation of Nova Scotia. Cullison (1938, Plate 1) illustrates what may be a similar record from Mississippian boulders of the Ozark region.

CHAPTER VI

FEATURES OF IGNEOUS ROCKS

184. Introduction.—The top and bottom features of igneous rocks will be considered with reference to the kind of body in which they occur. The features and structures in layered and tabular bodies such as pyroclastic deposits, lava flows, sills, and dikes can be used directly to determine the top or bottom of the mass. Those in plutons and also certain features in sills and dikes, however, indicate only the direction of gravity at the time when they were formed. The top of the body may be inferred from this information in some cases; in others, no inference can be drawn.

The top or bottom of a body of igneous rock or an accumulation of volcanic ejectamenta can be determined, in many cases, from features and structures preserved within the mass and from relations present along the surface of contact with contiguous rocks. Most of the useful features and structures were formed during the movement, solidification, fragmentation, and crystallization of molten rock materials. A few, however, were produced some time after solidification by hydrothermal alteration or by the processes and agencies of weathering and erosion.

Tabular bodies, formed in horizontal or nearly horizontal position, commonly exhibit certain top and bottom features at different levels in the layer and also on both upper- and undersurfaces. Nontabular bodies usually show marginal features that indicate whether the relations with contiguous rock are intrusive or unconformable. They may also contain a few internal features that indicate the direction of gravity at the time when the magma solidified.

For convenience of discussion and presentation of data, igneous rocks are here divided into the following categories:

1. Accumulations of volcanic ejectamenta (pyroclastic deposits)
2. Lava flows
3. Plutons
4. Sills and sheets
5. Dikes

Detailed descriptions of these categories and of the criteria by which they may be identified are available in many published works.[1]

[1] See "Petrography and Petrology," by Grout (1932: 32), "Igneous Rocks and the

The most common and reliable top and bottom features of igneous rocks are the following:

1. Textural variation in ash and tuff beds ranges from coarsest particles at the base to finest material at the top (Art. 186.)

2. Zones of mud balls are present in the upper part of some recently formed ash deposits, and piled-up mud pellets themselves may be significant (Art. 187.)

3. Bombs and large blocks, falling on ash, deform the laminae under and around themselves in a characteristic manner and are in turn buried by more ash of which the earlier laminae terminate at the object, whereas the later arch over it (Art. 188.)

4. Bombs and large blocks, falling on plastic lava, may become rafts on the lava or may be fused to it so as to form a rough protuberance.   In either case the relations of the object to the lava are usually clear enough to indicate that the object fell onto the lava (Art. 188.)

5. Objects coming to rest on the surface of an ash deposit or a hardened lava, without deforming the substratum as described in items 3 and 4, are buried with relations to surrounding and surmounting laminae similar to those described in item 3.   Relations to the underlying material, however, suffice to show that the object did not *fall* into or onto the substratal material (Art. 189.)

6. Pyroclastic deposits nearly always rest unconformably on underlying materials (Art. 190.)

7. A thin zone of stratified ash and tuff commonly marks the very top of a flow.   Such material is not likely to be present in the base of a flow (Art. 191.)

8. The upper surface of a flow has a ropy or rough nature entirely different from that of the undersurface.   The difference in the two surfaces is due to the fact that the molten lava is anchored against the substratum, whereas it can move more freely when in contact with air only (Arts. 194, 195.)

9. The chilled margin of a lava flow is thicker on top than at the bottom, typically with a ratio of 10 or 20 to 1 (Art. 196.)

10. The zone of vesicles and amygdules at the top of a flow is typically thicker than a similar zone at the base, and the vesicles themselves are larger.   Tubular vesicles, which may lie near either the top or bottom of a flow, usually fork downward (Arts. 197 to 200.)

11. Three types of amygdules are recognized—*complete, incomplete,* and *composite* (Fig. 309).   Complete amygdules fill the entire cavity and

Depths of the Earth," by Daly (1933), "Structural and Field Geology," by Geikie (1940: 213–216) and "Structural Geology," by Billings (1942: 315–316). These works also contain references to the more important publications on igneous rocks.

are without top and bottom significance. Incomplete amygdules have a hemispheroidal shape, and the flat part marks the upper surface (Art. 219). Composite amygdules consist of a bipartite spheroid or ellipsoid, with a separating plane of composition. This plane, marking horizontality at the time when the lower part of the filling was made, also marks the upper surface of the earlier incomplete filling. The upper part of the composite amygdule is rarely stratified and usually differs in composition from the earlier lower part (Arts. 198 to 200, 219.)

12. The upper surface of a lava flow, viewed on a regional scale, is likely to be fairly flat, whereas the undersurface is commonly quite uneven because it conforms to the relief of the surface that the lava overwhelmed (Art. 202.)

13. Pillows, squeeze-ups, spatter cones, pressure ridges, and certain other convex surface features are commonly reliable for determining the top of a flow. In general, the flat or slightly concave side of the bulbous mass is the underside; the strongly curved convex part, the upper (Arts. 203 to 212.)

14. Tonguelike marginal extensions of a flow, called "flow units," have certain of the usual top and bottom features of flows and in addition have a characteristic marginal profile that is planocurvilinear (Art. 209.)

15. Surficial cracks and their fillings generally extend downward into a flow (Arts. 213 to 216.)

16. Bubbles trapped in the upper part of inclusions in phenocrysts of rhyolite porphyries indicate the direction of gravity at the time when they were formed (Art. 218.)

17. Incomplete and composite amygdules, primary cavities and their fillings in pillows and squeeze-ups, and the cavities produced in lava flows by outward drainage of molten lava and subsequent collapse of the roof— all have one significant feature in common: a plane marking horizontality at the time when the structure was formed. The relation of cavities and fillings to this plane provides a means of orienting the features in the rock (Arts. 219 to 221.)

18. The weathered upper surface of a lava flow is indicated by lithified weathering profiles (Art. 223), decreased specific gravity (Art. 224), and interflow soil and forest beds (Art. 225).

19. Erosional features cut into the top surface of a flow show by their relation to the eroded rock and the material filling them that they mark the upper part of the flow (Art. 227.)

20. The base of a lava flow is characterized by inclusions of the substratum (Arts. 229, 236), spiracles and bubble aggregations (Art. 232), and enveloped trees (Art. 234). The substratum beneath a flow is commonly deformed, with masses incorporated in the flow itself, and may be

baked and jointed as a result of being heated by the lava (Arts. 230, 236, 237).

21. Crystallization differentiation, crystal settling, and volatile transfer of gases result in concentration of glass and ferric oxide (hence red tops) at the top of flows (Arts. 239, 240) and sills (Art. 251); concentration of the heavier mafic minerals below the median plane and of the lighter feldspathic ones above that plane in flows (Art. 241) and sills (Art. 251); and a specific gravity profile that shows the upper half of a flow or sill to be lighter than the lower (Arts. 242, 254). The textural profile of differentiated flows and sills shows an upper and lower chilled margin, the former much thicker than the latter in flows, and a gradual coarsening of grain downward from the upper chilled zone to a line somewhat below the median plane, thence rapid decrease in grain size to the basal chilled zone (Arts. 243, 255).

22. Some flows and sills display a characteristic bipartite or tripartite jointing that is constant in the order of succession of the different types of joints (Art. 244.)

23. Intrusive and unconformable relations between plutonic masses and juxtaposed rocks are useful in determining order of geologic events and may also indicate top and bottom in certain associated sedimentary and metamorphic rocks (Arts. 246 to 249.)

24. Gravity-stratified sheets are characterized by compositional layering, which provides a means of determining the top or bottom of such an intrusion (Arts. 253, 254.)

25. Thick differentiated dikes may have the heavier minerals concentrated in the foot wall part and the coarser texture in the hanging wall part (Art. 257.)

Certain other features and structures of limited and uncertain value or of restricted occurrence are not listed above but are discussed briefly in the following sections.

185. Accumulations of Pyroclastic Materials.—Solid and fluid materials ejected during a volcanic eruption settle back to earth sooner or later, forming some sort of deposit on the land or on the bottoms of water bodies. Commonly preserved in these accumulations are certain features and structures furnishing, if properly interpreted, a clue to which part of the deposit is the older or younger.

186. Textural Variation in Tuff and Ash Deposits.—Fragmental material ejected from a volcano is sorted as it falls back to earth so that the resulting deposit, whether on land or under water, is likely to show fairly good stratification and textural gradation within each distinct fall.[1]

[1] In a visit to the active volcano El Parícutin, in southwestern Mexico, in the summer of 1944, the author saw along the road from Uruapan to the volcano several

The coarser and heavier fragments fall most rapidly, hence make the basal part of the deposit. They are likely to be rather crudely stratified and usually do not show the same degree of sorting as the overlying material. The finer and lighter particles come last to rest and form a laminated, well-sorted upper part that grades downward into the coarser basal layer (Fig. 289). As pointed out in Art. 51, wind-laid ash and tuff are more crudely classified than water-laid deposits of the same material because of the additional sorting action of the water before the particles finally come to rest. Graded bedding thus produced by wind and water has been proved useful in the field for determining order of succession in ancient ash and tuff deposits (Arts. 50, 51).

187. MUD BALLS IN PYROCLASTIC DEPOSITS.—Concentrically laminated spheroidal and ellipsoidal mud pellets a centimeter or so in diameter have been observed to fall during several volcanic eruptions [Nichols (1944: 342–343)]. They have been called "mud pellets," "mud balls," "tuff balls," "mud raindrops," "fossil raindrops," "volcanic pisolites," "volcanic hailstones," "chalazoidites" (stone resembling hail), and "accretionary lapilli."

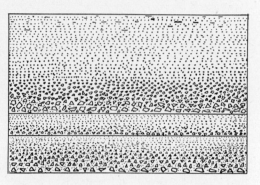

FIG. 289.—Diagram showing texture gradation from coarse tuffaceous material in the basal part to fine ash in the upper in three ash falls of different thickness. It is to be noted that the coarser material lacks well-defined stratification, whereas the finer ash usually has clearly defined bedding. Layers of graded ash may range in thickness from a few millimeters to more than half a meter. (Art. 186.) (*Sketch based on recent ash deposits in the vicinity of El Parícutin, Mexico.*)

They have been found in recent ash deposits around Kilauea, Mt. Pelé, Taal, and Vesuvius [Perrett (1924: 48)], all active volcanoes,[1] and they were formed in the eruption that overwhelmed Pompeii in A.D. 79. They have also been recorded from Triassic tuffs in

exposures of recently fallen ash showing good graded bedding. The individual layers, presumably representing successive ash falls, averaged 1 to 5 cm. thick and consisted of a black lower part and a lighter colored upper part. The black part, usually making up more than half the thickness of the layer, was much coarser in texture than the lighter colored upper part into which it graded.

[1] In a discussion (*Bull. Geol. Soc. Am.*, **32**: 27, 1921), it is reported that "Dr. H. S. Washington remarked on the globules of volcanic dust produced by rain descending through the eruption cloud of the 1790 explosive outbreak, of Kilauea, Hawaii, and preserved in the ash," and "Dr. E. O. Hovey cited the similar abundant globules formed during the explosive eruption of Mount Pelé, Martinique, in 1902." Additional references are cited in a recent article by Nichols (1944: 342–343).

New Zealand [Richards and Bryan (1927: 54–60)], from Miocene rocks in the Philippines [Pratt (1911, 1916)], and from ancient strata in Germany[1] [Nichols (1944: 342)].

The mode of formation of these unusual pellets has been a matter of some debate. Finch (1926: 1) suggests that they are formed by rain-drops falling through dust-laden atmosphere above and around erupting volcanoes; Wentworth and Williams (1932: 35, 37) ascribe their formation to condensation of steam around dust particles; and Nichols (1944: 343) concludes that both mechanisms just described are probably effective. It is likely that they form in most great volcanic eruptions where large quantities of steam and dust are erupted; hence there is every reason to believe that they may be more common in ancient pyroclastic deposits than has so far been reported.

Two aspects of the pellets merit consideration because of their pos-sible use in top and bottom determination. First is the possibility that plastic pellets may pile up in such a way as to show which is the older or oldest and which the younger. A single pellet possessing just the right plasticity would flatten out to some extent upon striking a surface and would assume a planoconvex form, the flat side being the bottom (Fig. 290B). If such a pellet happened to fall onto an earlier one, it would tend to fit down over the later, with the relationship shown in Fig. 290B. Some pellets would be too dry and nonplastic to change form appreciably upon striking a surface. These would not in themselves have top and bottom significance, but they might well be the cause of a softer pellet taking on a significant shape, as indicated in Fig. 290B. To the extent that pellets flatten upon impact or shortly thereafter as a result of the weight of superincumbent ash, they indicate the general plane of bedding by having their longer axes roughly parallel to that plane (Art. 9).

Second is the possibility that the pellets form during the waning stage of an ash eruption, clearing the air, so to speak, as they gather together the particles in the ash-laden atmosphere as they fall. If this happens,

---

[1] Foye (1924: 335–336) describes and illustrates a "pisolitic" sandy shale that consists of thin (5- to 25-cm.) layers alternating with six or seven agglomerate beds 15 to 60 cm.(6 to 24 in.) thick. He considers and then rejects the possibility that the pellets are mud balls rained down during an eruption, for they are composed of frag-ments of " . . . quartz, feldspar, and mica, with some basaltic fragments, surrounded by a film of clay or limonite containing bits of mica" and concludes: "The material forming the pellets is, therefore, largely derived from the sandstones. . . . " He points out that since the material is fine and angular it is of wind-blown origin, trans-ported by winds produced as a result of the updraft of hot air over a volcano, and concludes that " . . . the pellets were formed by raindrops which fell into fine, loose dust." This occurrence merits further study to determine whether or not some of the pellets could have been formed as mud balls [see Hodges (1928)].

the pellets should lie at or near the top of a recognizable ash fall. Hovey (1902: 343) and Pratt (1911: 63–86; 1916: 450–455) describe a case in point in a recent pyroclastic deposit having a zone of mud balls in the fine ash near the top (Fig. 291). These bodies, called "volcanic hailstones" by Pratt (1916: 452), range in size from tiny drops to large

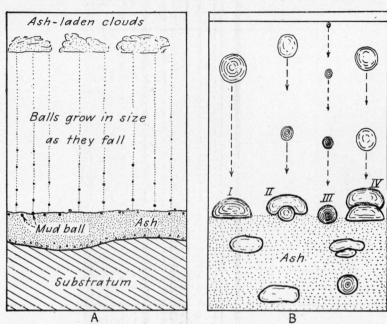

Fig. 290.—Mud balls in ash deposits. *A.* Diagrammatic sketch (not to scale) showing how mud balls, formed by the aggregation of falling particles of wet ash, may be incorporated in the surficial part of an ash deposit. Under favorable conditions mud pellets might also fall into water and be buried in the bottom sediments before disintegrating. *B.* Diagram showing different shapes and relations of mud balls in an ash deposit. Some balls are plastic enough to flatten out as they strike the ground, whereas others maintain their spheroidal shape. In some instances plastic balls mold themselves over other pellets on the surface, thus producing a relationship that has top and bottom significance (see Fig. 388*A* for mud pellets of another origin in tuffaceous rock). An ash deposit containing many mud pellets is likely to have some spheroidal ones, some of hemispheroidal shape with bottom being the flat side, and some showing molding over underlying pellets. It is probable that the weight of superincumbent materials plays a part in flattening many of the pellets. (Art. 187.) [*A based on description by Pratt (1911: 70–72). B based on suggestions by R. L. Nichols.*]

pellets as much as 15 cm. (6 in.) in diameter and commonly possess concentric structure.

The two investigators just cited conclude that the balls formed initially within the eruption cloud from some of the ash which had been made muddy by condensation of surrounding moisture (Fig. 290*A*). Mud and balls then fell to earth, the latter growing by concentric increments from the former. Many of the balls retained their shape and internal structure upon dropping into soft unconsolidated ash, and some even settled through water, to be incorporated finally in a subaqueous deposit. If the balls are always confined to the uppermost part of a single ash fall, they can serve as a means of determining top and bottom in the deposit.

188. BOMBS AND LARGE FRAGMENTS FALLEN INTO ASH DEPOSITS AND ONTO LAVA FLOWS.—Bombs and large rock fragments falling into soft unconsolidated ash are embedded with characteristic structural relations to the surrounding materials, as illustrated in Fig. 292.   The object, as

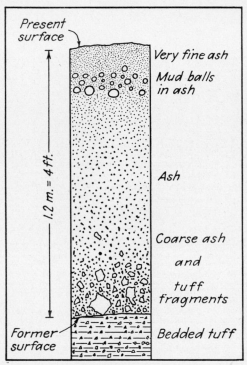

FIG. 291.—Section of ash that fell on the slope of Taal volcano (the Philippines) in January, 1911, showing balls of dried mud near the top of the deposit.   Coarse fragments were first ejected, and these were followed by coarse ash.   In the later phases of the eruption finer and finer ash settled out of the air. The mud balls are supposed to have been formed near the end of the eruption during a rain when the wet particles grew in size as they fell to earth.   See Fig. 290A for a diagrammatic sketch illustrating how the balls formed.   (Art. 187.)   (*Modified after Pratt, 1911, Philippine Jour. Sci.*, **6**: 70–72, *text Fig. 2. See also Pratt, 1916, Jour. Geology*, **24**: 451, *Fig.* 1.)

it sinks into the yielding ash, transects the uppermost laminae and bends downward those upon which it finally comes to rest.   The next ash to fall buries the object completely, and the laminae commonly sag down around it at first before arching over it.   Wentworth and Williams (1932: 34, Fig. 3) describe and illustrate an embedded bomb similar to that shown in Fig. 292 (both examples are from Hawaii).   Several years ago the author saw similar embedded bombs and blocks of lava in the quaquaversal peripheral pyroclastic beds of a volcanic crater in

Lago San José, about 70 km. northeast of Puebla, Mexico, and it is probable that similar occurrences have been observed by many geologists.

Not only do embedded bombs and rock fragments commonly indicate the top of the deposit in which they lie; they also show that there was once a volcano near by.

If an active volcano sends out tongues of lava, it is possible that bombs and large rock fragments might fall on such a flow and sink some distance into its soft, ropy crust without being melted later. Such objects would not adhere to the flow rock; hence they could be distinguished from

Courtesy of H. Winchell

FIG. 292.—Bomb sag in Koko tuff, south shore of Hanauma Bay, Oahu, T. H. The bomb, which is about 20 cm. (8 in.) in diameter, fell into unconsolidated tuff, depressing the laminae below and leaving a small circumferential moat. The material from a later ash fall filled the depression around and above the bomb. The first ash laminae show no arching. (Arts. 99, 101, 188, 189.) (*See Horace Winchell, 1941, "The Honolulu Series, Oahu, T.H.," p. 113 and Fig. 49, unpublished Ph. D. thesis, Harvard University. Illustration also published in Winchell, 1947, Bull. Geol. Soc. Am., 58, Plate 2, Fig. 1.*)

similar blocks incorporated in the base of a flow, since the latter almost certainly would be frozen in and altered.

Nichols and Stearns (1939: 433; 1940: 22–31) mention certain surface features (grooving, pockmarking, etc.) of Idaho flows that " . . . resulted from the falling of blocks, bombs, and lapilli onto the surfaces of still molten flows." Features of this sort may not be uncommon in ancient volcanics and should be expected.

189. OBJECTS BURIED BY PYROCLASTIC MATERIALS.—Plants and animals buried alive or in living position by a fall of ash or coarser pyroclastic material or by a lava flow show by their position in the rock which is top and which the surface on which they stood when overwhelmed (Art. 101). Molds remaining after decomposition of the organic matter show the same thing. The relationship of object (or mold) to surrounding material is essentially the same as that discussed in Arts. 99 and 107

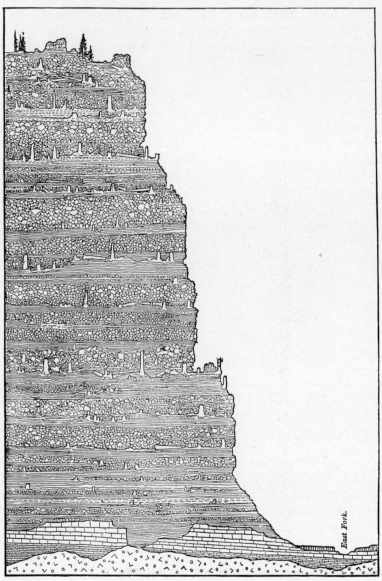

FIG. 293.—Section in the north face of Amethyst Mountain, Yellowstone National Park, showing 17 successive forests overwhelmed by lavas. Some of the stumps, buried in position of growth, still remain rooted in the soil that nourished them. (Arts. 162, 189, 225, 233 to 235.) [*After Holmes*, 1879, *Bull. U.S. Geol. Geog. Survey Terr.* (Hayden), **5**: 127, *Fig.* 1.]

except that in the present case the covering material is ash, tuff, or lava rather than mud or sand.

During the Tertiary there was great volcanic activity in many parts of the world, and in certain areas of the western United States successive forests were killed and overwhelmed by ash and tuff. The well-known Amethyst Mountain section, long ago described by Holmes (1880: 125–132), whose sketch of it is here reproduced as Fig. 293, has 17 successive forest beds. This same relationship of trees and pyroclastic material has been reported from many parts of the world and is to be expected in rocks of late Paleozoic to Recent age (Fig. 294).

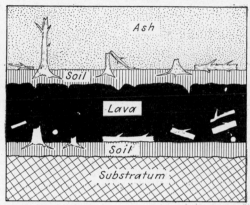

Fig. 294.—Trees buried *in situ* by lava and ash. The first soil layer developed on the rock of the substratum and supported a forest that was finally overwhelmed by a lava flow. Stumps were buried and consumed by fire to become tree molds; prostrate logs were rafted along in the lava to become suspended tree molds when the lava solidified. A second soil layer developed on the flow rock, and a second forest came into existence. The trees of this forest were overwhelmed by a heavy ash fall. Some of the shattered stumps, stripped largely of their limbs, were buried *in situ*. Some trunks were broken off to be prostrate on the ground, whereas others remained attached to the stump. Compare this diagram with Fig. 293. (Arts. 162, 189, 225.)

Boulders, blocks of rock, and prominences of a land surface, if buried beneath an ash or tuff deposit, commonly are surrounded and surmounted by quaquaversally dipping stratification that may be accentuated considerably by later differential compaction. The first materials to fall develop stratification that ends abruptly against the steep margin of a boulder or block (in this relation differing from the peripheral, downwardly bent transected laminae surrounding an embedded object as described in Art. 188); later laminae rise somewhat on approaching the object; and the materials finally covering it arch over in gently domed strata (Fig. 295; *cf.* Art. 188 and Fig. 292).

In dealing with buried boulders, blocks, and bombs, care always must be taken to differentiate those which lay on a firm surface when surrounded and covered by pyroclastic material (Fig. 295) from those which fell into soft unconsolidated materials (Fig. 292).   It seems likely that ancient volcanic formations, particularly those of Pre-Cambrian age, may contain examples of both kinds of burial.   Where the rocks are not too much deformed and altered, boulders and included blocks should yield significant information regarding the mode of burial.

190. BASAL RELATIONS OF ASH-TUFF DEPOSITS.—Structures and features in the basal part of an ash-tuff deposit commonly exhibit relations with the irregularities of the buried surface that at once suffice to

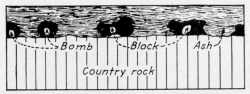

FIG. 295.—Diagram showing bombs and lava blocks lying on a rock surface where they came to rest and later were covered by ash.   The first ash laminae are horizontal, or parallel to surface irregularities, and end abruptly against the bombs and blocks.   Later laminae rise gently toward the objects and pass over them in a flat arch.   Had the bombs and blocks fallen into the ash, the laminae alongside and under them would be considerably deformed (*cf.* with Fig. 292.) (Art. 189.)

demonstrate the superincumbent position of the pyroclastic material (Figs. 295 to 297).   Wind is of special importance in producing some of the relations exhibited by ash deposits [Shrock (1946)].

The surface upon which volcanically ejected materials fall commonly has considerable relief.   It is likely, therefore, that the undersurface of an ash or tuff deposit will be somewhat more uneven than the top, for irregularities tend to be smoothed out by continued deposition and simultaneous redistribution by the wind (Figs. 296, 297).   Sagging or trunca-

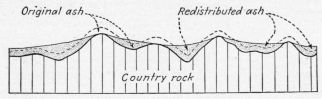

FIG. 296.—Diagram showing how an irregular surface may be smoothed out by erosion and redistribution of an ash mantle.   The original ash is eroded from the prominences and deposited in the lower areas. (Art. 190.)

tion of bedding and textural gradation may be used to corroborate interpretations based on assumed unconformable relations (Fig. 297).

Inasmuch as heavy rainfall commonly accompanies and immediately follows volcanic eruptions, freshly fallen ash is likely to be eroded, especially if the surface of the deposit is somewhat undulatory.   The finer materials, at least, will be washed or blown off the higher places and deposited in the lower, as shown in Fig. 296.   Bodies of ash may slide to lower positions, where they come to rest as internally deformed masses

(Fig. 298). The structural features thus formed by penecontemporaneous deformation should not differ greatly from those described in Art. 153.

Courtesy of H. Winchell

FIG. 297.—Unconformity in the Koko tuff, south shore of Hanauma Bay, Oahu, T. H., showing how the first laminae of an ash-tuff fall sag into the depressions on an irregular erosion surface, whereas later laminae soon gain essential horizontality. The irregular contact is about 5 m. (15 ft.) long. (Art. 190.) (*See Horace Winchell, 1941, "The Honolulu Series, Oahu, T.H.,", p. 110 and Fig. 47, unpublished Ph.D. thesis, Harvard University. Illustration also published in Winchell, 1947, Bull. Geol. Soc. Am., **58**, Plate 2, Fig. 2.*)

Local unconformities (Figs. 297, 299, 300) and evidence of subaerial as well as subaqueous sliding of freshly fallen ash and tuff are to be

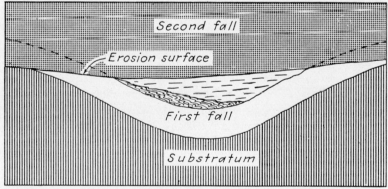

FIG. 298.—Diagram showing penecontemporaneous erosion, deformation, etc. First the substratum was channeled. Next the eroded uneven surface was covered by an ash fall. Later the ash slumped toward the depression from one side, and the slumped material was then covered by ash washed from the opposite bank. Finally the terrane was buried beneath a second ash fall. (Art. 190.)

expected in ancient volcanic shales and tuffstones, since both phenomena occur commonly in recent deposits of volcanic materials.[1]

[1] Kent (1945: 130–135) recently described a case in point in lacustrine ash deposits in Kenya, Africa.

191. Ash Deposits at Top of Flows.—A thin layer of finely stratified ash is commonly present at the very top of a flow or tuff deposit, indicating a brief eruption at the close of a period of more intense volcanic activity (see Art. 201 for a detailed discussion of this feature; Figs. 300, 315).

192. Summary of Features in Pyroclastic Materials.—There are many fine-grained, fragmental sedimentary rocks in the geologic column, particularly of Pre-Cambrian and early Paleozoic age, that may be ancient volcanic deposits made in either subaerial or subaqueous environments. If in the field there is any reason to believe that a certain

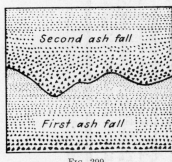
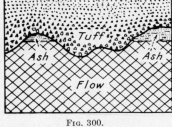

Fig. 299.   Fig. 300.

Fig. 299.—Basal relations of ash-tuff deposits. Diagram showing two ash-tuff deposits separated by an erosional unconformity. Both show gradation in texture from coarse tuff in the basal part to fine ash at the top. Much of the finer ash of the lower fall was eroded away before the second fall of pyroclastic material. Unconformable relations of this sort are common in ancient as well as in recent pyroclastic sequences (see Fig. 297). (Arts. 186, 190.)

Fig. 300.—Basal relations of ash-tuff deposits. Diagram showing an ash-tuff deposit resting with erosional unconformity on a flow that once had a layer of fine stratified ash overlying it. Erosion had removed much of this earlier ash deposit before the coarser tuff of the succeeding fall was deposited. Compare the unconformable relationship with that shown in Fig. 299. (Art. 190.)

formation or succession of formations had such origin, the beds should be scrutinized for features and relations like those just described.

193. Lava Flows.—Since lava flows vary in thickness, viscosity, and composition, the features and structures formed in them during crystallization, solidification, and contemporary deformation exhibit considerable variety. A few of these primary features may be modified or may acquire certain additional characteristics (*e.g.*, leached upper zones and filled or partly filled vesicles, or amygdules) through localized alteration by weathering or by circulating hot and cold waters [see Sandberg (1938: 809)].

The features, structures, and relationships shown by lava flows are often useful in determining the top or bottom of a flow, but one has always to be certain that he is dealing with a single flow or a succession of distinctly separated sheets or flow units.[1] Furthermore, it is of prime

[1] The field geologist who has to determine the upper and lower boundaries of a lava flow is often faced with a difficult task, for it is not always possible to determine them

importance to recognize the limitations of the particular features being used. In this connection, a warning well worth heeding has been sounded by Cooke, James, and Mawdsley (1931: 50–51), who write:

Although the methods of determining attitudes of lavas are apparently simple, the application of them in the field is a most difficult operation, and must be done with the greatest care and skill if correct results are to be obtained. It is evident that once the strike of the flows is known—and this is usually rather easy to obtain—a determination of attitude must show the top of the flow facing either to the one side or to the other. One of these directions is the correct attitude, the other wrong. There can thus be no compromise or half-way correctness about these determinations; in the nature of things they must be either entirely right or absolutely wrong. . . .

. . . several conditions must be fulfilled if satisfactory structure determinations are to be made. (1) The lavas must be of suitable composition—rhyolites can rarely be employed; (2) the flows must be neither too thin nor too thick; (3) the flows must not be pillowed from top to bottom—determination is possible when they are massive from top to bottom, but is easiest when they are partly pillowed and partly massive; (4) the outcrops must be very clean, so that the observer can view the rock across *every inch* of the width, and thus make absolutely certain that no line of contact has been overlooked; (5) the outcrops must be very wide, since not only the full width of the flow, in many cases 200 to 300 feet, must be exposed, but also a sufficient width of the rock with which it is in contact must be exposed to prove that it is likewise a flow and not a dyke or sill. It is because all

---

definitely and certainly. Cooke, James, and Mawdsley (1931. 50–51), in discussing the difficulties commonly encountered, state:

. . . In the best of circumstances, the contacts of flows of similar composition are lines that are difficult to detect, as there is no great difference in composition, grain, or weathering on the two sides. Again, contacts, being lines of weakness, are in many places somewhat sheared, or else rotted by circulation of water so as to be concealed by weathered materials. Again, as photographs of present-day lavas show, lava surfaces are commonly not planes, but rough, irregular, and covered with debris. If another lava were to flow out upon such a surface, the contact line might be almost impossible to detect. Still another difficulty, and one of the commonest in actual practice, is the common occurrence of dykes or sills intruded into the lavas parallel to the bedding or nearly so, and composed of rock similar both in composition and grain to the massive parts of the flows. Consequently the discovery of a line of contact is not alone proof that this line is a flow boundary; it may be, and in many cases is, a contact between an intrusive dyke and a flow; and the dyke may have broken through the flow at any horizon in it. It is never enough, therefore, merely to find a contact and assume that it is the upper or lower boundary of the flow. It is necessary, also, to determine whether the rock on the other side of the line of contact is itself a flow or a dyke. If a dyke, then the line of contact is of no value for purposes of structure determination.

Determination of the lines of contact is rendered easier and more certain when: (1) a band of bedded tuff or chert has been deposited between two flows [Fig. 306]; and (2) when the two flows in contact differ notably in composition. In the latter case it is not necessary to find the exact line of contact, but merely to establish the fact that the rocks on both sides of the contact are flows. Luckily for the geologist, one or other of these two conditions occurs with reasonable frequency.

these factors must be satisfied that structure determinations are so difficult to obtain.   The final factor, that of great widths of clean outcrop, is perhaps the hardest to satisfy, as in general such outcrops are rarely obtained except: (1) on the wave or current-washed shores of lakes or streams of clear water; and (2) in areas burnt long enough for rain to have washed away the ash and smoke from the rocks, but not so long that moss and lichen have recommenced their growth.

The chief top and bottom features of lava flows are summarized in Art. 184.   They are considered in detail in the following paragraphs.

194. NATURE OF LAVA SURFACES.—The top surface of a lava flow is nearly always strikingly different from the bottom (Fig. 301).   There are several reasons for this difference.   Lavas extruded subaqueously are chilled quickly on contact with the water or the wet sediments of the

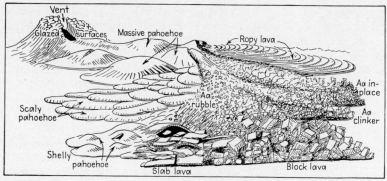

FIG. 301.—Idealized diagram illustrating the classification of lava surfaces suggested by Jones (1943: 265–268).   See tabular classification in Art. 194.   (*Redrawn after Jones, 1943, Am. Geophys. Union Trans.,* **1943***: 266, Fig. 2.*)

substratum.   Movement after the formation of the chilled crust produces certain features and structures in the flow that have generally been assumed to indicate the presence of water (*e.g.,* pillow lavas, spike and pipe amygdules).   Lavas extruded subaerially exhibit much greater differences in top- and bottom-surface features because of the different ways in which lava is affected by contact with air on the one hand and with wet or dry sediment or rock on the other.

Lava in contact with air chills fairly quickly, though not so rapidly as when in contact with water, and crusts over immediately.   Subsequent movement produces a variety of features on the surface, depending on several factors.   Since the carapaced lava can continue to move without restraint from the air, features such as ropes, grooved lava, spatter cones, squeeze-ups, and pressure ridges can form readily.

On the other hand, lava flowing over a wet or dry substratum becomes anchored against the rock or in unconsolidated sediment.   This anchoring effect is responsible for certain features commonly observed in the basal part of a flow which would never form in freely moving lava such as that at the surface. Among other things, the hot lava bakes the materials of the substratum, and as it moves along it is likely to disengage portions of the substratum and incorporate them in the fluid stream.

An added effect is produced in lavas flowing over wet sediments and rock or around living plants. In both instances the heat drives gases from the surrounded material, and these gases entering the lava produce certain characteristic features.

The action of gravity also is manifested in thicker flows by sinking of early-formed heavy crystals, rising of gases and lighter fluids during crystallization, incipient localized spurts of fresh lava breaking through thin surface crusts, collapse of the roofs of cavities formed when lava is drained out, and many other less conspicuous features.

It is evident, therefore, that there should be certain features in lava flows which could form on only one of the surfaces. These, when used properly, provide reliable top and bottom criteria.

195. *Ropy and Rough Surfaces.*—The upper surface of a lava flow is typically ropy (pahoehoe), spiny and rough (aa), or blocky[1] (see Figs.

[1] On the basis of field studies of the Modoc lava beds in northern California, Jones (1947: 265–268) formulated the following classification of lava surfaces (see Fig. 301):

CLASSIFICATION OF LAVA-FLOWS
[Jones (1947: 267)]

		Ordered smooth surfaces to Rough disordered surfaces	
Weak loose structure to solid structure	Glazed surfaces found inside caves, bubbles, and vents along with drip pendants and flow-lines	Massive pahoehoe of very thick cross-section (10 + feet) with hummocks or tumuli, and with cracks at infrequent intervals	Ropy lava (on surfaces, slabs and blocks) fine smooth ropes to coarse rough ropes (1 to 6 inches) formed by folding of viscous surfaces due to the drag of underlying mobile lava (grades to furroughed aa)
		Scaly pahoehoe thin (one-quarter to one foot) small flow-units overlapping like scales, but solid, may show pillows and toes	Aa-lava in place Fine-aa / Medium-aa / Gross-aa 0.1 to 1 cm / 1 to 10 cm / 10 to 100 cm < ½ in. / ½ to 4 in. / 4 to 40 in.
		Shelly pahoehoe thin bubbles of weak structure (one half foot) that break into slabs and plates of loose structure = slab-lava	Aa-rubble of fragmental scoriaceous character, few fractured surfaces (grades from rubble to aa-clinker) Block-lava usually four to five fractured sides (grades in size from one-half foot to 10 + feet)

Thirty years ago Jaggar (1917a: 280) proposed the term *dermolith* and *aphrolith* for wrinkled and lumpy vesicular lava surfaces, respectively, but these terms seem not to have met with general acceptance.

301 to 303).   A ropy surface forms on basaltic lavas which retain plasticity long enough so that the molten material can flow for considerable distances before solidifying (Figs. 301 to 303).   Lobate tongues, overlapping pancakelike units, ropy masses, and other characteristic forms are intimately intermingled in typical ropy lavas.   The more acid flows

Fig. 302.—Ropy and billowy surface of a recent lava flow in Valle dell' Inferno, Vesuvius, Italy.   Features like these form only on the surface of rather fluid lavas and would, if preserved by burial, provide an excellent criterion for determining the top of a flow.   (Arts. 194, 195.)   (*After Kuenen*, 1939, *Tijdschr. van het koninklijk Nederlandsch Aardrijksk. Genootschap, Deel* 56, *Plate* 3, *Fig.* 2.)

have a ragged and rough surface composed of a jumbled aggregation of lava blocks and fragments of all sizes[1] (Fig. 304).   As pointed out by

[1] MacDonald (1945: 1179), in discussing the common misconception that aa flows consist of clinker throughout, describes a typical present-day flow as follows:

.   .   the massive central part of the flow is both overlain and underlain by layers of clinker. The upper clinker layer is essentially continuous throughout the extent of the aa flow. The lower clinker layer is generally thinner and less continuous than the upper.   Locally, layers or irregular masses of clinker occur within the massive phase.   Only very rarely and locally is the flow clinker throughout.

In a section of 20 successive complete flows, the total thickness was about 82 m. (267 ft.), the range in thickness of the individual flows 1.2 to 9 m. (4 to 28 ft.), and the average clinker content 39 per cent.   These data are worth keeping in mind in investigating fragmental flows in the field.

Jaggar (1917: 255–258), both pahoehoe and aa lava may be formed in different parts of the same flow, the former near the vent and the latter at

Courtesy of R. L. Nichols

Fig. 303.—Ropy lava. *A.* Corded or ropy lava surface in Valle dell' Inferno, Vesuvius, Italy. Flow wrinkles of this kind are characteristic of the top surface of lava flows; they are rarely formed on the undersurface. They have been reported from flows as ancient as Pre-Cambrian (see Fig. 305). *B.* Ropy lava on the surface of the Quaternary McCartys basaltic flow of New Mexico. The width of the area shown is about a meter. (Art. 195.) (*A after Kuenen, 1939, Tijdschr. van het koninklijk Nederlandsch Aardrijksk. Genootschap, Deel 56, Plate 1, Fig. 4.*)

Courtesy of R. L. Nichols

Fig. 304.—Aa lava. View showing spiny surface of the Quaternary Big Obsidian flow from Newberry Crater, Oregon. (Art. 195.)

some distance away.[1] Neither ropy nor aa lava is likely to be developed

[1] Jaggar (1917: 255–288) observed that, in a 1916 flow from Mauna Loa, Hawaii, pahoehoe lava formed near the vent, whereas aa was characteristic away from the vent.

on an extensive scale elsewhere than in the upper part of a flow; hence their characteristic surficial expressions provide a good top and bottom criterion.

Logan (1863: 71) long ago called attention to concentrically wrinkled structure on certain Pre-Cambrian flow surfaces, explaining it as " . . . resulting from the flow of the volcanic matter when in a viscid condition," and Tanton (1930: 75), in describing and illustrating (Fig. 305) the feature, states: "The crests of flowage wrinkles on the surfaces of beds of

Courtesy of Geological Survey of Canada   *Courtesy of F. F. Grout*

A   B

FIG. 305.—Flow wrinkles in Pre-Cambrian lavas (light from upper right in both photographs).   (Art. 195.)   A. Flow wrinkles on a late Pre-Cambrian basaltic lava, Wilson Island, Lake Superior.   (*After Tanton, 1930, Geol. Mag.,* **67**: 75, *Plate* 7, *Fig.* 1.   *Original print from Tanton's negative* 48376 *furnished by the Geological Survey of Canada.*)   B. Flow wrinkles on a Keweenawan flow at Schroeder, Minn. (*Reproduced by permission of the James Furman Kemp Fund and D. Van Nostrand Company, Inc. This photograph, an original copy of which was furnished by F. F. Grout, appears as Fig.* 28b *on p.* 92 *of Kemp's "A Handbook of Rocks," 6th ed., revised by F. F. Grout.*)   The crests of flow wrinkles are broad and rounded, whereas the intervening grooves are narrow and V-shaped.   The counterpart, or undersurface, of the covering layer, therefore, has narrow, sharp-crested ridges and broad, rounded troughs.

mudstone or lava are more smoothly curved than the depressions between wrinkles.   The ability to distinguish between the wrinkled surface itself and the cast admits of determining the original top and bottom."

Cooke, James, and Mawdsley (1931: 43–44, 50) describe ropy structure in Pre-Cambrian lavas as follows:

The Keewatin lavas are commonly seen in cross-section, as the flows in most places have been forced into steeply inclined or vertical attitudes and afterwards planed off by erosional processes to form the present surface.   A flow, characterized by the ropy texture and seen in cross-section, exhibits a lower section of massive lava, which passes at the top into a zone of ribbon-like forms.   The individual ribbons are roughly parallel to the strike of the flow, that is, to the old surface; they exhibit flow textures; they are not of uniform size throughout their length, but pinch out usually within a few feet; they need not be perfectly parallel with one another but may show rather large variations in direction; in other words, the ropy zone has all the irregularity that one would see if a pile of interwoven cables were cut across with a sharp knife. The ropy zone is not commonly of great thickness; an average minimum thickness might be about 2 feet, and a maximum perhaps 10 feet. True ropy structures are rather rare within the Keewatin, perhaps because general conditions were more favourable

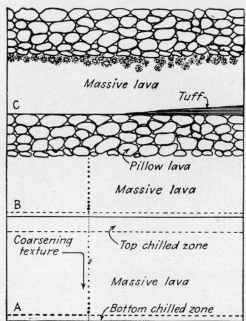

Fig. 306.—Diagrams illustrating the use of pillow lavas and grain-size variation as top and bottom criteria. *A.* A massive lava flow with a relatively thick upper chilled zone, a thin bottom chilled zone, and downward coarsening texture in the main part. Flows must be of the order of tens of meters thick before this textural profile is well developed. *B.* Bipartite flow consisting of a lower massive part with the usual texture gradation and an upper part composed of pillows. The reverse of this order does not occur in flows. If there is stratified ash or tuff between flows, it is commonly at the top rather than in the base, though the feature must be used with caution. In both *A* and *B* the size of the dots illustrates diagrammatically the change in size of the crystal grains from top to bottom. *C.* Tripartite flow consisting of a basal part of massive lava, a thin intermediate transitional zone a meter or two thick consisting of small spheroidal masses, and an upper and thicker layer of typical pillows. The intermediate zone, which always lies under the pillows and at the top of the massive lower part, contains small blocks of lava embedded in lava. Each block is surrounded by a shell of glassy lava 10 to 25 mm. thick marked by flow structure. This encircling shell suggests that the block was revolved in a viscous matrix. (Arts. 196, 204.) (*Modified after Cooke, James, and Mawdsley,* 1931, *Geol. Survey Canada Mem.,* **166: 47,** *Fig. 1.*)

to the production of pillow structure, which, as the previous descriptions show, is rather closely allied to the ropy structure in mode of origin. . . .

The ropy or corded structure is useful in occasional instances for making determinations of attitude. The ropy zone of the flow is, of course, the original upper side. It is rarely more than 10 feet thick, so far as noted, and passes downward into very fine-grained, massive lava [Fig. 305].

Flow wrinkles must be used with due caution, however, for they also form on the underside of flows that rest on dry scoria and ash. Hills (1940: 129–130, Plate II*B*) describes and illustrates such an occurrence in a basalt flow covering a steep scoria slope on Mt. Porndon, Victoria, Australia.

196. CHILLED TOP AND BOTTOM MARGINS.—Ancient flows, as well as those of recent formation, have a chilled zone along both upper and lower margins. The upper zone is usually much thicker than the lower. After the initial contact of lava with cold substratum, which results in the formation of a relatively thin basal crust, there is little or no additional

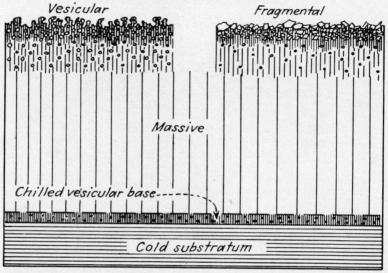

FIG. 307.—Diagram of a lava flow with a thin chilled base full of tiny vesicles, a thicker surface part full of larger vesicles and vesicular or fragmental, and the main body of the flow, which is massive and without vesicles. A dry cold substratum causes the hot lava to congeal almost instantly, tiny gas bubbles being frozen in before they can ascend very far into the lava. A wet substratum, on the other hand, when overwhelmed by hot lava, is likely to give off steam, which is driven upward with considerable force into the lava. This rising steam forms pipe and spike vesicles. See Figs. 311 and 313. (Art. 197.)

chilling. At the surface of the flow, however, there is continuous radiation of heat so that a crust of considerable thickness can form while the internal part of the flow remains fluid (Fig. 306).

Chilled margins have been mentioned repeatedly in geologic literature and have proved reliable for top and bottom determination when used with discrimination. The pitfalls attending their use are well stated by Cooke, James, and Mawdsley (1931: 50–51) (see quotation in Art. 193).

197. VESICULAR AND FRAGMENTAL TOPS; THIN VESICULAR BASES.— There is usually a relatively thick zone of vesicles, amygdules, scoriaceous rock, or fragmental material at the top of a flow, and there may be a vesicular or amygdaloidal zone, somewhat thinner and less conspicuous, at the base.[1] (Figs. 306, 307).

[1] Butler and Burbank (1929: 26), in describing the Keweenawan basaltic flows of

The top of many flows is frothy (pumiceous) or cindery (scoriaceous), a condition produced by gas bubbles that burst at the surface or were frozen in just below it. In many flows the vesicular crust, floating along on the molten stream beneath, is first fragmented and then partly engulfed by lava. Such flow surfaces have a rough and ragged appearance that is accentuated by weathering.

It has been suggested[1] that the following zonal arrangement might develop in the uppermost part of some acidic lavas (obsidians and rhyolites): (1) an upper zone of spherical or spheroidal vesicles at the very surface where gas bubbles were free to escape; (2) an intermediate zone of ellipsoidal vesicles elongated in the direction of flow; (3) a lower zone of amygdules developed in spherical cavities unaffected by the movement in the overlying lava (Fig. 308). So far as the author is aware, no example of this succession has been reported; hence its validity is so far unproved.

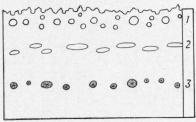

Fig. 308.—Diagram showing three zones of vesicles in the upper part of a flow. The spheroidal vesicles at the very top (1) are filled with gas bubbles, which were frozen in just before they could burst forth at the surface. The middle row of ellipsoidal vesicles (2) marks a zone in which the gas bubbles were elongated by lateral flowage of the lava. The lowest zone (3) contains spherulitic cavities. (Arts. 197, 199.) (*Sketch based on suggestion by W. L. Whitehead.*)

Thin zones of breccia and laminated ash not uncommonly mark the top of a flow, as illustrated in Fig. 315. Many examples of this phenomenon have been cited, and several representative occurrences are discussed in Art. 201.

The base of a flow is likely to have a fairly smooth contact with the substratum, and the vesicles present are confined to a rather thin chilled zone (thin as compared with a much thicker zone of similar nature at the top).

Vesicular and fragmental tops and thin basal vesicular zones have been cited as top and bottom criteria by so many writers that it is unnecessary to list specific references here. Mention of these criteria will be found in many of the articles referred to in connection with features of flows discussed in following paragraphs.

198. AMYGDULES.[2]—Two fundamental types of vesicles form in lavas as a result of the freezing in of ascending currents of gases generated at

---

Michigan, state: "The top of the flow, usually to a depth of several feet, is porous and cellular. . . . There is usually an amygdaloid portion at the base also, but as a rule it is only a few inches in thickness."

[1] Suggested to the author by Dr. Walter L. Whitehead, Nov. 27, 1942.

[2] The reader is referred to a paper entitled "Amygdules and Pseudo-amygdules" by Morris (1930: 383–404) for a classification of the kinds of cavities and cavity fillings present in igneous rocks.

different places in the flow.   These are (1), spherical to ellipsoidal cavities and (2) simple or variously branching tubes.   Rocks containing such vesicles are described as *vesicular—amygdaloidal*[1] if the vesicles are filled—and the partial or complete fillings of vesicles are designated *amygdules* or (*amygdales* by British geologists).

Three types of amygdules may be recognized for our present purpose—*complete, incomplete,* and *composite* (see Arts. 1 and 219).

A complete amygdule fills the entire vesicle and almost never has top and bottom significance (Fig. 309).   An incomplete amygdule is really

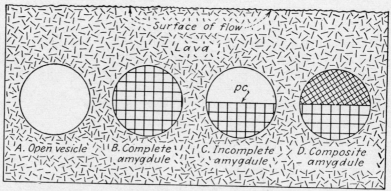

Fig. 309.—Diagram showing different kinds of fillings in the vesicles of a lava flow.   A complete amygdule *B* may be composed of some portion of the original magma that solidified to form the solid filling, or it may consist of mineral substances introduced long after solidification of the lava.   Stratification in the filling can be used as a geological level if it is parallel to the surface of the flow.   In *C* the upper part of the original vesicle is empty, and the flat surface of the incomplete amygdule, which is designated the plane of composition *pc*, is a reliable top and bottom criterion.   Composite amygdules *D* are also reliable indicators of top and bottom if the earlier part can be differentiated from the later. (Arts. 184, 198, 199.)

only a partial filling of a vesicle.   The hemispheroidal or hemiellipsoidal form of the amygdule is significant because the flat part—the plane of composition—represents the upper surface of the amygdule (Fig. 309). The plane of composition always represents horizontality at the time when the filling was made.   Its angular relation with bedding has structural significance, as pointed out in Arts. 199 and 219.   A composite amygdule is a bipartite filling of a vesicle.   The lower part is an incomplete amygdule; the upper, a later filling.   The separating surface is the plane of composition (Fig. 309).   The earlier part of the composite

[1] Butler and Burbank (1929: 27) describe ancient Keweenawan amygdaloidal flows of Michigan as follows:

The trap represents that portion of the flow from which the gas had escaped before consolidation and crystallization of the rock took place; the amygdaloid represents the upper bubbly or frothy crust in which the rising gas bubbles were frozen before they could escape because the top of the flow consolidated more quickly than the main portion underneath.   The thin amygdaloid layer at the base of a flow was likewise produced by the freezing-in of gas bubbles.

amygdule may constitute more or less than half of the filling, with the later part showing reverse variation, and it is commonly banded, whereas the latest material introduced is more likely to be unstratified. An additional difference is in composition. The lower part is likely to be composed of more than one substance and to be nearer the nature of the original magma, whereas the later filling is more likely to be mono-mineralic and composed of a common mineral such as calcite or quartz.

199. *Spheroidal Vesicles and Amygdules.*—Spherical, spheroidal, and ellipsoidal vesicles form during the solidification of lavas as a result of the trapping of bubbles of liquid and gas. The vesicles have a spheroidal shape if formed in essentially immobile lava and an ellipsoidal shape, with the longer axis parallel to the flow direction, if elongated in moving lava. They are filled initially with liquid or gas; later, material precipitated from the residual liquid or gas may form a hemispheroidal deposit in the bottom of the cavity.[1] Such penecontemporaneous amygdular fillings—incomplete amygdules—are reliable indicators of the top of a flow, for the flat or slightly concave upper surface of the incomplete amygdule is essentially parallel to the upper surface of the flow (Fig. 309). If the flow is later tilted, the flat or concave surface of the amygdule indicates the top and the angle between it and the horizontal gives the amount of tilting (Art. 219; Fig. 337).

If the angle between the surface of the incomplete amygdule and the general bedding of the flow is only a few degrees, this probably means that the flow had some initial dip. If, however, there is a larger angular relation between filling and bedding, it must be concluded that the filling is of secondary origin, having been made after the flow was tilted, and that it does not, therefore, necessarily indicate top and bottom (Fig. 337).

Primary vesicles and cavities may be secondarily filled, in part or completely, by infiltration of solutions followed by precipitation of the soluble substances so introduced. This phenomenon was described by Dana (1845: 54) as follows:

The mineral in these cavities . . . incrusts the upper half or roof, as if solidified on infiltrating through. In large geodes of chalcedony, stalactites depend from above like those of lime from the roofs of caverns, and . . . the stalactite is often found to correspond to an inferior stalagmite, the fluid silica having dripped to the bottom and there become solid; moreover the superior pendent stalactite is sometimes found united with the stalagmite below.

It may not always be possible to determine with complete satisfaction whether a partial amygdule was formed from residual substances or from

---

[1] Dana (1845: 54) long ago described such partial fillings of vesicles as follows: "The mineral in these cavities sometimes only fills the lower half, as if deposited from a solution. . . . ."

introduced materials, but this question does not affect the use of the feature for top and bottom determination if the plane of composition is essentially parallel to the general bedding of the flow.

200. *Pipe and Spike Vesicles and Amygdules.*—Gases formed within or at the base of a lava flow rise toward the surface and escape into the air unless they are arrested in their ascent (Figs. 310, 313). The path followed by the rising gas is marked by a string or strings of vesicles, which constitute the so-called "bubble trains" of some writers,[1] or by a

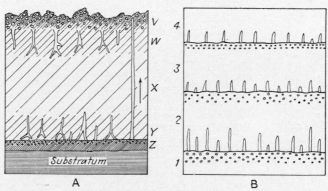

Fig. 310.—Pipe and spike vesicles. *A.* Diagram of a flow, showing a basal chilled zone containing tiny vesicles *Z*, a basal zone of simple and bifurcating tubular vesicles *Y*, the main central mass of the flow penetrated by a long tubular vesicle *X*, an upper zone of simple and forked tubular vesicles *W*, and a surface vesicular zone *V*. It should be noted that spike vesicles always fork downward. *B.* Diagram of a sequence of four flows each of which has a basal zone of simple tubular vesicles and a surface zone of ordinary vesicles. The medial zone lacks vesicles altogether. Some of the flows have red tops. This diagram is based on descriptions of Tertiary lavas of Scotland (see Bailey *et al.*, 1924, Tertiary and post-Tertiary geology of Mull, etc., *Geol. Survey Scotland Mem.*, p. 114), the successive flows of which are described as "intermittent advance of a lava, wave upon wave." (Art. 200.)

simple or downwardly forking tube. Tubes filled with zeolites and other minerals are designated *tubular, pipe,* and *spike amygdules.*

The pipes may be confined to the upper part. Those which are forked have the shape of an inverted Y (*i.e.*, ⅄) (Figs. 310 to 312), the lower tubular branches converging upward to make a somewhat larger tube, which may flare out at the top like a tiny funnel.[2] A zone of similar pipes may be

---

[1] Du Toit (1907: 13–17) was one of the first geologists who reported on pipe amygdules. The reader is referred to his paper for an excellent discussion of the subject.

[2] The use of the trumpet-shaped opening at the *top* of a pipe for top and bottom determination is well illustrated by an example in the Scottish Highlands described by Vogt (1930: 68) as follows: " . . . at Loch Eireboll, Murchison assumed the existence of an upper quartzite horizon which Nicol showed to be an inversion of the usual Cambrian quartzite, inasmuch as the trumpet-shaped openings of the 'pipes' were found to be on the lower faces, a condition which indicated a complete reversal of the beds."

present in the basal[1] part of a flow, separated from the actual bottom by a thin chilled zone and ending upward in the somewhat coarser part of the flow[2] (Figs. 310, 311).   Other pipes may traverse nearly the entire flow, rising from the vesicular basal part, continuing through the denser and coarser middle part, and terminating in the scoriaceous or pumiceous zone at the top (Figs. 310, 311).

Pipe amygdules range in diameter from 5 to 150 mm. (⅕ to 6 in.) and may be as much as 2 m. (6 ft.) long.

Certain aspects and relations of pipe amygdules make them reliable indicators of the top or bottom of a flow.   The tendency for several tubes

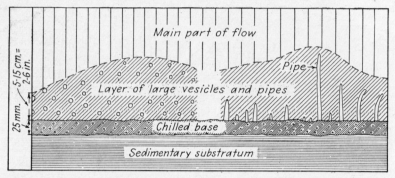

Fig. 311.—Diagram showing details of spherical and tubular vesicles in the basal zone of certain Keweenawan lava flows in Michigan. Some flows have only spherical vesicles, whereas others have well-developed tubular ones. In most flows the vesicles are filled, and the rock is referred to as *amygdaloid*. A few flows show some of the tubular vesicles or amygdules bent over uniformly in one direction, indicating some flowage of the lava after the tube was formed. Two such bent tubes are shown at the extreme right of the diagram. (Art. 200.) (*Sketch based on description by Butler, Burbank, et al., 1929, U.S. Geol. Survey Prof. Paper,* **144**: 27.)

to converge upward has already been mentioned.   Some pipes taper to a smaller diameter upward, probably reflecting increasing resistance by the lava to the further ascent of the gas.   In some lavas a zone of simple and

[1] Vogt (1930: 68) cites an example from the Scottish Highland schists and states: "Dr. Peach examined the Dalradian Tayvallich lava on the Knapdale peninsula and found the pipe-amygdales springing from the base, while the upper portion of the lava was wholly slaggy."

[2] Logan (1863: 71) called attention to amygdaloidal tops and bottoms in flows, stating: "The trap is in general of an amygdaloidal character, less so at the bottom than higher up . . . " and described tubular vesicles as follows:

Instances are occasionally met with where the cavities, generally filled with calcspar, present the shape of irregular vertical tubes of about a quarter of an inch in diameter, running up into a bed for several inches, sometimes as many as twelve.   Near the base of the bed the tubes often approach to within half an inch of one another; but higher up two of them often join in one, and this may unite with another which comes up singly from the bottom, or is perhaps the result of the combination of other two or more, and so on.   The combined tubes appear to be a little larger than the original separate ones.   None of the tubes were seen to divaricate upwards.

forking pipe amygdules passes downward through a finely vesicular band
into a chilled basal zone (Fig. 310).   This sequence has been accounted
for by assuming that the lava overflowed a wet surface whereupon the
steam[1] and other gases, generated in the substratum by the heat of the
molten lava, ascended into the lava as far as they could.   The gas, being
cooler than the lava, caused the wall of the tube to be chilled, so that it
usually is denser than the surrounding scoriaceous lava.   The base of the
flow, meanwhile, was chilled upon coming in contact with the cooler
substratum.

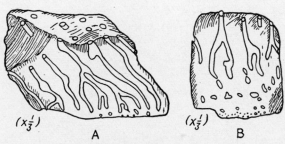

$(x\frac{1}{3})$

A

$(x\frac{1}{3})$

B

Fig. 312.—Pipe amygdules in lava from the Drakensberg, South Africa.   In *A* the pipes are inclined
with reference to the base of the flow, indicating that the lava flowed from right to left.   In *B* the tubes
are perpendicular to the base.   It should be noted that in both specimens the amygdules fork *downward*.
It is this feature which makes pipe amygdules a reliable top and bottom criterion.   (Art. 200.)   [*Modified after Du Toit*, 1907, *Geol. Mag.*, (5) **4**: 14, *Fig.* 1.]

If the upper part of a flow in which vesicles and pipes are forming or
have developed moves forward with reference to the lower part, the vesicles are elongated into ellipsoidal cavities and the pipes are bent forward
in the direction of movement (Figs. 312, 313).   The latter, vertical in
their lower part and inclined in the upper, indicate the top of the flow as
well as the direction of lava movement (Fig. 313).   Du Toit (1907: 17)
and Walker (1939: 305) report inclinations of tubes as great as 60°.

Du Toit (1907: 15), in describing the diabasic lavas of the Ventersdorp
system of South Africa, mentions that the nearly horizontal flows

. . . are in places traversed by nearly vertical cylinders or amygdaloidal rock
from one to six inches in diameter and with considerable length.   Cross-sections
are circular, elliptical, crescentiform, or a little irregular in outline; the spacing
of these vesicular portions is usually very irregular.

The cylinder walls are clearly defined from the enclosing compact diabase,
owing to the occurrence on their peripheries of closely-set vesicles elongated in a
vertical direction. . . .

The cylinders may terminate sharply upwards in the form of a cone-shaped
mass of vesicles, or the bubbles may become diffused through the diabase [Fig.
314.]

[1] Fuller (1939: 305) ascribes pipes to air imprisoned beneath advancing lava.

He explains these amygdaloidal cylinders as clusters of "bubble-trains" that formed in a lava too mobile for successful formation of

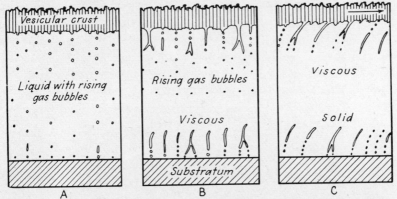

Fig. 313.—Spheroidal and pipe vesicles in lava flows. *A.* Diagram of a flow on which a vesicular crust has formed and within which gas bubbles are rising toward the surface crust. *B.* Diagram of a congealing flow in which the arrested vesicles in the lower viscous part are beginning to be dragged forward (to the right), while the upper part of the flow remains liquid enough so that gas bubbles can still rise toward the surface crust. *C.* Diagram of a flow nearing complete solidification. The vesicles of the basal part, dragged forward as the lava was congealing, are now frozen in solid lava, and the vesicles of the upper part, likewise bent forward, will soon be frozen in as the viscous lava solidifies. Pipe vesicles and rows of spheroidal vesicles have inclinations as great as 60°. (Art. 200.) [*For a somewhat comparable set of diagrams see Emmons, Thiel, Stauffer, and Allison* (1939: 312, *Fig.* 326).]

ordinary pipe amygdules when bubbles of gas (air, water vapor, etc.) derived from cavities and fissures in the substratum ascended from the bottom of the lava.

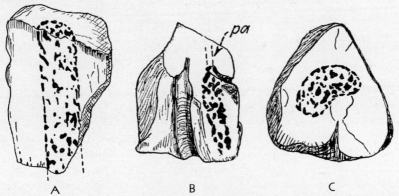

Fig. 314.—"Vesicle cylinders" in a South African diabasic lava. *A.* Longitudinal section of a cylinder. *B.* Specimen showing a cylindrical congregation of vesicles coalesced to form a "pipe amygdale" *pa.* *C.* Transverse section of an asymmetrical cylinder. All figures are one-third natural size. (Art. 200.) [*Modified after Du Toit,* 1907, *Geol. Mag.*, (5) **4**: 15, *Figs.* 2a, b, c.]

Pipe amygdules of several kinds have been described and illustrated by many writers[1] and are known to be present throughout the geologic

[1] Excellent lists of references on pipe amygdules are given in articles by Walker and Parsons (1922; 1923) and Fuller (1939) [see also Butler and Burbank (1929: 27)].

column in many parts of the world. The consensus, as fully reviewed by Walker and Parsons (1922: 5–12), seems to be that they are usually confined to the base of a flow and that they were formed by the upward escape through the lava of steam derived from materials of the substratum.[1] Fuller (1939: 305), on the contrary, believes that they are formed by the ascent of air caught beneath the advancing lava.

201. Breccia and Ash at Top and Bottom of Flows.—It is not unusual in presently active volcanic regions to find a thin deposit of

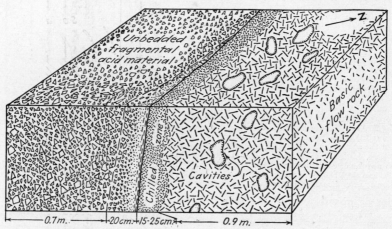

Fig. 315.—Contact zone between an acid and a somewhat basic flow, both of late Carboniferous age, in Dorchester, Mass. The upper basic flow contains scattered, irregularly shaped cavities as much as 15 cm. (6 in.) long, many small vesicles, and a prominent basal chilled zone averaging about 15 cm. thick. The acid flow, composed largely of unbedded and unsorted fragments, has at its top a prominent lenticular layer that shows distinct bedding and gradation of texture from coarse fragments at the base to ash at the contact with the chilled zone of the later flow. It is probable that there was some erosion of this top pyroclastic layer before the basic lava flowed over the surface. The flows, which are over a meter thick, now have a concordant southwesterly dip of 80° but face the northeast; hence they are slightly overturned. (Arts. 191, 197, 201.)

stratified ash over part or all of a flow, covering the scoriaceous or fragmental upper part (Art. 191), and the same relation is preserved in ancient volcanic successions (Fig. 300). Such an ash layer is present in vertical Carboniferous volcanics in Dorchester, Mass. (Fig. 315), and Wilson (1939: 1943; 1941: 21; 1942: 64) includes the feature in his com-

---

[1] Emerson (1905: 92) describes how lava flowing onto water-soaked sand had its chilled crust broken open, whereupon the steam generated by the hot lava bored a hole upward to the surface through the flow, thus producing a mud volcano. Butler and Burbank (1929: 27) found that the thin vesicular zone at the base of most of the Keweenawan flows is best developed where the substratum is sedimentary rock, and they suggest that this may be due to the fact that the sediment contained more water than other kinds of substratal material.

Bartrum (1930: 451) concludes that tubular vesicles which formed in subaqueously extruded lavas in New Zealand " . . . are obviously the result of evaporation of water from the basal tuffs by the heat of the covering flow rocks. . . . "

ments on the problem of determining tops of flows in the Keewatin of western Quebec. Wilson (1942: 64) reports two features that commonly mark the top of andesitic flows of the Abitibi series: "(1) a zone of breccia along the top of the flow, ranging from 3 inches to 20 feet in thickness . . . " and "(2) a zone of lamination up to 4 inches wide along the base of the flow above the contact or below the contact in places where breccia is absent at the top of the flow."

Courtesy of R. L. Nichols

FIG. 316.—Big Obsidian flow, Newberry Crater, Oregon. The view shows the tabular nature of an acidic lava flow with a rough, fairly level surface and quite steep marginal slopes. The height and breadth of the flow may be determined in a rough way by comparison with the surrounding trees. (Arts. 194, 202.)

The flows in which these features occur [Wilson (1941: 21)]

. . . range in width from 10 to 40 feet. They consist almost wholly of dense, massive andesite with well-defined flow contacts. On the south side of the contacts [in the Noranda district, Quebec] the margin of each flow is marked by a zone of breccia 3 to 6 inches thick. On the north side, on the other hand, the margins consist of massive andesite with a well-defined edge against the breccia. The zones of breccia are composed of round, sausage-like to tabular-shaped fragments lying roughly parallel to the strike. This breccia is, no doubt, the broken up top of the flow.

202. PLANAR TOP AND UNEVEN BASE.—The uneroded upper surface of a flow, despite being ropy (pahoehoe) or rough (aa), pillowed or fragmental, or in some other way uneven, is when viewed as a whole more or

less plane (Fig. 316).   This essential horizontality is due to the fact that
a lava flow usually remains fluid long enough to attain a relatively
horizontal surface before it hardens.   Butler and Burbank (1929: 23)
in contrasting ropy and rough surfaces in Keweenawan lavas state:

> In general it may be said that the flows having cellular or smooth tops are the
> most uniform in thickness and those having fragmental or rough tops the least
> uniform. . . .
>   . . . the smooth tops approach much more nearly a plane surface, but the
> rough tops were hummocky and irregular, with differences in altitude of probably
> 30 feet [page 28].

The undersurface, on the other hand, is typically uneven, in some
flows spectacularly so, for it had to conform to the irregularities over

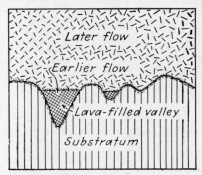

FIG. 317.—Diagram showing uneven base of a
flow that overwhelmed a surface of erosion.
An earlier thin flow had moved down the
larger valleys and possibly had covered some
of the interstream divides, but much of it
drained away so that remnants now remain
only in the deeper valleys.   Both flows have
thin basal chilled zones.   (Art. 202.)

which the lava flowed.   In areas of
considerable relief, valleys may drain
off so much of the lava that the ridges
will not be covered or will be only
thinly covered, and the solidified lava
stream then remains as a filling of the
original valley (Fig. 317).   Prominences of less magnitude, surrounded
and capped by lava, may have a
baked shell around and over them
(Art. 237) as a result of the proximity
of the hot lava (Figs. 360, 361).
Stearns (1942: 870) reports such a
zone of baking at the top of a pink
arkosic alluvium that is overlaid by
volcanic rubble and quartz basalt.
Trees overwhelmed by lava usually are set afire and consumed so that
only a charcoal-lined or -filled cylinder, erect or prone depending
on whether the tree stood or fell, marks the place where the plant once
grew (Arts. 233 to 235.)

If the top and bottom surfaces of lava flows are examined on a local
scale, the nature of the two surfaces may be the exact reverse of that
stated in the preceding discussion.   The reason for such a difference is
the fact that local conditions on a surface being overwhelmed by lava
vary greatly from place to place.   Furthermore, if the contact features
of small scale are brought into consideration, it will become obvious
immediately that no general rule can be formulated for the degree of
flatness or irregularity of either surface with reference to the other.

A case in point is reported by Capps (1915: 51) from Prince William

Sound, Alaska, where ellipsoidal lava flows have a rather flat contact with underlying shale but a billowy contact with the shale overlying.

203. SURFICIAL EXCRESCENCES AND IRREGULARITIES.—Lava flows commonly have surficial excrescences and internal ellipsoidal units that are useful for top and bottom determination. Several terms have been applied to such flows and to the bodies within them, and geologic literature contains many references to them. Since only a few of the surficial and internal structures are of importance in the present discussion [see Fuller (1932: 164–170)], attention is directed to them alone in the following paragraphs.

Courtesy of P. E. Auger

FIG. 318.—Pre-Cambrian pillow lava along Lake Mattagami, northwestern Quebec. The flow faces the top of the picture. Note that the lower sides of the pillows near the hammer fit into the irregularities of those underlying, whereas the tops are smoothly convex. (Arts. 204, 206.) *(Photograph furnished by P. E. Auger and published by permission of the Quebec Bureau of Mines.)*

204. Pillow Lavas.[1]—Under certain conditions pillowlike bodies develop on the surface of a lava flow. These bodies, which usually are disposed with respect to each other as though they were piled up like

---

[1] Pillow lavas are mentioned in many publications, for they are present throughout the geological column the world over. They have been used as top and bottom criteria by many geologists and rejected for this use by a few. Their mode and environment of formation have long been a subject for vigorous discussion. A few of the more important references to the pertinent literature follow, but this list makes no pretense at completeness.

Anderson (1910: 621–639); Dewey and Fleet (1911: 241–246); Lewis (1914: 591–654); Burling (1916: 235–237); Powers (1916: 265–266); Foye (1924: 329–346); Buddington (1926: 824–828); Moore (1926: 1–33; 1930: 137–139); MacGregor (1928: 19–20); Bartrum (1930: 447–455); Cooke, James, and Mawdsley (1931: 40–47); Fuller (1931: 281–300; 1932: 164–170); Hoffman (1933: 189); Stark (1938: 225–238; 1939: 205–209); Stearns (1938: 252–253); McKinstry (1939: 202–204); Wilson (1941: 18–19; 1942: 62–64).

plastic bags of grain, are present in many ancient flows, commonly designated "pillow lavas," and may be observed in the process of formation around some presently active volcanoes.

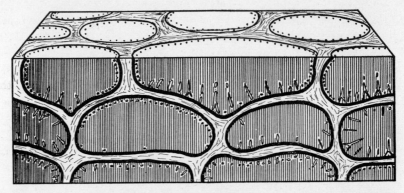

FIG. 319.—Idealized diagram of pillow lava as it appears in plan and cross section. Common shapes of pillows are those of a balloon, a loaf, and a bun. Some of the pillows have a row or two of vesicles just inside the outer glassy shell, some have inwardly directed pipe-stem vesicles, and some have both or lack them altogether. In plan pillows tend to have an elliptical outline [see Foye (1924: 338, Fig. 7)]. (Arts. 200, 204, 206.)

Typical pillow lavas[1] are characterized by more or less discrete

[1] Lewis (1914: 593–594), in the following description, which has been quoted often and accepted widely by geologists, points out the chief features of pillow lavas:

[Pillows] are separate or nearly separate masses of lava that yield rounded or oval cross-sections in all directions, though in many localities they are molded in varying degrees on one another or even flattened out like cushions or half-filled sacks, and in the latter case nearly or quite fill the space, without open interspaces. . . . These forms are to be clearly differentiated from the spheroidal jointing or exfoliation due to weathering. . . . Where spaces exist between the masses they tend toward a rude tetrahedral form, with concave sides (hence are roughly triangular in cross-section), and are generally filled in part with flakes and angular fragments of the same character as the curved surfaces of the bounding masses. Filling the remaining spaces in many localities and cementing the fragments into a breccia are a great variety of minerals that are commonly considered secondary. Prominent among these are chlorite, calcite, quartz, chalcedony, agate, and other cherty and flinty forms of silica, together with epidote and the wonderful series of the zeolites. In some regions but few of these minerals occur, while elsewhere, even in other parts of the same flow, they are developed in marvelous variety and abundance.

In some districts the interspaces are filled with radiolarian and other cherts, jaspers, and limestones or with shales and coarser terrigenous sediments. Some of these seem to have been gathered up from preexisting oozes or muds across or into which the lava flowed, and others appear to have fallen into the open spaces from subsequent deposits on the lava surface.

In many places the rounded masses are elongated and more or less flattened into a bale-like or bolster-like forms, and indeed some degree of elongation is a very general characteristic. . . . In such cases there is commonly also a pronounced parallelism of the longest axes of the masses and a like, though less prominent, parallelism of the intermediate and shortest axes as well. Gradations into more irregular twisted and ropy lavas have also been observed, with half-formed pillows or ellipsoids attached to each other and to the solid

ellipsoidal bodies of lava that generally are confined to rather definite zones and that may be present in any part of a flow—base, middle, or top (Figs. 306, 318, 319). Pillows may have the shape of a mattress, a bun, a flattened balloon with a downwardly directed "tail," or a somewhat deformed ellipsoid (Figs. 318, 321). They range in size from a few centimeters[1] to as much as 3 m. across, usually have a chilled and vesicular marginal shell, and may have a dense, vesicular, or hollow interior.

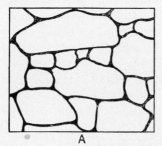 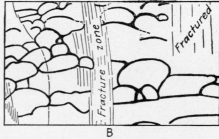

A   B

Fig. 320.—Pillow structure in ancient lavas. *A.* Diagram of a strike section in pillow lavas on Jacques Cartier Island, northern Newfoundland. The large planoconvex pillow in the uppermost part of the sketch is about 1.4 m. (4.5 ft.) long and is conspicuous for its flat base and smoothly biconvex top. *B.* Diagram based on a photograph of a vertical strike cross section through pillow structure in Pre-Cambrian andesite of the Noranda district, Canada. Three types of pillows are shown: (1) large mattresslike pillows (lower right) with flat surfaces at top and base; (2) bun-shaped forms; (3) balloon-shaped pillows with a prominent basal projection. If seen in plan (*i.e.*, parallel with the dip of the flow) the pillows would appear circular or elliptical in outline. Several of the pillows are nicely adjusted to the irregular tops of those underlying. Thin zones (5 to 25 mm. wide) of easily weathered glassy material separate the pillows and form gore-shaped areas where three of them meet. Individual pillows range from over 3 m. long and 1 m. wide to less than ⅓ m. in diameter. (Arts 204, 206.) (*A modified after Daly*, 1903, *Amer. Geologist*, **32**: 69, *Fig.* 3. *B based on a photograph by Wilson*, 1941, *Geol. Survey Canada Mem.*, **229**: 154, *Plate VIB.*)

Pillows are most commonly developed in basaltic and andesitic lavas, but they have also been reported in trachytes [Moore (1930: 139)] and

---

massive lava of the flow by necks or along the sides, as in the typical Mesozoic pillow greenstones of Alaska . . . and in the modern lavas of Hawaii and Samoa. . . .

The individual pillows are very commonly sheathed in a film of glass from 2 or 3 to 25 or more millimeters in thickness . . . , and the microscope shows that this passes gradually into the crystalline lava of the interior. In many cases the rock is massive or only slightly vesicular, although some very light and spongy lavas are also known in this form. A vesicular or variolitic zone (or both) very commonly lies just within the glassy crust, and in some localities a flow-structure is developed parallel to the outer surface of each mass. . . . Two or more concentric layers of alternating vesicular and solid lava are sometimes found, and the central portions of some pillows are extremely porous or even cavernous, the weathering out of such spongy interior leaving only hollow shells. . . . Some nonvesicular spheroidal lavas also have in many of the masses a central or axial hollow resembling the pipe in a steel ingot. . . .

[1] Moore (1930: 137; see also 1926: 1–33) has reported that in the matrix of some pillows (in the Mississagi Forest Reserve of Ontario) " . . . there is a structure on a very small scale similar to that in the pillow lava." These microscopic bodies, he believes, " . . . support the theory that pillows are due to the rolling of the congealing lava. . . . "

dacites [Cooke *et al.* (1931: 40)] and even in basic phases of rhyolites [Cooke *et al.* (1931: 40); Wilson (1942: 62)]. Pillow structure has come to be associated mainly with flows, but Moore (1930: 138) credits A. C. Lawson with the statement that " . . . pillows have been found in intrusive rocks—dikes, stocks and probably lopoliths—in California." If, as Wilson (1942: 64) comments on the Keewatin pillow lavas of the Noranda district, " . . . the pillows are discrete masses formed in succession in an upward direction from the bottom of the flow, each succeeding pillow having adjusted its form to the pillow or pillows directly beneath it," one is likely to agree with his conclusion that "it is scarcely conceivable that such forms could develop in magma confined in a dike."

Since the appearance of the classic paper by Lewis (1914: 591–654), there has been much discussion concerning the mode and environment of origin of pillow lavas. Most geologists now seem to accept the opinion that pillows form in lavas of intermediate to basic composition which come into contact with marine or fresh waters. Extrusion need not be subaqueous necessarily, but apparently extraneous water must be present in the environment,[1] although a few writers doubt the necessity for water at all.

Stearns (1938: 252–253), who studied several thousand lava flows in the Hawaiian Islands and in the Snake River Plain of Idaho, concludes that pillows[2] are

. . . found only where extraneous moisture was available as steam . . . [and that they] form only as a result of excess extraneous steam; hence are caused by lava either entering water, or being spread over or intruded into moist ground, a conclusion which has been reached by many others.

Bartrum (1930: 447–455), reporting on certain pillow lavas from New Zealand, concluded that they were extruded subaqueously because they are both underlain and overlain by tuffaceous rocks containing marine

---

[1] Cooke, James, and Mawdsley (1931: 42) would not agree with this generalization and cite writers who support their view that " . . . the presence of water is not essential to their [pillow lavas'] formation. . . ." [(See also Foye (1924: 329–346); Hoffman (1933: 184–195).]

[2] The definition by Stearn (1928: 252) of "pillow," which covers the "typical pillow" of McKinstry (1939: 202–204), is contained in the following statement: "Pillow lava consists of spheroidal and ellipsoidal ball-like masses of lava, coated with glass and generally detached from each other with fragmental glassy material in the interstices." Stearns (1938: 252–253) states, further:

No genuine pillow lavas have heretofore been described in Hawaii, although many spheroidal forms have been mistaken for pillow lava. . . .

The various bulbous forms of pahoehoe in Hawaii which are frequently cited as examples of pillow lavas are definitely not pillow lavas, but are elongate structures made during the normal process of subaerial pahoehoe spreading.

fossils. A good many years ago, Capps (1915: 45–51) described from Alaska an ellipsoidal lava that he concluded had been extruded subaqueously onto plastic mud and then buried beneath more mud without ever having been raised above water level. Wells (1923: 65) also emphasizes the necessity for the presence of water, and Sampson (1923: 577) concludes:

Although recognizing that pillow lavas may form on a small scale on land, the author believes that a review of the literature justifies the conclusion that a thick series of pillow lavas, covering a wide area and free from pahoehoe and massive flows, is in all probability a subaqueous flow, and such an origin is accepted for the pillow lavas with which the cherts in question [from Notre Dame Bay, Newfoundland] are associated.

Several observers[1] have seen pillow and ellipsoidal lavas actually form in both subaqueous and subaerial environments, so that disagreement over the origin of this type of lava has arisen as a consequence. That much of this difference of opinion results from confusion over the definition of pillow lava is brought out clearly in a series of articles by Stark (1938: 225–238; 1939: 205–209), Stearns (1938: 252), McKinstry (1939: 202–204), and Wilson (1942: 62–64).

For our present purpose we shall use the expression "pillow lava" in the sense that most Pre-Cambrian geologists have used it [see Cooke *et al.* (1931: 40–50); McKinstry (1939: 202–204); Wilson (1942: 53–70); etc.], for it has been found that such "typical" pillows are useful in structural determinations. It matters little here how the lava was extruded, for our purpose is to show how pillows may be useful in determining the top of a flow.

That typical pillows, properly interpreted, can be used to determine a flow top is proved by many statements to this effect in the Pre-Cambrian literature of North America.[2] Pillows take on added importance as a

---

[1] Anderson (1910: 621–639) describes recent pillow lavas actually seen in the process of formation.

[2] Wilson (1941: 18–19; also 1942: 62–64) gives a typical description of a Pre-Cambrian ellipsoidal lava as follows:

Wherever pillow structure is seen in transverse sections, most of the pillows have round tops and are either flattened on their under sides (bun-shaped) or have adjusted themselves to fit the "V-shaped" depressions between the tops of the pillows below (balloon-shaped). In the rock face shown in Plate VI*B* [see Fig. 320] there are three types of pillows: (1) large mattress-like pillows (in the lower right hand corner of the photograph) having flat surfaces both above and below; (2) bun-shaped pillows; and (3) balloon-shaped pillows. One of the balloon-shaped pillows rests on two bun-shaped pillows and has, therefore, a modified form with two V-shaped extensions at its base. At least two-thirds of the pillows seen in Plate VI*B* are bun-shaped and between one-third and one-quarter are balloon-shaped. In plan, that is in sections parallel to the dip of lava flows, the pillows are round or nearly round. The round tops, and the flat or V-shaped under sides of pillows resulting from their adjust-

top and bottom criterion when it is realized that they are present in lavas ranging in age from Pre-Cambrian to Recent and are world-wide in distribution (Figs. 318, 320).

205. *Relation of Shape of Pillows to the Top of a Flow.*—There has been considerable debate, at times friendly and at times heated, in both print and in the field or around the campfire, as to whether pillows (*i.e.*, the shape of pillows) can be trusted to indicate the top of the flow in which they lie.   Moore (1930: 139) reports an occasion when a party in the Porcupine district of Canada, challenging the statement of one of the members "that the flat side of the pillow is always on the lower side," repaired to the field to settle the question.   In an area of splendidly developed pillow structure they found about as many pillows with curved

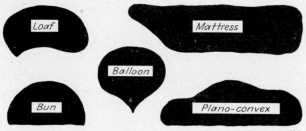

Fig. 321.—Diagram showing by cross section the more common shapes of pillows.   All have in common a relatively flat base, which tends to fit over the top surfaces of underlying pillows, and a gently rounded upper surface.   They generally have a somewhat flattened form.   Those shaped like loaves, buns, and balloons are reliable indicators of top and bottom in a flow.   Those shaped like a mattress are seldom reliable for this purpose.   Compare these diagrams with Figs. 318 and 320.   (Arts. 204 to 206.)

lower sides as with flat ones.   Moore concludes from this experiment "that it is dangerous to use this evidence in working out structure in areas underlain by pillow lavas."

Many other geologists, however, probably have had better success than Moore's party, for the literature of Canadian Pre-Cambrian geology contains many statements to the effect that structural determinations were made by using the shapes and relations of pillows. [See Wilson (1911: 276–277; 1914: 5; 1941: 18–19; 1942: 62–64); Cooke *et al.* (1931: 40 –44); etc.]

206. *Shapes of Pillows.*—There are four commonly observed shapes of pillows, and of these two provide reliable top and bottom criteria (Figs. 319 to 321).

Large tabular masses, as much as a meter thick and even broader, have the shape of a mattress (Fig. 321).   They do not indicate the top or bottom.

ment to the tops of underlying pillows, [are] important in ascertaining the structure of the rocks, for [they permit] the determination of not only the strike and dip of the pillow lavas but also the upper sides of the flows.

A second shape is flattened hemispheroidal. Wilson (1941) suggested that pillows of this kind be described as "bun-shaped" because of their resemblance to a bun. Bun-shaped pillows are typically flat on the bottom and convex upward; hence they indicate top and bottom (Figs. 320, 321).

A third shape is that of a flattened balloon with a prominent "tail" or cusp extending downward. The undersurface of the pillow conforms to the V-shaped crevice between the underlying pillows. Such pillows are

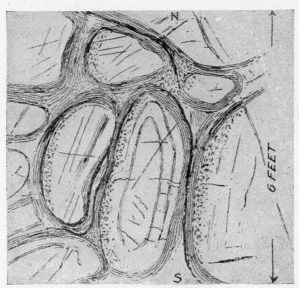

Fig. 322.—Sketch of part of an ellipsoidal, or pillow, lava, showing concentration of vesicles (amygdaloidal cavities) on what appears to be the upper side of the ellipsoids. (Art. 206.) [*After Clements and Smyth*, 1899, *U.S. Geol. Survey Ann. Rept.*, **19** (3): 54, *Fig.* 2.]

useful and reliable for determining the top or bottom of a flow (Figs. 318–321).

An unusual feature in certain balloon-shaped pillows has recently come to the attention of the author. The feature consists of planoconvex lenses of quartz, which singly or in several sheets lie in the upper half of many pillows in certain Keewatin lavas of Quebec. These lenses are described and illustrated in Art. 220.

The fourth shape is that of a deformed spheroid or ellipsoid (Figs. 320, 321). This type of pillow generally is not to be trusted for determining which is up or down in a flow, despite the fact that the undersurface tends to fit over the underlying pillows.

A significant aspect of pillows is mentioned by Clements, Smyth, *et al.* (1899: 54), who have described how they used the conspicuously vesicular upper part of certain pillows as a top and bottom criterion (Figs. 319, 322): "In exceptional cases the amygdules are much more numerous on the west side of the ellipsoids—that is toward the top of the

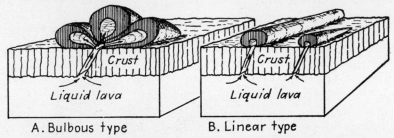

A. Bulbous type　　　　　　B. Linear type

Fig. 323.—Diagrams showing formation of "squeeze-ups." *A.* Bulbous squeeze-ups formed by successive extrusions of lava. When a bulbous mass is sealed off, the lava escapes along one of the sides and forms another. *B.* Linear squeeze-ups formed along a crack in the crust of a flow. Squeeze-ups are small surface features generally less than a meter in height. Compare with Figs. 324 and 325. (Art. 208.)

lava flows—than on the east side. . . . " Wilson (1941: 18) found a somewhat similar situation in certain Pre-Cambrian lavas containing ". . . a zone of amygdules along the margin or less commonly along the top." This feature is probably of limited use, however, for according to most descriptions ellipsoids have an almost complete vesicular shell rather than a concentration of vesicles in one part.

207. *False Pillow Lavas.*—Recently formed lava flows of intermediate and basic composition commonly have irregular or billowy surfaces due to formation of bulbous excrescences by pahoehoe spreading. These outgrowths exhibit diverse shapes and have received several designations. Inasmuch as some of them have the surficial appearance of pillows, the sectional heading False Pillow Lavas has been used, but this is not to imply that the features form in the same way as typical pillow lavas.

Courtesy of R. L. Nichols

Fig. 324.—A trilobate bulbous squeeze-up on the Quaternary McCartys basaltic lava flow of New Mexico. Excrescences of this sort are formed by localized extrusion of viscous lava in successive gushes (Fig. 323*A*). The individual lobes are left hollow if some of the lava drains out after the crust has formed. Squeeze-ups of this kind should not be confused with ellipsoids, or pillows. The latter have a different relation to the surface of a flow and form in a different way. (Art. 208.) (*After Nichols,* 1939, *Jour. Geology,* **47**: 422, *Fig.* 1.)

208. *Squeeze-ups.*—Viscous lava extruded through an opening in the hardened crust of a flow may take the form of a bulbous swelling (Figs.

323*A*, 324) or a linear ridge (Figs. 323*B*, 325). These surficial features, which form during subaerial extrusion, have been designated *squeeze-ups* by Colton and Park (1930: 579), *grooved squeeze-ups* by Nichols (1938: 609), *toes* by Jaggar (1931: 1–2), and *pushes* by Brigham [Nichols (1939: 421)].

Nichols (1939: 421–425) discusses the formation of both bulbous and linear types, as well as those which are intermediate. Bulbous excrescences may have a diameter as great as 3 to 5 m. but usually are much smaller. Linear types are as much as 6 m. long and 10 to 12.5 cm. high. Both kinds of squeeze-ups are commonly hollow (Art. 220).

Courtesy of R. L. Nichols

Fig. 325.—A linear squeeze-up on the Quaternary McCartys basaltic flow of New Mexico. Squeeze-ups of this kind may pass into bulbous forms (*cf.* Figs. 323*A*, 324) and are the result of localized extrusion of viscous lava through cracks in the crust of a flow (see Fig. 323*B*). (Art. 208.) (*After Nichols*, 1939, *Jour. Geology*, **47**: 424, *Fig.* 3.)

Nichols (1939: 425) points out that "squeeze-ups, where recognizable in cross section, would be useful in differentiating both successive superimposed flows and flow-units."

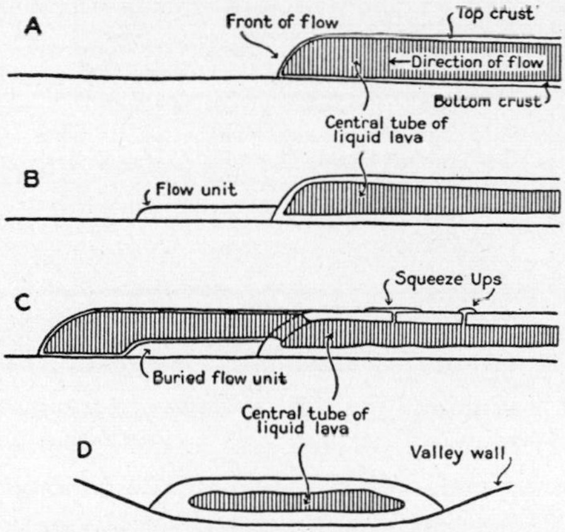

209. Flow Units.—Nichols (1936: 617–630) has applied the designation *flow unit* to crudely imbricating tongues of lava that are penecontemporaneous marginal extensions from a master flow (Fig. 326). The units are similar lithologically, have a tabular or lenticular form, and are characterized by a hoof-shaped marginal profile (Fig. 326). They range in thickness from 3 to 6 m. and in length from 30 to more than 100 m. As many as five units, one on top of the other, have been observed.

The units are much smaller than a typical flow but they can be oriented by certain of the same criteria used in determining the top of a

Fig. 326.—Diagrams showing mode of formation of flow units and squeeze-ups in Quaternary basaltic lava flows of New Mexico. The longitudinal and transverse sections show the central molten tube of lava whose motion downstream advances the lava front. The planoconvex, or hoof-shaped, front of a flow unit provides a profile by which the top or bottom of the flow can be determined with confidence. (Art. 209.) (*After Nichols*, 1936, *Jour. Geology*, **44**: 628, *Fig.* 9.)

flow.   Each unit has a thin zone of vesicular lava at its base and a much thicker similar zone at the top (Fig. 327).   Crude columnar jointing is usually present in the upper part of the unit and a type of horizontal sheeting in the lower.   If the unit margin can be viewed in a vertical section, the planocurvilinear, or hoof-shaped, profile furnishes a reliable criterion for determining the top.

Flow units do not seem to have been reported from ancient igneous rocks, but they constitute a feature that should be sought.

Courtesy of R. L. Nichols

FIG. 327.—A close-fitting contact between two flow units of the Quaternary Suwanee basaltic flow in Valencia County, New Mexico.   The upper part of the lower unit is highly vesicular and marked by two kinds of jointing.   Columnar jointing at the very top gives way downward to crude sheeting.   In contrast, the lower part of the overlying unit has a basal chilled zone with only scattered vesicles and lacks prominent jointing.   Since the reverse of the contact relations is not likely to occur, the sequence provides a reliable means of determining top and bottom in a series of overlapping, juxtaposed units. (Arts. 209, 244.)   (*After Nichols*, 1936, *Jour. Geology*, **44**: 618, *Fig. 1*.)

210. *Spatter Cones.*—Small spatter cones occasionally interrupt the smooth surface of a flow, producing a conspicuous protuberance, which, if buried, would provide a top and bottom criterion.   It seems entirely possible that some ancient flows had such surficial features as spatter cones, and there is good reason to believe that some of these may ultimately be found (Fig. 328).

211. *Pressure Ridges.*—Under strong lateral pressure the crustal part of a flow may buckle into linear ridges, and these commonly develop a medial crack that may remain open or be filled by lava welling up from the lava stream beneath (Figs. 329, 330).

Pressure ridges, as developed in the Quaternary McCartys basaltic flow of New Mexico, are described by Nichols (1939*b*: 432) as follows:

On the last mile of the Flow pressure-ridges are very common. The shortest are only 130 feet long while the longest are more than 1200 feet. They are from 10 to 25 feet high and as much as 100 feet wide. In transverse cross-section the sides of the pressure-ridges are steep, reminding one of the gable of a house or the cross-section of a broken anticline. They have a medial crack running along the crest of the ridge which may be as much as 15 feet in width but which is usually much less. They are almost without exception lined up parallel with the Flow and they are in general close to its margin [see Fig. 334].

212. *Miscellaneous Surface Irregularities.*—There are additional surface or near-surface features of lava flows that have not been con-

Courtesy of R. L. Nichols

FIG. 328.—Small spatter cone 6 miles from the terminus of the Quaternary McCartys basaltic flow of New Mexico. The man is 6 ft. (2 m.) tall. (Art. 210.) (*After Nichols*, 1946, *Bull. Geol. Soc. Am.*, **57**: 1062, *Plate 3, Fig. 2.*)

sidered in the preceding discussion, either because of their uncertain value as top and bottom criteria or because they have not been adequately described and illustrated. In the former category, (*i.e.*, of uncertain value) should be listed such features as "grooved lava" and "shark's-tooth" structure [see Nichols (1938: 601–614; 1939*a*: 188–194; 1939*b*: 432 –433) and Nichols and Stearns (1939: 433; 1940: 22–31)].

213. SURFICIAL CRACKS IN FLOWS.—Cracks, crevices, and prominent holes break the continuity of the surface of many recent flows, and similar features should be expected along the top margins of ancient flows. Under certain thermal and stress conditions (Arts. 214, 215) prominent surficial cracks are developed in the carapace of a flow. These may be filled later by upwelling lava from beneath, by a new flow on top of the cracked surface, or by clastic material washed in from the surrounding area (Figs. 331 to 333). Depressions formed by the collapse of tunnel and cavern roofs pit the surface of some flows and may be partly or completely filled by surface lava or with clastic material (Figs. 331, 345). Finally, the processes of weathering and erosion etch an exposed lava-flow

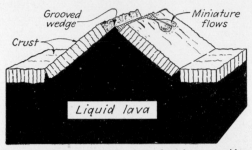

surface into secondary relief, and the negative features so produced can be backfilled with lava or clastic material in the way described in the preceding cases.

Fig. 329.—Diagram showing formation of pressure ridge and its medial wedge. The crust of the flow is cracked by arching, whereupon molten lava forces its way upward between the tilted blocks. At one point the lava has broken through to the surface with enough mobility to flow a short distance down the slope of one of the tilted blocks. Compare with Fig. 330. (Art. 211.)

The general rule in all the examples just cited is that the crack penetrates the older formation and is filled by the younger.

If lava advances across a preexisting flow surface that is cracked or pitted, it flows into and fills all depressions unless it is too stiff. In the latter case an inverted ridge or lobe of lava will hang down into the crack (Fig. 332). This feature should not be confused with a linear squeeze-up (Art. 208). The clastic fillings of cracks are likely to be tuffaceous

Courtesy of R. L. Nichols

Fig. 330.—Pressure ridge on the Quaternary McCartys flow in New Mexico, showing a small pahoehoe flow that issued from the medial crack. The ridge is 7 m. (21+ ft.) high and 20 m. (60+ ft.) across. (Art. 211.) (*After Nichols, 1946, Bull. Geol. Soc. Am.,* **57**: 1072, *Plate 8, Fig. 1.*)

because of the local origin of the material. Such fillings have been mentioned by a few writers [Fackler (1941: 550–556)] and are known to be present in ancient volcanic rocks.

Prominent cracks and hollows between pillows, blocks, and other surface irregularities will be filled under favorable conditions, and the laminae of the fillings tend to be parallel or concave[1] to the superjacent strata (Fig. 332). Burling (1916: 236), who found sedimentation of this sort while studying the ellipsoidal lavas in Glacier National Park, Montana, concludes that " . . . the silting up of cracks in the surface of the flow would seem more natural than the upward penetration, into

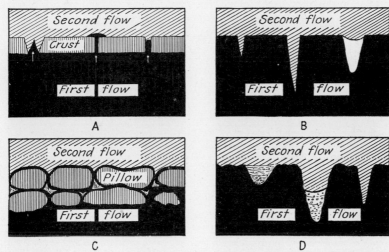

Fig. 331. Filled cracks in flow surfaces. *A*. Diagram showing cracks in the surface crust of a flow. Molten lava has ascended to fill the cracks partly or completely. The left triangular filling represents a grooved wedge of viscous lava; the central crack was filled with lava that was fluid enough to reach and locally overflow the surface; the right crack was not completely filled before the lava solidified. The second flow fits cleanly over the irregular surface of the first. *B*. Cracks in a lava flow filled partly or completely by a second flow. At the right is a large crack that was not filled because the lava was almost solid and could only sag slightly before solidifying. *C*. Diagram showing lava of a second flow fitting neatly over the irregularities of an earlier flow containing prominent pillow structure. *D*. Original cracks in a lava flow modified by weathering and erosion before being filled by sediments and the lava of a second flow. (Arts. 213, 214, 216.)

cracks several feet in height, of mud sufficiently resistant to flatten the bases of individual ellipsoids," but he emphasizes how this feature must be used with caution to prevent confusion with contemporaneous mud-filled crevices on the *underside* of a flow, like those described by Capps (1915: 49) from the Prince William Sound region in Alaska.

Capps (1915: 51) describes the difference between the mud-filled cracks at the top and bottom of the Alaskan flows as follows:

The difference in appearance of the flat bottom of an ellipsoidal flow, with its abundance of mud-filled cracks, from the uneven upper surface of the same flow, and the consequent unevenness of the bottom of the succeeding sedimentary bed

[1] Compaction and consequent downward sagging of laminae between adjacent prominences can produce concave lamination.

often made it possible to determine which surface of a steeply tilted bed was originally the upper surface, and was a valuable aid in working out the structure of the beds.

214. *Thermal Cracks.*—As the surface of a flow cools in contact with air, a carapace or crust forms. Later this crust shrinks, and tension cracks develop. These range in depth and breadth from tiny cracks to clefts many meters deep and wide (Figs. 333, 334). If they are filled by later lava or with surface debris, they and their fillings provide criteria for determining the top of the flow (Figs. 331, 332, 348).

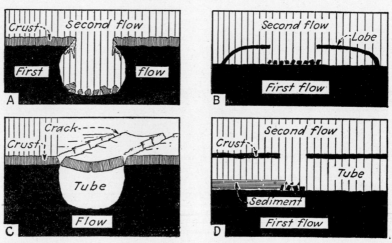

Fig. 332.—Collapse features on the surface of flows. *A.* Diagram of a tube of which the roof collapsed before a later flow filled it. Stalactites formed on the rim of the tube as the later lava flowed in. Fragments of the crust of the earlier flow lie on the bottom of the original tube. *B.* Diagram showing the collapsed roof of a small lobe on the surface of a larger flow. A second flow filled and buried the cavity left by the outflowing lava of the first. Fragments from the crust of the lobe lie buried on the bottom of the original tunnel. *C.* Diagram showing the sagging and cracking of a part of the roof over a lava tube. If the lava, as shown at the left by vertical lining, were to flow over the sagging roof, it is likely that the roof would collapse and the lava fill the tube. Incoming sediments could have the same effect. *D.* Diagram showing a small hole in the crust roofing over a lava tube. Both sediment and lava could enter such an opening and partly or completely fill the cavity. (Arts. 213, 214, 215.) (*Diagrams based on suggestions by R. L. Nichols.*)

Lane (1911:31) described sediment-filled thermal cracks in the Keweenawan lava flows of Michigan and used the term *clasolite* for the material filling the cracks. In discussing the sedimentary filling he stated:

. . . this red shaly or sandy sediment may work far down into the old lava beds or traps, following the cracks that formed as it cooled, and to such little red sediment-like veins I have applied Wadsworth's name of *clasolite* [may be defined as *clastic vein*].

The clasolite veins are composed of material similar to the matrix of the amygdaloidal conglomerates that lie between successive flows.

215. *Cracks and Crevices Due to Collapse.*—Collapse of the roofs of tunnels, caves, and other large cavities, caused by drainage of lava from an encased flow, produces a variety of cracks, crevices, and larger depressions. We shall mention here only those cracks of rectilinear nature. Larger collapse features are discussed in Art. 221.

Owing to their mode of origin, cracks and crevices formed as a result of collapse are likely to open downward into larger cavities. On the

Courtesy of R. L. Nichols

Fig. 333.—Surficial crack near margin of the Quaternary McCartys basaltic flow of New Mexico. Cracks of this kind are closely associated with pressure ridges and commonly lie near flow margins. Since they could not be formed in the base of a flow, they are reliable indicators of the top and would be further emphasized if filled with new lava or sediment. Under certain conditions they might remain open even though buried beneath a later flow (*e.g.*, if the covering lava were too stiff to flow downward and fill the crack). (Art. 214.)

other hand, if the roof of the cavity sagged without collapsing, the surface cracks lie along the margin of the depressed roof (Fig. 332).

Since features such as those just described are common in recent basaltic flows, it seems reasonable to conclude that they may also be preserved in some ancient flows (see Figs. 333, 334).

216. *Crevices Produced by Weathering and Erosion.*—Cracks, crevices, pits, and other depressions are etched or worn into lava flow surfaces by weathering and erosion. These may be formed entirely secondarily, but many represent primary features that have been enlarged and to some extent reshaped by wind and water. If the denuded lava flow is buried, the contact relations along the surface between the juxtaposed rocks should indicate which of the formations was denuded and which was

Courtesy of R. L. Nichols

FIG. 334.—A triangular wedge of lava in the medial crack of a pressure ridge developed in the McCartys basaltic flow (Quaternary) of New Mexico. Wedges of this kind are commonly grooved and fluted, showing that they were formed while the lava was plastic. Pressure ridges with their medial cracks and wedges form only in the top part of a flow, never in the basal part; hence if preserved in an ancient flow, they would provide a means of determining the top of that flow. (Arts. 211, 214.) (*After Nichols, 1938, Jour. Geology,* **46**: 610, *Fig. 7.*)

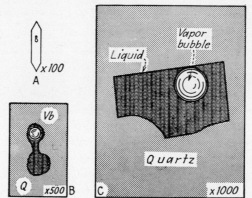

FIG. 335.—Vapor bubbles in liquid inclusions. *A.* Quartz crystal containing a liquid inclusion and vapor bubble. *B.* Enlarged diagram of part of *A,* showing hourglass shape of liquid inclusion that has a small vapor bubble in upper part. The vapor bubble would not change its position unless the crystal were rotated through about 180°. *C.* Liquid-filled negative crystal with vapor bubble floating near the top margin. If the thin section containing this inclusion is agitated, the bubble dances about and acts like a spirit level. (*A* and *B are diagrammatic. C is based on a specimen of rhyolite from Christiania, Norway, numbered 3038 in the Rosenbusch Collection of the Massachusetts Institute of Technology.*) (Art. 218.)

deposited on the surface of denudation.[1] Specific features produced by weathering on flow surfaces and within flows are discussed in Arts. 222 to 226; those produced by erosion, in Art. 227.

217. PRIMARY CAVITIES AND THEIR FILLINGS.—After solidification lava flows have many kinds and sizes of cavities. These include tiny vesicles, larger spheroidal, ellipsoidal, and tubular cavities, and still larger cavelike tunnels that may reach a diameter of tens of meters and persist for many kilometers. There may also be local collapse features that have the shape of a cistern (Figs. 344, 345). The smaller cavities are formed by trapped bubbles of gas and liquid; the larger, by the flowing out of molten lava from a partly solidified flow. All these cavities have top and bottom significance by virtue of the predictable position they hold within a flow or of the flat-topped incomplete filling deposited in them before the flow is tilted or folded to any extent.

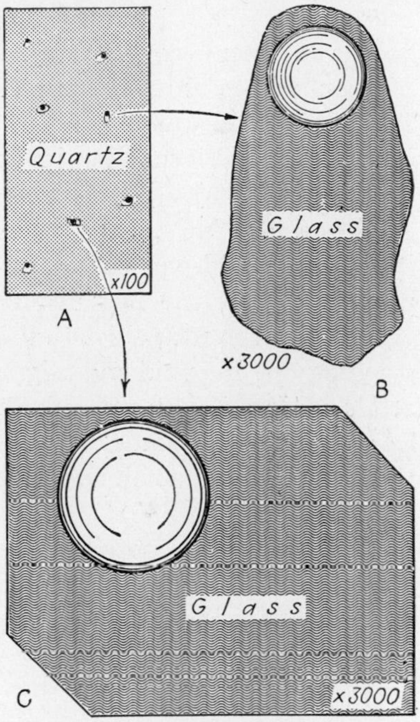

218. *Bubbles in Liquid and Solid Inclusions.*—Not only are globules of original magma and bubbles of gas and liquid caught and trapped in quickly cooling lava; their microscopic complements are also included in growing crystals, and these deserve brief notice here.[2]

FIG. 336.—Bubbles in glass-filled cavities in a quartz phenocryst. *A.* Portion of a quartz crystal containing several cavities with bubbles. *B.* An irregular cavity now filled with glass except for the prominent bubble in the upper part. *C.* Negative crystal cavity filled with glass except for large bubble. It is to be noted that the bubbles all lie in the same general position in the cavities, *i.e.*, near the upper margin. (*Sketches are based on a porphyritic rhyolite from Apati, Hungary, numbered 3183 in the Rosenbusch Collection of the Massachusetts Institute of Technology.*) (Art. 218.)

Let us assume that the original inclusion had an irregular shape, with an equatorial constriction of some sort, and consisted mainly of water.

[1] Wright (1932: 32–33) used the relations of an interflow chert bed to determine the top of a sequence.

One chert bed . . . appears to have been deposited on an irregular surface of a lava flow, perhaps developed in part by erosion in the interval between the extrusion of the flows. This bed was followed carefully along its strike and its north side is straight, whereas the south contact is irregular, causing the thickness of the bed to increase abruptly from 1 foot to as much as 14 feet at one point.

[2] The author is indebted to O. F. Tuttle for calling his attention to several types

As the crystal and the rock around it cooled, the water contracted faster than the mineral and some of it went into the vapor phase to fill the space resulting from the contraction. The vapor then migrated upward and collected at the top of the inclusion. Once the rock had cooled, the bubble of vapor became fixed and it would not thereafter change its general position unless the rock mass were rotated through more than 90°. Hence the vapor bubble, acting as a geological spirit level, indicates the direction of gravity at the time when the rock solidified about the parent crystal (Fig. 335).

Spheroidal inclusions of gas and liquid are commonly trapped in quartz and feldspar phenocrysts of rhyolites (Fig. 336). As in the preceding case, the included material, cooling faster than the parent crystal and the rock surrounding it, contracts somewhat, and the vapor resulting fills the void and migrates upward to the highest position it can attain. Here it is trapped by the fluid below or by the glass resulting from the solidification of the original included fluid. The final inclusion then consists of a small spheroid of liquid or solid with a tiny bubble at the very top (Fig. 336).

Tilting of the containing rock may destroy the usefulness of the inclusion as a top and bottom criterion if it consists of gas and liquid, but not if it consists of gas (or fluid) and solid. The position of the tiny bubble at the top of the inclusion gives a means of determining horizontality and verticality (up or down) in the rock mass at the time when it cooled. Similar inclusions are quite common in certain synthetic minerals. They constitute a criterion well worth seeking in porphyritic rhyolites and other igneous rocks of similar nature.

This type of criterion requires microscopic investigation of carefully oriented thin sections, supplemented by statistical study of the inclusions themselves. A few random determinations cannot be trusted, but a statistical treatment of all the inclusions that can be studied in a section usually suffices for satisfactory determination of the direction of gravity.

219. *Incomplete and Composite Amygdules.*—The shape, mode of formation, nature of fillings of vesicles, and the use of certain fillings in structural geology are discussed in Arts. 198 to 200. Here, only one type of amygdular filling will be considered—that which constitutes a hemispheroidal or hemiellipsoidal deposit in the lower part of a vesicle. These are started before the containing lava is tilted to any extent, as proved by the fact that the flat upper surface of the incomplete amygdule, which is in reality a geological spirit-level, is at first essentially parallel to the

---

of microscopic inclusions and for pointing out how the position of bubbles in these inclusions has top and bottom significance.

general surface plane of the flow. If there is no tilting during the deposition of successive layers of mineral substance on the bottom of the original vesicle, the laminae of the incomplete amygdule are parallel with one another, as well as being parallel with the general flow surface (Fig. 337). Such an amygdule commonly has the form of a concentrically layered geodelike shell, inside which lies the hemispheroidal or hemiellipsoidal deposit of parallel laminae[1] (Fig. 338). It may be composed of (1) original magmatic substances dissolved in trapped gases and liquids; (2) substances dissolved from the components of the surrounding rock and deposited in the cavity; and (3) materials brought into the vesicle from outside the flow. It follows, therefore, that the incomplete amygdules being described may be composed of any one of the three materials or

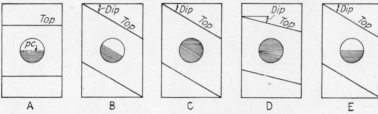

Fig. 337.—Incomplete amygdules as indexes of top and bottom in lava flows. *A*. An incomplete amygdule in a flat-lying flow. The plane of composition *pc* is parallel to the general top surface of the flow. *B*. An inclined flow with an incomplete amygdule which shows that the dip is 30° and the flow top side up. *C*. An inclined flow with a composite amygdule consisting of two distinct parts, an earlier part formed while the flow was horizontal and a later part deposited after tilting. The flow is top side up. *D*. A gently tilted flow (dip = 14°) containing an incomplete amygdule that was formed as tilting took place. The early part was deposited before tilting started; the converging laminae were deposited at successive stages during tilting. *E*. Incomplete amygdule formed in a vesicle after tilting. Although the plane of composition may be used to determine the amount of dip, it is of no use for top and bottom determination, for it appears the same in gently tilted and overturned flows. (Art. 219.)

of any combination of the three. However, the material of (1) must in every case be the bottom deposit.[2]

If there is tilting after an incomplete amygdule has formed, the flat upper surface of the filling indicates the direction in which the top of the containing flow lies and the angle between it and the horizontal gives the amount of tilting (Figs. 337, 339). Banded incomplete amygdules of this sort were long ago described from the Carboniferous Brighton flows in Allston, Mass., by Davis (1880: 426–428) and Burr (1901: 53–69), the former of whom concluded that they could be used to determine the top

[1] Probably the most widely known examples are the "water-level agates" from Serra do Mar, Brazil, and the "thunder eggs" in the Miocene Columbia River basalts of Oregon. Specimens of the former are to be seen in almost any large mineralogical museum (Figs. 338*A*, 339).

[2] The author is indebted to Prof. F. K. Morris for the information that the liquid in certain partly filled primary vesicles may deposit a tiny shelf or band of material around the margin. This marking, like the "bathtub ring," indicates original horizontality in the rock.

B–D courtesy of H. C. Dake

Fig. 338.—Geodelike concretions with stratified fillings weathered out of lava flows. *A.* "Water-level" agate from Brazil (×0.6) showing two stages of filling. In the first, silica was deposited in parallel laminae on the floor of the cavity and later on the ceiling and walls; in the second, the remaining hemiellipsoidal cavity was filled with unstratified silica that crystallized into quartz. *B.* Concretion ("thunder egg") from the Columbia River basalt of Oregon (×0.3) showing a rhyolitic shell and a partial filling of laminated silica. The upper part of the concretion is empty. This is not a common type of concretion according to a letter from H. C. Dake of Portland, Oreg., who wrote: "Perhaps less than 10% of all the 'thunder eggs' we find show hollow areas." *C.* Thunder egg from Oregon (×0.3) showing tubular stalactites hanging downward from the ceiling of the original cavity and surrounded by the laminated filling. These stalactites are believed to have formed during the early part of the filling stage. They constitute a reliable criterion for determining the top side of a concretion. *D.* Radially cracked thunder egg from the Columbia River basalt of Oregon (×0.3) consisting of a rhyolitic shell, broken into segments by radial fractures, and an internal cavity filled with silica that is stratified below and massive above. Concretionary masses like those illustrated above range in size from 5 mm. to several meters in diameter and usually have a rhyolitic shell surrounding a cavity partly or wholly filled with silica. (Art. 219.) (*Photographs B, C,* and *D furnished by H. C. Dake.*)

of the tilted flows. The banded amygdules are associated with others having concentric structure and which, because of this feature, are useless for top and bottom determination. The two kinds of amygdules are illustrated in Fig. 340, which is based on Davis's original sketch.

If the tilting of flows containing vesicles with primary incomplete amygdules is followed by renewed deposition of material in the vesicles,

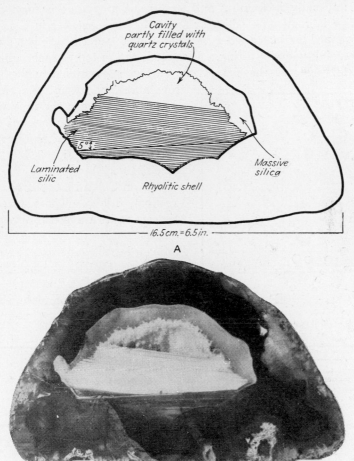

FIG. 339.—Geodelike cavity filling ("thunder egg") from the Columbia River basalt of Oregon. *A.* Diagram showing the main features of *B.* *B.* Polished cross section of a typical multilaminated thunder egg. The geode consists of a thick, glassy shell surrounding a cavity that is filled with two sets of differently inclined laminae and an uppermost unstratified mass of quartz crystals. Projection of the two planes of lamination shows a divergence of about 5°, indicating that the flow containing the geode was tilted through this angle after the first set of laminae was deposited and before deposition of the second started. In the third stage of filling, quartz crystals were formed in the highest part of the cavity. If geodes like this could be found *in situ* and carefully oriented before removal and splitting, they would constitute a reliable top and bottom feature. (Art. 219.)

Courtesy of H. C. Dake

the laminae of the second increment have an angular relation to those of the first and the angle indicates the amount of tilting that took place between the two periods of amygdular deposition (Fig. 337C). Composite chalcedonic amygdules of this sort are known to be present at certain Oregon localities in the Columbia River basalts.

An unusually interesting and significant amygdule is formed when successive increments of silica or some similar substance in the form of wedge-shaped laminae are deposited on the floor of a vesicle in a flow that is undergoing periodic tilting. Inasmuch as the top of each lamina is a horizontal plane at the time of formation, successive laminae diverge from a common point and the total divergence between the first and last laminae indicates the amount of tilting that took place after filling of the vesicles started (Fig. 337C). Reed (1937: 239–243) reported a case in point from Columbia River lavas near Freedom, Idaho. These lavas contain composite amygdules having two distinct parts: (1) a concentrically laminated shell composed of a sequence of minerals, that Reed concludes were deposited early from "deuteric emanations"; (2) an incomplete siliceous filling of the remaining cavity that consists of converging laminae. The latter are explained as successive increments of silica deposited in the bottom of the concentrically lined cavity during and between times of periodic tilting. The amygdules are present throughout two juxtaposed flows, which are parallel and now dip at an angle of 17°, and show a maximum divergence of 14° between the laminae. The remaining 3° may represent initial dip, though Reed states that there seems to have been little if any of this, or it may indicate that much tilting before the first increment of silica was deposited. The tilting took place between lower-middle Miocene and Pleistocene.

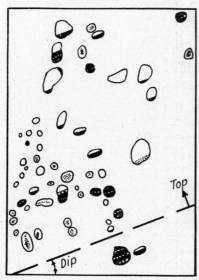

Fig. 340.—Banded and incomplete amygdules in the Carboniferous Brighton lavas of eastern Massachusetts. The flow, dipping gently to the left, is top side up as indicated by the numerous incomplete amygdular fillings of primary vesicles. (Art. 219.) (*Modified after Davis*, 1880, *Boston Soc. Nat. History Proc.*, **20**: 428, *Fig.* 2.)

If the vesicles of tilted flows contain incomplete amygdules with laminae or top surface now horizontal or with some inclination between that of the flow and horizontality, the filling was not made until folding or tilting had got under way and it is not, therefore, a trustworthy criterion of top and bottom (Fig. 337E). Such fillings, however, may suggest the direction in which the top of the flow lies by indicating the only direction in which the flow could have been rotated (Fig. 337F).

220. *Original Cavities in Pillows and Squeeze-ups.*—Planoconvex cavities and their lenticular quartz fillings are present in pillows and false pillow structures of some lava flows. Since they nearly always lie above the median horizontal plane of the bulbous mass, the flat part constituting the floor and the curved part being roughly parallel to the convex upper surface of the pillow, or ellipsoid, they provide a useful criterion for determining the top and bottom of lavas that have been folded and metamorphosed.

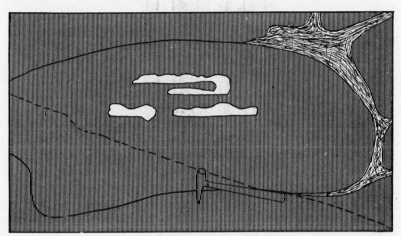

Fig. 341.—"Quartz eyes" in Pre-Cambrian ellipsoidal lavas along Lake Mattagami, northwestern Quebec. The quartz-filled cavities, flat on the bottom side and irregularly convex on the upper, always lie above the median horizontal plane of the ellipsoid and provide a reliable top and bottom feature. Some ellipsoids have a single large cavity rather than several smaller ones as shown above; in such ellipsoids the cavity has a convex roof that tends to parallel the upper boundary of the ellipsoid. The rounded ends of three adjacent ellipsoids are visible in the upper right-hand corner. Altered volcanic glass fills the interstitial space. A prominent fracture transects the large ellipsoid from left to right. (Art. 220.) *(Sketch based on a photograph by P. E. Auger, which was used by permission of the Quebec Bureau of Mines.)*

The attention of the author has been called to one example of this kind in certain Keewatin lavas of Quebec.[1] The lenses, as illustrated in Fig. 341, have a fairly flat base and usually a slightly convex upper surface. The flat base parallels the general horizontal plane of the flow, and the convex upper surface tends in a general way to parallel the upper margin of the pillow containing the cavity. If a median horizontal plane is drawn through a pillow having one or more of the quartz lenses, the latter always lie *above* the plane (Fig. 341). Dr. P. E. Auger, who discovered these lenses and used them for structural determinations, believes that the cavities now filled by secondary quartz were formed originally by the aggregation of gas bubbles which were trapped in the upper part

[1] The author is indebted to Dr. P. E. Auger, who described the feature to him and furnished the photograph used in making Fig. 341.

of the pillow while it was still partly plastic.   They may also have been formed, at least in certain flows, by the draining out of some still liquid lava, as described by Fuller (1931: 287), but this seems a less likely explanation.

Somewhat akin to the "quartz eyes" found by Auger are the "eye and eyebrow structures" reported by Burrows and Rickaby (1935: 17) from Pre-Huronian rhyolite of the Sudbury district, Ontario.   The writers describe the feature as follows:

One peculiar structure noted in some of the rhyolitic rocks consists of crescent-shaped bodies of quartz associated with rounded pea-like inclusions, also of quartz.

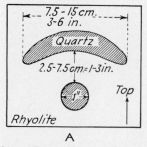
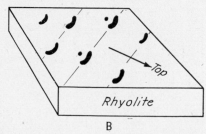

A   B

Fig. 342.—"Eye and eyebrow" structure in Pre-Cambrian rhyolite of the Sudbury district, Ontario. *A.* Typical eye and eyebrow structure consisting of a large crescentic mass of quartz with a smaller spheroidal body on the concave- and underside at a distance equal to about one-half the length of the crescent.   This diagram can be either a plan or a cross section.   *B.* Eye and eyebrow structure as it appears on the surface of a rhyolite flow.   The small, pealike quartz bodies are not always present. Since the crescents always have the convex side toward the flow top, they provide a reliable top and bottom feature.   (Art. 220.)   (*Sketches based on description and illustrations by Burrows and Rickaby,* 1935, *Ontario Bur. Min. Ann. Rept.,* **43**: 16–17, *Figs.*)

The crescents are from 3 to 6 inches long and the smaller pea-like masses are approximately an inch in diameter.   In many cases the two are together with the smaller mass from one to three inches from the crescent and always on the concave side.   In the same flow these crescents assume always the same attitude with respect to the flow, that is, with the convex side toward the flow top.

Figure 342 consists of two diagrams based on a photograph showing a number of these structures, which have obvious top and bottom significance.

Fuller (1931: 287) described and illustrated an original cavity in basalt formed by the draining out of some fluid from a chilled ellipsoid. The remaining cavity has a flat bottom and a domed top roughly paralleling the shell of the ellipsoid (Fig. 343).   This may be the way in which the Quebec cavities described above were formed, although it does not seem very likely.

Bulbous and linear squeeze-ups (Art. 208) are commonly left hollow by the draining away of some of the lava after the outer crust has formed.

The resulting cavity may be filled later with introduced material. Both cavity and filling might well be of use in determining the top or bottom of a squeeze-up as illustrated in Fig. 323.

221. *Tunnels, "Caves," Collapse Features, etc.*—Tunnels and similar cavities are known to form when lava drains out from under the solidified crust of a flow. If the roof is sufficiently strong, the cavity may persist for a long time and may even be buried and filled with sedimentary material. Stearns (1926: 539) describes a tunnel of this sort in Idaho that is 20 km. long.

If the roof of such a tunnel is weak or becomes weakened later and collapses, a cave or cisternlike cavity results and this may be filled with materials washed and blown in from the surface. Nichols (1938: 607–608)

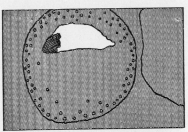

FIG. 343.—A hollow ellipsoid from foresetbedded volcanic breccia east of Columbia River about 2½ miles south of Moses Coulee. The vitreous margin, irregular distribution of marginal vesicles, and large central cavity with a horizontal floor are clearly defined. The ellipsoid is about 43 cm. (17 in.) in diameter. The planoconvex cavity indicates that the enclosed lava retained a relatively high degree of fluidity for some time after the chilled shell was formed. Compare with Fig. 352. (Art. 220.) [*Adapted from Fuller*, 1931, *Am. Jour. Sci.* (5) **21**: 287, *Fig. 3.*]

describes a collapse feature of this sort, and Fig. 344 is a diagrammatic sketch prepared for him by Dr. Erwin J. Raisz, with whose kind permission it is here reproduced. Nichols (1939*b*: 432) states:

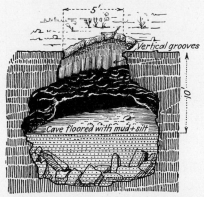

FIG. 344.—A cavelike collapse depression in a lava flow. The throat of the cavity is vertically grooved, and the angular blocks that fell from the collapsed roof are now covered by stratified mud and silt. (Arts. 217, 221.) (*Sketch by E. R. Raisz in Nichols*, 1938, *Jour. Geology*, **46**: 608, *Fig. 6.*)

In an area approximately two miles long, near the terminus of McCartys Flow [New Mexico], there are about 100 collapse-depressions. The largest depression is nearly a mile long and in places as much as 300 feet wide, whereas the smallest is only a few feet in diameter. They may be as much as 28 feet deep. They are formed by the collapse of the roofs of lava-tunnels [Fig. 345].

222. Weathered Upper Surface of Flows.—If a flow is weathered to any extent before burial by new lava or by sediments, certain indicators of this interflow, or preburial, weathering period are preserved at or near the top of the flow. The more common of these weathering effects are (1) weathering profiles,

(2) decreased specific gravity, (3) interflow soil and forest beds, and (4) secondarily filled vesicles and cavities.

223. *Weathering Profiles.*—Under intense and prolonged chemical weathering of basaltic lavas, the soluble alkalies, lime, and magnesia are lost to ground water, whereas less soluble silica, alumina, and the oxides of iron remain as a residue. The resulting residue is a combination of silica, hydrated aluminum silicate, and the hydrated oxides of iron and aluminum. Under certain climatic conditions it is an iron-stained clay;

Courtesy of R. L. Nichols

FIG. 345.—Small collapse depression about 5 m. (15 ft.) across in the Quaternary McCartys flow of New Mexico. The vegetation in the foreground is rooted in the bottom sediment that is visible near the right edge of the picture. Collapse depressions of this kind are commonly filled with carbonaceous muds. (Arts. 217, 221.) .(*After Nichols, 1946, Bull. Geol. Soc. Am., 57: 1064, Plate 6, Fig. 2.*)

under another set of conditions it will be a composite of the hydrated oxides of iron and aluminum with only a few per cent of silica; and under still other conditions it may be further simplified to a lateritic iron ore with low alumina and silica or a lateritic aluminum ore with low iron and silica content.

In addition to the profound chemical changes produced by weathering, the primary rock may undergo other modifications. Spheroidal weathering is to be expected in the upper part of the profile and may be so extensively developed that the rock has the appearance of a giant conglomerate. If there is any appreciable thickness of soil, the amount of carbonaceous matter will decrease with depth below the upper contact. Weathering of the primary zone of reddening at the tops of certain flows may further intensify the red color because of the oxidation of primary ferrous iron

(Art. 240).   The contact relations shown by the residual deposit should therefore indicate which formation covers it and which is its parent rock (Fig. 346).

Exposed and buried weathering profiles developed on ancient igneous rock have been reported from widely scattered places.[1] Two good examples are the lateritic iron ores of Cuba, developed on serpentine [Leith and Mead (1915)] and the recently discovered ferro-aluminous laterite of Oregon, developed on Columbia River basalt [Libbey, Lowry, and Mason (1945)].   Tomkeieff (1940: 97), in describing a series of basaltic flows near Giant's Causeway in Ireland, states that "each flow as

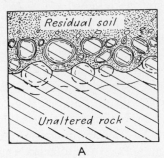
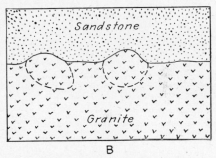

A   B

Fig. 346.—Weathering profiles.   A. Diagram showing residual soil resting upon spheroidally weathered source rock.   Several spheroids are outlined in the solid rock but have not yet become separated from it. Other concentrically weathered boulders lie in the basal part of the soil mantle.   The "soil" may be a ferruginous or aluminous laterite with low silica content or a red kaolinitic clay.   The carbon content of the soil is usually highest in the upper few centimeters, decreasing downward quite rapidly.   This general relationship of residual soil to spheroidally weathered rock is especially characteristic of weathered basic igneous rocks.   B. Cambrian sandstone resting unconformably upon Archean granite. The ellipsoidal masses outlined in the granite belong to a weathering profile developed before deposition of the sand.   The masses are about a meter long.   (Art. 223.)   (B is slightly modified after Crosby, 1899, Bull. Geol. Soc. Am., 10: 149–151, Figs. 17–20.)

a rule has a reddened upper surface, which when fully developed is composed of bole or laterite (interbasaltic zone)" (Art. 240).   There is every reason to expect that extensive deposits of iron, aluminum, manganese, and certain other metals will be discovered along ancient unconformities as future exploration proceeds (Fig. 347).

224. *Decreased Specific Gravity in Weathered Zone.*—Decomposition of the iron- and alkali-bearing minerals in the weathered zone at the top of a flow and subsequent removal of the soluble salts lower the specific gravity of the rock in the weathered zone.   Powers and Lane (1917: 445) report this condition at the top of the thick Cape Spencer flow in Nova Scotia, and similar examples almost certainly occur elsewhere (Fig. 366).

225. *Interflow Soil and Forest Beds.*—If lavas of intermediate and basic composition undergo prolonged weathering under the proper con-

[1] Leith and Mead (1915: 25–44), Frasché (1941: 280–305), and Libbey, Lowry, and Mason (1945).

ditions, a considerable regolith of mantle rock and soil develops and this ultimately supports a forest of some kind. If such a soil and forest are buried beneath an advancing flow[1] or under a sheet of sediments, the order of events is usually clear from the obvious relation of the forest and soil to the underlying lava. Trees overwhelmed in position of growth are discussed in Arts. 162 and 233 to 235 (see also Figs. 355, 358).

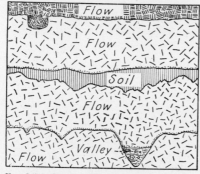

Fig. 347.—Erosional and weathering features along interflow contacts. The lowest flow was eroded and the deeper valleys partly filled with alluvium before the second flow overwhelmed the surface. Then ensued a long period of weathering with little erosion during which a thick cover of residual soil developed on the second flow. The third flow baked the upper part of the soil layer and itself developed a chilled basal zone. At one point (see the left side of the diagram) a channel was left in the surface of the flow, probably the result of a somewhat more fluid stream flowing on after the flanking lava had solidified. This channel, as well as the general level surface of the third flow, was covered by the fourth flow. All these relations and others that might be included may be observed in flow sequences in western United States and should be looked for in ancient metamorphosed sequences thought to be of flow origin. (Arts. 216, 227.)

Interflow soils and forest beds are to be expected in areas of intermittent volcanism, such as the well-known Amethyst Mountain section of Yellowstone Park (Fig. 293). Ancient soil beds are almost certainly present in the now greatly altered volcanics of the Pre-Cambrian and Paleozoic, but it is doubtful whether they can always be identified with certainty (Fig. 347). Intense metamorphism has done much to obliterate them. Inasmuch as their argillaceous nature made them more incompetent than the adjacent rock under shearing stress, they are almost certain to be the loci for interflow shear zones.

226. *Secondary Amygdules.*—The vesicular upper part of many flows is made doubly apparent by the development of partial or complete amygdular fillings in the vesicles. Fillings of the first type have top and bottom significance and are discussed in Art. 219. Complete fillings

---

[1] Emerson (1916: 322) years ago reported peculiar cylinders of scoriaceous diabase in the normal Holyoke (Massachusetts) diabase and considered them to have an origin associated with the overwhelming of trees, citing as a similar example the burial of trees by lava in Hawaii.

I have also seen at Kilauea a hollow tube in the lava 4–5 inches in diameter and perhaps a foot deep where the liquid lava had surrounded a small tree and became solid so quickly that the trunk on burning or rotting left a cylindrical cavity. A second scoriaceous flow might have filled this hole and made a result like that here described.

Alford (1937: 146–147) describes a locality in Oregon, where geologically recent lavas, as much as 6 + m. (20 ft.) thick, overwhelmed a pine forest, pushing over some of the trees and leaving others erect. The sap in the trees chilled the surrounding lava so that the cylindrical cavities left after the woody tissue had burned or rotted away show a chilled periphery.

made by ground water during an interflow weathering period are not likely to be of any use in determining the top of a flow. Ground water, however, may bring into the partly filled vesicles the mineral substance which now constitutes the upper part of a composite amygdule (Art. 198).

227. EROSIONAL FEATURES OF FLOW SURFACES.—If considerable rain accompanies the extrusion of a lava flow or if the surface of a flow is subjected to prolonged weathering and erosion, any surficial ash deposits are likely to be blown or washed away. Furthermore, the fragmental or scoriaceous upper part and even the dense middle portion of a flow may be eroded into a surface of considerable relief (Art. 216). The crevices,

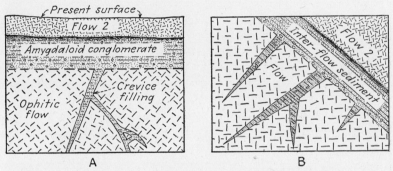

FIG. 348. Clastic dikes filling cracks thought to have been formed in a Keweenawan lava flow by thermal contraction. The sediment, derived from the erosion of neighboring areas, was washed into the crevices and stratified. Since stratification in the dike material is parallel to the dip of the tilted flow, it follows that the cracks were filled before tilting. The crevice fillings generally are confined to the upper 3 or 4 m. of the flow, but large ones may extend downward several times that distance. *A.* Cross section of two flows, showing relations of crevice fillings to overlying amygdaloid conglomerate in a Keweenawan flow. *B.* Diagram showing crevice fillings in tilted flows. (Arts. 214, 227.) (*A modified after Fackler, 1941, Jour. Geology, 49 : 554, Fig. 4. B diagrammatic.*)

channels, and valleys so produced may then be backfilled with new lava or with sediments transported from the land or deposited from superjacent water (Figs. 317, 347). Since the contact of the eroded flow and covering rock is unconformable, the true order of succession should be readily obvious.[1] Not so obvious, however, may be the origin of the original crevice or channel (Figs. 348, 349).

Conglomerates, sandstones, and shales commonly separate lava flows, indicating that sufficient time elapsed between flows for weathering to produce a residual regolith or for wind and water to bring in a transported regolith. Residual regolithic sediments—boulders, pebbles, sand grains, and soil particles—reflect in their lithological and mineralogical charac-

[1] Crevices produced by weathering and erosion and later backfilled by new lava or with sediments may be difficult to distinguish from similar openings due to thermal contraction [Fackler (1941: 550–556)] (Art. 214) and to rupture during the formation of pressure ridges [Nichols (1938: 610)] (Art. 211). This is very likely to be so in the more ancient volcanic rocks that have been folded and metamorphosed (Fig. 348).

teristics the nature of the original flow from which they were derived (*i.e.*, the underlying flow). Even if successive flows are similar lithologically, the sharp upward termination of the regolith against the later flow and the downward gradation into the solid rock of the parent flow ought usually to indicate the order of succession (see Art. 223.)

The relations between alternating flows and conglomerates are well exposed along the scenic Columbia River highway between Portland, Oreg., and the sea and are likely to be complex (Fig. 349). Similarly

Fig. 349.—View of a Columbia River basaltic flow that was eroded before burial by sediments. The V-shaped depressions are filled with red silt in which the bedding planes sag downward. The overlying gravel consists entirely of basaltic boulders. The hammer shown at the point of the deepest depression indicates the scale. The photograph was taken along a tributary of Columbia River a few miles west of Longview, Wash. (Art. 227.)

complex relations have been reported from the late Pre-Cambrian Keweenawan flows by Butler and Burbank (1929: 17–47), from Alaskan flows and interbedded shales by Capps (1915: 45–51), and from a similar sequence in Glacier National Park in Montana by Burling (1916: 235 –237). Additional examples are well known in the Triassic sequences of the North American Atlantic seaboard and probably are common on other continents. All these occurrences have in common certain features produced by lava flowing onto and over sediments and another group of surface relations produced by burial of weathered and eroded surfaces of some relief.[1] Careful study of contact relations usually makes it possible to determine the top or bottom of the flow (see Art. 194).

[1] Crevices and other depressions extending downward into a lava flow commonly

228. FEATURES IN BASAL PART OF FLOWS.—The distinct differences between the upper and lower surfaces of lava flows are discussed in Arts. 194, 196, 197, and 201. Here we shall consider features that are common in the basal part of flows and others that were formed in the substratum as a result of being covered by hot lava.

229. *Inclusions of Sediment and Country Rock.*—Lava flows commonly have basal inclusions of many kinds of material obviously derived from the substratum.[1] Such inclusions, commonly sedimentary in composition, must not be confused with the fragmental material formed from and at the same time as the lava flow itself.

As lava advances across a surface, either subaerially or subaqueously, it may, if its viscosity is favorable, flow into concavities and around and over irregular prominences, thus making a fairly smooth contact with the surface.[2] Again, it may plow up soil, sand, and gravel and roll over and over large blocks of the regolith, ultimately incorporating some or all of the disturbed materials in its basal part.[3] Lava extruded subaqueously is likely to incorporate some of the soft and unconsolidated sediments in its basal part. Since these sediments may contain shells and other animal hard parts, the flow may become fossil-bearing and its time of formation may be fairly accurately fixed (Art. 233).

An advancing sheet of lava may cool enough on the surface for a crust to form, and this crust, impelled forward by the continued motion of the lava beneath, is fragmented. Some of the blocks thus formed may roll down the advancing front and come ultimately to rest on the substratum, where they are buried by the passing flow. Although this is a common

---

are filled with sediments, new lava, etc., but such bodies would show by their relations to the underlying lava and their lack of thermal alteration by the adjacent lava that they had been emplaced after the flow had solidified and cooled (Arts. 213 to 215).

[1] It is worth while to note here that, whereas fragments of the substratum may be included in a flow, fragments from the overlying rock cannot be. In contrast, sills and flat dikes may contain inclusions from either sub- or superstratum, and apophyses of a sill or veinlets from a dike may penetrate either wall [see Billings (1942: 263*ff.*)].

[2] Substratal materials are likely to be baked by the hot lava, as described and illustrated by Stearns (1942: 870) and Bailey *et al.* (1924: 116) (Fig. 360 and Art. 237).

[3] Emerson (1905: 93) described how Triassic basaltic lavas, flowing over muds and sands, broke through the bottom crust and churned the substratal materials into a confused mass; Capps (1915: 45–51) describes how recently formed ellipsoids, rolling down the front of an advancing subaqueous flow, plunged into the soft bottom muds and squeezed these same muds upward into the interstices between the crudely piled ellipsoids; and Fuller (1931: 287, Fig. 3) illustrates an ellipsoid that became incorporated in the mud of the substratum in this manner. Burling (1916: 237) records similar displacement of underlying mud at the base of ellipsoidal lavas in Montana. The same phenomenon may be observed around the base of El Parícutin, the recently active volcano in Mexico (Fig. 350), and many other examples could be cited.

phenomenon in recent flows, there seem to be few references to ancient lava flows having such blocks in the basal part. Butler and Burbank (1929: 27) state that "in the Michigan [Keweenawan] lavas no such fragmental material is consistently present at the bottoms of the flows."

Finally, lava may enter cracks and crevices in the underlying rock floor and, by a kind of quarrying action, excavate large blocks of the bedrock and rotate them into all sorts of positions within the basal part of the flow. Masses of Cambridge slate, as much as 10 m. across, lie with

Courtesy of R. L. Nichols

Fig. 350.—View of a lava flow advancing over an ash-covered surface near El Parícutin, southwestern Mexico. Under conditions like these the flow commonly disturbs the surface materials over which it moves, causing overfolding, thrusting, sag bedding, and general churning of the unconsolidated ash. The churning results in an intimate mixing of ashy materials with the basal part of the flow. Such a relation of ash and lava would not be present at the top of a flow. (Arts. 228 to 230.)

random orientation in the basal part of the Carboniferous Brighton flows in Allston, Mass. (Fig. 351). They appear to have been excavated and buried in the manner just described. A second example is found at Vinegar Hill in Saugus, Mass., where the Lynn volcanics contain blocks of granite as much as 4 m. (12 ft.) in greatest dimension and large quantities of arkosic material originally derived from weathering of the same granite. These included materials, lying as they do in the basal part of the volcanic sequence, indicate that the lava flowed over a surface of weathered granite and plowed some of the surficial material into its basal part [Clapp (1921: 64)]. Similar occurrences have been reported from many parts of the world in rocks of all ages.

It is unlikely that inclusions of foreign, or country, rock would be present in the upper part of a lava flow and not also in the lower. Talus fragments and blocks ripped from cliffs might fall onto and sink into a flow, but such cases are probably not common.

After a flow has been weathered, zones of inclusions are likely to be very conspicuous because of projecting blocks, which are more resistant that the enclosing flow rock, and large irregular cavities produced by the decomposition and removal of masses less resistant than the surrounding volcanic rock.

230. *Deformed Materials Overridden by Flows.*—Unconsolidated materials overridden by a lava flow are subjected to abnormally high pressures

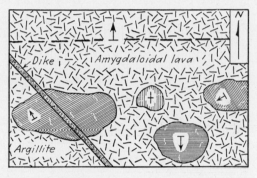

Fig. 351.—Inclusions of Carboniferous Cambridge slate in the basal part of northward-dipping Brighton flows in Allston, Mass. Inclusions do not appear north of the portion shown by the heavy dashed line, for the layer in which they are embedded passes under a younger part of the flow. The blocks of slate, measuring from 1 to 5 or 6 m. across, are tilted in every direction. It is believed they were torn loose from the rock floor over which the lava advanced. A postlava dike, probably of Triassic age, cuts both slate and lava. (Art. 229.) (*Sketch, which is diagrammatic, based on outcrops in the Allston playground.*)

and temperatures and as a result undergo deformation and alteration of several kinds. There usually is no difficulty in distinguishing between such deformed and altered materials and those of similar lithology overlying a flow.

In the vicinity of presently active volcanoes (*e.g.*, El Parícutin in Mexico) intensely deformed ash and tuff deposits may be observed beneath recent lava flows (Fig. 350). Folding, thrust faulting, and general contortions are everywhere in evidence in such deformed materials. Capps (1915: 49) described a somewhat similar situation on Prince William Sound in Alaska, where soft mud was squeezed into the basal ellipsoids of a lava.

The presence of this sedimentary material in the cracks of the fractured ellipsoids can be satisfactorily explained only by assuming that the bed of mud upon which the lava was extruded was at that time soft and plastic, and that upon the cooling of the lavas, and their cracking from shrinkage as they chilled, the weight of the lava bed forced the soft mud from below up into the cracks as fast as they were opened.

Certain Triassic flows of New England have prominent basal inclusions of argillaceous rock, which have been interpreted as muds first deposited on top of a moving flow and later carried forward and rolled under to be incorporated in the basal part of the flow [Emerson (1897: 59 –86)].

Many similar examples could be cited if the discussion warranted, showing that the phenomenon is common.

231. *Cross-bedded Flow Breccias.*—An unusual feature of brecciated lavas is a crude type of cross-bedding reported by Fuller (1931*a*: 281–300;

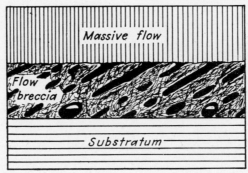

Fig. 352.—Foreset-bedded flow breccia.   Traced upward, the diagonal tongues of lava merge into basal extensions of the overlying flow.   Two partly hollow spheroids are shown.   After these rolled into place, the internal fluid sought its level within the chilled shell and a planoconvex cavity was left in the upper part (see Fig. 342 and Art. 220).   [*Diagram is based on a description by Fuller* (1931: 281–300) *of a Columbia River basaltic flow.*]   (Art. 231.)

1934: 311–320) and Hoffman (1933: 184–195; 1934: 320–328) from the Columbia River lavas of central Washington.   Hoffman (1933: 189) states that "at a number of places the stringers and rows of pillows are arranged more or less parallel to each other and give the flow a rude, cross-bedded appearance."   This feature should not be mistaken for true bedding in a pillow lava [see Wilson (1941: 18–19)].   One characteristic to be noted is the fact that some of the inclined and elongated pillows are joined to the base of the overlying flow (Fig. 352), indicating that they represent forward extensions of the lava down the foreset slope.

232. *Spiracles, Vesicular Masses, and Bubble Aggregations.*—Molten lava flowing over wet sediments or growing vegetation traps the gases driven off from the substratum as a result of the sudden elevation of temperature.   These gases are forced upward into the viscous lava for some distance and form several distinctive vesicular structures in the basal part of the flow.

Spiracles are irregularly walled tubular cavities that rise into the basal part of a flow from underlying sediments. They are formed by gases released during the burial of wet muds and sap-filled vegetation. In many flows mud flakes and carbonized wood are found enclosed in the roughened walls of the tube (Fig. 353). Fuller (1931a: 299–300) describes and illustrates spiracles in the basal part of certain Columbia River basaltic flows. These extend upward from the base of the flow for a distance of 3 to 6 m. (10 to 20 ft.).

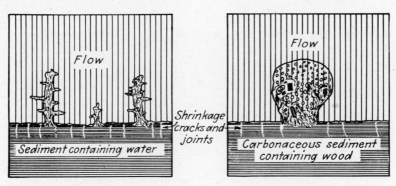

FIG. 353.

FIG. 354.

FIG. 353.—Spiracles in the base of a lava flow overlying argillaceous sedimentary rock. These are formed by gases that rise into hot fluid lava as it flows over damp sediments or sap-filled vegetation. Mud flakes and carbonized wood are commonly embedded in the irregular walls of the spiracle, and the spiracle itself was filled with mud forced upward into the viscous lava along with steam and other gases. When exposed to weathering, spiracles usually appear as irregular cavities because of removal of the easily weathered sedimentary material. Spiracles may extend into the lava several meters and may be quite closely spaced. (Art. 232.) [*Sketch adapted from Fuller, 1931, Am. Jour. Sci., (5) 21: 299, Fig. 13.*]

FIG. 354.—Balloon-shaped vesicular body about a meter in diameter in the base of a basaltic flow. The feature formed in the base of a flow as the hot lava advanced over carbonaceous muds containing wood and other vegetation. Steam from the mud and gases from the destructive distillation of the plant matter were forced upward into the plastic lava, causing the balloon-shaped vesicular mass to form. Chunks of sediment and fragments of carbonized wood were carried upward with the gases and mixed with the vesicular lava in chaotic fashion. The mass as a whole is less resistant to weathering than the enclosing flow rock, so that the weathered exposures are marked by large cavities where the vesicular material has been removed. (Art. 232.) (*Sketch based on suggestion by R. L. Nichols.*)

[They] invariably are at least partially filled with the light-colored basal sediments, which quite commonly contain fragments of carbonized wood. In fact, similar fragments have been found actually incorporated in the flow. At intervals of 1 to 2 feet, these vertical cavities locally exhibit horizontal marginal extensions 1 to 4 feet long. Between these embayments the lava forms a succession of rounded surfaces that suggest segments of pillows.

Dr. R. L. Nichols has called the attention of the author to an unusual vesicular feature he has observed in the base of flows that were extruded onto muds containing wood. Steam from the mud and gases from the destructive distillation of the entombed wood ascended into the base of the plastic lava and formed there a balloon-shaped vesicular mass containing chunks of sediment, fragments of carbonized wood, and vesicular lava mixed together in confused fashion. These masses are made conspicuous because they weather readily into prominent cavities (Fig. 354).

Other vesicles owing their origin to gas bubbles rising into the lava from the substratum are discussed in Art. 200.

233. *Lava-enveloped Trees and Other Organisms.*—Some lavas of recent formation contain certain unusual features formed as the result of

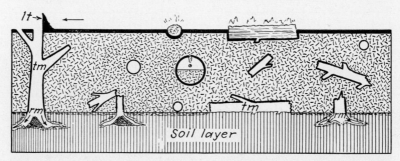

Fig. 355.—Diagram showing features produced by a lava flow overwhelming a forest. On the surface of the flow two floating logs are burning. They will probably leave their imprint in the crust that has formed about them. At the extreme left is a large tree mold *tm* with a lava tree *lt* above the surface. The latter indicates that the lava flowed from right to left. Within the flow are tree molds with different orientations, and in about the middle is an unusually large mold into which secondary lava is dripping from a rupture in the encircling shell. The original tree mold thus becomes a partly filled cylindrical cavity, the flat surface of the filling indicating the upward direction in the flow. Stumps and prostrate logs lie at the base of the flow where the lava overwhelmed them, and root molds *rm* extend from the stumps into the underlying soil. The soil is baked for some distance downward from its contact with the lava. The stumps and logs have hardened lava shells that were produced by the chilling action of steam and other gases escaping from the sap-filled wood. The soil surrounding the stump bases and roots was baked as the wood burned out. Some tree molds contain carbonized wood—the unconsumed residue from the original tree. This is particularly true of stump molds. (Arts. 234, 235.) (*Sketch based on suggestions by R. L. Nichols.*)

molten lava invading a forest (Figs. 293, 359) or flowing over shell-bearing unconsolidated sediments. In the first case, cylindrical sheaths are formed about the trees and later, when the tree itself has disappeared. constitute "tree molds" and "lava trees." In the second case, moving lava churns the unconsolidated sediment into the basal part of the flow. In this way shells and other organic hard parts become fossils in the base of a lava flow.

234. *Tree Molds.*—Lavas that invade forests and surround scattered trees affect the trees in different ways. The sap, driven out by the excessive heat of the lava, causes a shell of chilled lava to form around the tree, which may burn or later disappear through decay.[1] The resulting cavity is called a "tree mold."

Trees buried *in situ* give essentially erect molds, which are rooted in the substratum and may extend through the entire flow to become a

[1] See Emerson (1916: 322) and Alford (1937: 146–147).

"lava tree" at the surface (Art. 235; Figs. 355, 358, 359). Logs and limbs broken off by the lava may be buried near the mother stump or rafted along for some distance. Upon disappearing by burning or decay they leave molds with random orientation that have no top and bottom significance (Figs. 355, 356). The molds may be filled later with new lava or with introduced mineral matter, if open to the surface or in connection with it by joints and crevices, or with detritus washed and blown in from the surface. The lava may be too stiff to make any adjustment to the cavity other than to sag into it slightly (Fig. 356); if less viscous, it forms lava stalactites on the walls of the mold (Fig. 357); and if still more fluid, it fills the cavity partly or completely (Fig. 356). In all cases

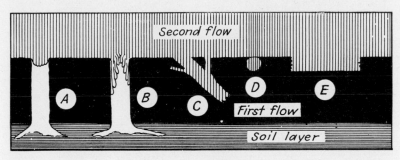

FIG. 356.—Tree molds. *A.* A tree mold into which lava from the overlying flow sagged for a few centimeters. The lava was not fluid enough to fill the entire mold as in *C.* *B.* Lava stalactites on the upper wall of a tree mold (see Fig. 357). *C, D.* Tree molds completely filled with lava from the second flow. *E.* Lava from second flow filling cylindrical depression originally occupied by a floating log. These same molds (*C* to *E*) could be filled with sediment before the second flow covered the area. (Art. 234.) (*Sketch based on suggestions by R. L. Nichols.*)

the contact relations of the two juxtaposed lavas should indicate clearly which is the younger and which the older.

Mold fillings of surficial detritus should exhibit crude stratification, and the individual laminae should sag downward to some extent in many of the deposites.

The top of a flow that has invaded forests and surrounded and engulfed trees should be determinable from observing the relations of erect trunks or their molds with reference to the general layering of the flow. The concavity of sandstone and shale laminae in filled molds should furnish corroborative data.

235. *Lava Trees.*—As a lava flow overwhelms a forest, a shell of chilled lava forms around the upstream side of trees that remain erect, and after the flow has subsided a hemicylindrical tube of chilled lava, open on the downstream side, remains as a surficial projection (Figs. 355, 358, 359). These have been called lava trees and are common in the Lava-cast Forest of Oregon. Downward into the flow they become tree molds.

Lava trees are an unusual feature and have been observed so far only on recent flows. Under unusual conditions, however, they may have been preserved in ancient flows.

236. *Incorporation of organic hard parts contained in unconsolidated substratum.*—If a lava were to flow over a substratum composed of unconsolidated sediments containing shells, leaves, and other organic hard parts, it is likely that some of the sediment and organic debris would be churned into the basal part of the flow. In this way a lava flow could become fossiliferous, and the fossils would provide a means of determining

Courtesy of R. L. Nichols

Fig. 357.—Lava stalactites on the wall of a tree mold in a flow in Lava-cast Forest of Oregon. The stalactites indicate the direction of gravity at the time when they were formed, and if found *in situ* in a tree mold they indicate the general direction of the flow top. See Fig. 356*B*. (Art. 234.)

the age of the extrusion. Since it is not likely that fossiliferous shales and sandstones would be churned into the upper part of a flow, it follows that contorted masses of sediment along one surface of a flow indicate that that surface is the underside.

237. *Baking of Underlying Material.*—Unconsolidated sediments and little-indurated sedimentary rocks are likely to be baked along their contact with an overlying flow. Bailey *et al.* (1924: 116) describe a massive sandstone that was baked through several centimeters along its marginal contact with a basaltic lava (Fig. 360). The baked margin developed a rude columnar jointing. Dr. R. L. Nichols informs the author that he has observed similar rude columnar jointing in baked argillaceous sediment beneath Quaternary lava flows in New Mexico, particularly around tree molds (Fig. 358).

Gray shale and other sedimentary materials containing ferrous iron take on a conspicuous red color when baked by contact with molten lava. This reddening is caused by oxidation of ferrous iron to ferric. Red-

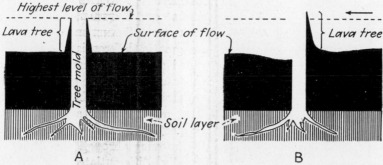

FIG. 358.—Lava tree and its relation to a tree mold. *A.* Section at right angles to the direction of flow, showing the lava sheath rising above the general flow surface to a height determined by the highest level attained by the fluid lava. *B.* Section parallel to the direction of flow, showing the prominent upstream partial sheath and the lack of an appreciable deposit on the downstream side of the original tree. Piling up of fluid lava against the upstream side of the tree causes the sheath to rise slightly above the highest level attained by the lava. Lava trees pass downward into tree molds in the body of the flow. The mold is produced by consumption and removal of the original tree (*i.e.*, the trunk, stump, and roots). Compare these diagrams with Figs. 355 and 359. (Arts. 234, 235.) (*Sketches based on orginal drawings by R. L. Nichols.*)

Courtesy of R. L. Nichols

FIG. 359.—Lava trees on a Quaternary flow in Lava-cast Forest, Oregon. *A.* Irregular, sheathlike lava tree with upstream side higher than the downstream. It becomes a tree mold below the surface. The lava moved from rear to front in the area shown. *B.* Semicylindrical lava tree passing downward into a tree mold. The lava moved from rear to front, and its highest position was the plane marked by the top of the semicylinder. Compare with Fig. 358. (Arts. 233 to 235.)

topped argillaceous materials of the type just described are common along the Columbia River gorge and have been observed under Quaternary flows in New Mexico.

Steptoes—hills of rock surrounded but not surmounted by lava—

commonly show a marginal zone of baking, and their stratigraphic relations together with this baked zone provide a criterion for determining the order of succession (Fig. 361).

238. CRYSTALLIZATION DIFFERENTIATION[1] AND THE GENERAL PROBLEMS OF CRYSTAL SETTLING AND VOLATILE TRANSFER.—Gravitational

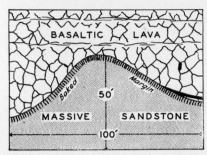

magmatic differentiation may be defined as that process of internal adjustment between gas, liquid, and crystal by which the constituents of the magma seek and attain their respective gravity-determined levels by moving through the liquid. An ideally differentiated tabular body of igneous rock should have a chilled zone at both top and bottom margin, between which the main mass of rock should consist of a lower portion composed dominantly of dark-colored, heavy minerals, the crystals

FIG. 360.—A low sandstone hillock covered by a horizontal bedded Tertary lava flow that baked the rock for several centimeters inward. The baked margin is hardened and has a system of rude columnar joints. (Art. 237.) (*Modified after Bailey et al., 1924, Tertiary and post-Tertiary geology of Mull, etc., Geol. Survey Scotland Mem., p. 116, Fig. 17.*)

of which could sink through the liquid, and an upper portion composed dominantly of lighter colored minerals with specific gravities less than those of the lower part. The two chief portions of the differentiated body may be distinct rock types, rather sharply differentiated one from the other, or each may pass into the other by gradation. In

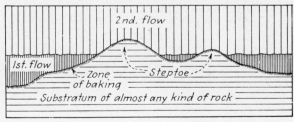

FIG. 361.—Steptoes—rock hills surrounded by lava. The first flow was not thick enough to cover the two prominent hills, which were buried by the second. A zone of baking lies just below the base of each flow along the surface of the buried hills. The baking produced by one flow is probably indistinguishable from that of another. See Fig. 360. (Art. 237.) (*Sketch based on suggestions by R. L. Nichols.*)

general, mafic minerals increase in amount from the upper chilled zone downward almost or quite to the lower chilled zone, and the felsic min-

[1] For comprehensive discussions of the general subject of differentiation, see Lane (1898: 106–151; 1911: 79–83), Harker (1909), Fenner (1926), Bowen (1928), Tyrell (1929), and Daly (1933). For numerous aspects of differentiation in an ancient flow, see Broderick (1935: 503–558).

erals show reverse distribution.[1] Under certain conditions, however, the systematic arrangement of minerals does not obtain, causing concentration at some levels and depletion at others. Gravity-stratified sheets have many successive bipartite layers of two different minerals, which maintain constant stratigraphic position within the layer relative to each other. Some basic plutonic rocks have primary banding, which has been ascribed to *rhythmic differential settling* (Art. 247).

In the early stage of differentiation volatile substances rise to the surface, causing slight concentration of iron oxides in the upper part of the body and strong oxidation of the iron near the surface. Red tops of flows are explained in this way (Art. 240). In the closing stages, liquids and gases rise to the upper portion of the body and there crystallize into felsic minerals or those with some volatile content. The latter commonly line vugs. Mobile residues of variable composition may produce pegmatitic schlieren and certain other features in the upper part of the mass, where most of the liquid remains [Broderick (1935: 512–517); Walker (1940: 1093)].

That crystals heavier than the liquid around them sink to or toward the bottom of a magma was cited twenty years ago as a primary cause of differentiation [Bowen (1928); Tyrrell (1929: 156)], and the investigations of Bowen (1928) and others have established the importance of gravity differentiation in producing the mineralogical distribution mentioned in the previous paragraph. Trommsdorf (1934: 329–332) has even found magmas in which sinking and rising crystals caused a streaming of the groundmass crystals in their wake (Figs. 362, 363). Although there no longer is any doubt about the sinking of crystals in a magma, there is present disagreement on the extent to which the felsic minerals rise to the position they hold in a flow or sill. That some crystals do rise appears certain from Trommsdorf's figures (Figs. 362, 363) and the reference of Broderick (1935: 505) to concentration of labradorite phenocrysts near the top of Keweenawan flows in Michigan,[2] but general

---

[1] In order to determine whether or not crystal fractionation produced a progressive change in the constituent minerals, Lund (1930: 540) investigated a 170-m. (556-ft.) basaltic flow (Cape Spencer) in Nova Scotia and found " . . . a noticeable enrichment of pyroxene . . . just below the middle [median plane of flow] and an even more striking enrichment of feldspar . . . above the middle part of the flow."

Chapman (1936: 33–57) studied a 336-m. (1100-ft.) differentiated diabase sill to determine whether there was any variation in the nature of the feldspar twinning with change in rock composition. She found that, whereas the type of twinning remained the same with change in rock composition, there was a statistical increase in the number of twins with increase in basicity or anorthite content. The feldspars ranged from An_{75} to An_{32}.

[2] Broderick (1935: 505–506), however, does qualify the significance of this con-

opinion seems to favor the conclusion that rising of crystals is not so important as sinking in gravitative differentiation.[1]

Differentiated flows and sills have been reported from many parts of the world—Daly (1933: 333–344) lists over 50 examples—but differentiated dikes seem to be rare [Quinn (1943: 272–281)]. Certain features

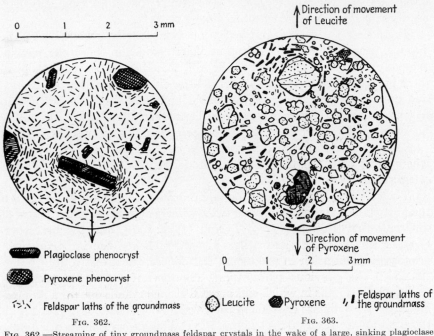

Fig. 362.
Fig. 363.

Fig. 362.—Streaming of tiny groundmass feldspar crystals in the wake of a large, sinking plagioclase crystal. The tiny laths are crowded together under the settling crystal and stream around its extremities to arrange themselves in more or less parallel fashion in the wake. Other plagioclase crystals are visible at 9 and 11 o'clock, and a sinking pyroxene crystal is partly visible at 1 o'clock. Compare with Fig. 363. Art. 238. (*After Trommsdorff*, 1934, *Naturwissenschaften*, **22**: 330, *Fig.* 1.)

Fig. 363.—Magnified thin section of a leucite basanite from Vesuvius showing a pyroxene crystal arrested in its downward path, after causing feldspar laths to pile up ahead and to string out alongside, and a leucite crystal arrested in its upward path after causing a similar concentration of feldspar laths. Compare with Fig. 362. (Art. 238.) (*After Trommsdorff*, 1934, *Naturwissenschaften*, **22**: 331, *Fig.* 2.)

of differentiated tabular igneous bodies are useful in determining top and bottom and will be considered in the following sections.

239. *Concentration of Glass and Magnetite at the Top and Bottom of a Flow.*—Thick flows commonly show a marked concentration of glass—

centration as follows: "This would seem to be a case of crystal floating because of low specific gravity, although the possibility should be admitted that gas bubbles may have attached themselves to the phenocrysts and helped to lift them."

[1] Butler and Burbank (1929: 26) report a thin zone (a few centimeters to a meter thick) at the base of the upper amygdaloidal part of a Keweenawan flow where there are " . . . abundant feldspar phenocrysts that collected by rising from the underlying lava," but such concentrations do not seem to be common.

and in some cases of iron[1] (magnetite, hematite, etc.)—in the top and bottom parts, the greater amount of each of these constituents being at the top (Figs. 364, 365).

This concentration is well shown in the 170-m. (556-ft.) Triassic Cape Spencer flow of Nova Scotia, which has been described in considerable detail by Powers and Lane (1916: 540) and by Lund (1930: 547, 577), and in other flows of the Acadian Triassic [Powers (1916: 256–266)]. Similar concentration of glassy constituents, especially at the surface, can be observed in the plateau flows along the Columbia River gorge in Washington and Oregon.

240. *Red Tops and Variation in Iron in Upper Part of Flows.*—Lavas with red tops have been reported from recent and ancient volcanic sequences in many parts of the world. The color, often brilliant or intense, is due to the oxidation of the iron to hematite (which increases in amount and fineness of division upward) during the solidification of the lava. Butler and Burbank (1929: xi; see also 35–36), in discussing this feature of the Keweenawan flows of Michigan, state:

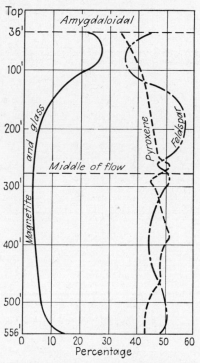

Fig. 364.—Diagram showing variation with depth in percentage of magnetite and glass and of the minerals pyroxene and feldspar in the 556-ft. (170-m.) Triassic Cape Spencer basaltic flow of Nova Scotia. (Arts. 239, 241.) (*Adapted from Lund*, 1930, *Am. Mineralogist*, **15**: 547, Plate 1.)

The tops of nearly all the flows are distinctly red, and the fragmental tops are decidedly red. Chemical analyses show that there is in general a steady decrease in the proportion of ferric iron and an increase in ferrous iron from the top of a flow nearly to the bottom. In the fragmental flows there is also more total iron in the top—as much as 40 per cent more than in the compact portion of the flow.

It is thought that the oxidation and concentration of the iron were accomplished in large part by the gases given off by the lava during solidification. The evidence indicates that at the temperature at which the lavas emerged the

---

[1] Broderick (1935: 505), in discussing the red tops of Keweenawan lavas, states: "In some cases this hematite not only is the equivalent of the normal iron content of the lava, but is much greater and represents an actual addition of considerable iron to the upper part of the flow by the ascending gases."

inclosed gases were either neutral or reducing in their action on ferric oxide, but as they cooled in their ascent through the flow they became strongly oxidizing toward ferrous oxide.

This variation in the iron content of the upper part of a flow and in an entire flow is well illustrated by the following comparative tables from a report by Butler and Burbank (1929: 35–36) (Fig. 365).

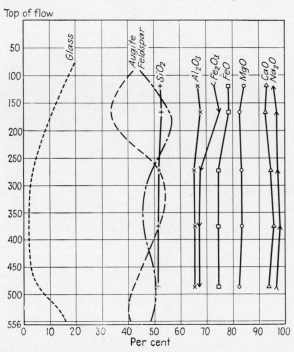

FIG. 365.—Compositional profile of the Triassic Cape Spencer basaltic flow of Nova Scotia. Curves show variation with depth in the amount of glass, augite, feldspar, and the chief oxides. The flow has a total thickness of 556 ft. (170 m.). (Arts. 239, 241.) [*After Lane and Powers*, 1916, *Am. Inst. Min. Eng. Trans.*, **54**: 456, (*Discussion following p.* 455), *Fig.* 1.]

Excellently exposed red-topped lava flows with little dip may be seen at many points along the gorge of the Columbia River between Portland, Oreg., and Longview, Wash., on U.S. Highway 30 and westward from Longview on U.S. Highway 830. Fuller (1939: 305) mentions the same feature in describing a late Tertiary basaltic flow in Steens Mountain, Oregon: "As is usually characteristic of the series, each flow had sufficient fluidity to attain a relatively level upper surface, which locally shows a thin aphanitic coating superficially oxidized to a fairly brilliant shade of red."

For other references to red-topped lavas, see Bailey *et al.* (1924),

I. Iron Content of Upper 25 Ft. of 40-Ft. Unaltered Flow (Snake River Lava
Plain) at Twin Falls, Idaho
(H. C. Kenny, analyst)

Distance from top of flow, ft.	Iron, %		
	Ferric	Ferrous	Total
0	7.7	3.7	11.4
3	4.9	6.8	11.7
6	3.0	9.0	12.0
12	1.6	9.9	11.5
25	1.3	10.1	11.4

II. Iron Content of Typical Smooth-top Keweenawan Flow
(H. C. Kenny, analyst)

Distance from top of flow, ft.	Iron, %		
	Ferric	Ferrous	Total
0– 30	4.5	3.7	8.2
30– 60	4.4	3.4	7.8
60– 90	3.7	4.7	8.4
90–120	2.7	5.1	7.8

III. Iron Content of Entire Brecciated-top Keweenawan Flow (Kearsarge
Flow)
(H. C. Kenny, analyst)

Distance from top of flow, ft.	Iron, %		
	Ferric	Ferrous	Total
0– 30	6.7	2.4	9.1
30– 60	4.4	3.3	7.7
60– 90	4.2	3.6	7.8
90–120	3.9	3.7	7.6
120–150	3.1	4.9	8.0
150–180	3.0	5.6	8.6

Bailey and Anderson (1925: 65*ff*.), Butler and Burbank (1929: xi, 34–37),
Richey and Thomas (1930: 51, 72), and Broderick (1935: 505*ff*).

Similar increase of iron oxide near the top of thick sills has been
reported by some investigators [Walker (1940: 1099)] (Fig. 373).

241. *Compositional Profiles Produced by Gravitative Differentiation.—*
The compositional profile of an ideally differentiated flow should exhibit
in descending order

1. A surface chilled zone of vesicular rock having essentially the chemical composition of the original magma
2. A zone of light-colored minerals of relatively low specific gravity
3. A zone of dark-colored, relatively heavy minerals
4. A basal chilled zone similar to (1), but much thinner

Deviations from this ideal sequence obviously affect adversely the reliability of the sequence as a top and bottom criterion.   Daly (1933: 333 –344) discusses factors that interrupt or alter the ideal sequence and lists 54 examples showing differentiation of some sort.

The upward or downward movement of newly formed crystals in a lava flow or in a sill and the subsequent concentration of certain minerals into gravity-stratified layers have been recognized and reported by several investigators.   The heavier minerals—olivine, pyroxenes, and magnetite and more rarely calcic plagioclases—sink through the liquid lava, whereas the felsic minerals and quartz tend to rise.

Lane (1897: 403–407; 1903: 369–384) long ago demonstrated gravitative differentiation by fractional crystallization and gravitative separation in the Keweenawan flows of Michigan.   It was shown that the feldspars were concentrated in the upper part of the flows, whereas the heavier olivine and pyroxene were concentrated in the lower part (Fig. 365). A similar mineralogical profile is reported to be present in the 170-m. (550-ft.) Triassic Cape Spencer flow of Nova Scotia, where Powers and Lane (1916: 548) report " . . . a concentration of the leucocratic, felsic constituents at the top of the flow; the melanocratic, mafic constituents at the base.   The quickly chilled top and bottom of the flow show approximately, when free from alteration, the original composition of the magma."

A special example of crystal settling was reported by Fuller (1931: 190; 1931*b*: 119; 1939: 303–313) in a 10-m. late Tertiary basaltic flow in Steens Mountain, Oregon, where the upper third of the flow lacks olivine, whereas the lower two-thirds shows a marked concentration (up to 30 per cent) of that mineral.   The writer (1939: 303) states: "Late Tertiary basaltic flows in southeastern Oregon show locally a surface depletion and a basal concentration of olivine above a chilled basal zone containing scattered phenocrysts of that mineral."   This unusual situation is ascribed (page 312) to " . . . gradual accumulation of the olivine phenocrysts at the base of a relatively stagnant flood of basalt, which was being continuously augmented in depth by the advance of a very fluid surface lava."

A similar mineralogical profile has been reported from a number of thick differentiated sills, as pointed out in Art. 251.

Reasoning that the fractionation just described should be reflected by progressive change in the composition and properties of the chief constituent minerals, Lund (1930: 540) reinvestigated the 170-m. (556-ft.) Acadian Cape Spencer flow and found "a noticeable enrichment of pyroxene . . . just below the middle [median plane of flow] and an even more striking enrichment of feldspar . . . above the middle part of the flow" (Fig. 364).

242. *Specific-gravity Profile in Flows.* As a consequence of the thicker zone of vesicles at the top of a flow (as compared with the thinner zone at the base) and concentration of the lighter minerals above and the heavier below the median plane and finally because in thick flows there tends to be a downward increase in the tenor of iron and calcium, it follows that the specific gravity of flow rock should be least at and near the top and should increase downward therefrom to within a short distance of the base of the flow (Fig. 366).

Lane (1899: 15–18) found this gravity profile to be present in the Keweenawan lava flows of Michigan, and Powers and Lane (1916: 548), after investigating the same problem in the Triassic flows of Nova Scotia, concluded that specific-gravity determinations have " . . . sufficient accuracy to be of much practical use." Their graph is reproduced in Fig. 366.

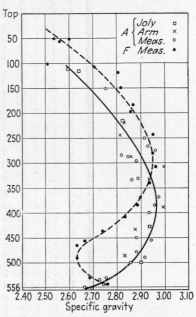

Fig. 366.—Specific-gravity profile of the Triassic Cape Spencer basaltic flow of Nova Scotia. The curves show variation with depth in specific gravity. The data on which the curves are based were secured by use of a Jolly balance, a two-arm balance, and a system of measurements. Each curve represents a different core. (Art. 242.) (*After Powers and Lane*, 1916, *Am. Inst. Min. Eng. Trans.*, **54**: 450, *Fig.* 4.)

243. *Textural Profile in Flows.*—The top portion of a flow crusts over quickly, particularly if in contact with cool air or under water, and the result is a chilled, glassy upper layer. The bottom margin likewise is chilled upon coming in contact with the cooler substratum, and a lower glassy border forms. The internal portion of the flow, on the other hand, being more or less insulated by the glassy or very dense upper- and undercrusts, loses heat slowly and crystallizes into a rock of phaneritic texture. If the flow is thick enough for differentiation to take place and if other conditions are similarly favorable, the resulting texture tends to increase in coarseness from the upper chilled border downward to a broad zone slightly below the median plane of the flow. This zone, which is rather uniformly coarse-grained, grades downward with decreasing coarseness into the basal chilled border (Fig. 367).

The following section through a 20-m. (61¼-ft.) flow is more or less typical of the usual textural profile. It is based on field notes and thin sections kindly furnished by Dr. Paul E. Auger and is used here by permission of the Quebec Bureau of Mines.

FLOW IN SOUTHEAST CORNER OF TOWNSHIP 209, ABITIBI COUNTY, PROVINCE OF QUEBEC

(About 80 Miles North of Senneterre—Lat. 49°5′N.; Long. 77°30′20″W.)*

Distance of Specimen from Top of Flow, Ft.	Description of Rock
0	Brecciated pillows; glassy
5	Brecciated pillows; glassy
10	Pillow lava; glassy
15	Very good pillows; glassy
20	Basic lava with flow lines and traces of pillows. Fine texture
25	Massive basalt with minor fracturing. Fine texture
30	Massive gabbro; no schistosity
35	Massive gabbro; mineralization
40	Massive gabbro; coarser
45	Massive gabbro; coarser
50	Massive gabbro; very coarse
55	Massive gabbro; coarse but finer than overlying and slightly schisted
60	Fine-grained andesite
61¼ (*bottom*)	Very fine-textured breccia—acid

* Dr. P. E. Auger, who described the flow and collected the specimens from which the thin sections were made, states in a letter to the author that the strike of the schistosity and of the flow is N.15°W., and the dip ranges from 75° northeast (top of flow is toward the east), through vertical, to an overturned position with the flow inclined 80° to the southwest. The specimens were taken at 5-ft. intervals (except for the two lowest) along a line trending N.75°E., hence transverse to the strike of the flow.

The thin sections of the 14 specimens show a gradual coarsening in grain from the surface downward to within about 5 ft. of the bottom, where the texture changes rapidly to almost rhyolitic fineness in the chilled border.

Queneau (1902: 181–195), Lane 1898: 106–151; 1902: 393–396), and Powers and Lane (1916: 540–542), among others, have investigated grain size in igneous rocks, and the last-named report as follows on their investigation of the Cape Spencer flow, the textural profile of which is shown in Fig. 367 (page 542):

[The flow shows] a fine grain at the top of the flow, and a coarse grain at or near the middle, with apparently a sudden transition between the two. At the base of the flow it is almost impossible to tell what is the true grain, on account of the phenocrysts, but there is apparently another sudden change to a finer grain.

It is obvious from the above description, and the same may also be said of the Quebec flow, that the textural profile of a flow is only a crude top and bottom feature and should therefore be employed with considerable caution because of the several factors which may have modified the ideal cooling history of the lava.

244. *Jointing Variation in Flows.*—As lava cools and solidifies, shrinkage cracks develop. These commonly have regular arrangement and outline columns with polygonal cross section. Such columnar jointing is common in both flows and sills. Some lava flows have a bipartite joint system, and since one type of jointing characteristically succeeds another in the same flow the order of succession provides a means of determining the top or bottom of the flow where it is steeply inclined.

Nichols (1936: 618–619) states that the upper vesicular zone of flow units is crudely jointed and sheeted, whereas the lower part is massive. In a typical unit, crude columnar jointing at the very top gives way downward to interrupted sheeting, which is produced by thin, horizontally disposed spaces probably due to laminar accumulation of gas bubbles arrested at certain levels (Fig. 327).

Bipartite jointing is well developed in a series of flows exposed near the well-known Giant's Causeway in Ireland. In a recent article on these

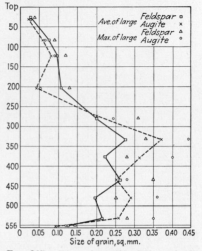

FIG. 367.—Textural profile of the Triassic Cape Spencer basaltic flow of Nova Scotia. Curves show variation with depth in grain size of feldspar and augite. The average area of the five largest crystals of each mineral is plotted, and the points connected by a continuous line for feldspar and a dashed line for augite. The area of the largest crystal of each mineral for each slide is also plotted, but the points are not connected. The curves show that the coarsest part of the flow lies slightly below the median horizontal plane, and the profile made by the curves is typical of many flows. The profile, therefore, provides a means of determining top and bottom in thick flows. (Art. 243.) (*After Powers and Lane*, 1916, *Am. Inst.Min. Eng. Trans.*, **54**: 448, *Fig.* 3.)

flows, Tomkeieff (1940: 96) characterizes the upper part, which he names the *entablature*, and the lower part, the *colonnade*, as follows: "(*a*) upper zone composed of closely spaced wavy columns or of thick vertical columns (pseudo-columnar jointing), or both. The uppermost part of this zone is usually vesicular and slaggy. (*b*) lower zone composed of regular vertical columns."

In a succession of flows with the sort of jointing just described, there should be no difficulty in distinguishing the upper or lower part, particularly when there is an interflow lateritic soil layer separating individual flows[1] (Fig. 368).

245. *Summary on Flows.*—Many structures and features of lava flows have been described and illustrated so that the field geologist may have

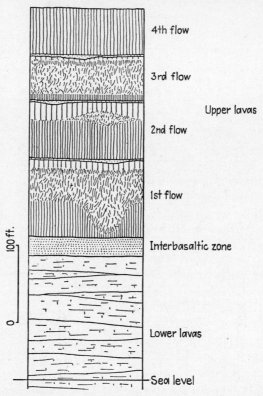

FIG. 368.—Jointing sequence in a succession of lava flows. Diagrammatic vertical section of the upper lavas in the sea cliff near Giant's Causeway, Ireland. The first, second, and third flows consist of two parts, (1) the lower zone, the *colonnade,* consisting of regular vertical columns and (2) the upper *entablature,* consisting of an upper vesicular zone, an intermediate zone of short, thick blocks having a false columnar appearance, and a basal zone composed of curved, thin columns. The fourth flow apparently has been denuded of its entablature. The interbasaltic zones of lateritic soil are shown stippled. (Art. 244.)   (*After Tomkeieff,* 1940, *Bull. volcanologique,* (2) **6:** 100, *Fig.* 1.)

them in mind when he is actually observing ancient volcanic rocks or collecting from them specimens which he intends to study later in the laboratory. Certain of the features are time-tested and are known to be reliable; others must be used with proper care and a regard for their limitations. Still other features have been observed only in recently

[1] In a letter dated Aug. 1, 1947, Tomkeieff writes that "the 'entablature-colonnade' type of lava structure is a very common one and there are many good examples of this among the Snake River plateau lavas of the Western States."

formed flows; these should be sought in the field and tested when found. Only in this way can their usefulness and reliability be determined.

246. Intrusive Bodies of Igneous Rock.—The principle of igneous intrusion—*the rock intruded is older than the intruding rock*—is one of the oldest and most widely used means of determining the age relations of contraposed rocks, and in some terranes the relations are such that it is possible also to determine the order of succession in associated sedimentary and metamorphic rocks. In addition, certain features within and along the peripheries of intrusive bodies may be useful in determining the top and base of the body itself.

In the present discussion we shall consider the following aspects of intrusive igneous bodies: (1) marginal relations and internal features of batholiths and plutons, including unconformities between eroded igneous masses and adjacent sedimentary rocks; (2) internal features of small tabular bodies intruded between sedimentary layers; (3) internal features of dikes.

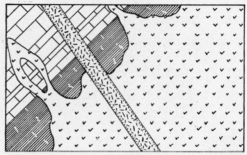

Fig. 369.—Diagram showing a shale-limestone sequence invaded by granite. A postinvasion dike cuts both granite and sediments. The diagram can be considered a plan or a cross section. Zones of contact metamorphism usually extend some distance into the host rock from its contact with the invading rock. Compare with Fig. 25. (Arts. 32, 248.)

247. MARGINAL RELATIONS AND INTERNAL FEATURES OF PLUTONS.— Where margins or peripheries of igneous bodies can be examined, it is usually possible to determine which of the juxtaposed rocks is the older. If the contact is between igneous and sedimentary rocks, the problem usually is simple. If both contacting rocks are igneous, determination of younger and older may be difficult. The present discussion will be confined mainly to those relations which may be useful in determining order of succession in sedimentary and metamorphic rocks.

An internal feature of plutons that might have top and bottom significance is the primary banding found in some basic plutonic rocks. Mineralogically dissimilar bands in certain bodies of basic rock are thought by Coats (1936: 407) to have been produced by " . . . simultaneous crystallization and settling of two or more minerals in a magma lighter than any of them. By a process of *rhythmic differential settling*, rhythmically alternating bands of differing composition may be produced."

This kind of banding, which may be repeated many times in a pluton, has top and bottom significance if the mineral sequence in successive layers is consistent. Banded plutons of this type should be compared with the gravity-stratified sheets discussed in Art. 253.

248. *Intrusive Relations.*—Certain features and structural relations are to be expected along the contact between an igneous body and a sedimentary (or metamorphosed sedimentary) succession (Figs. 25, 369). Xenoliths of sedimentary material may be incorporated in the igneous rock, and roof pendants with jagged margins may extend into the igneous body. There may be a zone on both sides of the contact in which both igneous and sedimentary rock have been changed somewhat in texture and mineralogical composition. Finally, dikes of igneous rock may cut through hundreds of feet of bedding before ending abruptly against an unconformity. All these relations and others that might be mentioned serve only to prove that the sedimentary rock has been invaded by the igneous and is therefore the older. They do not indicate the order of succession in the sedimentary rock. That must be determined by other means.

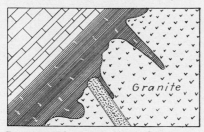

FIG. 370.—Diagram showing a shale formation resting unconformably on a granite that was intruded by a preshale dike. The contact between the two rock bodies is uneven, for the granite was weathered and eroded before the mud was deposited. Compare with Figs. 25, 26, and 369. (Art. 249.)

249. *Unconformable Relations.*— Sedimentary rocks (and their metamorphosed equivalents) deposited on an erosion surface transecting plutonic rocks show no basal alteration from proximity to the igneous rock. They commonly contain boulders and smaller fragments of the underlying rock, and many fill crevices and depressions in the surface of the igneous mass. The strata may also first end abruptly against a prominence of igneous rock and then, at a slightly higher horizon, arch gently over the same feature (Fig. 370). Observations of contact relations usually can be supplemented by a study of regional relations, and in general the task of determining unconformity is relatively simple except where sedimentary rocks have undergone intense folding and metamorphism.

250. FEATURES AND RELATIONS OF SILLS.—Sills, sheets, and similar tabular bodies of igneous rock are formed by magma invading a flat-lying or gently tilted sequence of sedimentary rocks between the beds. Hence, if the top or bottom of the invading body can be determined from some internal feature or marginal relation it shows, the order of succession of the sedimentary rocks should be obvious. Such a statement, of course, ignores the possibility that the sedimentary section was turned almost completely over before being invaded—a situation that would be exceedingly rare.

The following features are useful in determining the top or bottom of sills:

1. A differentiated sill (*i.e.*, differentiation *in situ* of a magma which was homogeneous when emplaced) has a distinctive mineralogical profile in which mafic minerals, especially olivine and pyroxene, are concentrated in the lower part and lighter feldspathic minerals are concentrated in the upper part.

2. A sill that was differentiated by crystal settling and gaseous transfer has minerals with volatile constituents (*e.g.*, apatite, calcite, chlorite, hornblende, and zeolites) concentrated in a zone in the upper part of the body.

3. Differentiated sills commonly have an upper zone of micropegmatite and vugs, suggesting that gases and mineralizers migrated upward through the main body of the magma.

4. Gravitational sorting may produce stratified sheets consisting of successive bipartite layers that are of dual mineralogical nature—each layer has mafic minerals at its base, grades upward into felsic minerals, and ends abruptly downward against the top of the felsic portion of the underlying layer. If the couplet is constant in the relative positions of the minerals and is repeated again and again, it can be used as a criterion of top and bottom.

5. Differentiation may produce a stratified rock mass of dual lithological character and density (*e.g.*, a gabbroic lower layer and a dioritic upper).

6. Xenoliths of rock lighter than the magma may float to a position in the top part of the sill.

251. *Compositional Profile in Sills.*—If there is gravitative separation of the newly formed crystals in a cooling sill, the heavier mafic minerals sink toward the bottom, whereas the lighter felsic ones concentrate in the upper part of the intrusive. Likewise, the compositional variation in the same mineral, from bottom to top, is from higher to lower content of mafic constituents. This mineralogical profile is essentially the same as that found in thick differentiated flows (Art. 241).

If such sills are folded or faulted into steeply inclined or overturned positions, the mineral profile outlined in the previous paragraph offers one good means of determining the top of the body.

Lewis (1908: 155–162; 1908a: 129–134) years ago described differentiation in the Palisade diabase along the Hudson River, and Walker (1940: 1059–1106) recently published a comprehensive report on this world-famous example of gravitative differentiation, explaining certain features that heretofore have caused some confusion. He called special attention to the stratum of olivine diabase at the bottom of the sill.

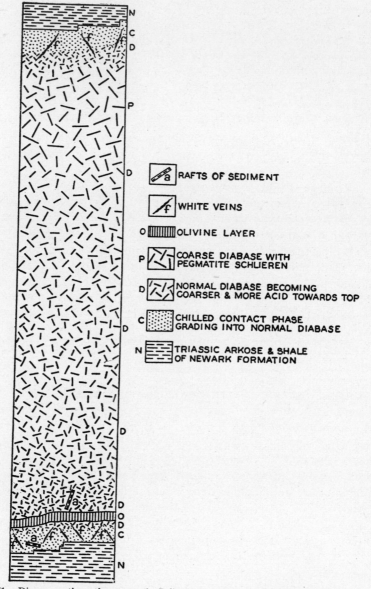

FIG. 371.—Diagrammatic section across the Palisade sill of New Jersey, showing chilled borders, basal olivine layer, rafts of sediments, and textural profile.   (Art. 251.)   (*After Walker, 1940, Bull. Geol. Soc. Am.*, **51**: 1066, *Fig. 2.*)

The top and bottom of the sill are chilled. There is an olivine-rich zone just above the chilled base, a concentration of augite above the olivine zone and below the median plane of the sill, and a concentration of feldspar above the middle. Throughout the sill as a whole, calcic feldspars predominate in the lower part, whereas the lighter sodic plagioclase and orthoclase are preponderant in the upper part (Fig. 371).

Emmons (1927: 73–82) described a Pre-Cambrian diabase sill in Ontario that changes progressively from pyroxene gabbro in the basal part to pegmatitic quartz-hornblende diorite at the top. He explains the sequence as follows (page 82):

The residual liquor of the magma, formed as crystallization progressed, tended to rise, aided by the mineralizers present. This liquor was of course high in silica and alkalies and therefore carried these substances upward with it. Progressively upward the liquor became more concentrated and crystals in contact with it approached equilibrium with it—hence the *progressively* more sodic feldspars higher in the sill.

Merriam (1945: 456–465) describes two gabbro sills with dioritic facies that intrude Eocene sediments in Oregon (Fig. 372) and show progressive changes in mineral composition similar to those described by Emmons (1927: 73–82).

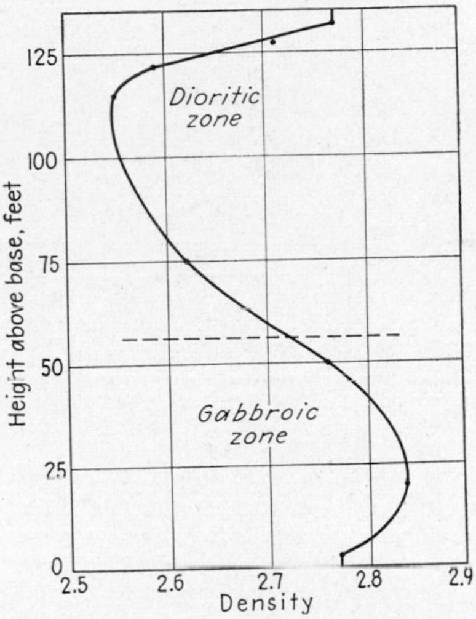

FIG. 372.—Density variation in the upper of two sills intruding the Eocene Umpqua sedimentary rocks near Ashland, Ore. (Arts. 251, 254.) (*After Merriam*, 1945, *Am. Jour. Sci.*, **243**: 461, *Fig.* 3.)

A well-known differentiated sill is the Lugar sill in Ayr, Scotland, which, according to Tyrrell (1929: 150–151),

. . . is composed of ultra-basic analcite-bearing rocks in which an increasing abundance of olivine from top to bottom of the mass can be traced. The uppermost layer consists of theralite with 13.6 per cent. of olivine. This passes downward into picrite with 30.1 per cent. of olivine, and finally to peridotite at the base with 65.2 per cent. of olivine. . . .

Some 50 other examples of differentiation in sills and sheets are cited from widely separated areas and abstracted by Daly (1933: 333–344) and Walker (1940: 1099–1104).

The prominent increase in iron oxide in the upper third of the Palisade diabase and a less prominent increase near the base [Walker (1940: 1099)]

show that distribution of iron in a sill is essentially similar to that in a thick flow (Art. 240; Fig. 373).

252. *Micropegmatite and Vugs in Upper Part of Sills.*—Micropegmatite is present in the upper part of differentiated sills, reaching 6 per cent by weight at the top of the Palisade diabase [Walker (1940: 1075)]. It is most abundant in the top of the Ontario sill described by Emmons (1927: 73–82) and exceeds 20 per cent in some parts of the upper zone of the Oregon sill described by Merriam (1945: 460).

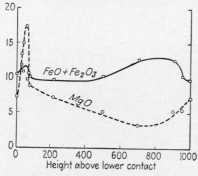

Certain minerals with volatile constituents (*e.g.*, zeolites, calcite, and chlorite) line sporadic vugs in the upper part of sills that were gas-rich in the closing phases of crystallization. These are thought to have been formed possibly as a result of differentiation by volatile transfer [Merriam (1945: 456)].

FIG. 373.—Graphs showing MgO and FeO + Fe₂O₃ plotted against height above lower contact of Palisade sill of New Jersey. (Art. 251.) (*After Walker*, 1940, *Bull. Geol. Soc. Am.*, **51**: 1099, *Fig. 9.*)

Pegmatitic schlieren are commonly present in the upper part of differentiated sills [Walker (1940: 1092); Merriam (1945: 456, 460)]. They are explained as the result of local concentrations of volatiles that were expelled by crystallization.

253. *Gravity-stratified Sheets.*—Gravity-stratified sheets have the following general characteristics: (1) a relatively thin chilled basal zone of a composition intermediate between the extreme variations present above; (2) an ultrabasic segregate directly above the chilled facies; (3) a thick portion of intermediate composition that is more feldspathic or felsic than (2) and that, in its uppermost part, may be a granite; (4) alternating bands or layers of different mineral composition.

The top or bottom of a gravity-stratified sheet can be determined from the order of succession of rock and mineral facies or from the gravity stratification within individual layers, which, in some sheets, are only a few centimeters thick.

Typical examples of gravity-stratified sills or sheets are (1) the Bushveld complex of South Africa [Peoples (1936: 356, 359–360)]; (2) the Diana complex of the Adirondack region, New York [Buddington (1936)]; (3) the Palisade complex of New Jersey [Lewis (1908); Walker (1940)]; and (4) the Stillwater complex of Montana [Peoples (1936)] [see also Daly (1933: 333–344)].

As an example of a gravity-stratified sheet, Buddington (1936: 347) cites the Diana complex of the northwestern Adirondacks, which he describes as follows:

. . . the border consists of a pyroxene-quartz syenite considered to be a chill facies similar to the primary magma (65 to 67 per cent SiO_2), and this grades successively inward into pyroxene syenite (56 to 60 per cent SiO_2), locally with thin lenses of shonkinite (46 to 48 per cent SiO_2), transitional pyroxene-quartz syenite (61 to 64 per cent SiO_2), hornblende-quartz syenite (63 to 66 per cent SiO_2), and finally into hornblende-quartz syenite and hornblende granite (66 to 69 per cent SiO_2). Relics of country rock are practically confined to the granitic part and are interpreted as synclinal infolded portions of the roof. The reverse of the foregoing succession occurs toward the axis of an anticline in the foliation. There is locally in the shonkinite a banding of mafic and felsic minerals in layers as much as a few inches thick, whose positions relative to one another, if interpreted as due to gravity sorting, suggest overturning of the limb of the fold, as do also the large-scale features and the general structure of the country rock.

Inasmuch as the igneous complexes interpreted by Buddington as "isoclinally folded gravity-stratified sheets," were previously interpreted as batholithic or stocklike intrusions, it follows, obviously, that if his hypothesis of origin is correct, then, as he states (1936: 347), " . . . many modifications in current interpretations of the early geologic history of the Adirondacks must follow." He might well have generalized for a broader geographic area, for Peoples (1936: 353–360) points out, in an article immediately following that of Buddington, that the hypothesis of gravity stratification offers a satisfactory explanation for the Stillwater complex of Montana. Because this complex is greatly different from the one described by Buddington in the Adirondacks, a brief description of it is added here [Peoples (1936: 353)]:

The pre-Cambrian Stillwater complex of Montana consists of a norite (interpreted as a basal chilled facies) on the south, adjoined successively on the north by ultrabasic rocks 2,500 feet thick and by banded noritic anorthositic facies. By analogy with the Bushveld complex, this arrangement may be interpreted as gravity stratification. The banding of the complex dips steeply, and the intrusive, formerly interpreted as a dike, is here considered a sheet or lopolith tilted up on edge and locally overturned. In the banded zone many layers of norite and anorthosite alternate. The base of many of the norite layers is sharper than the upper contact, which is gradational into anorthosite through a gradual decrease of pyroxene crystals. *The tops and bottoms of layers may be determined by a study of such features.*[1]

The bedding of the Cambrian sediments that rest on the eroded surface of the igneous mass is roughly conformable with the layering of the complex and shows

---

[1] The italics are those of the present author.

that the complex must have been essentially horizontal when erosion of its upper portion and deposition of the sediments took place.

A thin layer of metamorphosed iron formation found near the base, except where cut out by later intrusive granite, is thought to represent the floor and is in general conformable with the complex.

254. *Density and Lithological Variation in Differentiated Sills.*— Merriam (1945: 456–465) recently described two differentiated sills from Oregon that are composed of a higher density gabbroic lower part that

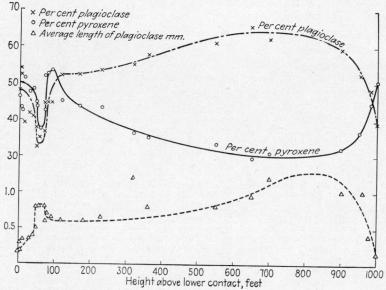

Fɪɢ. 374.—Graphs showing amount of plagioclase and pyroxene and size of plagioclase crystals in the Triassic Palisade diabasic sill at George Washington Bridge in New Jersey. (Art. 255.) (*After Walker*, 1940, *Bull. Geol. Soc. Am.*, **51**: 1075, *Fig. 6.*)

passes by gradation into a lower density dioritic upper part (Fig. 372). Geologic literature contains reports of other similarly differentiated sills in which the upper part is granite, the lower diorite or some other more basic rock; etc. Careful field work would be necessary to prove the existence of such a bipartite sill.

255. *Textural Variation in Differentiated Sills.*—As a general rule the mafic minerals are coarser in the lower part of a differentiated sill, where they are typically concentrated, whereas the lighter felsic minerals show greatest grain size in the upper part of the sill. Walker (1940: 1075) found this to be the case in the Palisade diabase (Fig. 374), and the same textural profile has been reported by certain other writers.

256. *Xenoliths in Sills.*—One of the thicker sills intruding the landward-tilted Cambrian strata on East Point, Nahant, Mass., has several granite boulders 25 to 30 cm. (a foot or so) in diameter near the upper margin (Fig. 375). These foreign rocks are believed to have been torn loose from the underlying basement and carried upward by the invading magma, coming to rest near the top of the sill, to which position they had floated because of being lighter than the magma. How useful this feature might be in determining the top of a sill is uncertain, but it is one that should be looked for and tested in the field. It should be emphasized that blocks of wall rock caught up in the sill must not be confused with obviously foreign rocks of the basement.

257. INTERNAL FEATURES OF DIKES.—Flow structure, in the form of lunate bands convex in the direction of flow, are preserved in some dikes

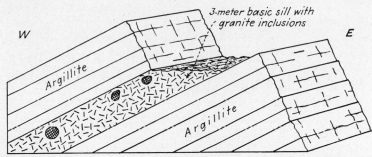

FIG. 375.—Inclusions in a sill. The westward-dipping Cambrian argillites are intruded by a 3-m. (9-ft.) basic sill that has three small granite inclusions 0.2 to 0.3 m. in diameter near the upper boundary. These are believed to have been torn loose from the basement rock by the rising magma and to have been floated up to their present position. Being lighter than the magma they floated toward the top of the sill, where they were frozen in. The sketch is based on exposures on East Point, Big Nahant, Mass. (Art. 256.)

and indicate which way the invading magma moved.[1] Such dikes, transecting lava flows and sills, have been reported from a few localities. If it can be demonstrated that the intrusion of the dike was essentially contemporaneous with the outpouring of lava or invasion of magma and that the dike material moved upward rather than laterally, the flow structure mentioned above could be used to determine the top of the invaded flow or sill. This feature needs a rigid test to determine whether or not it is worth anything for top and bottom determination.

Powers (1915: 1–10, 166–182) reports several examples of inclusions that were carried or floated upward in dike magmas for hundreds to thousands of meters, but he also found some inclusions that had been carried downward. It does not seem likely, therefore, that inclusions can be used with confidence to determine direction of movement of dike magmas.

[1] See Nevin (1942: 172, Fig. 121*B*). The author has observed lunate flow structure in thin lamprophyre dikes cutting Silurian and basement rocks on New World Island, Newfoundland, and the feature is probably common in certain types of dikes.

Belyea (1935: 154–155), in listing top and bottom criteria, states that "the inclination of a pegmatite dyke may be recognized. When the dip is inclined the coarse crystallization favours the hanging wall, and when the dip is vertical the coarse crystallization is in the centre." This textural feature may be useful not only in determining the original attitude of the dike, and under certain conditions the top of the invaded sequence, but also in showing whether or not the dike has been tilted to any extent since its crystallization.

If thick dikes gently inclined at the time of crystallization undergo differentiation, they should exhibit some of the same effects of gravitative separation of minerals as those in differentiated flows (Art. 241) and sills (Arts. 250 to 255). Quinn (1943: 272–281) reports one such example from the Triassic terrane of Rhode Island. A 20-m. (65-ft.) granodiorite dike, with a south dip of about 28°, shows a systematic increase in the heavy mineral content from south to north (*i.e.*, from top to bottom). Attention is called to the fact that the heavy minerals are especially concentrated in a dark zone along the base and seem to fill shallow depressions in the slightly irregular floor. Quinn ascribes this unusual distribution of heavy minerals to crystal settling because (page 280) "the minerals which are concentrated toward the base are heavier than the magma of granodiorite . . . and crystallized early in the solidification of the rock."

CHAPTER VII

FEATURES OF METAMORPHOSED ROCKS

258. Introduction.—Most metamorphosed rocks, even though they have undergone intense alteration, retain some features and structures inherited from their predecessors.[1]   Leith (1923a: 288) states:

Rarely does the deformation of rocks go so far as to destroy beyond the possibility of reconstruction, the main outlines of formations, their thickness, continuity, field relations, or even some of their textures.   A formation may be thickened or thinned by folding and flowage, and it may be much fractured and faulted, but it is usually possible to get some idea of its original morphology. Even deformation as extreme as rock flowage, producing schists, does not always destroy evidences of original structures, like bedding, or ellipsoids, or amygdules."

Such inherited structures include textural variations (varves and graded bedding), ripple marks, inorganic and organically produced imprints, mud cracks, scour-and-fill structures, cross-lamination, features produced by penecontemporaneous deformation, and fossils and organic structures in original sedimentary rocks; textural gradation in ash and tuff deposits, vesicular and fragmental flow tops, pillow lavas, amygdules, chilled borders, and occasionally other less common features in original

---

[1] A case in point is the greatly metamorphosed Pre-Cambrian Vishnu schist of the Grand Canyon.   Recently this highly altered rock has been shown to be derived from a sedimentary clastic formation, for it contains well-preserved cross-lamination and lenticular bodies of what were once lenses of quartz sand.   Campbell and Maxson (1933: 808–809), who discovered the sedimentary structures, state that

. . . the origin of many of the schists might be obscure, were it not for their association and interbedding with the types of undoubted sedimentary character, for igneous invasions have greatly complicated the picture.   Thus not infrequently it is possible to trace, by almost imperceptible gradations, a quartz-mica paraschist into a typical granite.

It is worth further comment that, by determining the top and bottom of the schists, Campbell and Maxson were able to demonstrate the order of succession of a great series of rocks which previously had not been worked out.

A second instructive example of a primary sedimentary structure that persisted through metamorphism intense enough to produce a rock of granitoid nature is found in the Eocambrian Sparagmite of Scandinavia.   In an address on "The West-Scandinavian Mountain Range," delivered before the Boston Geological Society on Dec. 3, 1946, Dr. Olaf Holtedahl remarked that current bedding (cross-lamination) in an originally arkosic phase of the Sparagmite is still perfectly preserved even though the rock is now granitized.

igneous rocks. The excellence of preservation of these original features, which are described on preceding pages, usually varies inversely as the intensity of deformation and recrystallization, other factors being equal. Lithology is also an important factor, as we shall see later, for quartzose and highly siliceous rocks react differently from argillaceous and calcareous sedimentary rocks and basic igneous rocks.

In addition to the inherited characteristics just mentioned, metamorphosed rocks commonly have certain features and structures that are a consequence of their thermal and deformational history. These secondary features and structures fall into two classes: (1) those produced by elevated temperatures and pressures and hydrothermal action; (2) those resulting from application of stress. The former involve recrystallization and the formation of new minerals that are in equilibrium with the environment. The latter include drag folds and fracture cleavage, resulting from rock failure, and flow cleavage and foliation formed by recrystallization under differential stress, with consequent development of the platy so-called "stress" minerals, which assume a definite orientation with respect to direction of stress.

259. Features Produced by Thermal Metamorphism.—Sediments and sedimentary rocks, upon being subjected to abnormal temperatures and pressures and to invading solutions, undergo important mineralogical and textural alterations. Grubenmann (1910), Eskola (1920: 143–194), Tilley (1924: 167–171), Harker (1939), and many others have shown that the diversity of mineralogical composition exhibited by metamorphosed rocks depends on two independent variables: (1) the original composition of the rock that is to be altered and (2) the pressure-temperature conditions that prevail during metamorphism.

The alterations may be on a regional scale and of very complex nature —these are not important enough for our present purpose to be discussed further[1]—or they may be exhibited in individual beds or sequences of beds. The latter are of interest here in that they have produced certain features which in the field prove to have top and bottom significance.

260. REVERSE OF TEXTURAL GRADATION IN METAMORPHOSED ROCKS WITH ORIGINAL GRADED BEDDING.—Thermal metamorphism of a succession of sandstone, siltstone, and shale layers originally having graded bedding is known to have produced a reversal in the usual texture gradation.

The coarser sandy or silty material constituting the lower part of the

---

[1] For examples of complex regional metamorphism the reader is referred to the following writers: Tilley (1924: 167–171), Elles and Tilley (1930: 621–646), Jeffreys (1935: 158), Harker (1939: 185–189), Gunning and Ambrose (1940: 52–53), and Geikie (1940: 228).

bipartite graded layer, being composed dominantly of relatively coarse quartz grains, is little affected and retains its characteristic texture.

The much finer argillaceous material in the upper part of the bed, on the other hand, since it is more susceptible to chemical change (because of its fine state of division and appreciable content of alumina and the basic oxides), is greatly affected. The most obvious megascopic effect is the development of large crystals (metacrysts or porphyroblasts) of the following minerals, approximately in order of their metamorphic grade:

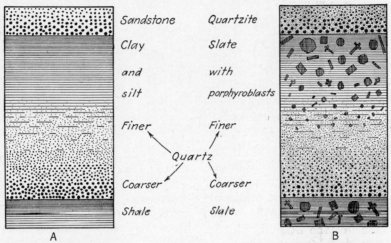

A   B

Fig. 376. —Reversal of textural gradation by metamorphism. *A.* One complete layer and parts of two contiguous layers, all showing textural gradation from coarse at the base to fine at the top. The lithology of the layers consists of sandstone, siltstone, and shale. Individual layers range in thickness from less than 1 mm. to more than 15 cm. (6 in.). *B.* The same sequence as shown in *A* metamorphosed. Porphyroblasts of staurolite, garnet, andalusite, cordierite, and muscovite are known to have developed in the aluminous, finely divided upper part of graded beds, whereas sillimanite has been reported from the sand-silt part of the layer. The quartz of the coarser lower part of the bipartite layer is little altered by metamorphism, but the interstitial spaces are filled with siliceous or other cement, rendering the rock quartzitic. Examples of this type of metamorphism have been reported from widely separated localities throughout the world. See Figs. 377 to 379. (Art. 260.)

chlorite, sericite, and muscovite; biotite; garnet; staurolite, andalusite, and cordierite [Grout (1932: 356)].

The metacrysts may not be much larger than the coarsest grains of the lower part of the bed, but commonly they grow to sizes of tenfold or even a hundredfold. If they are unusually large, the *true* upper part of the bed, studded with conspicuous crystals, appears at a casual glance to be the coarser basal part (Fig. 376). It is doubtful, however, as pointed out by Gunning and Ambrose (1940: 52), whether the upper fine-grained part of a graded bed would ever become uniformly the coarser grained; hence the reversal of grain size will probably be limited to the metacrysts alone.

Inasmuch as this interesting metamorphic phenomenon has proved a useful top and bottom criterion in a number of widely separated localities, a few specific examples will be described briefly to illustrate the variation in mineral suites.

261. *Broken Hill District, Australia.*[1]—Strata exhibiting reversal of textural gradation are exposed in the Footwall tunnel of the Central Mine, Broken Hill, Australia. In single beds, which range in thickness from a few centimeters to a meter (a few inches to several feet), the base of the bed is strongly quartzose and also contains considerable sillimanite. Upward these minerals give way to small garnets, which increase in size and abundance toward the top of the bed, reaching a maximum near and at the top. Since most of the garnet crystals are considerably larger than the quartz and sillimanite grains, the true top of the bed exhibits much coarser texture than the basal part, a reversal of the usual gradation in unmetamorphosed sedimentary rock. In this sequence the upward increase in garnets seemingly reflects a similar increase of alumina in the original argillaceous material constituting the upper part of the layer.

262. *Pre-Cambrian of Canadian Shield.*—Metamorphosed Pre-Cambrian sediments (Yellow-knife formation in the Wray Lake district) in the Northwest Territories of Canada exhibit pseudogradational bedding with cordierite or that mineral associated with nodules of andalusite well developed in the upper, originally argillaceous parts of the beds[2] (Fig. 377). Similar metamorphic effects are present in the McKim arkosic sandstone of the Sudbury district, where varvelike bands have large pseudomorphs after staurolite as much as 15 cm. long in the finer and more argillaceous portions (*i.e.*, in the upper part) of the layers (Fig. 378). The lithology of the rock is described by Coleman (1914: 213) as follows:

Usually the rock [McKim graywacke] is banded with finer and coarser layers, the bands varying from half an inch to two or three inches in thickness, probably an indication of seasonal changes. The finer-grained parts are slaty and usually contain pseudomorphs after staurolite, sometimes small like "rice grains," but occasionally reaching 5 or 6 inches in length, with a breadth of one inch. The pseudomorphs now consist of fine-grained quartz and sericite. In thin sections one finds in the matrix a good deal of chlorite and sericite besides obscure opaque material.

Gunning and Ambrose (1940: 51–52) report strata at the Dempsy Cadillac mines (Malartic area, Quebec) that exhibit pseudogradational bedding.

[1] The author is greatly indebted to H. C. Burrell for the data on this occurrence. Burrell and his associates recognized and used the criterion constantly in mapping underground structure.

[2] Reported to the author by J. D. Allan, who observed the rocks while engaged in field work and kindly furnished the photograph for Fig. 377.

Courtesy of J. D. Allan

FIG. 377.—Pseudogradational bedding in early Pre-Cambrian Yellowknife strata in the Wray Lake area, N. W. T., Canada. The rock has been metamorphosed by a near-by granite. The white arrow and the head of the hammer point toward the top of the vertically dipping beds. The hammer is 40 cm. (16 in.) long.

J. D. Allan, who took the photograph, describes the rock as follows (personal communication, Apr. 18, 1941): "Before metamorphism the rock was probably much like that seen in [Fig. 42]. Metamorphism has caused recrystallization of the constituents. Nodules of andalusite as much as 25 mm. across have developed in parts of the beds. The parts where the nodules have developed are believed to be the original fine-grained tops of the beds. The composition of the shaly part was more highly aluminous and so would be suitable for the formation of andalusite. Also the fine grain of the shaly part permits reaction between constituents to take place at an earlier stage of metamorphism than in the coarser parts. The arrow points in the direction of the tops of the beds as indicated by the greater development of nodules in that direction in each successive bed. In some beds cordierite nodules develop with or instead of andalusite. This is governed by the original composition of the bed." Compare with Figs. 376 and 379. (Arts. 51, 262.)

FIG. 378.—Pre-Cambrian McKim argillite showing graded bedding in which the texture has been reversed by metamorphism. The original graded beds may have been deposited as varved clays. *A.* Glacially striated outcrop along the main highway near Cutler, Ont. The beds are nearly vertical. *B.* Successive bipartite layers with coarser texture at the top, which is toward the top of the page. The glacial striae trend northeast-southwest. The white cap is 40 mm. (1.6 in.) in diameter. (Art. 262.)

. . . the lower 2 or 3 inches [50 to 75 mm.] of each of a pair of beds is medium-to fine-grained greywacke with clastic quartz grains 0.2 mm. or so in diameter. This grades upwards into very fine, argillaceous material, also 2 or 3 inches thick, with quartz grains 0.01 mm. or less in diameter. However, the fine-grained, argillaceous top is thickly sprinkled with biotite crystals to 0.5 mm. in diameter, in marked contrast with those in the coarser bottom when the biotite flakes about equal the quartz grains in size. As in the other rocks in the area, sieve textures and sutured borders of the biotite flakes indicate beyond doubt that they are actually secondary and not original constituents. The size distribution of the biotite flakes illustrates the familiar principle that one of the main factors controlling the speed of a reaction is the fineness of subdivision of the reacting substances. The more finely divided the material the more surface is exposed, so that reaction, once initiated, can proceed more rapidly towards completion.

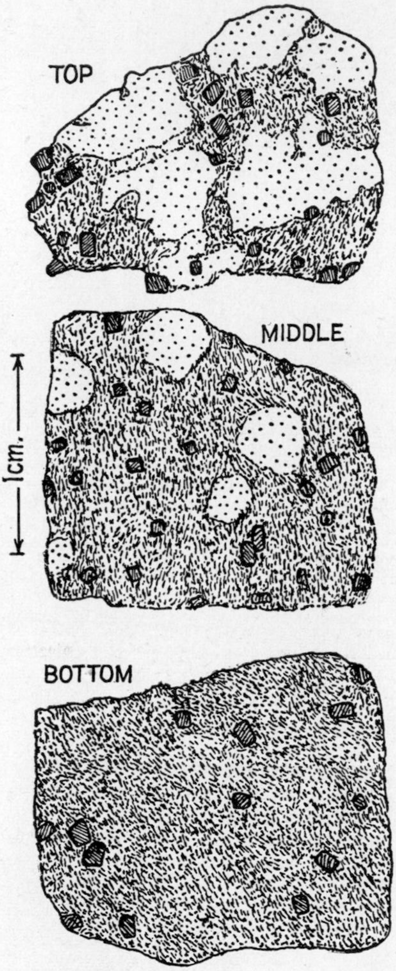

The situation described has another important application. One of the methods most commonly employed for determination of the tops of beds is observation of gradation in grain size from coarse at the bottom to fine at the top. However, in the beds illustrated, the net effect of alteration has been to produce a complete reversal of the grain size in so far as the biotite flakes are concerned. At first glance the lower side might easily be mistaken for the top.

Fig. 379.—Pseudogradational bedding in Dalradian rocks of Scotland. Three sections show the inferred bottom, middle, and top of an andalusite schist bed. The bottom section shows a few small staurolites in a base of quartz and mica. The middle section shows the addition of a few patches of andalusite. The top shows an abundance of andalusite in large crystals. The quartz-mica-staurolite groundmass remains the same throughout the bed, whereas the andalusite crystals increase in size upward. (Art. 263.) (*After Read*, 1936, *Geol. Mag.*, **73**: 474, *text Fig. 2.*)

263. *Scotland.*—Read (1936: 468–476) has reported marked pseudogradational bedding from metamorphosed Pre-Cambrian Dalradian rocks of Banff, Scotland.[1] Individual bipartite strata 15 to 30 cm. (6 to 12 in.) thick have large andalusite

[1] Read states (p. 468) that he used current bedding and graded bedding " . . .

crystals or porphyroblasts in the finer argillaceous upper part of the bed but lack these in the coarser quartzose lower part (Fig. 379). He emphasizes the reliability of this criterion when he shows that other sedimentary structures (*e.g.*, cross-bedding) indicate that the porphyroblastic argillaceous portion of the bed constitutes the upper part.

Read's detailed description (pages 472 to 473) will not be included here but is given in the footnote below.[1]

---

along the lines developed by Prof. E. B. Bailey and the Glasgow School. . . . " This reference is to the work of Bailey (1930: 77; 1934: 462–525) and later that of Allison (1933: 125–144), Anderson (1935:74), and McCallien (1935: 407–442), all of whom applied the criteria of cross-lamination and graded bedding after becoming acquainted with their top and bottom significance as a result of a visit to Scotland by two American geologists, S. Buckstaff and O. N. Rove, in 1924 and a later visit by a third, R. M. Field, who led the Princeton University Summer School of Geology to the Scottish Highlands in the summer of 1929. The observations made during these field trips resulted in important revisions of existing stratigraphic and structural interpretations according to Bailey (1930: 77), Vogt (1930: 68–73), and Tanton (1930: 73), the latter of whom was one of the members of the Princeton group.

[1] The rocks of importance in this connection are pebbly grits and andalusite-schists; these are exceptionally well exposed at Whitehills, Knock Head, and in the south-west corner of Boyndie Bay. The *pebbly grits* form beds from 1 foot to 4 or 5 feet in thickness. They are coarse, pebbly rocks, showing large grains, sometimes 1 cm. long, of quartz and felspars in a matrix of fine quartz grains, little felspars, magnetite grains, and much yellow to brown biotite in small laths. In numerous localities, and especially on Knock Head, the grit bands show graded bedding. The structural dip is at fairly high angles to the east and east-south-east, and the grit bands are interbedded in andalusite-schists. It can be observed repeatedly that the western edge of each grit band is coarsely pebbly, and that toward the east in each band the pebbles become finer and that at the east margin of each bed a few crystals of andalusite appear. The change in grain-size and abundance of pebbles takes place perfectly gradually from one side to the other of innumerable grit bands up to 5 feet in thickness. This can be interpreted only as graded bedding, however disquieting the scale may be. The episode of sedimentation of each grit bed began with the deposition of coarse materials, gradually becoming finer till a portion of the clay fraction appeared in the final deposition that closed the episode—on metamorphism, this clay fraction appears as andalusite. All the observations on graded bedding in grits hereabouts point to an upward succession towards the east or east-south-east. Such observations can be made in Whitehills, everywhere around Knock Head, and in Boyndie Bay.

The andalusite-schists provide a very pretty case of graded bedding in totally recrystallized rocks. When the andalusite-schists are examined in detail it is seen that the andalusite is not uniformly distributed in them. I had noted this fact many years ago when I stated "it is at once apparent that the development of andalusite is intimately connected with the nature and composition of the original sediment; the andalusite is often confined to thin beds, often under 1 inch in thickness, interbanded with slightly more siliceous but still somewhat clayey, non-andalusite-bearing phyllites. . . .

In innumerable examples the rocks grouped as andalusite-schists are formed of distinct beds, 6 inches to 1 foot in thickness. The west side of each bed shows little or no andalusite; towards the east in each bed, andalusite appears, first as a few crystals, then in greater abundance, till at the east margin of each band the rock is largely composed of granular andalusite. . . .

Examination of a series of thin sections cut from different parts of such beds supplies the explanation. The western margins of the beds consist of a medium-grained association of

264. *Summary of Pseudogradational Bedding.*—Undoubtedly there are many examples similar to those cited above where metamorphosed beds with original graded bedding now exhibit a reversal in the texture gradation (*i.e.*, pseudogradational bedding) because of the development of porphyroblasts in the finer upper parts of layers. Such metamorphosed beds need occasion no difficulty in structural work if their history and the significance of the secondary minerals are appreciated.

265. CAVITIES AND CAVITY FILLINGS PRODUCED BY HYDROTHERMAL ACTION.[1]—Wahlstrom (1941: 551–561) has described from the Spencer Mountain volcanics of Colorado some interesting cavities of hydrothermal origin that have top and bottom significance. The cavities are confined to two 5-m. layers of pitchstone that represent quickly chilled lava flows associated with an ancient volcano (Fig. 380). Cessation of volcanic activity was followed by reverse faulting; following this came a period of hydrothermal activity during which the mineralizing solutions, moving along the fault zones, extensively replaced the glassy flow rock there; but "at a distance from the faults the only manifestations of replacement are jasper geodes, or concretions, which are localized by closely spaced, onion-like spherical shrinkage fractures."

Our interest here is in the geodes and concretions thus formed, for when the mineralizing solutions later changed in character they dissolved out the interiors of many isolated jasper concretions and then partly or completely backfilled the cavities thus produced. Therefore now (page 556)

Gray and green *agate, onyx, opal* and *calcite* partially or completely fill the interiors of hollow concentrations, or geodes. . . .

The *agate* coats the walls and roof of the cavities and on the floor grades into flat intercalated layers of opal and chalcedony in the form of *onyx*. The thickness

---

biotite and quartz, with which occur abundant ore-grains, many small euhedral staurolite crystals, and rare tiny garnets and prisms of tourmaline. The eastern margins of the beds show exactly the same association, but in this as a groundmass are set large porphyroblasts of andalusite, up to 1 inch in length, with a few patches of cordierite. In many cases, more than half of the eastern parts of the beds consists of granular andalusite porphyroblasts. Slices cut between the western and eastern margins of beds show intermediate characters—the same groundmass with fewer andalusite porphyroblasts. Rock slices showing the variation are figured in [Fig. 379]. Since the aluminum silicate, andalusite, registers the amount of original clayey material it can be inferred that the amount of this clayey material increased gradually from the western margins of each of these beds towards their eastern margins: that is, each bed is graded from coarse on the west to fine on the east. Further, since the andalusite occurs as large porphyroblasts, the top, which was originally the finest part of the bed, becomes on metamorphism the coarsest-grained portion. It is therefore possible to deduce the stratigraphical order in these totally recrystallized regionally metamorphosed sediments.

[1] These features would not ordinarily be included under the usual definition of metamorphism. They are inserted here merely for convenience and because they do not fit elsewhere into our outline.

of the agate layer rarely exceeds an eighth of an inch, but some oynx masses are several inches thick. Agate and onxy were deposited contemporaneously. The greater thickness and flat layering of the oynx indicate gravitative control.

Inasmuch as (page 556) "[the] floors of many of the cavities are covered with corroded angular jasper fragments cemented by the younger minerals" and the stratified partial fillings (Fig. 381) lie at the bottom of the cavity, we have in these relations a means of determining the direction of

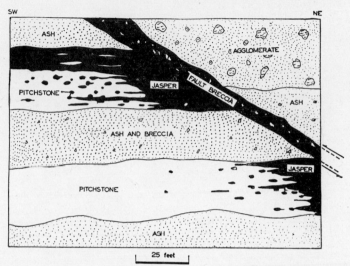

Fig. 380.—Idealized cross section showing jasperization of pitchstone flows adjacent to a thrust fault on the southwest side of Specimen Mountain, Colorado. Scattered geodes like that illustrated in Fig. 381 are present in the pitchstone layers at some distance from the fault zone. (Art. 265.) (*After Wahlstrom*, 1941, *Am. Mineralogist*, **26**: 555, *Fig. 4.*)

gravity at the time when the filling was made. Comparison of the plane of stratification in the filling with the general plane of the tabular flow should indicate (1) whether the filling was made while the flow was essentially horizontal or after it was tilted and (2) the amount of tilting.

Ross (1941: 727–732) has described from Oregon certain peculiar chalcedony-filled spherulites having a star-shaped cross section. Some of these are filled with horizontally laminated chalcedony (Fig. 338*D*.), and Ross (1941:732) concludes that "the resultant cavity [which was formed in glassy ash while it was still hot] was later filled by chalcedony that was probably deposited during the alteration of the enclosing material to a clay."

Incomplete and composite amygdular and spherulitic fillings, discussed in Art. 219, have certain features that are similar to those here described, and it may not always be possible in the field to determine the time and mode of formation of the original cavity and of the subsequent filling.

In an address on "Some aspects of the Geology, Petrology, and Mineralogy of Switzerland," delivered before the Boston Geological Society on Jan. 29, 1948, Prof. Paul Niggli described the crystals lining large cavities, presumably tensional in nature, that were formed when

Courtesy of E. E. Wahlstrom

A

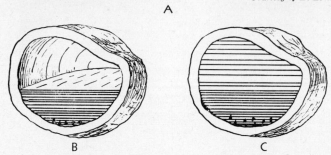

B   C

FIG. 381.—Geodes in lavas. *A.* Partly filled geodelike concretion from a lava flow in the Specimen Mountain volcanic complex of Rocky Mountain National Park, Colorado. The two parts of the transected concretion show a partial filling that consists of alternating layers of opal (white) and chalcedony (gray). The original cavity was dissolved out of a pitchstone flow by hydrothermal solutions. Following this came a second stage during which the cavity was lined with agate. In the last phase, successive horizontal layers of onyx (opal and chalcedony) were deposited in the bottom of the cavity (*cf.* Figs. 338 and 380). The flat surface of the partial filling indicates horizontality at the time when it was formed and also indicates the top of the cavity. This concretion, if found *in situ*, could therefore be used to determine the top of the enclosing flow as well as to establish whether the flow had been tilted before or after the partial filling was deposited. *B.* Diagram to show relation of incomplete filling to shell enclosing cavity. Fragments of shell material lie in the basal laminae of the stratified filling. *C.* Completely filled cavity, the bottom of which is indicated by fragments similar to those in *B,* (Art. 265.) (*After Wahlstrom, 1941, Am. Mineralogist,* **26:** 557, *Fig. 5.*)

the strata of the Swiss Alps were folded. The lower side of some of the cavities can be determined by the fact that large quartz crystals projecting into the cavity with variable inclination to the lower surface are coated with small chlorite crystals on their upper surfaces. Presumably the chlorite crystals formed in the fluid filling the cavity and then settled to the bottom, coming to rest on the upper surfaces of the large quartz crystals. This relationship of coated and uncoated crystal surfaces should be useful in determining whether or not the terrane has been tilted since the crystals were formed.

266. Features and Structures Produced by Folding, Faulting, and Dynamic Metamorphism.—Any sediment or rock subjected to sufficient stress fails in a manner determined largely by the physical properties of the material and the nature of the stress. Consequent on increasing stress, the following hypothetical sequence of events may be set up:

1. *Penecontemporaneous deformation*—folding and faulting of soft or unconsolidated sediments under little or no load. Structures so formed are discussed in Arts. 145 to 153.

2. *Local and regional folding* of stratified rocks with development of major anticlines and synclines and of minor features[1] bearing genetic relations to the major structures. These minor features—drag folds, fracture cleavage, and flow cleavage—are of much importance in the present discussion because of their structural significance.

3. *Dynamic metamorphism*, commonly accompanied by hydrothermal action, results in the formation of new minerals more or less in equilibrium with the rigorous environmental conditions present. These minerals, generally platy in shape, are characteristically oriented with reference to the direction of stress.

Structural features referable to all three types of deformation are of common occurrence and frequently are useful criteria for determining the original order of succession in much-deformed and altered sedimentary rocks. It is of course true that in the later phases of dynamic metamorphism fluids and increased temperature come into play and greatly modify or obliterate many details of structure.

Here we shall consider only the three minor structures mentioned in (2)—drag folds, fracture cleavage, and flow cleavage. These are commonly the only top and bottom criteria present in highly folded rocks; for, as Mead (1940: 1007) points out, " . . . sedimentation features useful as indicators [of top or bottom], such as cross-bedding, ripple marks, and grain-size gradation, are not always available and have a perverse way of being absent when most vitally needed."

267. DRAG FOLDS.—Drag folds are small[2] asymmetrical flexures formed in relatively incompetent beds during folding or faulting or by

---

[1] Decker (1920: 1–89), in a concise treatment of minor folds that is seldom cited in reference lists, points out many kinds of major and minor folds and calls special attention to the less conspicuous flexures of gently folded and flat-lying sedimentary rocks.

[2] Gunning and Ambrose (1940: 45) report a drag-folded conglomerate bed 13 m. (40 ft.) thick, but this probably had a different origin from structures usually classified as drag folds.

the sliding of unconsolidated sediments.   The type of drag fold in which we are particularly interested here is that formed during the folding of a succession of competent and incompetent strata.   Such drag folds are

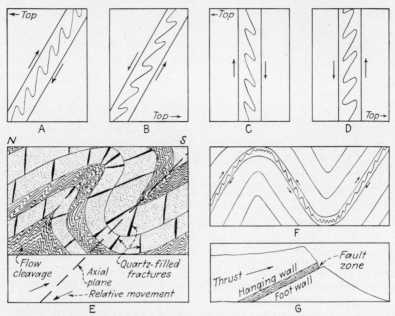

Fig. 382.—Drag folds.   *A–D*. A drag-folded layer in an incompetent bed sheared between two competent beds.   Since the top bed of a pair moves upward relative to the underlying, *A* is right side up, *B* is overturned, *C* faces to the left, and *D* faces to the right.   In these drag folds an axial plane of any of them is approximately parallel to the axial plane of the major fold.   *E*. Drag-folded quartzite beds with intervening sericitic schist layers in the Pre-Cambrian Baraboo quartzite near Devil's Lake, Wisconsin.   The brittle and competent quartzite layers, averaging about 0.3 m. (1 ft.) thick, have numerous plane, lenticular, and wedge-shaped fractures filled with quartz.   The plane fractures are mainly on the flatter parts of the folds, whereas the lenticular and wedge-shaped ones are near and at the crests, respectively, where the brittle quartzite cracked open upon bending.   The quartz was introduced later.   The originally argillaceous layers between the quartzite beds are now intensely crumpled sericite schist in which there has been considerable flowage.   This unusually large drag fold is but a miniature of the large Baraboo syncline on the south flank of which it now lies.   *F*. Diagram showing the general relation of drag folds to beds in a normal anticline and syncline with vertical axial plane. *G*. Drag folding along a thrust-fault zone where the hanging wall has ridden upward on a layer of incompetent material.   This type of drag fold has no top and bottom significance.   Miller (1922: 588) and Brock (1904: 1–17) cite examples of this type.   (Arts. 152, 267, 270.)

produced in incompetent layers sheared between oppositely moving competent layers (Fig. 382).

Leith (1923: 167) states that "most folds are probably *drag* folds on a larger or smaller scale," and this statement takes on its full significance when one reads the analysis of folds by Van Hise (1896: 581–633) and studies his illustrations.   It seems appropriate, therefore, to review briefly the several kinds of drag folds before proceeding to a more detailed consideration of the ones which are of present interest.

268. *Types of Drag Folds.*—There are at least five general types of drag folds, and it is important that the fold be identified correctly before it is used as a basis for structural determination. The types are:

1. Drag folds in thin layers and lenticular masses intercalated with normally stratified beds. These are assigned to penecontemporaneous deformation and are described in Arts. 145 to 153.

2. Drag folds associated with fault zones and produced by the differential movements of contraposed rock masses. These may indicate direction of movement in the faulting but are of no use in top and bottom determination (Art. 152; Figs. 229, 382*G*).

3. Drag folds formed at the same time as major folding. These may consistently parallel the major structures, in which case they are most useful, but they may also be oriented across major structural features, in which case they are of little or no use in top and bottom determination and will, in fact, prove misleading unless their true relations are recognized.

4. Drag folds associated with domal folding—*e.g.*, igneous intrusions, salt domes, cryptovolcanic structures, and magmatic intrusions [Miller (1922: 607–610)]. These are the reverse of (3) in their relationships to bedding planes but otherwise are not greatly different.

5. Drag folds in recrystallized or originally molten rocks [Miller (1922: 607–610)]. Intense folding of the drag-fold type is commonly present in certain kinds of salinastone (Art. 147; Fig. 228) and in marble [see Prouty (1916: 27) and Bain (1931: 503–530)], in various kinds of igneous rocks, and in gneisses. These drag-fold structures are not generally related to major folding forces, hence are valueless for working out major structures or stratigraphic successions.

269. *Drag Folds Produced in Folding of Stratified Rocks.*—In the folding of stratified or layered rocks, adjacent layers tend to slip by each other in opposite directions relatively. Incompetent rocks which can be deformed rather easily are thrown into small intricate folds referred to as *drag folds*. Several kinds of drag folds have thus far been recognized, depending on their position with reference to the axial plane or to some other part of the fold. Axial-plane and cross-structure drag folds are the commonest, but other unusual types have been reported. Drag folds are much used in some areas for structural determinations, hence a brief consideration of them follows.

270. *Axial-plane drag folds*[1].—In the folding of a sequence of bedded rocks the upper of a pair of adjacent beds moves out of a syncline or up

[1] Hills (1940: 90) suggests that these be termed *congruous* in order to differentiate them from other drag folds, not related to the major folding forces, which he designates *incongruous* [See Cope (1946: 139–176)].

the flank of an anticline relative to the lower bed. This differential movement between adjacent layers causes the more competent to fold gently and then to fail by fracture when the elastic limit is passed, whereas the less competent layers first become intensely crumpled and finally fail by flowage. Competent beds are thrown into large drag folds, which are miniatures of the major regional folds, whereas incompetent layers are intricately crumpled in making adjustment to the convolutions of the former (Fig. 382). Drag folds so produced are characteristically asymmetrical, and their axial plane is approximately parallel to that of the major fold of which they are a part.

By relating drag folds of this kind to bedding, it is possible to determine the position of the axial plane of the major fold, the relative movement between contiguous beds, and from the latter the top of the folded sequence.[1] Furthermore, if *Pumpelly's rule*,[2] *i.e.*, that "the degree and direction of the pitch of a fold are often indicated by those of the axes of the minor plications on its sides," is applicable to axial-plane drag folds, as most structural geologists now seem to assume [Leith (1923: 176–181) Willis and Willis (1934: 97–99), Hills (1940: 89–91), Billings (1942: 81, 97), Nevin (1942: 68–72), and Wilson (1947: 263–302)], it follows that the direction and angle of pitch of the drag folds should closely approximate those of the major fold.

Axial-plane drag folds have long been one of the most important tools for deciphering the structure of complexly folded rocks in the Pre-Cambrian Canadian Shield, from Minnesota to Labrador, and most of the more comprehensive reports on this vast geologic complex refer to the usefulness of drag folds (see the reports of Van Hise, Pumpelly, Van Hise and Leith, and the long list of Canadian geologists who have slowly but surely unraveled one by one so many of the complicated structural knots of the Pre-Cambrian). Furthermore, drag folds are cited as a top and bottom criterion in nearly all recent textbooks on structural geology (see table in Chap. I, pages. 22–23).

[1] Gruner (1941: 1621), in studying the complexly folded Pre-Cambrian Knife Lake slates of Minnesota, found that

Drag folds are usually very helpful, not only by showing the positions of the anticlines and synclines, but also by indicating in some measure the distance the observer is away from the main crests and troughs. Experience has taught the writer that the closer a given outcrop is to the crest or trough of a major fold the more numerous are the drag folds, other conditions being equal. On long limbs, however, they may be absent, or, what is worse, contradictory.

[2] Hills (1940: 89) applies this designation to the statement of Dale [Pumpelly, Wolff, and Dale (1894: 158)] that "the degree and direction of the pitch of a fold are often indicated by those of the axes of the minor plications on its sides" and credits its formulation to Dale, who worked under Pumpelly's guidance.

271. *Cross-structure drag folds.*—Only a cursory examination of an intensely folded sedimentary succession is necessary to prove the existence, in addition to axial-plane drag folds, of numerous minor flexures and plications that are not parallel to the general trend of the major structure. These have caused endless confusion when attempts were made to use them in the same way as axial-plane drag folds. Because they may be oriented in almost any direction in the beds of a fold, they cannot be used for top and bottom determination.

Examples of this type of drag fold are usually assumed to have formed after the major folding, hence to be related, not to the original major folding forces, but to forces that acted later in another direction.

Van Hise and Leith (1911: 123) found that in the Vermilion district of the Lake Superior Pre-Cambrian, where cross folding and at least three orders of drag folds are present, the axes of one common type of drag fold lie " . . . in any direction in the plane of bedding"; Derry (1939: 109–134) has described from the same terrane steeply pitching drag folds which, though independent of the major folding, are associated with drag folds which are dependent on that folding; and Gunning and Ambrose (1940: 45) report that in a gently pitching syncline—again in the Lake Superior Pre-Cambrian—steeply pitching drag folds have axes essentially perpendicular to the axis of the main fold. The last-named writers conclude that these Z-shaped secondary drag folds, which are present on both flanks of the major structure, were formed after the main folding; *i.e.*, " . . . after the strata had been thrown into vertical positions, the beds slipped past one another as a result of nearly horizontal movements."

Hills (1940: 90) suggests that drag folds which do not conform to Pumpelly's rule (Art. 270), whether dependent on or independent of the major folding forces, be designated *incongruous*. He cites a case in point from the lower Paleozoic rocks of Victoria, where steeply pitching drag folds are related " . . . to nearly horizontal bedding plane slip developed in already steeply dipping beds."

These examples and others that could be cited make it clear that the field geologist must be certain of the type of drag fold with which he is dealing before using it as a basis for structural determinations.

272. *Drag folds in domal structures.*—In those structural situations where beds have been domed or thrust upward by a vertically directed force, the under of a pair of adjacent beds moves upward relative to the upper. If drag folds and cleavage are formed, both are reversed from the usual situation (Fig. 383). Such reversed drag folds and cleavage have been observed in a supposed cryptovolcanic structure at Kentland, Ind.,[1]

[1] On a field excursion to this unusual structural area in northern Indiana [Shrock

and are to be expected in stratified rocks domed by igneous or saline plugs.

The author is indebted to Prof. W. J. Mead for the description of unusual drag folds in the peripheral zone of a volcanic plug that is exposed in the river gorge at the site of the Owyhee Dam in Oregon. The plug, which consists of rhyolite, intrudes a series of sediments. The peripheral shell of the plug cooled first; and as the viscosity here increased, the still plastic magma was drag-folded by the upward thrust of the fluid central

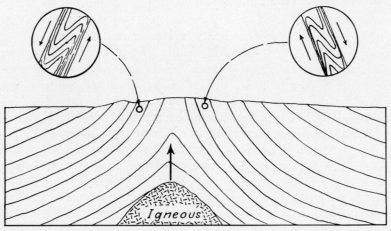

Fig. 383.—Hypothetical diagram of a cryptovolcanic structure, showing the upward thrust that arches the overlying strata. The extensive faulting associated with these structures is omitted. In this type of deformation the upward thrust from the igneous mass causes the under bed of a pair to move upward relative to the overlying, so that both drag folds and cleavage are oppositely oriented from those in the usual folds. Reversed drag folds are common in the steeply inclined argillaceous limestones in the supposed cryptovolcanic structure near Kentland, Ind. Compare with Fig. 384. (Art. 272.)

mass. The result is a peripheral zone of intense drag folding where, by observing the orientation of the drag folds, it is possible to determine one's position with reference to the center of the plug and whether, in advancing along a radial path, one is going toward the central part of the plug or away from it.

273. *Summary on Drag Folds.*—Drag folds are common and widespread in folded and otherwise deformed rocks and are variously oriented with reference to the planes bounding the tabular masses in which they are present. Certain of them can be used as top and bottom criteria and for determining the nature and extent of major structural features provided that their true nature is first determined. Many of them, on the

(1937: 471–531)], Dr. R. T. Chamberlin and the author discovered on the northern wall of the large central quarry, where the thin-bedded Ordovician limestones are vertical, numerous well-developed reverse drag folds which show that the eastern (lower) of a pair of beds moved upward relative to the western (upper) (see Fig. 384).

other hand, can be contradictory and misleading if used indiscriminately. A few, obviously formed while the containing sediments were still soft and under little or no load or as a result of recrystallization, may or may not have top and bottom significance.

274. Foliate Structure or Cleavage.—Foliate structure may be defined as that community of textural and structural properties of a rock which permits it to cleave or part along approximately parallel surfaces. It is formed in several ways and may be differentiated into the following varieties [Mead (1940: 1009–1011)]:

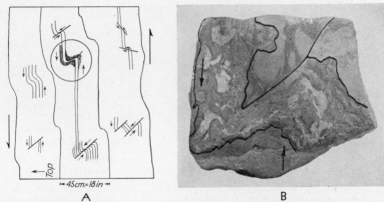

A   B

Fig. 384.—Reversed drag folds in thin-bedded Ordovician limestones of the supposed cryptovolcanic disturbance near Kentland, Ind.   These beds, which are highly inclined or vertical, have been thrust upward over 300 m. (1,000 ft.).   In the thrusting the lower bed slipped upward relative to the upper— the reverse of the movement in normal folding.   *A.* Three layers averaging about 45 cm. (18 in.) in thickness show drag folds and faults in thin laminae averaging about 25 mm. (1 in.) in thickness.   The top of the sequence is to the left.   *B.* Photograph of the drag fold enclosed in the circle on *A*, showing prominent thinning of layer along plane of movement.   The sketch is based on exposures along the northern wall of the main quarry, and the specimen was taken from the middle layer of the sequence shown in the sketch.   (Art. 272.)

1. *Bedding fissility*—the capacity of many of the finer grained sedimentary rocks to part along surfaces parallel to the stratification.   This property, which is ascribed largely to compositional and grain-size variation between layers, is a primary sedimentary structure modified to some extent probably during the consolidation of the rock.   It has no top and bottom significance.

2. *Bedding foliation*—a schistlike or gneissoid structure produced by metamorphic accentuation of original bedding fissility, with or without subsequent deformation.   This type of foliation, called "load cleavage" by Daly (1917: 375), has no apparent use as a top and bottom criterion.

3. *Fracture cleavage*—this type of foliation results from the fracture of relatively weaker rock layers, which are sheared between stronger layers during moderate folding, but may also occur along shear and fault zones. It consists of closely spaced, parallel shear fractures that are independent

of the orientation of the constituent minerals.   The fractures divide the layer into plates that are not cleavable into thinner foliations.

Fracture cleavage, as Mead (1940: 1010) points out, is " . . . an admirable indicator of the direction of shear displacement" and has been proved a reliable top and bottom criterion when used with proper discrimination.   It is discussed more fully in Art. 275.

4. *Flow cleavage*[1]—this type of foliation, which pervades the entire rock in contrast to the more widely spaced fracture and shear cleavages,

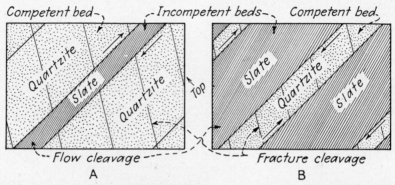

Fig. 385.—Cleavage in incompetent and competent beds.   *A.* Flow, or axial-plane, cleavage in an incompetent slate layer between competent quartzite beds that have fracture cleavage.   *B.* Competent quartzite beds with fracture cleavage in a slate series with flow, or axial-plane, cleavage.   The arrows in both diagrams indicate relative movement between beds.   In each diagram the top of the sequence is to the left, for the left-hand bed of any pair has moved upward relative to the right-hand.   (Art. 276.)

is a result of dynamic metamorphism and is due to the parallel orientation of platy and elongate minerals.   According to Mead (1940: 1010),

> Its orientation is perpendicular to the short axis of strain, which is equivalent to saying that it is perpendicular to the direction of the resultant of compressional stresses . . . [which] relationship to strain places it approximately parallel to the axial plane of folds.   The simple relationship between flow cleavage and strain makes it reliably useful in the interpretation of folds.

Flow cleavage, like fracture cleavage, has been proved a reliable top and bottom criterion.   It is more fully discussed in Art. 275.

5. *Shear cleavage*—Mead (1940: 1010–1011) defines shear cleavage as follows:

> This type of cleavage consists of roughly parallel, closely spaced surfaces of shear displacement on which platy minerals may have developed and into which they may have been dragged. . . .
> Shear cleavage may be developed in rocks having earlier flow cleavage or bedding foliation. . . . Shear cleavage, although commonly found in folded rocks, is not a consequence of folding. . . .

[1] Leith (1905: 23*ff.*) first used the term "flow cleavage" and also pointed out that it had previously been called "slaty cleavage" and "schistosity."   Fairbairn (1935: 591) later described this type of foliation as "axial-plane cleavage."

Hence the structure cannot be used for determining the tops and bottoms of folded beds.

Inasmuch as certain of the foliate structures just described may be so much alike that they are indistinguishable in the field, the greatest effort must always be made to establish the correct identity of the structure before using it as a top and bottom criterion.

The reader will find an excellent review of slaty cleavage and kindred structures in a recent article by G. Wilson (1947: 263–302), which was published too late for the author to take full advantage of it.

275. *Fracture and Flow Cleavage.*—The manner in which fracture and flow cleavage are formed and their orientation with reference to the stress which produces them have been widely discussed, not always with unanimity of opinion. Since we are not interested here in these aspects of cleavage, it will suffice to list some of the more important references in a footnote.[1] The interested investigator will find in this brief list enough references to take him far into the general problem of rock cleavage and particularly into the mechanics of folding and cleavage formation. We turn then to consideration of those features of cleavage which are useful for top and bottom determination.

276. *Relation of cleavage to bedding and to folds.*—It has been pointed out repeatedly, following the original analysis by Leith (1905: 1–216), that fracture and flow cleavage can be used successfully to determine tops and bottoms of beds in stratified rocks (see table, Chap. I, pages 22–23). In folding produced by compressional or rotational stress the top bed of a pair always moves upward with reference to the underlying bed (Fig. 385); hence, by following the fracture or flow cleavage to its two boundaries within a single layer, it is possible to determine how contiguous beds moved and from this observation to fix the top and bottom of the beds.

Flow cleavage is approximately parallel to the axial plane of the fold in which it is developed, whereas fracture cleavage makes an appreciable acute angle with the axial plane (Fig. 386). In symmetrical folds the cleavage is steeper than the bedding in every part of the fold[2] (Fig. 386).

[1] Laugel (1854–1855: 363–368), Heim (1878), Loretz (1882), Becker (1893: 13–90; 1904: 1–34), Dale (1896: 543–570; 1902: 9–22), Van Hise (1896: 633–668; 1909: 97–104), Hoskins (1896: 845–874), Leith (1905: 1–216; 1923: 113–158, 181–185), Swanson (1927: 193–223; 1939: 1938; 1941: 1245–1263), Lovering (1928: 709–717), Cloos and Martin (1932: 74), Fairbairn (1935: 591–608; 1936: 670–680; 1942), A. Leith (1937: 360–368), Derry (1939: 109–134), Rowland (1939: 449–471), Mead (1920: 505–523; 1940: 1007–1021), Broughton (1946: 1–18), and Wilson (1947: 263–302).

[2] Even in closely compressed folds there is usually a slight inclination of cleavage to bedding, though the angle may be only a few degrees and so small that cleavage is scarcely distinguishable from bedding. Leith (1923: 128) states that in his wide observations of Pre-Cambrian rocks he " . . . has never yet found cleavage exactly parallel to the bedding for any distance. When followed out in strike or dip for even a few yards, it is found to cut the bedding."

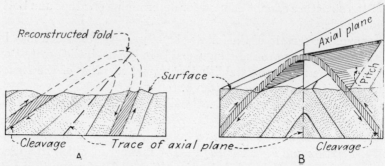

FIG. 386.—Axial-plane cleavage in overturned and normal anticlines. *A*. From cleavage-bedding relations in surface exposures it is possible to reconstruct the part of the fold that has been eroded away and also to construct the subsurface structure. The left limb of the fold is normal, the right overturned. The cleavage has the same inclination in both limbs and is approximately parallel to the axial plane. *B*. An upright symmetrical anticline with axial-plane cleavage. The suprasurface part of the fold is reconstructed and the position of the axial plane indicated. The pitch is the angle between the horizontal and the trace of bedding on cleavage. In both folds the upper bed of a pair moved upward toward the anticlinal axis relative to the underlying bed. Compare Figs. 387, 389, 391, and 392. (Art. 276.)

In asymmetrical folds with the steeper limb vertical or overturned and in overturned symmetrical folds, cleavage is steeper than bedding on the normal limb, but bedding is steeper than cleavage on the overturned limb (Fig. 386). These relations were long ago recognized and used by Irving, Van Hise, Leith, Mead, and many others in working out the structure of the folded Pre-Cambrian rocks of North America, and they have been found equally useful when applied in other folded areas. A. Leith (1931: 625–640), for example, found that both fracture and flow cleavage are extensively developed in the western Alps and can be used successfully to work out the structure of that complex terrane (Fig. 387). Hills (1940: 102) reports similar cleavage development in the Bendigo gold field of Victoria, Australia [see also Dunn (1896)].[1]

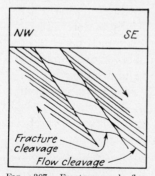

FIG. 387.—Fracture and flow cleavage on the overturned limb in the root zone of the Wildhorn nappe in the Helvetian Alps. A bed of limestone lies in the midst of black calcareous schist. The beds dip about 68° to the southeast, the flow cleavage about 45°, and the fracture cleavage at a much flatter angle. The beds are obviously overturned since bedding is steeper than cleavage. (Art. 276.) (*Modified after A. Leith,* 1931, *Jour. Geology,* **39**: 631, *Fig.* 3.)

[1] Cleavage may be formed in relatively soft rocks during intense folding, as illustrated by an instructive example in the Carboniferous Wamsutta red beds of the Narragansett Basin. About half a mile southwest of Sheldonville, Mass., is a roadside exposure showing steeply inclined layers of fairly fine-grained red sandstone with numerous discoidal shale masses disposed at right angles to the bedding along the southern side of each bed. The shale discoids show well-developed cleavage, whereas the surrounding

Courtesy of R. L. Nichols

A

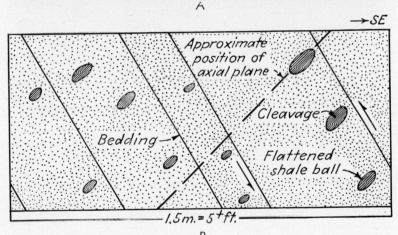

B

FIG. 388.—Shale pellets. *A.* Massive conglomerate in the Eocene Calapooya formation at Hobart Butte, Oregon. The photograph is slightly less than natural size. The rock consists of ovate kaolinitic pellets lying in a gray clay matrix and elongated in the general plane of bedding, which is shown across the photograph from left to right. The rock is thought to represent a water-laid sediment of pyroclastic origin, and the pellets have been interpreted as eroded fragments derived from desiccated clay layers. Many of the pellets appear to have been plastic when deposited, for they are molded against and over particles on which they came to rest. Compare these pellets, elongated in the general plane of stratification, with those of Fig. 388*B*, which have been dynamically elongated in a direction perpendicular to bedding. *B.* Flattened shale pellets with well-developed cleavage in sandstone layers of the Pennsylvanian Wamsutta formation near Sheldonville, Mass. The original mud pellets were probably spheroidal or flattened in the general plane of stratification, but as a result of deformation during folding they were elongated in the direction of cleavage, so that they now have their longest axis perpendicular to bedding. The incompetent shale readily developed cleavage, whereas the more competent sandstone did not. In massive formations that lack well-defined bedding, shale pellets not only indicate the general plane of stratification but also indicate differential movement between beds, hence top and bottom, provided that cleavage is developed. (Arts. 122, 276.) (*A after Allen and Nichols,* 1945, *Jour. Sedimentary Petrology,* **15**: 25–33, *Fig.* 1.)

An important correlative use of the cleavage-bedding relation is stated by Leith (1923: 127) as follows: "The trace of bedding on the cleavage planes indicates the pitch of the fold." Once the direction of pitch is determined, a traverse in that direction crosses successively younger strata regardless of whether the fold is an anticline or syncline. A means is thus afforded for determining the order of succession in pitching folds, and since most folds have some pitch the criterion is one worth remembering.

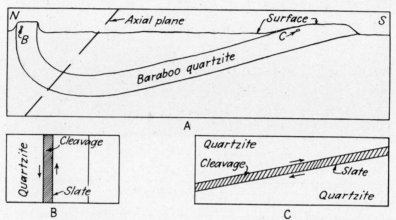

Fig. 389.—Diagrammatic cross section of the Pre-Cambrian Baraboo syncline of Wisconsin, and enlarged parts, showing the relation of cleavage to bedding and to the axial plane of the fold. The basement rocks, the Pre-Cambrian iron-bearing formations directly overlying the quartzite, and the Upper Cambrian strata, which lie unconformably upon the Pre-Cambrian, both inside and outside the syncline, are omitted from the diagram. In *B* and *C* the top bed of a pair moved upward or toward the anticlinal axis—*i.e.*, away from the synclinal axis—relative to the underlying bed. See Figs. 391 and 392. (Art. 277.)

277. *Identification of fracture and flow cleavage.*—Since, as Mead (1940: 1017) points out, "intelligent utilization of cleavage in the inter-

---

sandstone is devoid of secondary structure.

It appears that the shale masses were originally spheroidal or ellipsoidal mud balls which were elongated essentially parallel to the axial plane of the fold during folding. The cleavage-bedding relations now visible indicate that the exposure is on the limb of an asymmetrical anticline which has little if any pitch (Fig. 388). The unusual feature of their exposure is that the structural record is to be read from the deformed shale balls, which here serve the same purpose as slaty layers in other areas.

Cloos (1947: 843–918) recently called attention to several structurally significant relations between deformed oölites, cleavage, and axial planes of folds.

An instructive example of preferential development of cleavage is reported by Rowland (1939: 449–471) from the Moccasin clastic member of the Ordovician Lowville formation of Virginia. The cleavage is confined to incompetent beds of fine to coarse sand with calcite and clay matrix, the whole intimately intermixed and unassorted. Cleavage is lacking in contiguous members that have no calcitic and argillaceous matrix.

pretation of the structures of folded rocks requires correct classification of the type or types of foliate structures observed," identification of fracture and flow cleavage becomes the first step in solving the problem of what is top and what bottom in a folded succession of sedimentary rocks. Unfortunately there are no completely reliable criteria for this identification, but there are some general aspects of these types of cleavage that should be noted here.

The general principle, that flow cleavage is essentially parallel to the axial plane of the fold in which it is developed, is strictly applicable only to relatively incompetent beds, as Leith (1923: 113, 132), Swanson (1927: 193–223), and others have pointed out. Flow cleavage should be sought, therefore, in originally argillaceous beds and may be expected to have its best development where such beds, alternating with competent sandstones and quartzites, have been subjected to considerable deformation (Fig. 389).

Fracture cleavage, being the result of rupture by shearing, may be expected in hard, brittle rocks such as limestones, sandstones, and quartzites as well as in slightly deformed argillaceous beds. Its acutely angular relation to the axial plane is especially obvious where it gives way to

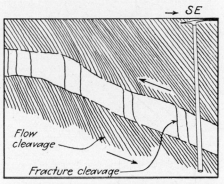

Fig. 390.—Fracture and flow cleavage in the root zone of the Diableret nappe in the Helvetian Alps. The limestone layer in the midst of black calcareous schist dips 15° to the southeast, the flow cleavage about 65° in the same direction, and the fracture cleavage in the limestone is essentially vertical. Since the cleavage is steeper than the bedding, the beds are right side up and on the normal limb of an anticline. The arrows indicate relative movement between beds. (Art. 277.) (*Adapted from A. Leith*, 1931, *Jour. Geology*, **39**: 632, *Fig.* 4.)

flow cleavage in adjacent less competent beds (Figs. 390, 394). A. Leith (1931: 631–640) describes and illustrates several cases in point from the western Alps, Du Toit (1939: 242, Plate 23) describes and illustrates well-developed fracture cleavage in vertical beds of Permian Dwyka tillite of South Africa, and Shenon and McConnel (1940: 440 *ff.*) found fracture cleavage in quartzite layers to be useful in determining the tops of beds. Both Leith (1931: 631) and Shenon and McConnel (1940: 440) call attention to the fact that the usefulness of fracture cleavage is increased if it has a pronounced attenuated S shape when viewed in transverse section, each end of the S being approximately parallel to the axial plane of the fold (Fig. 391). Such S cleavage is to be expected in the finer grained and silty layers of sandstones and quartzites and in limestones. Shenon and McConnel (1940: 442) remark:

This turning of fracture cleavage from its attitude in the middle of a bed to a position nearly parallel to the argillaceous parting at the bedding plane is the result of slight differences in grain size and therefore in relative competency and response to stress between the quartzite in the middle and outer parts of a bed. "S"-shaped cleavage is not seen in massive quartzite beds which do not have somewhat finer-grained material near the bedding surfaces.

Leith (1923: 154–155) years ago described and illustrated the same point from the Baraboo quartzite of Wisconsin (see Fig. 392); and in a

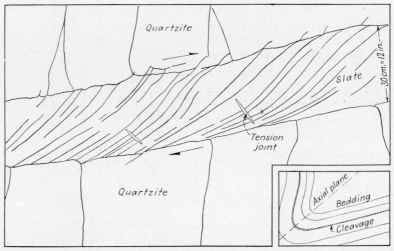

Fig. 391.—Fracture cleavage in an argillaceous layer between massive beds of Pre-Cambrian Baraboo quartzite on the south limb of the Baraboo syncline at Devil's Lake, Wisconsin. The partings in the slaty layer vary in continuity and curvature; some have the shape of an attenuated S, whereas others resemble foreset bedding. All show the differential movement indicated by the arrows. The joints in the massive quartzite are continuous with fracture-cleavage partings. Two short tension joints—open gashes—cross the fracture cleavage with opposite inclination (see Art. 279 and Figs. 396 and 397). The small inset indicates the general regional structure to be inferred from the cleavage-bedding relation in the exposure (see Fig. 392). Art. 277. (*Sketch based on a photograph by W. J. Mead.*)

recent article on the closely folded Ordovician rocks of Victoria, Australia, Hills and Thomas (1945: 54) report that "in graded beds, however, there is a gradual change in the attitude of the structures [*i.e.*, cleavage] as the bed becomes more argillaceous."

Tanton (1926: 44–45) points out a relationship between fracture cleavage and the lithology of varvelike layers that he found useful in determining order of succession in Coutchiching sedimentary rocks near Steeprock Lake, Ontario. His observations follow:

Between one-quarter and one-half mile east of the northeast end of Lerome Lake cross bedding was observed, and nearby there are varve-like groups of beds in the same series. The interpretation[s] of both of these, by the standard

Courtesy of W. J. Mead

FIG. 392.—Fracture cleavage in an argillacous layer of the Pre-Cambrian Baraboo quartzite at Devil's Lake, Wisconsin. The view is to the left of that sketched in Fig. 391. (Art. 277.)

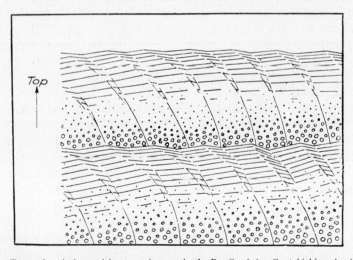

FIG. 393.—Textural variation and fracture cleavage in the Pre-Cambrian Coutchiching clastic rocks of the Lerome Lake area, Ontario. The two complete layers grade from coarse at the base to fine texture at the top, where there is a sharp break as the coarse basal part of the overlying layer begins. The fracture cleavage makes a larger acute angle with the bedding in the sandy part of the layer than in the upper argillaceous part. Both cleavage and texture variation indicate the top of the beds. (Art. 277.) (*After Tanton, 1926, Royal Soc. Canada Trans.*, **20**: 45, *Fig.* 3.)

methods, agree in showing the tops of the beds to be in the same direction.   The false bedding is abruptly cut off by overlying beds while it comes in contact with the lower beds by a tangential curve; the concave side of the curvature in the false bedding is toward the original top.   In the varve-like beds the texture changes more or less gradually from relatively coarse at the bottom to fine at the top within each sharply bounded compound unit.   A dependable interpretation cannot be made when, as sometimes happens, the gradations within the associated beds are either not uniformly in the same direction or admit of doubt.   It was observed that the fracture cleavage as developed in the varve-like beds also provided a means for recognizing the attitude, and in some cases this is more readily observable than the gradational texture variation itself.   The fracture cleavage in the varve-like beds curves and the convex side of the curvature is toward the top; in the coarser textured part of such beds the fracture cleavage makes a greater acute angle with the bedding than in the finer grained part of the same bed [Fig. 393].

Tanton's example illustrates, among other things, the possibility of confusing fracture cleavage and cross-lamination in medium- and fine-grained clastic rocks (Art. 142).

An interesting structural use of a modified type of fracture cleavage is described in a recent article by Hills and Thomas (1945: 51), who point out how "closely spaced fissures in sandstones and puckered arenaceous laminae in slates are used in field work to indicate center country (fold axes) where dip readings are difficult to obtain. . . ." Their Fig. 1, here reproduced with slight modification as Fig. 394, shows not only the usual intense deformation along the anticlinal crest but also the change in attitude of the cleavage as it passes from sandstone, through laminated sandstone, into slate.

The surface of contact between a brittle quartzite and cleaved shale typically has a serrated profile when viewed in cross section and a ridged topography when seen in plan (Fig. 87).   The parallel asymmetrical ridges of shale adhering to the quartzite should not be mistaken for ripple marks.   Maxson and Campbell (1934, 1939) made this mistake but corrected it when petrofabric analysis by Ingerson (1939, 1940) showed the true nature of the structure (see Art. 82).   Bucher (1919: 203) calls attention to a peculiar rippling of cleavage surfaces under certain conditions, stating: "True ripple-marks must, however, not be mistaken for it [the friction rippling] in rocks showing slaty cleavage in argillaceous layers.   For an interesting discussion see Krause, Zeitschr. Deutsch. Geol. Ges. Monatsberichte, 1911, p. 196–202."

There is one specific case in which cleavage developed by differential movement between beds in a fold is the reverse of the general rule. This exception is found in domal folding where the deforming stress, acting from below, forces the underbed of a pair to slide upward relative to the overlying bed (Fig. 395). More or less faulting is associated with

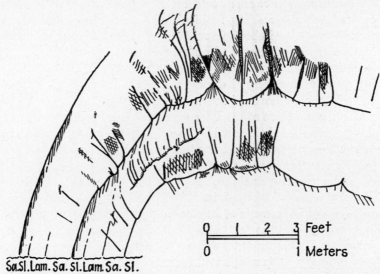

Sa.Sl.Lam.Sa.Sl.Lam.Sa.Sl.

FIG. 394.—Detail of east limb and axis of Napoleon anticline at surface, Golden Square, Bendigo, Australia. (*Sa*, sandstone; *Sl*, slate; *Lam*, laminated sandstone.) The two main beds of the diagram consist of the same tripartite succession—sandstone at the base, laminated sandstone in the middle, and slate (shale) at the top. The cleavage changes attitude sharply in passing from one type of lithology to another. Prominent fissures and fracture cleavage are well developed in the sandstone but do not extend into the laminated sandstone. Flow cleavage (axial-plane cleavage), with almost vertical dip, characterizes the slaty layers. On the flank of the fold the fracture cleavage has an inclination of about 45°, whereas the flow cleavage is essentially vertical. Inasmuch as the beds have been thickened somewhat along the crest of the fold, deformation is most intense there. (Arts. 276, 277.) (*Modified after Hills and Thomas*, 1945, *Econ. Geology*, **40**: 52, *Fig.* 1.)

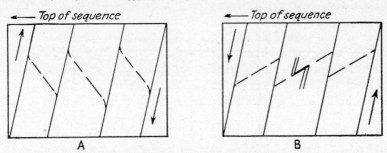

FIG. 395.—Normal and reversed fracture cleavage. *A.* Normal fracture cleavage on the left flank of an asymmetrical anticline. The top bed has moved upward relative to the underlying. *B.* Reversed fracture cleavage in the supposed cryptovolcanic disturbance near Kentland, Ind., where, in a steeply dipping sequence of middle Ordovician limestones, the underlying bed moved upward relative to the overlying. A small faulted reverse drag fold is indicated in the middle layer. Compare with Figs. 383 and 384. (Art. 277.)

this kind of cleavage, and the complication is likely to render it of little use for structural work. Cleavage of this sort is associated with reverse drag folds in the supposed "cryptovolcanic" structure at Kentland, Ind.

(Art. 272) and may be expected in other similar structures as well as in domal folds produced by laccolithic intrusions.

278. *Summary of Foliation, or Cleavage.*—Five kinds of foliate structure are recognized—bedding fissility, bedding foliation, fracture cleavage, flow cleavage, and shear cleavage. Of these only fracture and flow cleavage are reliable for top and bottom determination.

The following generalized rules may be set up for the structural use of cleavage and bedding as applied by geologists of the so-called "Wisconsin School." It should be emphasized in this connection that Van Hise, Leith, Mead, and others of the Wisconsin group did most of their work in the relatively unaltered sedimentary rocks of the Pre-Cambrian Canadian Shield, in which metamorphism has not been so intense as to obliterate all the primary sedimentary structures. Although the principles they applied and refined—principles, incidentally, that had been developed abroad many years before by Heim (1878), Loretz (1882), and others—are also quite useful in terranes of intense folding and metamorphism, as in the Appalachians and the Scottish Highlands, they cannot be expected to give in every case clean-cut answers to structural problems involving the more intensely metamorphosed rocks.

1. Since flow and fracture cleavage tend to parallel the axial plane of the fold in which they occur, the former more nearly than the latter, it follows that the trace of bedding on cleavage indicates the approximate angle and direction of the pitch of the fold.

2. Since flow and fracture cleavage indicate the direction of relative movement of contiguous beds and since in normal folding the upper of a pair of beds moves upward from the synclinal axis toward the anticlinal axis, it is possible to determine from the cleavage-bedding relation whether a sequence of strata is right side up or overturned.

3. Since during folding the upper of a pair of beds moves upward toward the anticlinal axis relative to the lower, the cleavage-bedding relation indicates the observer's position with reference to the axial plane and this holds for all pitching folds whether viewed in plan or in cross section.

4. In an upright symmetrical fold, cleavage is steeper than bedding in every part of the fold, being perpendicular to bedding on the crest and approaching but rarely attaining parallelism with bedding on the steepest part of the limbs.

5. In asymmetrical folds with one limb vertical or overturned and in overturned symmetrical folds, cleavage is steeper than bedding on the normal limb (*cf.* 4 above), but bedding is steeper than cleavage on the overturned limb.

6. From 4 and 5 it follows that

a. If cleavage dips more steeply than bedding and in the same direction, the beds are right side up and the cleavage direction, if continued into the top bed, indicates the direction in which that bed slipped as it moved toward the anticlinal axis.

b. If cleavage dips more steeply than bedding but in the opposite direction, the upper surface of the bed is the top side and the cleavage direction, if continued into the top bed, indicates the direction in which that bed slipped as it moved toward the anticlinal axis.

c. If bedding is steeper than cleavage, the beds are overturned and the continuation of cleavage direction into the upper bed indicates the direction in which that bed slipped as it moved toward the anticlinal axis.

d. If bedding and cleavage are perpendicular and vertical or steeply inclined, it is not possible to determine the top and bottom since the exposure shows the crest of a fold. In this case, a few steps in one direction or another along the strike of the bedding should suffice to determine whether the fold is an anticline or syncline.

Only the simple cases of cleavage have been considered in formulating the above rules. If later deformation attended by metamorphism has affected an earlier system of cleavage, the structure of the resulting rock may be too complex for the original cleavage to have any top and bottom significance.

Cleavage surfaces commonly are the only partings in metamorphosed rocks, and it is on them that sedimentary features of many kinds should be sought. In viewing these features, however, it must be kept in mind that one is observing a section which is inclined to the plane of stratification. Only in this way can one avoid misinterpreting features that appear to be distorted or out of proportion.

279. TENSION CRACKS.—At least one type of tension crack in deformed beds can be used indirectly for top and bottom determination. It consists of open, thinly lenticular gashes which incline in a direction opposite to that of fracture cleavage (Figs. 382*E*, 391, 396). These characteristically shaped cracks, commonly made conspicuous by a quartz filling, are usually best developed in relatively competent materials such as thin quartzite beds or the pebbles and small boulders of conglomeratic layers. They are widely spaced as a rule and usually do not extend completely to the margin of the bed or pebble. They are commonly associated with fracture cleavage but can be differentiated from it by the fact that they are open cracks and incline in the opposite direction.

Mead (1920: 512–513), in deforming a paraffin-coated rubber sheet by shearing, found that "the first fractures to appear in any one locality

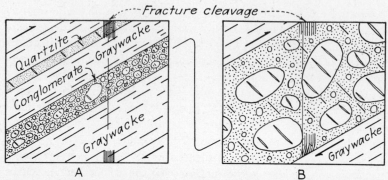

Fig. 396.—Tension cracks in pebbles and brittle layers. *A.* Cross section of tilted clastic sedimentary rocks showing tension cracks in a quartzite layer and in some of the pebbles and boulders of a conglomerate. Arrows indicate the differential movement between beds. The trace of the tension cracks inclines in a direction opposite that of fracture cleavage. *B.* Enlarged sketch of a small part of the conglomerate of *A,* showing the nature and relations of tension cracks in the pebbles. Not all pebbles have cracks, and larger boulders generally lack the feature altogether. It is the general rule that tension cracks do not reach to the periphery of the pebble or to the margin of the layer in which they occur. Scattered tension cracks are also to be expected in the main body of the conglomerate, but they are not likely to have the characteristic form of a lenticular cleft. Fracture cleavage is here shown to have a vertical orientation, pointing in the direction of movement, whereas the tension clefts are inclined in the opposite direction, pointing against the direction of movement between beds. A further difference between the two features is that the foliations of fracture cleavage are relatively closely spaced, whereas tension clefts are widely spaced. The latter are also commonly filled with quartz or some other introduced mineral. (Art. 279.) (*Sketches based on suggestions by H. W. Fairbairn.*)

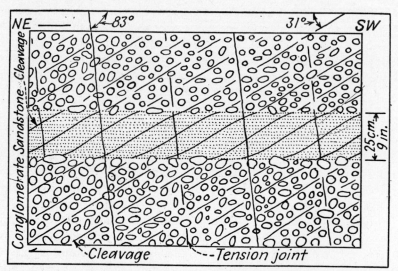

Fig. 397.—Horizontal layer of fine sand in a massive conglomerate showing prominent fracture cleavage dipping about 31° to the northeast. Steeply inclined tension joints dip to the southwest. The arrows indicate the relative movement between beds. The sketch is based on an exposure of Carboniferous Roxbury conglomerate along the Hammond Pond Parkway, Newton, Mass. (Art. 279.)

on the rubber sheet are usually tension cracks inclined about 45° to the direction of the shearing movement. These are at right angles to the direction of maximum elongation and appear as vertical open cracks." This observation probably explains why the tension cracks are usually found in competent rocks, inasmuch as these fail early in the shearing.

Tension cracks of this type were called to the attention of the author many years ago by Prof. C. K. Leith[1] and Prof. W. J. Mead, and recently Prof. H. W. Fairbairn informed him that he had used them to determine direction of differential movement between beds. From this observation Professor Fairbairn determined the top and bottom of beds in the Sutton Mountains of Quebec and in the Patricia district of Ontario. The cracks are present in parts of the Lower Cambrian Oak Hill series of quartzites and pebble beds in the Sutton Mountains and in the Pre-Cambrian Shabu sedimentary series consisting " . . . largely of clastic material ranging from boulder conglomerate to fine graywacke and slate" [Fairbairn (1936: 671)]. Tension cracks of the type here discussed are also well developed in certain brittle beds of the Carboniferous Roxbury conglomerate south of Boston (Fig. 397).

It is of added interest that this same feature develops on a microscopic scale, as described and illustrated by Sander (1930: 222–225). He reports such tension cracks in quartz layers in schists, limestone layers in phyllites, and garnets in garnetiferous schists.[2] Sander did not discuss the significance of these cracks with reference to their use in interpreting structural relations, but there is every reason to expect that such cracks in minerals and thin quartz bands should correlate with megascopic openings of the same sort.

[1] See Leith (1923: 154–155) for description and illustration of this feature.

[2] Professor H. W. Fairbairn informs the author that he has seen similar tension cracks having the form of fine hairlike gashes in elongate quartz masses surrounded by less competent foliated minerals (*e.g.*, mica).

CHAPTER VIII

BIBLIOGRAPHY

INDEX TO REFERENCES

GENERAL

Criteria of Succession.—45,* 50, 54, 103, 135, 145, 229, 262, 268, 399, 576, 601, 628, 629, 658, 668, 670, 671, 673, 723.

Stratification.—4, 17, 67, 72, 109, 114, 156, 157, 262, 323–325, 378, 413, 427, 428, 517, 569, 664, 707.

Cyclic Sedimentation.—13, 17, 33, 51, 65, 68, 71, 73, 168, 185, 235, 262, 265, 323–325, 345, 378, 466, 468, 504, 531, 546, 553–557, 620, 636, 638, 658, 661, 664, 667, 685, 687–691, 696–701, 707.

Cyclothems.—13, 466, 468, 504, 532, 553, 620, 650, 661, 685, 687–691, 696–701.

Correlation by Fossils.—119, 193, 195, 243, 277, 334–336, 470, 472, 560, 562, 577, 639, 659.

Unconformity.—39, 57, 131–133, 138, 139, 145, 148, 149, 163, 212, 213, 232, 254, 255, 262, 378, 393, 399, 401, 415, 431, 436, 452, 519, 529, 538, 597, 605, 606, 632, 656, 658, 665, 668, 676, 702, 705, 712.

Features along Contacts of Sedimentary Layers: Erosional Features; Stylolites; Buried Objects; Etc.—40, 41, 131–133, 148, 212, 213, 252, 254, 305, 378, 393, 409, 452, 513, 574, 610, 611, 614, 615, 617–619, 630, 648, 668, 672, 684, 686, 737.

Conglomerates.—4, 213, 229, 307, 326, 378, 500, 668, 675, 677.

Weathering Profiles.—232, 234, 308, 331–333, 394, 401, 402, 406, 407, 415, 442, 447, 452, 487, 538, 541, 581, 623, 632, 658, 666, 668, 686, 708, 714, 731–734.

SEDIMENTARY ROCKS

General Sedimentary Features: Large Sedimentary Bodies; Deltas; Beach Deposits; Processes of Sedimentation; Environments of Deposition; Etc.—3, 4, 8, 12, 14–16, 18–21, 29–32, 36, 45, 51, 60, 67, 76, 87, 109, 110, 135, 145, 164–166, 200, 204, 215, 226, 232, 250, 255–257, 259–262, 266, 268, 270, 274, 278, 281, 283, 326, 329, 330, 342, 346, 351, 352, 358, 359, 369–371, 378, 411, 419, 426, 431, 458, 463, 472, 489, 500, 502, 504, 534, 545, 562, 566, 583, 588, 593, 622, 641, 643, 646, 655, 657, 658, 668, 706, 714, 717.

Lithologic Sequences.—12, 14, 17, 18, 164, 463, 601, 621, 622, 686, 717.

Graded Bedding.—5, 6, 20–22, 51, 135, 140, 145, 185, 268, 345, 378, 399, 502, 528, 545, 628, 629, 658.

Varved Sediments and Sedimentary Rocks.—10, 11, 65, 68, 70, 71, 106, 133, 235, 262, 323–325, 338, 378, 501, 502, 540, 554–557, 636, 637, 643, 658, 683.

Ripple-mark.—19, 38, 53, 74, 83, 94–96, 130, 145, 150, 159, 206, 245, 247–250, 262, 268, 272, 274, 290, 303, 309–311, 320, 339, 348, 353, 359, 360, 362, 378, 399, 427, 440, 441, 465, 496, 516, 524, 564, 566, 586, 587, 593, 595, 635, 658, 662, 668, 726.

* The numbers listed here designate the numbered references that follow this index.

Inorganically Produced Ridges and Depressions:—Rill Marks; Flow Casts; Groove Casts; Etc.—3, 9, 36, 97, 125, 137, 202, 215, 221, 236, 262, 274–277, 315, 330, 378, 388, 420, 422, 437–439, 450, 453, 494, 499, 503, 523, 539, 561, 570, 571, 606, 652, 658, 663, 694.

Pit and Mound.—120, 347, 437, 559, 658.

Impressions: Raindrop Imprints; Crystal Impressions; Etc.—3, 9, 61, 145, 172, 176, 181, 186, 262, 356, 357, 378, 399, 419, 421, 422, 527, 658, 672, 736.

Buried Inorganic Objects.—28, 42, 79, 88, 89, 91, 135, 145, 167, 228, 467, 483, 507, 508, 558, 631, 633, 658, 684, 716.

Organically Produced Ridges and Depressions: Tracks; Trails; Borings; Burrows; Etc.—1, 34, 35, 47–49, 75, 83, 98, 102, 113, 120, 145, 175–177, 201, 262, 294–296, 306, 315, 378, 416, 417, 448, 526, 552, 585, 607, 608, 658, 710, 729.

Shrinkage Cracks.—66, 69, 116, 145, 172, 190, 207, 218, 221, 226, 246, 262, 307, 346, 349, 353–355, 361, 363, 378, 399, 410, 419, 434, 459, 460, 514, 524, 525, 580, 627, 642, 653, 658, 692, 711.

Clastic Dikes.—62, 111, 115, 122, 123, 146, 147, 149, 183, 192, 207, 216, 251, 264, 282, 284, 298, 317–319, 341, 366, 368, 373, 378, 383, 392, 424, 433, 445, 476, 492, 493, 512, 542, 547, 597, 713.

Weathering and Erosion Features.—52, 55, 77, 90–93, 137–139, 147, 163, 164, 174, 179, 184, 196, 254, 262, 263, 305, 344, 401, 415, 452, 495, 519, 529, 565, 572, 581, 592, 600, 658, 702, 705, 712, 714.

Cross-lamination.—19, 20–22, 134, 144, 145, 170, 258, 259, 262, 268, 297, 340, 364, 365, 370, 378, 380, 399, 427–430, 451, 457, 491, 520, 533, 566, 589, 593, 594, 628, 629, 658, 668, 673, 728.

Penecontemporaneous Deformation.—15, 16, 25, 26, 54, 60, 80, 91, 92, 114, 124, 131, 143, 179, 184, 191, 208, 214, 229, 262, 271, 273, 285, 286, 288, 289, 292, 328, 343, 344, 350, 374–379, 381, 399, 408, 409, 446, 454–456, 471, 475, 495, 535, 536, 548, 572, 573, 590, 596, 634, 640, 647, 658, 668, 675, 677, 709, 716, 725, 727, 730, 735.

Buried Fossils and Organic Structures.—34, 35, 46, 49, 56, 59, 84–86, 142, 145, 151, 152, 171, 173, 270, 277, 278, 302, 389, 420, 423, 448, 464, 472, 490, 515, 529, 552, 563, 577, 578, 584, 600, 602, 654, 658, 659, 693, 695, 705, 710, 719.

Algal Structures (Stromatolites).—58, 59, 64, 121, 128, 145, 220, 223–227, 253, 255–257, 321, 488, 563, 651, 658, 678,

Bioherms (Organic Reefs).—107, 153–155, 219, 222, 253, 256, 390, 494, 515, 579, 591, 612, 613, 616, 658.

IGNEOUS ROCKS

General Features of Igneous Rocks.—2, 23, 24, 63, 129, 136, 141, 145, 161, 199, 217, 230, 239, 266, 269, 279, 342, 372, 378, 382, 385, 387, 403, 404, 505, 506, 521, 550, 603, 649, 660, 668, 703, 721.

Pyroclastics.—7, 230, 299, 304, 484, 498, 510, 511, 537, 582, 704.

Lava Flows.—2, 23, 24, 37, 101, 104, 105, 108, 118, 126, 136, 141, 197–199, 238, 239, 241, 268, 269, 300–302, 312–314, 327, 372, 378, 383–385, 387, 399, 435, 461, 477–482, 485, 486, 538, 543, 603, 604, 645, 682, 712–724.

Amygdules.—104, 105, 108, 126, 162, 169, 187, 188, 469, 530, 543, 674, 680–682.

Pillow Lavas.—37, 99, 101, 112, 126, 141, 158, 182, 233, 238, 240, 241, 268, 378, 399, 405, 432, 436, 461, 462, 598, 599, 604, 703, 720–723.

Differentiation Features.—63, 81, 100, 117, 129, 203, 237, 242, 384, 403, 404, 418, 449, 497, 509, 522, 649, 679.

REFERENCES

1. ALBRITTON, C. C., JR., 1942, Dinosaur tracks near Comanche, Texas, *Field and Lab.*, **10**: 160–181.
2. ALFORD, E. C., 1937, The Lava Casts Forest of Oregon, *Rocks and Minerals*, **12** (5): 146–147.
3. ALLAN, J. A., 1926, Ice crystal markings, *Am. Jour. Sci.* (5) **11**: 494–500.
4. ALLEN, V. T., and R. L. NICHOLS, 1945, Clay-pellet conglomerates at Hobart Butte, Lane County, Oregon, *Jour. Sedimentary Petrology*, **15**: 25–33.
5. ALLISON, A., 1933, The Dalradian succession in Islay and Jura, *Geol. Soc. London Quart. Jour.*, **89**: 125–144.
6. ANDERSON, J. G. C., 1935, The Dalradian succession in the Pass of Brander District, Argyll, *Geol. Mag.*, **72**: 74–80.
7. ANDERSON, T., 1910, The volcano of Matavanu in Savii, *Geol. Soc. London Quart. Jour.*, **46**: 621 639.
8. ANDRÉE, K., 1915, Wesen, Ursachen, und Arten der Schichtung, *Geol. Rundschau*, **6**: 351–397.
9. ANONYMOUS, 1939, Fossil prints of slanting raindrops that marked the earth during a northeast gale in Colorado 250 million years ago are on exhibit at Chicago's Field Museum, *Science News Letter*, **35**: 18.
10. ANTEVS, E., 1922, The recession of the last ice sheet in New England, *Am. Geog. Soc. Research Ser.*, **2**: 1–120.
11. ———, 1925, Conditions of formation of the varved glacial clay [Abstract], *Bull. Geol. Soc. Am.*, **36**: 171–172.
12. ASHLEY, G. H., 1899, The coal deposits of Indiana, *Indiana Dept. Geol. Nat. Resources Ann. Rept.*, **23**: 1–1741.
13. ———, 1931, Pennsylvanian cycles in Pennsylvania, *Bull. Illinois Geol. Survey*, **60**: 241–245.
14. ——— et al., 1933, 1939, Classification and nomenclature of rock units, *Bull. Geol. Soc. Am.*, **44**: 423–459, 1933; *Bull. Am. Assoc. Petroleum Geologists*, **17**: 843 –868, 1933, *ibid.*, **23**: 1068–1098, 1939.
15. ATHY, L. F., 1930, Density, porosity and compaction of sedimentary rocks, *Bull. Am. Assoc. Petroleum Geologists*, **14**: 1–24.
16. ———, 1934, Compaction and its effects on local structure, *Prob. Petroleum Geology, Am. Assoc. Petroleum Geologists*, pp. 811–823.
17. ATWOOD, W. W., JR., 1933, Alternating layers of lava and glacial till in the rim rocks surrounding Crater Lake [Abstract], *Bull. Geol. Soc. Am.*, **44**: 214.
18. AUTHORS (many different writers; see also Ashley *et. al.*, 1933, 1939), 1933, 1939, Classification and nomenclature of rock units, *Bull. Geol. Soc. Am.*, **44**: 423–459, 1933; *Am. Assoc. Petroleum Geologists*, **17**: 843–868, 1933, *ibid.*, **23**: 1068–1098, 1939.
19. BAGNOLD, R. A., 1942, "The Physics of Blown Sand and Desert Dunes," William Morrow and Company, Inc., New York. 265 pp.
20. BAILEY, E. B., 1930, New light on sedimentation and tectonics, *Geol. Mag.*, **67**: 77–92.

21. ———, 1934, West Highland tectonics, *Geol. Soc. London Quart. Jour.*, **90**: 462–525.

22. ———, 1936, Sedimentation in relation to tectonics, *Bull. Geol. Soc. Am.*, **47**: 1713–1726.

23. ——— *et al.*, 1924, Tertiary and post-Tertiary geology of Mull, Loch Aline, and Oban, *Geol. Survey Scotland Mem.*, pp. 1–445.

24. ——— and E. M. ANDERSON, 1925, The geology of Staffa, Iona, and western Mull, *Geol. Survey Scotland Mem.*, pp. 1–107.

25. ———, L. W. COLLET, and R. M. FIELD, 1928, Paleozoic submarine landslips near Quebec City, *Jour. Geology*, **36**: 577–614.

26. ——— and J. WEIR, 1933, Submarine faulting in Kimmeridgian time: East Sutherland, *Royal Soc. Edinburgh Trans.*, **57** (2): 429–467.

27. BAIN, G. W., 1931, Flowage folding, *Am. Jour. Sci.* (5) **22**: 503–530.

28. BARNES, V. E., and G. A. PARKINSON, 1940, Dreikanters from the basal Hickory sandstone of central Texas, *Texas Univ. Pub.*, **3945**: 665–670.

29. BARRELL, J., 1906, Relative geological importance of continental, littoral, and marine sedimentation, *Jour. Geology*, **14**: 316–356, 430–457, 524–568.

30. ———, 1912, Criteria for the recognition of ancient delta deposits, *Bull. Geol. Soc. Am.*, **23**: 377–446.

31. ———, 1913, The Upper Devonian delta of the Appalachian geosyncline; Part I, The delta and its relations to the interior sea, *Am. Jour. Sci.* (4) **36**: 429–472.

32. ———, 1916, Dominantly fluviatile origin under seasonal rainfall of the Old Red Sandstone, *Bull. Geol. Soc. Am.*, **27**: 345–386.

33. ———, 1917, Rhythms and measurements of geologic time, *Bull. Geol. Soc. Am.*, **28**: 745–904.

34. BARROWS, A. L., 1913, Preliminary inquiry into the geological significance of rock-boring shells [Abstract], *Bull. Geol. Soc. Am.*, **24**: 130–131.

35. ———, 1917, Geologic significance of fossil rock-boring animals, *Bull. Geol. Soc. Am.*, **28**: 965–972.

36. BARROWS, W. L., 1910, A fulgurite from the Raritan sands of New Jersey, with an historical sketch and bibliography of fulgurites in general, *Columbia School Mines Quart.*, **31** (4): 294–319 (*Contr. Geol. Dept.* 20, No. 10).

37. BARTRUM, J. A., 1930, Pillow lava and columnar structure, New Zealand; *Jour. Geology*, **38**: 447–455.

38. BASCHIN, O., 1899, Die Entstehung wellenaehnlicher Oberflaechenformen, *Zs. Gesell. Erdkunde, Berlin*, **34**: 408–421.

39. BASSLER, R. S., 1932, The stratigraphy of the Central Basin of Tennessee, *Bull. Tennessee Div. Geology*, **38**: 1–268.

40. BASTIN, E. S., 1933, Relations of cherts to stylolites at Carthage, Missouri, *Jour. Geology*, **41**: 371–381.

41. ———, 1940, Discussion; a note on pressure stylolites, *Jour. Geology*, **48**: 214–216.

42. BATHER, F. A., 1900, Windworn pebbles in the British Isles, *Geol. Assoc. Proc.*, **1900**: 396–420.

43. BECKER, G. F., 1893, Finite homogeneous strain, flow, and rupture of rocks, *Bull. Geol. Soc. Am.*, **4**: 13–90.

44. ———, 1904, Experiments on schistosity and slaty cleavage, *Bull. U.S. Geol. Survey*, **241**: 1–34.

45. BECKER, H., 1939, "Gebirgsbildung und Vulkanismus," Verlagsbuchhandlung Gebrüder Borntraeger, Berlin. 220 pp.

46. BEECHER, C. E., 1894, On the structure and development of trilobites, *Am. Geologist*, **13**: 38–43.

47. BELL, W. A., 1912, 1914, Joggins Carboniferous section of Nova Scotia, *Geol. Survey Canada Summary Rept.*, **1911**: 328–333, *Summary Rept.*, **1912**: 360–371.

48. ———, 1921, The Mississippian formations of the Horton-Windsor district, Nova Scotia, *Am. Jour. Sci.*, (5) **1**: 153–173.

49. ———, 1929, Horton-Windsor district, Nova Scotia, *Geol. Survey Canada Mem.*, **155**: 1–268

50. BELYEA, H. R., 1935, Notes on the criteria for determining the tops of stratified beds [Abstract], *Nova Scotian Inst. Sci. Proc.*, **19**: 154–155.

51. ——— and A. W. SCOTT, 1935, Conditions of sedimentation of the Halifax formation as observed in Point Pleasant Park [Halifax, N. S.], *Nova Scotian Inst. Sci. Proc.*, **18** (iv): 225–239.

52. BERKEY, C. P., and J. E. HYDE, 1911, Original ice structures preserved in unconsolidated sands, *Jour. Geology*, **19**: 223–231.

53. BÉTHUNE, P. DE, 1936, "Ripple-marks" rhombiques fossiles du Carbonifère de l'Oklahoma, *Bull. soc. géol. Belgique*, **46**: 291–296.

54. BILLINGS, M. P., 1942, "Structural Geology," Prentice-Hall, Inc., New York. 473 pp.

55. BLACK, M., 1928, "Washouts" in the Estuarine Series of Yorkshire, *Geol. Mag.*, **65**: 301–307.

56. ———, 1929, Rooted land plants in a Jurassic limestone [Abstract], *Bull. Geol. Soc. Am.*, **40**: 222–223.

57. BLACKWELDER, E., 1909, The valuation of unconformities, *Jour. Geology*, **17**: 289–299.

58. ———, 1915, A fully exposed reef of calcareous algae (?) in the Middle Cambrian of the Teton Mountains [Wyoming]; *Am. Jour. Sci.* (4) **39**: 646–650.

59. ———, 1926, Pre-Cambrian geology of the Medicine Bow Mountains [Wyoming], *Bull. Geol. Soc. Am.*, **37**: 615–658.

60. ———, 1938, Mudflow as a geologic agent in semiarid mountains, *Bull. Geol. Soc. Am.*, **39**: 465–484.

61. ———, 1941, Significance of rain prints [Abstract], *Bull. Geol. Soc. Am.*, **52**: 1944.

62. BLOOMER, R. O., 1947, A tectonic intrusion of shale in Rockbridge County, Virginia, *Jour. Geology*, **55**: 48–51.

63. BOWEN, N. L., 1928, "The Evolution of the Igneous Rocks," Princeton University Press, Princeton, N. J. 332 pp.

64. BRADLEY, W. H., 1929, Algae reefs and oölites of the Green River formation, *U.S. Geol. Survey Prof. Paper*, **154**: 203–223.

65. ———, 1929a, The varves and climate of the Green River epoch, *U.S. Geol. Survey Prof. Paper*, **158**: 87–110.

66. ———, 1930, The behavior of certain mud-crack casts during compaction, *Am. Jour. Sci.* (5) **20**: 136–144.

67. ———, 1931, Origin and microfossils of the oil shale of the Green River formation of Colorado and Utah, *U.S. Geol. Survey Prof. Paper*, **168**: 1–58.

68. ———, 1931a, Nonglacial marine varves, *Am. Jour. Sci.* (5) **22**: 318–330.

69. ———, 1933, Factors that determine the curvature of mud-cracked layers, *Am. Jour. Sci.* (5) **26**: 55–71.

70. ———, 1937, Non-glacial varves, with selected bibliography, *Nat. Research Council Ann. Rept. Appendix A, Rept. Comm. Geol. Time*, pp. 32–42.

71. ———, 1938, A brief annotated bibliography on cyclic variations in climate as

indicated by pre-Pleistocene non-glacial varves, *Bull Am. Meteorol. Soc.*, **19**; 162–163.

72. BRAMLETTE, M. N., 1928, Pseudo-stratification in core recoveries, *Bull. Am. Assoc. Petroleum Geologists*, **12** : 1167–1169.

73. ———, 1934, Rhythmic bedding in the Monterey rocks of California [Abstract]; *Washington Acad. Sci. Jour.*, **23** : 575. See also 1946, The Monterey formation of California and the origin of its siliceous rocks, *U.S. Geol. Survey Prof. Paper*, **212** : 1–57.

74. BRANNER, J. C., 1901, Ripples of the Medina sandstone, *Jour. Geology*, **9** : 535–536.

75. BRANSON, E. B., and M. G. MEHL, 1932, Footprint records from the Paleozoic and Mesozoic of Missouri, Kansas, and Wyoming, *Bull. Geol. Soc. Am.*, **43** : 383–398.

76. ——— and W. A. Tarr, 1941, "Introduction to Geology," 2d ed., McGraw-Hill Book Company, Inc., New York. 482 pp.

77. BRETZ, J H., 1940, Solution cavities in the Joliet limestone of northeastern Illinois, *Jour. Geology*, **48** : 337–384.

78. BRIDGE, J., and C. L. DAKE, 1929, Initial dips peripheral to resurrected hills, *Missouri Bur. Geology and Mines Bienn. Rept. State Geologist* (1927–1928), pp. 93–99.

79. BRIGHAM, E. M., 1932, Concerning a granite pebble included in a varved pre-Cambrian sediment, *Michigan Acad. Sci. Papers*, **16** : 373–378.

80. BROCK, R. W., with R. G. McCONNEL, 1904, Report on the great landslide at Frank, Alberta, Canada, *Can. Dept. Interior Ann. Rept.*, **8** (1902–1903), (Appendix), pp. 1–17.

81. BRODERICK, T. M., 1935, Differentiation in lavas of the Michigan Keweenawan, *Bull. Geol. Soc. Am.*, **46** : 503–558.

82. BROUGHTON, J. C., 1946, An example of the development of cleavages, *Jour. Geology*, **54** : 1–18.

83. BROWN, A. P., 1912, The formation of ripple-marks, tracks, and trails, *Acad. Nat. Sci. Philadelphia Proc.*, **63** : 536–547.

84. BROWN, R., 1846, On a group of erect fossil trees in the Sydney coal field of Cape Breton, *Geol. Soc. London Quart. Jour.*, **2** : 393–396.

85. ———, 1848, Description of an upright Lepidodendron with Stigmaria roots in the roof of the Sydney main coal in the Island of Breton, *Geol. Soc. London Quart. Jour.*, **4** : 46–50.

86. ———, 1849, Description of erect Sigillariae with conical tap roots found in the roof of the Sydney main coal in the Island of Cape Breton, *Geol. Soc. London Quart. Jour.*, **5** : 354–360.

87. BROWN, T. C., 1913, Notes on the origin of certain Paleozoic sediments, illustrated by the Cambrian and Ordovician rocks of Center County, Pennsylvania, *Jour. Geology*, **21** : 232–250.

88. BRYAN, K., 1929, Solution-facetted limestone pebbles, *Am. Jour. Sci.* (5) **18** : 193–208.

89. ———, 1931, Wind-worn stones or ventifacts—a discussion and bibliography, *Nat. Research Council, Reprint and Circ. Ser.* 98, *Rept. Comm. Sedimentation*, pp. 29–50.

90. ———, 1936, Geologic features in New England ground water supply, *New England Water Works Assoc. Jour.*, **50** : 222–228.

91. ———, 1946, Letter and comment, *Military Engineer*, **38**: 168.

92. ——, 1946a, Cryopedology—the study of frozen ground and intensive frost-action with suggestions on nomenclature, Am. Jour. Sci., **244**: 622–642.

93. —— and R. L. NICHOLS, 1939, Discussion: wind-deposition shorelines, Jour. Geology, **47**: 431–435.

94. BUCHER, W. H., 1917, Large current-ripples as indicators of paleogeography, Nat. Acad. Sci. Proc., **3**: 285–291.

95. ——, 1919, On ripples and related sedimentary surface forms and their paleogeographic interpretation, Am. Jour. Sci. (4) **47**: 149–210, 241–269.

96. ——, 1938, Key to papers published by an institute for the study of modern sediments in shallow seas, Jour. Geology, **46**: 726–755.

97. BUCKLAND, W., 1842, On recent and fossil semi-circular cavities caused by air-bubbles on the surface of soft clay, and resembling impressions of rain-drops, Rept. British Assoc., Tr. Sect., p, 57.

98. ——, 1842a, Notice of perforations in limestone, Rept. British Assoc., Tr. Sect., p. 57.

99. BUDDINGTON, A. F., 1926, Submarine pillow lavas of southeastern Alaska, Jour. Geology, **34**: 824–828.

100. ——, 1936, Gravity stratification as a criterion in the interpretation of the structure of certain intrusives of the northwestern Adirondacks, 16th Int. Geol. Cong. 1933 Rept., **1**: 347–352.

101. BURLING, L. D., 1916, Ellipsoidal lavas in the Glacier National Park, Montana, Jour. Geology, **24**: 235–237.

102. ——, 1917, Protichnites and Climactichnites; a critical study of some Cambrian trails, Am. Jour. Sci. (4) **44**: 387–398.

103. ——, 1917a, Criteria of attitude in bedded deposits [Abstract], Bull. Geol. Soc. Am., **28**: 208.

104. BURR, H. T., 1901, The structural relations of the amygdaloidal melaphyr in Brookline, Newton, and Brighton, Mass., Bull. Mus. Comp. Zoology (Harvard), **38** (g.s. 5): 53–69.

105. BURROWS, A. G., and H. C. RICKABY, 1935, Sudbury nickel field restudied, Ontario Dept. Mines, **43** (2): 1–49.

106. BURWASH, E. M. J., 1938, The deposition and alteration of varved clays, Royal Canadian Inst. Trans., **22**(47): 3–6.

107. BUTLER, A. J., 1904, The stratigraphy of the Wenlock limestone of Dudley, Geol. Soc. London Quart. Jour., **95**: 37–74.

108. BUTLER, B. S., W. S. BURBANK, et al., 1929, The copper deposits of Michigan, U.S. Geol. Survey Prof. Paper, **144**: 1–238.

109. CALKINS, F. C., 1941, "Band," "layer," and some kindred terms, Econ. Geology, **36**: 345–349.

110. CAMPBELL, I., and J. H. MAXSON, 1933, Some observations on the Archean metamorphics of the Grand Canyon, Nat. Acad. Sci. Proc., **19**: 806–809; Abstract, Science (n.s.), **77**: 460.

111. CAMPBELL, M. R., 1904, Conglomerate dikes in southern Arizona, Am. Geologist, **33**: 135–138.

112. CAPPS, S. R., 1915, Some ellipsoidal lavas on Prince William Sound, Alaska, Jour. Geology, **23**: 45–51.

113. CARMAN, J. E., 1927, Fossil footprints from the Pennsylvanian system in Ohio, Bull. Geol. Soc. Am., **38**: 385–396.

114. CARRUTHERS, R. G., 1939, On northern glacial drifts: some peculiarities and their significance, Geol. Soc. London Quart. Jour., **95**: 299–333.

115. CASE, E. C., 1895, Mud and sand dikes of the White River Eocene, *Am. Geologist*, **15**: 248–254.

116. CHADWICK, G. H., 1940, Columnar limestone produced by sun-cracking [Abstract], *Bull. Geol. Soc. Am.*, **51**: 1923.

117. CHAPMAN, W. M., 1936, A study of feldspar twinning in a differentiated sill, *Am. Mineralogist*, **21**: 33–57.

118. CLAPP, C. H., 1921, Geology of the igneous rocks of Essex County, Massachusetts , *Bull. U.S. Geol. Survey*, **704**: 1–132.

119. CLARK, B. L., 1937, Correlation as based on the Mollusca [Abstract], *Geol. Soc. Am. Proc.*, **1936**: 389.

120. CLARK, T. H., 1923, Aspidella-like markings from the Cambridge slate, *Boston Soc. Nat. History Proc.*, **36**: 482–485.

121. CLARKE, E. DE C., and C. TEICHERT, 1946, Algal studies in a western Australia salt lake, *Am. Jour. Sci.*, **244**: 271–276.

122. CLARKE, J. M., 1900, The Oriskany fauna of Becraft Mountain, Columbia Co., N.Y., *N.Y. State Mus. Mem.*, **3**: 5–128.

123. ———, 1907, An interesting style of sand-filled vein, *Bull. N.Y. State Mus.*, **107**: 293–294.

124. ———, 1914, Illustrations of intraformational corrugation [Abstract and Discussion], *Bull. Geol. Soc. Am.*, **25**: 37.

125. ———, 1918, Strand and undertow markings of Upper Devonian time as indicators of the prevailing climate, *Bull. N.Y. State Mus.*, **196**: 199–238 (Abstract, *Bull. Geol. Soc. Am.*, **29**: 83).

126. CLEMENTS, J. M., H. L. SMYTH, W. S. BAYLEY, and C. R. VAN HISE, 1899, The Crystal Falls iron-bearing district of Michigan, *U.S. Geol. Survey Ann. Rept.*, **19** (3): 1–151.

126a. CLOOS, E., 1947, Oölite deformation in the South Mountain fold, Maryland, *Bull. Geol. Soc. Am.*, **58**: 843–918.

127. CLOOS, H., and H. MARTIN, 1932, Der Gang einer Falte, *Fortschr. Geologie*, **11**.

128. CLOUD, P. E., 1942, Notes on stromatolites, *Am. Jour. Sci.*, **240**: 363–379.

129. COATS, R. R., 1936, Primary banding in basic plutonic rocks, *Jour. Geology*, **44**: 407–419.

130. COFFEY, G. N., 1909, Clay dunes [southern Texas]; *Jour, Geology*, **17**: 754–755.

131. COLEMAN, A. P., 1905, The Sudbury nickel field, *Ontario Bureau Mines*, **14** (3): 1–188.

132. ———, 1914, The Pre-Cambrian rocks north of Lake Huron, with special reference to the Sudbury series, *Ontario Bureau Mines Ann. Rept.*, **23**: 202–236.

133. ———, 1926, "Ice Ages, Recent and Ancient," The Macmillan Company, New York. 296 pp.

134. COLLETT, J., 1883, Geological Survey of Newton Co., Indiana, *Indiana Dept. Geol. Nat. History Ann. Rept.*, **12**: 48–64.

135. COLLINS, W. H., 1925, North Shore of Lake Huron, *Geol. Survey Canada Mem.*, **143**: 1–160.

136. COLTON, H. S., and C. F. PARK, JR., 1930, Anosma or "squeeze-ups," *Science*, **72**: 579.

137. CONRAD, V., 1946, Polygon nets and their physical development, *Am. Jour. Sci.*, **244**: 277–296.

138. COOKE, C. W., 1926, The Cenozoic formations in Geology of Alabama, *Alabama Geol. Survey Special Rept.*, **14**: 1–312.

139. ———, 1943, Geology of the Coastal Plain of Georgia, *Bull. U.S. Geol. Survey*, **941**: 1–121.

140. COOKE, H. C., 1931, Anomalous grain relationship in the Caldwell quartzites of Thetford District, Quebec, *Royal Soc. Canada Proc. Trans.* (3) **25**: 71–74.

141. ———, W. F. JAMES, and J. B. MAWDSLEY, 1931, Geology and ore deposits of Rouyn-Harricanaw Region, Quebec, *Geol. Survey Canada Mem.*, **166**: 1–314.

142. COOPER, G. A., 1936–1937, Brachiopod ecology and paleoecology, *Nat. Research Council, Div. Geology and Geography Rept. Comm. Paleoecology*, **1936–1937**: 26–53.

143. COPE, F. W., 1946, Intraformational contorted rocks in the Upper Carboniferous of the Southern Pennines, *Geol. Soc. London Quart. Jour.*, **101**: 139–176.

144. CORBETT, C. S., 1937, Cross-bedding and formation thickness determinations, *Jour. Geology*, **45**: 89–94.

145. Cox, G. H., and C. L. DAKE, 1916, Geological criteria for determining the structural position of sedimentary beds, *Bull. Missouri Univ. School Mines*, **2** (4): 1–59.

146. CRONEIS, C., 1930, Geology of the Arkansas Paleozoic area, with special reference to oil and gas possibilities, *Bull. Arkansas Geol. Survey*, **3**: 1–457.

147. ——— and H. W. SCOTT, 1933, Scolecodonts and Conodonts from fissure fillings in the Niagaran of Illinois [Abstract], *Bull. Geol. Soc. Am.*, **44**: 207–208.

148. CROSBY, W. O., 1899, Archean-Cambrian contact near Manitou, Colorado, *Bull. Geol. Soc. Am.*, **10**: 141–164.

149. CROSS, C. W., 1894, Intrusive sandstone dikes in granite, *Bull. Geol. Soc. Am.*, **5**: 225–230.

150. CULBERTSON, G., 1903, Ripple marks in Hudson limestone of Jefferson Co., Indiana, *Indiana Acad. Sci. Proc.*, **1902**: 202–205.

151. CULLISON, J. S., 1937, Origin and structural relationships of incomplete internal moulds, *Geol. Soc. Am. Proc.*, **1936**: 69.

152. ———, 1938, Origin of composite and incomplete internal moulds and their possible use as criteria of structure, *Bull. Geol. Soc. Am.*, **49**: 981–988.

153. CUMINGS, E. R., 1932, Reefs or bioherms, *Bull. Geol. Soc. Am.*, **43**: 331–352.

154. ——— and R. R. SHROCK, 1928, Niagaran coral reefs of Indiana and adjacent states and their stratigraphic relations, *Bull. Geol. Soc. Am.*, **39**: 579–620.

155. ——— and ———, 1928a, The geology of the Silurian rocks of northern Indiana, *Indiana Div. Geology, Conservation Comm., Pub.*, **75**: 1–226.

156. DALE, T. N., 1893, The Rensselaer grit plateau in New York, *U.S. Geol. Survey Ann. Rept.*, **13**(2): 291–340.

157. ———, 1896, 1902, Structural details in the Green Mountain region and in eastern New York, *U.S. Geol. Survey Ann. Rept.*, **16** (1): 543–570, 1896; *Bull. U.S. Geol. Survey*, **195**: 9–22, 1902.

158. DALY, R. A., 1903, Variolitic pillow lava from Newfoundland, *Am. Geologist*, **32**: 62–78.

159. ———, 1912, Geology of the North American Cordillera at the 49th Parallel; *Geol. Survey Canada Dept. Mines Mem.*, **38**: 1–857 (in 3 parts).

160. ———, 1917, Metamorphism and its phases, *Bull. Geol. Soc. Am.*, **28**: 126–127 (Abstract), 375–418.

161. ———, 1933, "Igneous Rocks and the Depths of the Earth," 2d ed., McGraw Hill Book Company, Inc., New York. 598 pp.

162. DANA, J. D., 1845, Origin of the constituent and adventitious minerals of **trap** and the allied rocks, *Am. Jour. Sci.*, **49**: 59–64.

163. DANE, C. H., and W. G. PIERCE, 1934, Fossil sink holes in Cretaceous beds **of** Prowers County, Colorado, *Bull. Am. Assoc. Petroleum Geologists*, **18**: 1493–1505.

164. DANNENBERG, A., 1915, "Geologie der Steinkohlenlager," Vol. I, Parts II and III, Verlagsbuchhandlung Gebrüder Borntraeger, Berlin.

165. DAPPLES, E. C., 1938, The sedimentational effects of the work of marine scavengers, Am. Jour. Sci. (5) 36 : 54–65.

166. ————, 1942, The effect of macro-organisms upon near-shore marine sediments, Jour. Sedimentary Petrology, 12 : 118–126.

167. DARWIN, C., 1860, "Journal of Researches during the Voyage of H.M.S. 'Beagle,' " Thomas Nelson & Sons, Ltd., London.   543 pp.

168. DAVIS, E. F., 1918, The radiolarian cherts of the Franciscan group, Univ. California Pub. Bull. Dept. Geology, 11 : 235–432.

169. DAVIS, W. M., 1880, Banded amygdules of the Brighton amygdaloid, Boston Soc. Nat. History Proc., 24 : 426–428.

170. ————, 1890, Structure and origin of glacial sand plains, Bull. Geol. Soc. Am., 1 : 195–202.

171. DAWSON, J. W., 1851, Notice of the occurrence of upright Calamites near Pictou, N.S., Geol. Soc. London Quart. Jour., 7 : 194–196.

172. ————, 1855, 1868, "Acadian Geology," Oliver and Boyd, Edinburgh, 1855; 2d ed., Macmillan & Company, Ltd., London, 1868.   694 pp.

173. ————, 1861, On an erect Sigillaria from the South Joggins, Nova Scotia, Geol. Soc. London Quart. Jour., 17 : 522–524; Canadian Naturalist, 7 : 106–111.

174. DAY, A. E., 1928, Pipes in the coast sandstone of Syria, Geol. Mag., 65 : 412–415.

175. DEANE, J., 1844, On the fossil footmarks of Turner's Falls, Massachusetts, Am. Jour. Sci., 46 : 73–77.

176. ————, 1845, Fossil footmarks and raindrops, Am. Jour. Sci., 49 : 213–215.

177. ————, 1861, "Ichnographs from the Sandstone of Connecticut River," Boston. 61 pp.

178. DECKER, C. E., 1920, "Studies in Minor Folds," University of Chicago Press, Chicago.   89 pp.

179. DEELEY, R. M., 1916, Trail and underplight, Geol. Mag., 3 : 2–5.

180. DERRY, D. R., 1939, Some examples of detailed structure in early pre-Cambrian rocks of Canada, Geol. Soc. London Quart. Jour., 95 : 109–133.

181. DESOR, E., 1850, 1852, [On the probable origin of so-called fossil raindrops] Raindrop impressions, etc., Boston Soc. Nat. History Proc., 3 : 200–202, 1850, 4 : 131–132, 1852.

182. DEWEY, H., and J. S. FLEET, 1911, On some British pillow-lavas and the rocks associated with them, Geol. Mag., 48 : 241–246.

183. DILLER, J. S., 1890, Sandstone dikes [with discussion by W. M. Davis and B. K. Emerson], Bull. Geol. Soc. Am., 1 : 411–442.

184. DINES, H. G., S. E. HOLLINGWORTH, W. EDWARDS, S. BUCHAN, and F. B. A. WELCH, 1940, The mapping of Head deposits, Geol. Mag., 77 : 198–226.

185. DOUGLAS, G. V., R. L. MILNER, and J. MACLEAN, 1937, The deposition of the Halifax series, Nova Scotian Dept. Pub. Works and Mines Ann. Rept., 1937(2): 34–45.

186. DUNBAR, C. O., 1924, Kansas Permian insects.   Part I.   The geologic occurrence and the environment of the insects, Am. Jour. Sci. (5) 7 : 171–209.

187. DU TOIT, A. L., 1907, Pipe amygdaloids, Geol. Mag. (5) 4 : 4–17.

188. ————, 1939, "The Geology of South Africa," 2d ed., Oliver and Boyd, Edinburgh and London.   539 pp.

189. DUNN, E. J., 1896, Reports on the Bendigo goldfield (Nos. I and II); Dept. Mines Victoria Special Rept.

190. EARDLEY, A. J., 1938, Sediments of Great Salt Lake, Utah, *Bull. Am. Assoc. Petroleum Geologists*, **22**: 1305–1411.

191. EARP, J. R., 1938, The higher Silurian rocks of the Kerry District, Montgomeryshire, *Geol. Soc. London Quart Jour.*, **94**: 125–160.

192. ELDRIDGE, G. H., 1906, The formation of asphalt veins, *Econ. Geology*, **1**: 437–444.

193. ELIAS, M. K., 1937, Evolutionary series versus species-range method in stratigraphic paleontology [Abstract], *Geol. Soc. Am. Proc.*, **1936**: 374.

194. ELLES, G. L., and C. E. TILLEY, 1930, Metamorphism in relation to structure in the Scottish Highlands, *Royal Soc. Edinburgh Trans.*, **56**: 621–646.

195. ELLISON, S. P., JR., 1946, Conodonts as Paleozoic guide fossils, *Bull. Am. Assoc. Petroleum Geologists*, **30**: 93–110.

196. ELSTON, E. D., 1917–1918, Potholes: their variety, origin and significance, *Sci. Monthly*, December, **1917**: 554–567, January, **1918**: 37–51.

197. EMERSON, B. K., 1897, Diabase pitchstone and mud enclosures of the Triassic trap of New England, *Bull. Geol. Soc. Am.*, **8**: 59–86.

198. ———, 1905, Plumose diabase and palagonite from the Holyoke trap sheet [with discussion by A. C. Lane], *Bull. Geol. Soc. Am.*, **16**: 91–130.

199. ———, 1916, Description of large cylinders of scoriaceous diabase in the normal Holyoke diabase, *Am. Jour. Sci.* (4) **41**: 321–322.

200. EMERY, K. O., 1941, Transportation of rock particles by sea-mammals, *Jour. Sedimentary Petrology*, **11**: 92–93.

201. ———, 1944, Beach markings made by sand hoppers, *Jour. Sedimentary Petrology*, **14**: 26–28.

202. ———, and R. H. TSCHUDY, 1941, Transportation of rock by kelp, *Bull. Geol. Soc. Am.*, **52**: 855–862.

203. EMMONS, R. C., 1927, Diabase differentiation, *Am. Jour. Sci.* (5) **13**: 73–82.

204. EMMONS, W. H., G. A. THIEL, C. R. STAUFFER, and I. S. ALLISON, 1939, "Geology," 2d ed., McGraw-Hill Book Company, Inc., New York. 451 pp.

205. ESKOLA, P., 1920, The mineral facies of rocks, *Norsk geol. tidsskr.*, **6**: 141–194.

206. EVANS, O. F., 1941, The classification of wave-formed ripple marks, *Jour. Sedimentary Petrology*, **11**: 37–41.

207. FACKLER, W. C., 1941, Clastic crevice fillings in the Keweenawan lavas, *Jour. Geology*, **49**: 550–556.

208. FAIRBAIRN, H. W., 1932, Structure and metamorphism of Brome County, Quebec, Ph. D. thesis, Harvard University (Geology), unpublished.

209. ———, 1935, Notes on the mechanics of rock foliation, *Jour. Geology*, **43**: 591–608.

210. ———, 1936, Elongation in deformed rocks, *Jour. Geology*, **44**: 670–680.

211. ———, 1942, "Structural Petrology of Deformed Rocks," Addison-Wesley Press, Inc., Cambridge, Mass., 143 pp.

212. ———, 1944, The relations of the Sudbury series to the Bruce series in the vicinity of Sudbury, *Ontario Dept. Mines 15th Ann. Rept.*, **50** (6): 1–13.

213. ———, and G. M. ROBSON, 1944, Breccia at Sudbury, *Ontario Dept. Mines 15th Ann Rept.*, **50** (6): 18–33.

214. FAIRBRIDGE, R. W., 1946, Submarine slumping and location of oil bodies, *Bull. Am. Assoc. Petroleum Geologist*, **30**: 84–92.

215. FAIRCHILD, H. L., 1901, Beach structure in Medina sandstone, *Am. Geologist*, **28**: 9–14.

216. FARMIN, R., 1934, "Pebble dikes" and associated mineralization at Tintic, Utah, *Econ. Geology*, **29** : 356–370.

217. FENNER, C. N., 1926, The Katmai magmatic province, *Jour. Geology*, **34** : 675–772.

218. FENTON, C. L., 1918, A prominent mud-crack horizon of the Cedar Valley stage of the Iowa Devonian, *Ottawa Naturalist*, **32** : 113–115.

219. ———, 1931, Niagaran stromatoporoid reefs of the Chicago region, *Am. Midland Naturalist*, **12** : 203–212.

220. ———, and M. A. FENTON, 1931, Algae and algal beds in the Belt series of Glacier National Park, *Jour. Geology*, **39** : 670–686.

221. ——— and ———, 1933, Hail prints and mud cracks of Proterozoic age, *Science*, **77** : 491.

222. ——— and ———, 1933a, Algal reefs or bioherms in the Belt series of Montana, *Bull. Geol. Soc. Am.*, **44** : 1135–1142.

223. ——— and ———, 1936, Walcott's "Pre-Cambrian Algonkian Algal Flora" and associated animals, *Bull. Geol. Soc. Am.*, **47** : 609–620.

224. ——— and ———, 1937, Cambrian calcareous algae from Pennsylvania, *Am. Midland Naturalist*, **18** : 435–441.

225. ——— and ———, 1937a, Collecting fossil algae of the Canadian Rockies, *Sci. Monthly*, **44** : 497–508.

226. ——— and ———, 1937b, Belt series of the north: stratigraphy, sedimentation, paleontology, *Bull. Geol. Soc. Am.*, **48** : 1873–1970.

227. ——— and ———, 1939, Pre-Cambrian and Paleozoic algae, *Bull. Geol. Soc. Am.*, **50** : 89–126.

228. FIEDLER, A. G., and S. S. NYE, 1933, Geology and ground-water resources of the Roswell artesian basin, New Mexico, *U.S. Geol. Survey Water Supply Paper*, **639** : 1–372.

229. FIELD, R. M., 1916, A preliminary paper on the origin and classification of intraformational conglomerates and breccias, *Ottawa Naturalist*, **30** : 29–36, 47–52, 58–66.

230. FINCH, R. H., 1926, Ancient volcanoes, *Volcano Letter, Hawaiian Volcano Research Assoc.*, **75**.

231. FORRESTER, J. D., 1946, "Principles of Field and Mining Geology," John Wiley & Sons, Inc., New York. 647 pp.

232. FOWLER, G. M., J. P. LYDEN, F. E. GREGORY, and W. M. AGAR, 1934, Chertification in the Tri-State (Oklahoma-Kansas-Missouri) mining district, *Am. Inst. Min. Eng. Tech. Pub.*, **532** : 1–50.

233. FOYE, W. G., 1924, Pillow structure in Triassic basalts of Connecticut, *Bull. Geol. Soc. Am.*, **35** : 329–346.

234. FRASCHE, D. F., 1941, Origin of the Surigao iron ores, *Econ. Geology*, **36** : 280–305.

235. FRASER, H. J., 1929, An experimental study of varve deposition, *Royal Soc. Canada Trans.* (3) **23** (4) : 49–60.

236. FUCHS, T., 1895, Studien über Fucoiden und Hieroglyphen, *K. Akad. Wiss., Wien*, **62** : 369–448.

237. FULLER, R. E., 1931, Evidence on the gravitational accumulation of olivine during the advance of a basaltic flow [Abstract], *Bull Geol. Soc. Am.*, **42** : 190.

238. ———, 1931a, The aqueous chilling of basaltic lava on the Columbia River Plateau, *Am. Jour. Sci.* (5) **21** : 281–300.

239. ———, 1931b, The geomorphology and volcanic sequence of Steens Mountain in southeastern Oregon, *Univ. Washington Pub. Geology*, **3** (1) : 1–130.

240. ———, 1932, Tensional surface features of certain basaltic ellipsoids, *Jour. Geology*, **40**: 164–170.

241. ———, 1934, Structural features in the Columbia River lavas of Central Washington—a criticism, *Jour. Geology*, **42**: 311–320.

242. ———, 1939, Gravitational accumulation of olivine during the advance of basaltic flows, *Jour. Geology*, **47**: 303–313.

243. GALLOWAY, J. J., 1926, Methods of correlation by means of Foraminifera, *Bull. Am. Assoc. Petroleum Geologists*, **10**: 562–567.

244. GEIKIE, J., 1940, "Structural and Field Geology," "5th ed., revised by R. Campbell and R. M. Craig, Oliver and Boyd, Edinburgh and London. 395 pp.

245. GEINITZ, E., 1911, Ripplemarks auf Ziegesteinen, *Centralbl. Mineralogie*, etc., **1911** (20): 640–642.

246. GILBERT, G. K., 1880, Report on the geology of the Henry Mountains [Utah], *U.S. Geog. and Geolog. Survey Rocky Mtn. Region* (Powell), pp. 1–160, 1877, 2d ed., pp 1–170, 1880.

247. ———, 1880*a*, Ripple-marks [Abstract], *Bull. Philos. Soc. Washington*, **2**: 61–62.

248. ———, 1884, Ripple-marks, *Science*, **3**: 375–376.

249. ———, 1899, Ripple marks and cross bedding, *Bull. Geol. Soc. Am.*, **10**: 135–140.

250. ———, 1914, The transportation of debris by running water, *U.S. Geol. Survey Prof. Paper*, **86**: 1–263.

251. GLENN, L. C., 1904, Fossiliferous sandstone dikes in the Eocene of Tennessee and Kentucky [Abstract], *Science* (n.s.), **19**: 522.

251*a*. GOLDICH, S. S., and H. R. Berquist, 1947, Aluminous lateritic soil of the Sierra de Bahoruco area, Dominican Republic, *Bull. U.S. Geol. Survey*, **953** (*C*): 53–84.

252. GOLDMAN, M. I., 1940, Stylolites, *Jour. Sedimentary Petrology*, **10**: 146–147.

253. GOLDRING, W., 1938, Algal barrier reefs in the Lower Ozarkian of New York with a chapter on the importance of coralline algae as reef builders through the ages, *Bull. N.Y. State Mus.*, **315**: 1–75.

254. GRABAU, A. W., 1900, Siluro-Devonic contact in Erie Co., New York, *Bull. Geol. Soc. Am.*, **11**: 347–376.

255. ———, 1901, A guide to the geology and paleontology of Niagara Falls and vicinity, *Bull. N.Y. State Mus.*, **45**: 1–284.

256. ———, 1903, Paleozoic coral reefs, *Bull. Geol. Soc. Am.*, **14**: 337–352.

257. ———, 1905, Physical characters and history of some New York formations, *Science* (n.s.), **22**: 528–525.

258. ———, 1907, Types of cross-bedding and their stratigraphic significance [Abstract], *Science* (n.s.), **25**: 296.

259. ———, 1913, Early Paleozoic delta deposits of North America, *Bull. Geol. Soc. Am.*, **24**: 399–528.

260. ———, 1920, "Principles of Salt Deposition," McGraw-Hill Book Company, Inc., New York. 435 pp.

261. ———, 1921, "A Textbook of Geology," Part II. Historical Geology, D. C. Heath and Company, Boston. 976 pp.

262. ———, 1924, "Principles of Stratigraphy," 2d ed., A. G. Seiler, New York. 1185 pp.

263. GREENLY, E., 1900, On sandstone pipes in the Carboniferous limestone at Dwlban Point, East Anglesey, *Geol. Mag.*, **7**: 20–24.

264. GRESLEY, W. S., 1898, Clay veins vertically intersecting coal measures, *Bull. Geol. Soc. Am.*, **9**: 35–58.

265. GRISWOLD, L. S., 1892, Whetstones and the Novaculites of Arkansas, *Arkansas Geol. Survey Ann. Rept.* 1890, **3**: 1–443.

266. GROUT, F. F., 1932, "Petrography and Petrology," McGraw-Hill Book Company, Inc., New York. 522 pp.

267. GRUBENMANN, U., 1910, "Die Kristallinen Schiefer," 2d ed., Verlagsbuchhandlung-Gebrüder Borntraeger, Berlin. 298 pp.

268. GRUNER, J. W. (with C. E. Dutton, G. R. Gibson, and F. F. Grout as contributors), 1941, Structural geology of the Knife Lake area of northeastern Minnesota, *Bull. Geol. Soc. Am.*, **52**: 1577–1642.

269. GUNNING, H. C., and J. W. AMBROSE, 1940, Malartic Area, Quebec, *Geol. Survey Canada Mem.*, **222** (*Pub.* 2454), pp. 1-142.

270. HADDING, A., 1929, The Pre-Quaternary Sedimentary Rocks of Sweden, III. The Paleozoic and Mesozoic sandstones of Sweden, *Lunds Geol.-Mineralog. Inst., Meddelanden*, **41**: 1–287 [*Lunds Univ. Årsskrift, N.F. Avd* 2, **25** (3): 1–287; *Kungl. Fysiograf. Sällskapets Handl. N. F.*, **40** (3): 1–287].

271. ———, 1932, On subaqueous slides, *Lunds Geol. Mineralog. Inst., Meddelanden*, **47**: 377–393 [reprinted from *Geol. Fören. Förh.*, **53** (4): 377–393].

272. HAENTZSCHEL, W., 1938, Bau und Bildung von Gros-Rippeln in Wattenmeer, *Senckenberg., Naturf. Gesell. Abh.*, **20**: 1–42.

273. HAHN, F. F., 1913, Untermeerische Gleitung bei Trenton Falls (Nordamerika) und ihr Verhältnis zu Ähnlichen Störungsbilden, *Neues Jahrb. Mineral., Geol.*, etc., **36**: 1–41.

274. HALL, J., 1843, Geology of New York," Part IV, comprising the survey of the Fourth Geological District, Albany. 683 pp.

275. ———, 1843*a*, Remarks upon casts of mud furrows, wave lines, and other markings upon rocks of the New York system, *Assoc. Am. Geol. Rept.*, pp. 422–432.

276. ———, 1843*b*, On wave lines and casts of mud furrows [Abstract], *Am. Jour. Sci.*, **45**: 148–149.

277. ———, 1852, Descriptions of the organic remains of the New York system, *Paleontology N.Y.*, **2**: 1–362.

278. HAPP, S. C., 1945, Sedimentation in South Carolina Piedmont valley, *Am. Jour. Sci.*, **243**: 114–126.

279. HARKER, A., 1909, "The Natural History of Igneous Rocks," The Macmillan Company, New York. 384 pp.

280. ———, 1939, Metamorphism—a study of the transformations of rock-masses, Methuen & Co., Ltd., London. 362 pp.

281. HART, R. C., and J. E. HAWLEY, 1934, Cylindrical structures in basal Paleozoic sandstones near Kingston, Ontario [Abstract], *Geol. Soc. Am. Proc.*, **1933**: 85–86.

282. HARTNAGEL, C. A., 1903, Preliminary observations on the Cobleskill ("Coralline") limestone of New York, *Bull. N.Y. State Mus.*, **69**: 1109–1175.

283. HAWLEY, J. E., and R. C. HART, 1934, Cylindrical structures in sandstones, *Bull. Geol. Soc. Am.*, **45**: 1017–1034.

284. HAY, R., 1892, Sandstone dikes in northwestern Nebraska, *Bull. Geol. Soc. Am.*, **3**: 50–55.

285. HEDBERG, H., 1926, Effect of differential compaction on structure of sedimentary rocks, *Bull. Am. Assoc. Petroleum Geologists*, **10**: 1035–1072.

286. ———, 1936, Gravitational compaction of clays and shales, *Am. Jour. Sci.* (5) **31**: 241–287.

287. HEIM, A., 1878, "Mechanismus der Gebirgsbildung," Vol. II.

288. ———, 1908, Über rezente und fossile subaquatische Rutschungen und deren lithologische Bedeutung, *Neues Jahrb. Mineral., Geol.*, etc., **2**: 136–157.

289. HENDERSON, S. M. K., 1935, Ordovician submarine disturbances in the Girvan district, *Royal Soc. Edinburgh Trans.*, **58** (2): 487–509.

290. HENKE, W., 1911, Wirkungen des Gebirgsdrucks auf devonische Gesteine, *Zeitschr. deut. geol. Ges.*, **2**: 98–110.

291. HILLS, E. S., 1940, "Outlines of Structural Geology," Methuen & Co., Ltd., London, 2d ed. (1943). 172 pp.

292. ———, 1941, The Silurian rocks of the Studley Park district, *Royal Soc. Victoria Proc.*, **53** (1): 167–191.

293. ———, and D. E. THOMAS, 1945, Fissuring in sandstones, *Econ. Geology*, **40**: 51–61.

294. HITCHCOCK, E., 1844, Report on ichnolithology or fossil footmarks with descriptions of several new species and the coprolites of birds, etc., *Am. Jour. Sci.*, **47**: 292–322.

295. ———, 1848, An attempt to discriminate and describe the animals that made the fossil footmarks of the United States and especially of New England, *Am. Acad. Arts Mem. (n.s.)*, **3**: 129–256.

296. ———, 1858, Ichnology of New England, William White, Printer to the State, Boston.

297. HOBBS, W. H., 1906, Guadix formation of Granada, Spain, *Bull. Geol. Soc. Am.*, **17**: 285–294.

298. ———, 1907, "Earthquakes—an introduction to seismic geology," D. Appleton-Century Company, New York. 336 pp.

299. HODGES, R. B., 1928, Pisolites, *Volcano Letter, Hawaiian Volcano Research Assoc.*, **182**.

300. HOFFMAN, M. G., 1933, Structural features in the Columbia River lavas of central Washington, *Jour. Geology*, **41**: 184–195.

301. ———, 1934, Reply [Structural features in the Columbia River lavas of central Washington], *Jour. Geology*, **42**: 320–328.

302. HOLMES, W. H., 1879, Fossil forests of the volcanic Tertiary formations of the Yellowstone National Park, *Bull. U.S. Geol. and Geog. Survey Terr. (Hayden)*, **5**: 125–132.

303. HORE, R. E., 1913, Ripple-marked Huronian quartzite at Nipissing Mine, Cobalt, Ontario, *Michigan Acad. Sci. Rept.*, **15**: 59.

304. HOVEY, E. O., 1902, Martinique and St. Vincent; a preliminary report upon the eruption of 1902, *Bull. Am. Mus. Nat. History*, **16**: 333–372.

305. HUDSON, G. H., 1910, Joint caves of Valcour Island—their age and their origin, *Bull. N.Y. State Mus.*, **140**: 161–196.

306. HUGHES, T. M'KENNY, 1884, On some tracks of terrestrial and freshwater animals, *Geol. Soc. London Quart. Jour.*, **40**: 178–186.

307. HYDE, J. E., 1908, Desiccation conglomerates in the Coal Measures limestone of Ohio, *Am. Jour. Sci.* (4) **25**: 400–408.

308. ———, 1911, Notes on the absence of a soil bed at the base of the Pennsylvanian of southern Ohio, *Am. Jour. Sci.* (4) **31**: 557–560.

309. ———, 1911a, The ripples of the Bedford and Berea formations of central and southern Ohio, with notes on the palaeogeography of that epoch, *Jour. Geology*, **19**: 257–269.

310. INGERSON, E., 1939, 1940. Fabric criteria for distinguishing pseudo ripple marks from ripple marks [Abstract], *Bull. Geol. Soc. Am.*, **50**: 1953, 1939, **51**: 557–569, 1940.

311. JAGGAR, T. A., JR., 1894, Some conditions for ripple mark, *Am. Geologist*, **13**: 199–201.

312. ———, 1917, Lava flow from Mauna Loa, 1916, *Am. Jour. Sci.*, (4) **43**: 255–288.

313. ———, 1917a, On the terms aphrolith and dermolith, *Washington Acad. Sci. Jour.*, **7**: 277–281.

314. ———, 1931, Lava stalactites, stalagmites, toes, and "squeeze-ups," *Volcano Letter*, **345**: 1–4.

315. JAMES, L. F., 1884, The fucoids of the Cincinnati group, *Cincinnati Soc. Nat. History Jour.*, **7**: 124–132, 151–166.

316. JEFFREYS, H., 1935, "Earthquakes and Mountains," Methuen & Co., Ltd., London. 183 pp.

317. JENKINS, O. P., 1925, Clastic dikes of southeastern Washington [Abstract], *Bull. Geol. Soc. Am.*, **36**: 202.

318. ———, 1925a, Mechanics of clastic dike intrusion, *Eng. and Min. Jour.-Press*, **120**: 12.

319. ———, 1925b, Clastic dikes of eastern Washington and their geologic significance, *Am. Jour. Sci.* (5) **10**: 234–246.

320. JOHNSON, D. W., 1916, Contributions to the study of ripple marks, *Jour. Geology*, **24**: 809–819.

321. JOHNSON, J. H., 1940, Lime-secreting algae and algal limestones from the Pennsylvanian of central Colorado, *Bull. Geol. Soc. Am.*, **51**: 571–596.

322. JOHNSTON, W. A., 1915, Rainy River district, Ont.; surficial geology and soils, *Geol. Survey Canada Mem.*, **82**: 1–123.

323. ———, 1921, Sedimentation of the Fraser River delta, *Geol. Survey Canada Mem.*, **125**: 1–46.

324. ———, 1922, The character of the stratification of the sediments in the recent delta of Fraser River, British Columbia, Canada, *Jour. Geology*, **30**: 115–129.

325. ———, 1922a, Sedimentation in Lake Louise, Alberta, Canada, *Am. Jour. Sci.* (5) **4**: 376–386.

326. ———, 1922b, Imbricated structure in river gravels, *Am. Jour. Sci.* (5) **4**: 387–390.

327. JONES, A., 1943, Classification of lava-surfaces, *Am. Geophys. Union Trans.*, **1943**: 265–268.

328. JONES, O. T., 1940, The geology of the Colwyn Bay district: a study of submarine slumping during the Salopian period, *Geol. Soc. London Quart. Jour.*, **95**: 335–382.

329. JUKES, J. B., 1872, "The Student's Manual of Geology" (edited by A. Geikie), A. & C. Black, Ltd., London. 778 pp.

330. JULIEN, A. A., 1901, A study of the structure of fulgurites, *Jour. Geology*, **9**: 673–693.

331. KAY, G. F., 1931, Classification and duration of the Pleistocene period, *Bull. Geol. Soc. Am.*, **42**: 425–466.

332. ——— and E. T. APFEL, 1929, The pre-Illinoian Pleistocene geology of Iowa, *Iowa Geol. Survey*, **34**: 1–304.

333. ——— and J. N. PEARCE, 1920, The origin of gumbotil, *Jour. Geology*, **28**: 89–125.

334. KEEN, M. A., 1937, Percentage method of correlation [Abstract], *Geol. Soc. Am. Proc.*, **1936**: 390–391.

335. ———, 1937a, Statistical methods applied to paleontology [Abstract], *Geol. Soc. Am. Proc.*, **1936**: 396.

336. ———, 1939, The percentage method of stratigraphic dating, *6th Pacific Sci. Cong. Proc.*, **2**: 659–663 (preprint 1939).

337. KEILHACK, K., 1921, "Lehrbuch der praktischen Geologie," Vol I, F. Enke, Stuttgart. 548 pp.

338. KELLER, W. D., 1939, Varve-like deposit in a solution channel, *Jour. Sedimentary Petrology*, **9**: 32–33.

339. KELLOGG, J. L., 1905, Notes on marine mollusks of Louisiana, *Bull. Gulf Biol. Sta.* (*Cameron, La.*), **3**: 1–43.

340. KELLY, J., 1864, "Notes upon the Errors of Geology Illustrated by Reference to Facts Observed in Ireland," Longmans, Roberts and Green, London.

341. KELSEY, M., and H. DENTON, 1932, Sandstone dikes near Rockwall, Texas; *Texas Univ. Bull.*, **3201**: 139–148.

342. KEMP, J. F., 1940, "A Handbook of Rocks for Use without the Petrographic Microscope," 6th ed. (completely revised and edited by F. F. Grout), D. Van Nostrand Company, Inc., New York. 300 pp.

343. KENT, P. E., 1945, Contemporaneous disturbances in lacustrine beds in Kenya, *Geol. Mag.*, **82**: 130–135.

344. KERR, W. C., 1881, On the action of frost in the arrangement of superficial earthy material, *Am. Jour. Sci.* (3) **21**: 345–358.

345. KINDLE, E. M., 1895, The whetstone and grindstone rocks of Indiana, *Indiana Dept. Geol. Nat. History 20th Ann. Rept.*, pp. 329–368.

346. ———, 1914, Columnar structure in limestone, *Mus. Bull., Geol. Survey Canada* **2** (g.s. 14): 35–44.

347. ———, 1916, Small pit and mound structures developed during sedimentation, *Geol. Mag.*, **3**: 542–547.

348. ———, 1917, Recent and fossil ripple mark, *Mus. Bull., Geol. Survey Canada*, **25**: 1–56.

349. ———, 1917a, Some factors affecting the development of mud cracks, *Jour. Geology*, **25**: 135–144.

350. ———, 1917b, Deformation of unconsolidated beds in Nova Scotia and southern Ontario, *Bull. Geol. Soc. Am.*, **28**: 323–334.

351. ———, 1917c, Diagnostic characteristics of marine clastics, *Bull. Geol. Soc. Am.*, **28**: 905–916.

352. ———, 1919, Inequalities of sedimentation, *Jour. Geology*, **27**: 339–366.

353. ———, 1923, Notes on mud cracks and ripple marks in recent calcareous sediments, *Jour. Geology*, **31**: 138–145.

354. ———, 1923a, A note on mud crack and associated joint structure, *Am. Jour. Sci.* (5) **5**: 329–330.

355. ———, 1926, Contrasted types of mud cracks, *Royal Soc. Canada Proc. and Trans.* (3) **20** (4): 71–75.

356. ———, 1929, The Geological Story of Jasper National Park, National Parks of Canada, Department of the Interior, Ottawa. 48 pp.

357. ———, 1929a, The succession of fossil faunas in the eastern part of Jasper Peak, *Am. Jour. Sci.*, (5) **18**: 177–192.

358. ———, 1936, Dominant factors in the formation of firm and soft sand beaches, *Jour. Sedimentary Petrology*, **6**: 16–22.

359. ———, 1936a, Notes on shallow water sand structures, *Jour. Geology*, **44**: 861–869.

360. ——— and W. H. BUCHER, 1932, Ripple mark and its interpretation, in Twenhofel *et al.*, "Treatise on Sedimentation," pp. 632–668, The Williams and Wilkins Company, Baltimore.

361. ——— and L. H. COLE, 1938, Some mud crack experiments, *Geol. Meere und Binnengewässer*, **2** (2): 278–283.

362. ——— and E. M. EDWARDS, 1924, Literature of ripplemark, *Pan-Am. Geologist*, **41**: 191–203.

363. KING, R. H., 1946, Carnallite-filled mud cracks in salt clay, *Jour. Sedimentary Petrology*, **12**: 14.

364. KNIGHT, S. H., 1929, The Fountain and the Casper formations of the Laramie Basin, *Univ. Wyoming Pub. Sci. Geol.*, **1**: 1–82.

365. ———, 1930, Festoon cross lamination [Abstract], *Bull. Geol. Soc. Am.*, **41**: 86.

366. KRAMER, W. B., 1934, Dolomite dikes in the Texas Permian, *Jour. Geology*, **42**: 193–196.

367. KRAUSE, P. G., 1911, Wellenfurchen in linksrheinischen Unterdevon, *Zeitschr. deut. geol. Ges.*, **4**: 196–202.

368. KRUGER, F. C., 1938, A clastic dike of glacial origin, *Am. Jour. Sci.* (5) **35**: 305–307.

368a. KRUMBEIN, W. C., 1942, Criteria for subsurface recognition of unconformities, *Bull. Am. Assoc. Petroleum Geologists*, **26**: 36–62.

369. KRYNINE, P., 1935, Formation and preservation of desiccation features in a humid climate, *Am. Jour. Sci.* (5) **30**: 96–97.

370. ———, 1939, Annotated bibliography of recent Russian publications on sedimentation, National Research Council, Report of the Committee on Sedimentation (App. *B*, Exhibit *D*), pp. 51–64.

371. ———, 1940, Petrology and genesis of the third Bradford sand, *Pennsylvania State Coll. Bull. Min. Ind. Exper. Sta.*, **29**: 1–134.

372. KUENEN, PH. H., 1939, Lavaformen van den Vesuvius, *Tijdschr. koninklijk nederland. Aardrijksk. Genootschap*, **56** (1): 106–110.

373. KUGLER, H. G., 1938, Nature and significance of sedimentary vulcanism. "Science of Petroleum," Vol. I, pp. 297–299, Oxford University Press, New York.

374. KUKUK, P., 1920, Bemerkenswerte Einzelerschienungen der Gasflammkohlenschichten in der Lippemulde, *Glückauf*, **56**: 805–810.

375. ———, 1924, Das Nebengestein der Steinkohlenflöze in Ruhrbezirk, *Glückauf*, **60**: 1167–1175.

376. ———, 1936, Flözunregelmässigkeiten nichttektonischer Art im Ruhrbezirk und ihre Bedeutung für den betrieb untertage, *Glückauf*, **72**: 1021–1029.

377. LAHEE, F. H., 1914, Contemporaneous deformation: a criterion for aqueoglacial sedimentation, *Jour. Geology*, **22**: 786–790.

378. ———, 1941, "Field Geology," 4th ed., McGraw-Hill Book Company, Inc., New York. 853 pp.

379. LAMONT, A., 1938, Contemporaneous slumping and other problems at Bray series, Ordovician, and Lower Carboniferous horizons, County Dublin, *Royal Irish Acad. Proc.*, **45**: 1–32.

380. ———, 1940, First use of current-bedding to determine orientation of strata, *Nature*, **145**: 1016–1017.

381. ———, 1941. Irish submarine disturbance, *Quarry Manager's Jour.*, **24**: 123 –127, 150–151.

382. LANE, A. C., 1897, Grain of rocks [Abstract], *Bull. Geol. Soc. Am.*, **8**: 403–407; *Jour. Geology*, **5**: 222–223; *Science* (n.s.), **5**: 97–98.

383. ———, 1898, Geological report on Isle Royal, Michigan, *Michigan Geol. Survey*, **6** (1): 1–281.

384. ———, 1899, Magmatic differentiation in rocks of the copper-bearing series [Abstract], *Bull. Geol. Soc. Am.*, **10**: 15–18.

385. ———, 1902, Queneau on size of grain in igneous rocks, *Am. Jour. Sci.* (4) **14**: 393–396.

386. ———, 1903, Studies of the grain of igneous intrusives, *Bull Geol. Soc. Am.*, **14**: 369–384.

387. ———, 1911, The Keweenawan Series of Michigan, *Michigan Geol. Biol. Survey Pub.*, **6** (g.s. 4): 1–983.

388. LAUDERMILK, J. D., and A. O. WOODFORD, 1932, Concerning rillensteine, *Am. Jour. Sci.* (5) **23**: 135–154.

389. LAUDON, L. R., 1939, Unusual occurrence of *Isotelus gigas* Dekay in the Bromide formation (Ordovician) of southern Oklahoma, *Jour. Paleontology*, **13**: 211–213.

390. ——— and A. L. Bowsher, 1941, Mississippian formations of Sacramento Mountains, New Mexico, *Bull. Am. Assoc. Petroleum Geologists*, **25**: 2107–2160.

391. LAUGEL, A., 1854–1855, The cleavage of rocks, *Bull. Soc. géol. France*, (2) **12**: 363–368.

392. LAWLER, T. B., 1923, On the occurrence of sandstone dikes and chalcedony veins in the White River Oligocene, *Am. Jour. Sci.* (5) **5**: 160–172.

393. LAWSON, A. C., 1929, Some Huronian problems, *Bull. Geol. Soc. Am.*, **40**: 361–383.

394. LEIGHTON, M. M., and P. MacCLINTOCK, 1930, Weathered zones of the drift-sheets of Illinois, *Jour. Geology*, **38**: 28–53.

395. LEITH, A., 1931, The application of mechanical structural principles in the western Alps, *Jour. Geology*, **39**: 625–640.

396. ———, 1937, The strain ellipsoid, *Am. Jour. Sci.* (5) **33**: 360–368.

397. LEITH, C. K., 1905, Rock cleavage, *Bull. U.S. Geol. Survey*, **239**: 1–216.

398. ———, 1913, "Structural Geology," Henry Holt and Company, Inc., New York. 169 pp.

399. ———, 1923, "Structural Geology," rev. ed., Henry Holt and Company, Inc., New York. 390 pp.

400. ———, 1923a, Field versus laboratory evidence in the identification of metamorphic rocks, *Econ. Geology*, **18**: 288–290.

401. ———, 1925, Silicification of erosion surfaces, *Econ. Geology*, **20**: 513–523.

402. ——— and W. J. MEAD, 1915, "Metamorphic Geology," Henry Holt and Company, Inc., New York. 337 pp.

403. LEWIS, J. V., 1908, The Palisade diabase of New Jersey, *Am. Jour. Sci.*, (4) **26**: 155–162.

404. ———, 1908a, Petrography of the Newark igneous rocks of New Jersey, *N.J. Geol. Survey Ann. Rept. State Geologist*, **1907**: 97–167.

405. ———, 1914, Origin of pillow lavas, *Bull. Geol. Soc. Am.*, **25**: 591–654 (Abstract with Discussion, pp. 32–33).

406. LIBBEY, F. W., W. D. LOWRY, and R. S. MASON, 1945, Ferruginous bauxite deposits in northwestern Oregon, *Bull. Oregon Dept. Geol. Min. Industry*, **29**: 1–97; *Econ. Geology*, **41**: 245–265, 1946.

407. LINDGREN, W., 1928, "Mineral Deposits," 3d ed., McGraw-Hill Book Company, Inc., New York. 1049 pp.

408. LIPPERT, H., 1938, Gleit-Faltung in subaquatischen und subaerischen Gestein, *Senckenberg. Naturf. Gesell. Abh.*, **19**: 355–374.

409. LOGAN, W. N., 1863, Geology of Canada, *Geol. Survey Canada Rept. Prog.*, 1863: 1–983.

410. LONGWELL, C. R., 1928, Three common types of desert mud cracks, *Am. Jour. Sci.*, (5) **15**: 136–145.

411. ———, A. KNOPF, and R. F. FLINT, 1939, "A Textbook of Geology," Part I Physical Geology, John Wiley & Sons, Inc., New York. 543 pp.

412. LORETZ, H., 1882, Über transversale Schieferung, etc., *Jahrb. preuss. geol. Landesanstalt*, pp. 258–306.

413. LOUDERBACK, G. D., 1912, Pseudostratification in Santa Barbara County, California, *Univ. California Pub., Bull. Dept. Geology*, 7 (2): 21–38.

414. LOVERING, T. S., 1928, The fracturing of incompetent beds, *Jour. Geology*, 36 : 709–717.

415. LOWENSTAM, H. A., and E. P. DU BOIS, 1946, Marine Pool, Madison County. A new type of oil reservoir in Illinois, *Illinois Geol. Survey, Rept. Inv.*, 114 : 1–30.

416. LULL, R. S., 1904, Fossil footprints of the Jura-Trias of North America, *Boston Soc. Nat. History Mem.*, 5 (11): 461–557.

417. ———, 1915, Triassic life of the Connecticut Valley, *Bull. Connecticut Geol. Nat. History Survey*, 24 : 1–285.

418. LUND, R. J., 1930, Differentiation in the Cape Spencer flow [Nova Scotia], *Am. Mineralogist*, 15 : 539–565.

419. LYELL, C., 1841, "The Student's Elements of Geology," London.

420. ———, 1843, On the upright fossil trees found at different levels in the coal strata of Cumberland, N.S., *Geol. Soc. London Proc.*, 4 : 176–178; *Am. Jour. Sci.*, 45 : 353–356

421. ———, 1845, "Travels in North America," Vols. I and II.

422. ———, 1851, On fossil rain-marks of the Recent, Triassic, and Carboniferous periods, *Geol. Soc. London Quart. Jour.*, 7 : 238–247.

423. ——— and J. W. DAWSON, 1853, On the remains of a reptile . . . and of a land shell discovered in the interior of an erect fossil tree in the Coal Measures of Nova Scotia, *Geol. Soc. London Quart. Jour.*, 9 : 58–63.

424. McCALLIE, S. W., 1903, Sandstone dikes near Columbus, Georgia, *Am. Geologist*, 32 : 199–202.

425. McCALLIEN, W. J., 1935, The metamorphic rocks of Inishowen, County Donegal, *Royal Irish Acad. Proc.*, 42, Sec. B, 15 : 407–442.

426. McKEE, E. D., 1938, Structures in modern sediments aid in interpreting ancient rocks, *Carnegie Inst. Washington Pub.*, 501 : 683–694.

427. ———, 1938a, Original structures in Colorado River flood deposits of Grand Canyon, *Jour. Sedimentary Petrology*, 8 : 77–83.

428. ———, 1939, Some types of bedding in the Colorado River delta, *Jour. Geology*, 47 : 64–81.

429. ———, 1940, Three types of cross-lamination in Paleozoic rocks of northern Arizona, *Am. Jour. Sci.*, 238 : 811–824.

430. ———, 1945, Small-scale structures in the Coconino sandstone of northern Arizona, *Jour. Geology*, 53 : 313–325.

431. ———, 1945a, Cambrian history of the Grand Canyon region, *Carnegie Inst. Washington, Pub.*, 563 (1): 1–168.

432. McKINSTRY, H. E., 1939, Discussion—Pillow lavas of Borabora Society Islands, *Jour. Geology*, 47 : 202–204.

433. McMILLAN, J. M., JR., 1931, Clastic dike in Fort Hays chalk, Kansas, *Bull. Am. Assoc. Petroleum Geologists*, 15 : 842–843.

434. MacCARTHY, G. R., 1922, Mud cracks on steeply inclined surfaces, *Jour. Geology*, 30 : 702.

435. MacDONALD, G., 1945, Structure of aa lava flows [Abstract], *Bull. Geol. Soc. Am.*, 56 : 1179–1180.

436. MacGregor, A. M., 1928, The geology of the country around the Lonely mine, Bubi district, *Southern Rhodesia Geol. Bull.*, **11**: 1–96.

437. Madigan, C. T., 1928, Preliminary note on new evidence as to the age of formations on the north coast of Kangaroo Island [South Australia], *Royal Soc. South Australia Trans. and Proc.*, **52**: 210–216.

438. Mark, W. D., 1932, Fossil impressions of ice crystals in Lake Bonneville beds, *Jour. Geology*, **40**: 171–176.

439. Maxson, J. H., 1940, Gas pits in non-marine sediments, *Jour. Sedimentary Petrology*, **10**: 142–145.

440. ———— and I. Campbell, 1934, Archean ripple mark in the Grand Canyon, *Am. Jour. Sci.* (5) **28**: 298–303.

441. ———— and ————, 1939, Archean pseudo ripple mark in the Grand Canyon, *Am. Jour. Sci.* **237**: 606.

442. Mead, W. J., 1915, Occurrence and origin of the bauxite deposits of Arkansas, *Econ. Geology*, **10**: 28–54.

443. ————, 1920, Notes on the mechanics of geologic structures, *Jour. Geology*, **28**: 505–523.

444. ————, 1940, Folding, rock flowage, and foliate structures, *Jour. Geology*, **48**: 1007–1021.

445. Meek, C. E., 1928, Genesis of a sandstone dike as indicated by heavy minerals, *Bull. Am. Assoc. Petroleum Geologists*, **12**: 271–277.

446. Mehl, M. G., 1920, Influence of differential compression of sediments on attitude of bedded rocks [Abstract], *Science*, **51**: 520.

447. Mellen, F. F., 1937, The Little Bear residuum, *Bull. Mississippi State Geol. Survey*, **34**: 1–36.

448. Merriam, J. C., 1930, The past as living, *Carnegie Inst. Washington News Service Bull.*, **2** (11): 79–84.

449. Merriam, R., 1945, Magmatic differentiation in gabbro sills near Ashland, Oregon, *Am. Jour. Sci.*, **243**: 456–465.

450. Merrill, G. P., 1886, On fulgurites, *U.S. Nat. Mus. Proc.*, **9**: 83–91.

451. Merritt, P. L., 1934, Seine-Coutchiching problem, *Bull. Geol. Soc. Am.*, **45**: 333–374.

452. Meyerhoff, H. A., and R. F. Collins, 1935, Mississippian-Pennsylvanian contact in western South Dakota [Abstract], *Geol. Soc. Am. Proc.*, **1934**: 94–95.

453. Miller, B. L., 1937, Casts of halite crystals in the Beekmantown limestone, *Pennsylvania Acad. Sci. Proc.*, **11**: 55–57.

454. Miller, W. J., 1908, Highly folded between nonfolded strata at Trenton Falls, N.Y., *Jour. Geology*, **16**: 428–433.

455. ————, 1915, Notes on the intraformational contorted strata at Trenton Falls [N.Y.], *Bull. N.Y. State Mus.*, **177**: 135–143.

456. ————, 1922, Intraformational corrugated rocks, *Jour. Geology*, **30**: 587–610.

457. Mills, F. S., 1903, The Delta plain at Andover, Massachusetts, *Am. Geologist*, **32**: 162–170.

458. Milner, H. B., 1940, "Sedimentary Petrography," 3d. ed., Thomas Murby and Co., London. 666 pp.

459. Monroe, W. H., 1932, Earth cracks in Mississippi, *Bull. Am. Assoc. Petroleum Geologists*, **16**: 214–215.

460. Moore, E. S., 1914, Mud cracks open under water, *Am. Jour. Sci.* (4) **38**: 101–102.

461. ——, 1926, Mississagi Reserve and Goulais River iron ranges, district of Algoma, *Ontario Dept. Min. Ann. Rept.*, **34** (4): 1–33.

462. ——, 1930, Notes on the origin of pillow lavas, *Royal Soc. Canada Trans.* (3) **24** (4): 137–139.

463. ——, 1940, "Coal: Its Properties, Analysis, Classification, Geology, Extraction, Uses and Distribution," 2d ed., John Wiley & Sons, Inc., New York. 473 pp.

464. MOORE, H. B., 1939, Faecal pellets in relation to marine deposits, in "Recent Marine Sediments," pp. 516–524 (Trask, editor), American Association of Petroleum Geologists.

465. MOORE, J., and A. D. HOLE, 1902, Concerning well-defined ripple marks in Hudson River limestone, Richmond, Indiana, *Indiana Acad. Sci. Proc..* **1901**: 216–220.

466. MOORE, R. C., 1931, Pennsylvanian cycles in the northern Mid-Continent region, *Bull. Illinois Geol. Survey*, **60**: 247–257.

467. ——, 1934, The origin and age of the boulder-bearing Johns Valley shale in the Ouachita Mountains of Arkansas and Oklahoma, *Am. Jour. Sci.* (5) **27**: 432–453.

468. ——, 1936, Stratigraphic classification of the Pennsylvanian rocks of Kansas, *Kansas Univ. Bull.*, **22**: 1–256.

469. MORRIS, F. K., 1930, Amygdules and pseudo-amygdules, *Bull. Geol. Soc. Am.*, **41**: 383–404.

470. MULLER, S. W., 1937, Correlation of faunizones, *Geol. Soc. Am. Proc.*, **1936**: 390.

471. NASON, F. L., 1894, The economic geology of Albany County [New York], *N.Y. State Geologist Ann. Rept.*, **13**: 263–287; *N.Y. State Mus. Rept.*, **47**: 459–481.

472. NEAVERSON, E., 1928, "Stratigraphical Palaeontology, A Manual for Students and Field Geologists," Macmillan & Company, Ltd., London.   525 pp.

473. NETTLETON, L. L., 1936, Fluid mechanics of salt domes, in "Gulf Coast Oil Fields," pp. 79–108, American Association of Petroleum Geologists.

474. NEVIN, C. M., 1942, "Principles of Structural Geology," 3d ed., John Wiley & Sons, Inc., New York.   320 pp.

475. —— and R. E. SHERRILL, 1929, Studies in differential compacting, *Bull. Am. Assoc. Petroleum Geologists*, **13**: 1–22.

476. NEWSOM, J. F., 1903, Clastic dikes, *Bull. Geol. Soc. Am.*, **14**: 227–268.

477. NICHOLS, R. L., 1936, Flow-units in basalt, *Jour. Geology*, **44**: 617–630.

478. ——, 1938, Grooved lava, *Jour. Geology*, **46**: 601–614.

479. ——, 1939, Squeeze-ups, *Jour. Geology*, **47**: 421–425.

480. ——, 1939*a*, Surficial banding and shark's-tooth projections in the cracks of basaltic lava, *Am. Jour. Sci.*, **237**: 188–194.

481. ——, 1939*b*, Pressure-ridges and collapse-depressions on the McCartys basalt flow, New Mexico [Abstract], *Am. Geophys. Union 29th Ann. Meeting*, Part 3, pp. 432–433.

482. ——, 1940, The flow mechanism of basalts, Ph. D. thesis, Harvard University (Geology), unpublished.

483. ——, 1941, The geology of Plum Island, Castle Neck, and Great Neck, in N. E. Chute and R. L. Nichols, "The Geology of the Coast of Northeastern Massachusetts," *Bull. Massachusetts Department of Public Works*, (and *U.S. Dept. Interior, Geol. Survey*), **7**: 1–48.

484. ——, 1944, Mud pellet rains, *Bull. Am. Meteor. Soc.*, **25**: 342–346.

485. ———, 1946, McCartys basalt flow, Valencia County, New Mexico, *Bull Geol. Soc. Am.*, **57**: 1049–1086.

486. ——— and C. E. STEARNS, 1939, 1940, Grooved lava in the cross-section of Big Craters, Idaho, *Am. Geophys. Union Trans. 20th Ann. Meeting*, Part 3, p. 433 (Abstract), 1939; *Am. Jour. Sci.*, **238**: 22–31, 1940.

487. NIKIFOROFF, C. C., 1943, Introduction to paleopedology, *Am. Jour. Sci.*, **241**: 194–200.

488. NORMAN, G. W. H., 1935, Lake Ainslie map-area, N.S., *Geol. Survey Canada Mem.*, **177**: 1–103.

489. NORTH, F. J., 1930, "Limestones, their origins, distributions, and uses," Thomas Murby and Co., London. 467 pp.

490. ÖPIK, A., 1930, Brachiopoda Protremata der Estländischen Ordovizischen Kukruse-Stufe, *Pub. Geol. Inst., Univ. Tartu (Esthonia)*, **20**: 1–261.

491. ORTON, E., 1889, The Trenton limestone as a source of petroleum and inflammable gas in Ohio and Indiana, *U.S. Geol. Survey Ann Rept.*, **8**: 475–662.

492. PARKER, B. H., 1930, Notes on the occurrence of clastic plugs and dikes in the Cimarron valley area of Union County, New Mexico, Guidebook, 4th Annual Field Conference Colorado, New Mexico, Texas, September, 1930, pp. 131–136.

493. ———, 1933, Clastic plugs and dikes of the Cimarron valley area of Union County, New Mexico, *Jour. Geology*, **41**: 38–51.

494. PARKINSON, D., 1945, The origin and structure of the Lower Viséan reef-knolls of the Clitheroe District, Lancashire, *Geol. Soc. London Quart. Jour.*, **99**: 155–168.

495. PATERSON, T. T., 1940, The effects of frost action and solifluxion around Baffin Bay and in the Cambridge district, *Geol. Soc. London Quart. Jour.*, **96**: 99–130.

496. PATTON, L. T., 1933, Ripple marks of the Merkle dolomite of western Texas and their paleogeographic interpretation, *Jour. Sedimentary Petrology*, **3**: 77–82.

497. PEOPLES, J. W., 1936, Gravity stratification as a criterion in the interpretation of the structure of the Stillwater complex, Montana, *16th Internat. Geol. Cong. 1933 Rept.*, **1**: 353–360.

498. PERRET, F. A., 1924, The Vesuvius eruption of 1906, *Carnegie Inst. Washington Pub.*, **339**: 1–151.

499. PERRY, N. W., 1889, The Cincinnati rocks; what has been their physical history, *Am. Geologist*, **4**: 326–336.

500. PETTIJOHN, F. J., 1930, Imbricate arrangement of pebbles in a pre-Cambrian conglomerate, *Jour. Geology*, **38**: 568–573.

501. ———, 1936, Early pre-Cambrian varved slate in northwestern Ontario, *Bull. Geol. Soc. Am.*, **47**: 621–628.

502. ———, 1943, Archean sedimentation, *Bull. Geol. Soc. Am.*, **54**: 925–972.

503. PETTY, J. J., 1936, The origin and occurrence of fulgurites in the Atlantic coastal plain, *Am. Jour. Sci.* (5) **31**: 188–201.

504. PLUMMER, F. B., 1931, Pennsylvanian sedimentation in Texas, *Bull. Illinois Geol. Survey*, **60**: 259–269.

505. POWERS, S., 1915, The origin of the inclusions in dikes, *Jour. Geology*, **23**: 1–10, 166–182.

506. ———, 1916, The Acadian Triassic, *Jour. Geology*, **24**: 1–26, 105–122, 254–268.

507. ———, 1922, Reflected buried hills and their importance in petroleum geology, *Econ. Geology*, **17**: 233–259.

508. ———, 1926, Reflected buried hills, *Bull. Am. Assoc. Petroleum Geologists*, **10**: 422–442.

509. ———— and A. C. LANE, 1916, Magmatic differentiation in effusive rocks, *Bull. Am. Inst. Min. Eng.*, **110**: 535–548; *Am. Inst. Min. Eng. Trans.*, **54**: 442–457, 1917.

510. PRATT, W. E., 1911, The eruption of Taal volcano, Jan. 30, 1911, *Philippine Jour. Sci.*, **6**: 63–86.

511. ————, 1916, An unusual form of volcanic ejecta, *Jour. Geology*, **24**: 450–455.

512. PRICE, P. H., 1933, Clay dikes in Redstone coal, West Virginia and Pennsylvania, *Bull. Am. Assoc. Petroleum Geologists*, **17**: 1527–1533.

513. ————, 1934, Stylolites in sandstone, *Jour. Geology*, **42**: 188–192.

514. ———— and J. B. LUCKE, 1942, Primary limestone structures of West Virginia, *Am. Jour. Sci.*, **240**: 601–616.

515. PRINGLE, J., and R. ECKFORD, 1945, Structures in Silurian greywackes near Innleithen, Peeblesshire, *Edinburgh Geol. Soc. Trans.*, **14** (1): 5–7.

516. PROSSER, C. S., 1916, Ripple marks in Ohio limestones, *Jour. Geology*, **24**: 456–475.

517. PROUTY, W. F., 1916, Preliminary report on the crystalline and other marbles of Alabama, *Bull. Alabama Geol. Survey*, **18**: 1–212.

518. PUMPELLY, R., J. E. WOLFF, and T. N. DALE, 1894, Geology of the Green Mountains, Massachusetts, *U.S. Geol. Survey, Monograph*, **23**: 1–206.

519. PURDUE, A. H., 1907, Cave-sandstone deposits of the southern Ozarks, *Bull. Geol. Soc. Am.*, **18**: 251–256.

520. PUSTOVALOV, L. V., 1937, Conditions of sediment formation during the Upper Permian, *Problems Soviet Geology*, **7** (11): 963–964.

521. QUENEAU, A. L., 1902, Size of grain in igneous rocks in relation to the distance from the cooling wall, *School Mines Quart.*, **23**: 181–195 [Abstract, *Am. Geologist*, **29**: 125–126; *Annals N.Y. Acad. Sci.*, **14**: 163].

522. QUINN, A. W., 1943, Settling of heavy minerals in a granodiorite dike at Bradford, Rhode Island, *Am. Mineralogist*, **28** (4): 272–281.

523. QUIRKE, T. T., 1930, Spring pits, sedimentation phenomena, *Jour. Geology*, **38**: 88–91.

524. RADCLIFFE, D. H., 1913, The preservation and interpretation of ripple marks and sun cracks, pp. 1–23, B.S. thesis, University of Missouri, School of Mines & Metallurgy (unpublished).

525. RANSOME, F. L., and F. C. CALKINS, 1908, The geology and ore deposits of the Coeur d'Alene district, Idaho, *U.S. Geol. Survey Prof. Paper*, **62**: 1–203.

526. RAYMOND, P. E., 1922, Seaside notes [formation of trails], *Am. Jour. Sci.*, (5) **3**: 108–114.

527. ————, 1930, The Paleozoic formations in Jasper Peak, Alberta, *Am. Jour. Sci.* (5) **20**: 289–311.

528. READ, H. H., 1936, The stratigraphical order of the Dalradian rocks of the Banffshire coast, *Geol. Mag.*, **73**: 468–476.

529. READ, W. F., 1940, "Bone pocket" in Lower Permian Leuders formation of Baylor County, Texas [Abstract], *Bull. Geol. Soc. Am.*, **51**: 1975.

530. REED, J. C., 1937, Amygdales in Columbia River lavas near Freedom, Idaho, *Am. Geophys. Union Trans.*, 18th Ann. Meeting, Part 1, pp. 239–243.

531. REEDS, C. A., 1923, Seasonal records of geologic time, *Nat. History*, **23**: 371–380.

532. REGER, D. B., 1931, Pennsylvanian cycles in West Virginia, *Bull. Illinois Geol. Survey*, **60**: 217–239.

533. REICHE, P., 1938, An analysis of cross-lamination; the Coconino sandstone, *Jour. Geology*, **46**: 905–932.

534. REIS, O. M., 1910, Beobachtung über Schichtenfolge, *Geogn. Jahresh., München,* **22** : 1–285.

535. RETTGER, R. E., 1935, Experiments on soft-rock deformation, *Bull. Am. Assoc. Petroleum Geologists,* **19** : 271–292.

536. RICE, R. C., 1939, Contorted bedding in the Trias of N.W. Wirral, *Liverpool Geol. Soc. Proc.,* **17** (iv): 361–370.

537. RICHARDS, H. C., and W. H. BRYAN, 1927, Volcanic mud balls from the Brisbane tuff, *Royal Soc. Queensland Proc.,* **39** : 54–60.

538. RICHEY, J. E., and H. H. THOMAS, 1930, The geology of Ardnamurchan, north-west Mull and Coll, *Scotland Geol. Survey Mem.,* pp. 1–393.

539. RICHTER, R., 1937, Marken und Spuren aus allen Zeiten I–II, *Senckenberg. Naturf. Gesell. Abh.,* **19** : 159–163.

540. RITTENHOUSE, G., 1934, A laboratory study of an unusual series of varved clays from northern Ontario, *Am. Jour. Sci.* (5) **28** : 110–120.

541. ROBINSON, G. W., 1936, Soils, their origin, constitution and classification, D. Van Nostrand Company, Inc., New York. 442 pp.

542. ROE, W. B., 1934, Clay veins in the Springfield (No. 5) coal [Abstract], *Illinois Acad. Sci. Trans.,* **27** : 115.

543. ROSS, C. P., 1941, Origin and geometric form of chalcedony-filled spherulites from Oregon, *Am. Mineralogist,* **26** : 727–732.

544. ROWLAND, R. A., 1939, A petrotectonic analysis of cleavage in otherwise unmeta-morphosed sediments, *Jour. Geology,* **47** : 449–471.

545. RUBEY, W. W., 1933, Settling velocities of gravel, sand, and silt particles, *Am. Jour. Sci.* (5) **25** : 325–338.

546. RUEDEMANN, R., 1942, Geology of the Catskill and Kaaterskill quadrangles. Part I. Cambrian and Ordovician geology of the Catskill quadrangle, *Bull. N.Y. State Mus.,* **331** : 7–188.

547. RUSSELL, W. L., 1927, The origin of the sandstone dikes of the Black Hills region, *Am. Jour. Sci.* (5) **14** : 402–408.

548. SALISBURY, R. D., and W. W. ATWOOD, 1897, Drift phenomena in the vicinity of Devil's Lake, Baraboo, Wisconsin, *Jour. Geology,* **5** : 131–147.

549. SAMPSON, E., 1923, The ferruginous chert formations of Notre Dame Bay, Newfoundland, *Jour. Geology,* **31** : 571–598.

550. SANDBERG, A. E., 1938, Section across Keweenawan lavas at Duluth, Minnesota, *Bull. Geol. Soc. Am.,* **49** : 795–830.

551. SANDER, B., 1930, Gefügekunde der Gesteine, Verlag Julius Springer, Berlin. 352 pp.

552. SARLE, C. J., 1906, Arthrophycus and Daedalus of burrow origin, *Rochester Acad. Sci. Proc.,* **4** : 203–210.

553. SAVAGE, T. E., 1930, Sedimentary cycles in the Pennsylvanian strata, *Am. Jour. Sci.* (5) **20** : 125–135.

554. SAYLES, R. W., 1914, The Squantum tillite, *Bull. Mus. Comp. Zoology (Harvard),* **66** : 141–175.

555. ———, 1919, Seasonal deposition in aqueo-glacial sediments, *Mus. Comp. Zoology (Harvard) Mem.,* **47** (1): 1–67.

556. ———, 1924, Variability of summer deposition in glacial varves [Abstract, with discussion by C. A. Reeds], *Bull. Geol. Soc. Am.,* **35** : 67–68.

557. ———, 1929, New interpretation of the Permo-Carboniferous varves at Squan-tum [Mass.], *Bull. Geol. Soc. Am.,* **40** : 541–546.

558. SCHOEWE, W. H., 1938, "Fossil" ventifacts [Abstract], *Geol. Soc. Am. Proc.*, **1937**: 11.

559. SCHOFIELD, R. K., and B. A. KEEN, 1929, Rigidity in weak clay suspensions, *Nature*, **123**: 492–493.

560. SCHUCHERT, C., 1924, The value of micro-fossils in petroleum exploration, *Bull. Am. Assoc. Petroleum Geologists*, **8**: 539–553.

561. ———, 1927, Winters in the Upper Devonian of New York and Acadia, *Am. Jour. Sci.* (5) **13**: 123–131.

562. ——— and C. O. DUNBAR, 1941, "Historical Geology," 4th ed., John Wiley & Sons, Inc., New York. 544 pp.

563. SCHWELLNUS, C. M., and H. D. LE ROEX, 1945, Columnar, conical and other growths in the dolomites of the Otavi system, Southwest Africa, *Geol. Soc. South Africa Trans.*, **47**: 93–106.

564. SCOTT, G., 1930, Ripple marks of large size in the Fredericksburg rocks west of Fort Worth, Texas, *Texas Univ. Bull.*, **3001**: 53–56.

565. SCOTT, H. W., 1947, Solution sculpturing in limestone pebbles, *Bull. Geol. Soc. Am.*, **58**: 141–152.

566. SEDERHOLM, J. J., 1899, Über eine Archäische Sediment Formation im Sudwestlichen Finland, *Bull. comm. géol. Finlande*, No. 6, pp. 1–254.

567. SELLARDS, E. H , 1932, Pre-Paleozoic and Paleozoic systems in Texas, *Texas Univ. Bull.*, **3232**: 1–238.

568. SHACKLETON, R. M., 1940, The succession of rocks in the Dingle Peninsula, County Derry, *Royal Irish Acad. Proc.*, **46**: 1–12.

569. SHALER, N. S., 1888, Origin of the divisions between the layers of stratified rocks, *Boston Soc. Nat. History Proc.*, **23**: 408–419.

570. ———, J. B. WOODWORTH, and C. F. MARBUT, 1896, The glacial brick clays of Rhode Island and southeastern Massachusetts, *U.S. Geol. Survey Ann. Rept.*, **17** (1): 951–1004.

571. SHANNON, W. P., 1895, Wave marks on Cincinnati limestone, *Indiana Acad. Sci. Proc.*, **1894**: 53–54.

572. SHARPE, C. F. S., 1938, "Landslides and Related Phenomena. A Study of Mass-movements of Soil and Rock," Columbia University Press, New York. 137 pp.

573. SHARP, R. P., 1940, A Cambrian slide breccia, Grand Canyon, Arizona, *Am. Jour. Sci.*, **238**: 668–672.

574. SHAUB, B. M., 1939, The origin of stylolites, *Jour. Sedimentary Petrology*, **9**: 47–61.

575. SHELDON, P. G., 1928, Some sedimentation conditions in Middle Portage rocks, *Am. Jour. Sci.* (5) **15**: 243–252.

576. SHENON, P. J., and R. H. MCCONNEL, 1940, Use of sedimentation features and cleavage in the recognition of overturned strata, *Econ. Geology*, **35**: 430–444.

577. SHIMER, H. W., and R. R. SHROCK, 1944, "Index Fossils of North America," John Wiley & Sons, Inc., New York. 837 pp.

578. SHROCK, R. R., 1937, Stratigraphy and structure of the area of disturbed Ordovician rocks near Kentland, Indiana, *Am. Midland Naturalist*, **18**: 471–531.

579. ———, 1938, Wisconsin Silurian bioherms (organic reefs), *Bull. Geol. Soc. Am.*, **50**: 529–562.

580. ———, 1940, Rectangular mud cracks [in Wisconsin Silurian dolomitic limestone], *Wisconsin Acad. Sci. Trans.*, **32**: 229–232.

581. ——, 1946, Surficial breccia produced from chemical weathering of Eocene limestone in Haiti, West Indies, *Indiana Acad. Sci. Proc.*, **55**: 107–110.

582. ——, 1946a, Sedimentation and wind action around Volcan Parícutin, Mexico. *Indiana Acad. Sci. Proc.*, **55**: 117–120.

583. ——, 1946b, A classification of sedimentary rocks [Abstract], *Bull. Geol. Soc. Am.*, **57**: 1231; 1948, *Jour. Geology*, **56**: 118–129.

583a. ——, 1947, Loiponic deposits [Abstract], *Bull. Geol. Soc. Am.*, **58**: 1228.

584. —— and C. A. MALOTT, 1933, The Kentland area of disturbed Ordovician rocks in northwestern Indiana, *Jour. Geology*, **41**: 337–370.

585. SHULER, E. W., 1917, Dinosaur tracks in the Glen Rose limestone near Glen Rose, Texas, *Am. Jour. Sci.* (5) **44**: 294–298.

586. SIAU, M., 1841, Observations diverses faites en 1839 et 1840, pendant un voyage à l'Ile Bourbon, *Acad. sci. Paris Comptes rendus*, **12**: 774–775.

587. ——, 1841a. Action des vagues à de grandes profondeurs, *Ann. chim. phys.*, **2**.

588. SIMPSON, G. G., 1936, Cylindrical structures in sandstones in Patagonia [Abstract], *Geol. Soc. Am. Proc.*, **1935**: 106.

589. SINGEWALD, Q. D., 1931, Depositional features of the "Parting" quartzite near Alma, Colorado, *Am. Jour. Sci.* (5) **22**: 404–413.

590. SMITH, B., 1916, Ball or pillow-form structures in sandstones, *Geol. Mag.*, (6) **3**: 146–156.

591. ——, 1935, Geology and Mineral Resources of the Skaneateles quadrangle, *Bull. N.Y. State Mus.*, **300**: 1–120.

592. SMITH, J. F., and C. C. ALBRITTON, JR., 1941, Solution effects on limestone as a function of slope, *Bull. Geol. Soc. Am.*, **52**: 61–78.

593. SORBY, H. C. S., 1908, On the application of quantitative methods to the study of the structure and history of rocks, *Geol. Soc. London Quart. Jour.*, **64**: 171–233.

594. SPURR, J. E., 1894, False bedding in stratified drift deposits, *Am. Geologist*, **13**: 43–47.

595. ——, 1894a, Oscillation and single current ripple marks, *Am. Geologist*, **13**: 201–206.

596. SPURRELL, F. C. J., 1887, A Sketch of the History of the Rivers and Denudation of West Kent, etc., Greenwich, 1886. Review reprinted in *Geol. Mag.* (3) **4**: 121–122, 1887; from *Rept. West Kent Nat. History Soc.*, 1886.

597. STAINBROOK, M. A., 1945, The stratigraphy of the Independence shale of Iowa, *Am. Jour. Sci.*, **243**: 138–158.

598. STARK, J. T., 1938, Vesicular dikes and subaerial pillow lavas of Borabora, Society Islands, *Jour. Geology*, **46**: 225–238.

599. ——, 1939, Discussion, Pillow lavas, *Jour. Geology*, **47**: 205–209.

600. STAUFFER, C. R., 1939, Middle Devonian Polychaeta from the Lake Erie district, *Jour. Paleontology*, **13**: 500–511.

601. STEARN, N. H., 1934, Structure from sedimentation at Parnell Hill quicksilver mine, Arkansas, *Econ. Geology*, **29**: 146–156.

602. STEARNS, C. E., 1942, A fossil marmot from New Mexico and its climatic significance, *Am. Jour. Sci.*, **240**: 867–878.

603. STEARNS, H. T., 1926, Volcanism in the Mud Lake area, Idaho, *Am. Jour. Sci.* (5) **11**: 539–563.

604. ——, 1938, Pillow lavas in Hawaii [Abstract], *Geol. Soc. Am. Proc.* **1937**: 252–253.

605. STEPHENSON, L. W., 1929, Unconformities in Upper Cretaceous series of Texas, *Bull. Am. Assoc. Petroleum Geologists*, **13**: 1323–1334.

606. ——— and W. H. MONROE, 1940, The Upper Cretaceous deposits, *Bull. Mississippi State Geol. Survey*, **40**: 1–296.

607. STERNBERG, C. M., 1931, 1932, Dinosaur tracks from Peace River, British Columbia [Abstract], *Bull. Geol. Soc. Am.*, **42**: 362–363; *Canada Nat. Mus. Bull.*, **68**: 59–85.

608. ———, 1933, Carboniferous tracks from Nova Scotia, *Bull. Geol. Soc. Am.*, **44**: 951–964.

609. STOČES, B., and C. H. WHITE, 1935, "Structural Geology, with Special Reference to Economic Deposits," D. Van Nostrand Company, Inc., New York. 460 pp.

610. STOCKDALE, P. B., 1922, Stylolites; their nature and origin, *Indiana Univ. Studies*, **9** (55): 1–97.

611. ———, 1923, Solutive genesis of stylolitic structures, *Pan-Am. Geologist*, **39**: 353–364.

612. ———, 1931, The Borden (Knobstone) rocks of southern Indiana, *Indiana Dept. Cons., Div. Geology, Pub.*, **98**: 1–330.

613. ———, 1931a, Bioherms in the Borden group of Indiana, *Bull. Geol. Soc. Am.*, **42**: 707–718.

614. ———, 1936, Rare stylolites, *Am. Jour. Sci.* (5) **32**: 129–133.

615. ———, 1939, Stylolites [Abstract], *Bull. Geol. Soc. Am.*, **50**: 1989.

616. ———, 1939a, Lower Mississippian rocks of the east-central interior, *Geol. Soc. Am. Special Paper*, **22**: 1–248.

617. ———, 1941, Stylolites, primary or secondary? [Abstract], *Ohio Jour. Sci.*, **41**: 415–416.

618. ———, 1943, Stylolites: primary or secondary, *Jour. Sedimentary Petrology*, **13**: 3–12.

619. ———, 1945, Stylolites with films of coal, *Jour. Geology*, **53**: 133–136.

620. STOUT, W. E., 1931, Pennsylvanian cycles in Ohio, *Bull. Illinois Geol. Survey*, **60**: 195–216.

621. STRONG, M. W., 1937, Micropetrographic methods as an aid to the stratigraphy of chemical deposits, 11ᵐᵉ Congrès mondial du pétrole, Paris, 1937, Vol. I, Sec. 1, Géologie—Géophysique—Forage.   1021 pp.

622. STUTZER, O., 1940, "Geology of Coal" (translation by A. C. Noé), University of Chicago Press, Chicago.   461 pp.

623. SUTTON, A. H., 1931, A Pre-Cretaceous soil horizon in western Kentucky, *Am. Jour Sci.* (5) **22**: 449–452.

624. SWANSON, C. O., 1927, Notes on stress, strain, and joints, *Jour. Geology*, **35**: 193–223.

625. ———, 1939, Flow cleavage in folded rocks [Abstract], *Bull. Geol. Soc. Am.*, **50**: 1938.

626. ———, 1940, Flow cleavage in folded beds, *Bull. Geol. Soc. Am.*, **52**: 1245–1263.

627. SWARTZ, J. H., 1927, Subaerial sun cracks, *Am. Jour. Sci.* (5) **14**: 69–70.

628. TANTON, T. L., 1926, Recognition of the Coutchiching near Steeprock Lake, Ontario, *Royal Soc. Canada Trans.*, **20** (4): 39–49.

629. ———, 1930, Determination of age-relations of folded rocks, *Geol. Mag.*, **67**: 73–76.

630. TARR, W. A., 1916, Stylolites in quartzite, *Science*, **43**: 819–820.

631. ———, 1921, Syngenetic origin of concretions in shale, *Bull. Geol. Soc. Am.*, **32**: 373–384.

632. ———, 1926, Silicification of erosion surfaces [Discussion], *Econ. Geology*, **21**: 511–513.

633. ———, 1935, Concretions in the Champlain formation of the Connecticut Valley, *Bull. Geol. Soc. Am.*, **46**: 1493–1534.

634. TERZAGHI, R. A. D., 1940, Compaction of lime mud as a cause of secondary structure, *Jour. Sedimentary Petrology*, **10**: 78–90.

635. THIEL, G. A., 1932, Giant current ripples in coarse fluvial gravel, *Jour. Geology*, **40**: 452–458

636. THIESMEYER, L. R., 1938, Criteria of seasonal and annual accumulations in sediments [Abstract], *Geol. Soc. Am. Proc.*, **1937**: 326–327.

637. ———, 1939, Varved slates in Fauquier County, Virginia, *Bull. Virginia Geol. Survey*, **51**(*D*): 105–118.

638. ——— and R. R. STORM, 1938, Features indicative of seasonal banding in silicified argillites in Chapel Hill, North Carolina [Abstract], *Bull. Geol. Soc. Am.*, **49**: 1964.

639. THOMAS, N. L., 1937, Horizons of extinction, an aid to correlation [Abstract], *Geol. Soc. Am. Proc.*, **1936**: 373.

640. THOMPSON, B., 1894, Landscape marble, *Geol. Soc. London Quart. Jour.*, **50**: 393–410.

641. THOMPSON, W. O., 1937, Original structures of beaches, bars, and dunes, *Bull. Geol. Soc. Am.*, **48**: 723–751.

642. THWAITES, F. T., 1912, Sandstones of the Wisconsin coast of Lake Superior, *Bull. Wisconsin Geol. Survey*, **25**: 1–117.

643. ———, 1937, "Outlines of Glacial Geology," Edwards Bros., Inc., Ann Arbor, Mich. 115 pp.

644. TILLEY, C. E., 1924, The facies classification of metamorphic rocks, *Geol. Mag.*, **61**: 167–171.

645. TOMKEIEFF, S. I., 1940, The basalt lavas of the Giant's Causeway district of Northern Ireland, *Bull. volcanologique* (2) **6**: 89–143.

646. TOMLINSON, C. W., 1940, Technique of stratigraphic nomenclature, *Bull. Am. Assoc. Petroleum Geologists*, **24**: 2038–2046.

647. TRASK, P. D., 1931, Compaction of sediments, *Bull. Am. Assoc. Petroleum Geologists*, **15**: 271–276.

648. TREFETHEN, J. M., 1947, Some features of the cherts in the vicinity of Columbia, Missouri, *Am. Jour. Sci.*, **245**: 56–58.

649. TROMMSDORFF, W. E., 1934, "Fahrtströmungen" in Eruptivmagmen, *Naturwissenschaften*, **22**: 329–332.

650. TRUEMAN, A. E., 1946, Stratigraphical problems in the coal measures of Europe and North America, *Geol. Soc. London Quart. Jour.*, **102** (2): xlix–xciii.

651. TWENHOFEL, W. H., 1919, Pre-Cambrian and Carboniferous algal deposits, *Am. Jour. Sci.* (5) **48**: 339–352.

652. ———, 1921, Impressions made by bubbles, raindrops, and other agencies, *Bull. Geol. Soc. Am.*, **32**: 359–371.

653. ———, 1923, Development of shrinkage cracks in sediments without exposure to the atmosphere [Abstract], *Bull. Geol. Soc. Am.*, **34**: 64.

654. ———, 1927, Geology of Anticosti, *Geol. Survey Canada Mem.*, **154**: 1–481.

655. ———, 1931, Environment in sedimentation and stratigraphy, *Bull. Geol. Soc. Am.*, **42**: 407–424.

656. ———, 1936, Marine unconformities, marine conglomerates, and thicknesses of strata, *Bull. Am. Assoc. Petroleum Geologists*, **20**: 677–703.

657. ———, 1939, Principles of Sedimentation, McGraw-Hill Book Company, Inc., New York. 610 pp.

658. ——— and collaborators, 1932, "Treatise on Sedimentation," The Williams & Wilkins Company, Baltimore. 926 pp.

659. ——— and R. R. SHROCK, 1935, "Invertebrate Paleontology," McGraw-Hill Book Company, Inc., New York. 511 pp.

660. TYRRELL, G. W., 1929, "The Principles of Petrology," E. P. Dutton & Company, Inc., New York. 349 pp.

661. UDDEN, J. A., 1912, Geology and mineral resources of the Peoria quadrangle, Illinois, *Bull. U.S. Geol. Survey*, **506**: 1–103.

662. ———, 1916, Notes on ripple marks, *Jour. Geology*, **24**: 123–129.

663. ———, 1918, Fossil ice crystals—an instance of the practical value of "pure science," *Univ. Texas Bull.*, **1821**: 1–8.

664. ———, 1924, Laminated anhydrite in Texas, *Bull. Geol. Soc. Am.*, **35**: 347–354.

665. ULRICH, E. O., 1924, Notes on new names in table of formations and on physical evidence of breaks between Paleozoic systems in Wisconsin, *Wisconsin Acad. Sci. Trans.*, **21**: 71–107.

666. VAN BEMMELEN, R. W., 1941, Origin and mining of bauxite in Netherlands-India, *Econ. Geology*, **36**: 630–640.

667. VANDERHOOF, V. L., 1935, Seasonal bandings in an asphalt deposit at McKittrick (California) [Abstract], *Geol. Soc. Am. Proc.*, **1934**: 332.

668. VAN HISE, C. R., 1896, Principles of North American Pre-Cambrian geology, *U.S. Geol. Survey Ann. Rept.* **16** (1): 571–843; also *Am. Jour. Sci.*, (4) **2**: 205–213.

669. ———, 1896a, Deformation of rocks, *Jour. Geology*, **4**: 195–213, 312–353, 449–453, 593–629, **5**: 178–193, 1897.

670. ———, 1909, Principles of the classification and correlation of the Pre-Cambrian rocks, *Jour. Geology*, **17**: 97–104.

671. ——— and C. K. LEITH, 1911, The geology of the Lake Superior region, *U.S. Geol. Survey Monograph*, **52**: 1–641.

672. VANUXEM, L., 1842, "Geology of New York. Part III, Comprising the Survey of the Third Geological District," Albany. 306 pp.

673. VOGT, T., 1930, On the chronological order of deposition of the Highland schists, *Geol. Mag.*, **67**: 68–73.

674. WAHLSTROM, E. E., 1941, Hydrothermal deposits in the Specimen Mountain volcanics, Rocky Mountain National Park, Colorado, *Am. Mineralogist*, **26**: 551–561.

675. WALCOTT, C. D., 1894, Paleozoic intraformational conglomerates, *Bull. Geol. Soc. Am.*, **5**: 191–198.

676. ———, 1894a, Pre-Cambrian igneous rocks of the Unkar terrane, Grand Canyon of the Colorado, Arizona, *U.S. Geol. Survey Ann. Rept.* **14** (2): 497–524.

677. ———, 1896. The Cambrian rocks of Pennsylvania, *Bull. U.S. Geol. Survey*, **134**: 1–43.

678. ———, 1914, Pre-Cambrian Algonkian algal flora, *Smithsonian Misc. Coll.*, **64** (2): 77–156.

679. WALKER, F., 1940, Differentiation of the Palisade diabase, New Jersey, *Bull. Geol. Soc. Am.*, **51**: 1059–1105.

680. WALKER, T. L., and A. L. PARSONS, 1922, Tubular amygdaloid from Nova Scotia, *Univ. Toronto Studies*, geological studies, **14**: 5–12.

681. ――――, 1922a, The zeolites of Nova Scotia, *Univ. Toronto Studies*, geological studies, **14**: 13–73.

682. ――――, 1923, The North Mountain basalt of Nova Scotia; glaciation, tubular amygdaloid, mordenite, and louisite, *Univ. Toronto Studies*, geological studies, **16**: 5–12.

683. WALLACE, R. C., 1927, Varve materials and banded rocks, *Royal Soc. Canada Trans.* (3) **21** (4): 109–118.

684. WALTERS, R. F., 1946, Buried Pre-Cambrian hills in northeastern Barton County, Central Kansas, *Bull. Am. Assoc. Petroleum Geologists*, **30**: 660–710.

685. WANLESS, H. R., 1931, Pennsylvanian cycles in western Illinois, *Bull. Illinois Geol. Survey*, **60**: 179–193.

686. ――――, 1934, Relations between Pennsylvanian coals and their underclays, as revealed by field studies [Abstract], *Geol. Soc. Am. Proc.*, **1933**: 115–116.

687. ――――, 1938, Geological records of a rhythmic nature, *Illinois Acad. Sci. Trans.*, **31**: 7–14.

688. ――――, 1939, Pennsylvanian correlations in the Eastern Interior and Appalachian coal fields, *Geol. Soc. Am. Special Paper*, **17**: 1–130.

689. ――――, 1946, Pennsylvanian geology of a part of the Southern Appalachian coal field, *Geol. Soc. Am. Mem.*, **13**: 1–162.

690. ―――― and F. P. SHEPARD, 1936, Sea level and climatic changes related to late Paleozoic cycles, *Bull. Geol. Soc. Am.*, **47**: 1177–1206.

691. ―――― and J. M. WELLER, 1932, Correlation and extent of Pennsylvanian cyclothems, *Bull. Geol. Soc. Am.*, **43**: 1003–1016.

692. WARD, F., 1923, Note on mud cracks, *Am. Jour. Sci.* (5) **6**: 308–309.

693. WARD, L. F., 1896, Some analogies in the Lower Cretaceous of Europe and America, *U.S. Geol. Survey Ann. Rept.* **16** (1): 463–542.

694. WARREN, J. C., 1855, [On fossil raindrops], *Boston Soc. Nat. History Proc.*, **5**: 187–188.

695. WASMUND, E., 1926, Biocoenose und Thanatocoenose, Biosoziologische Studie über Lebensgemeinschaften und Totengesellschaften, *Archiv Hydrobiologie*, **17**: 1–116.

696. WELLER, J. M., 1930, Cyclical sedimentation of the Pennsylvanian period and its significance, *Jour. Geology*, **38**: 97–135.

697. ――――, 1931, The conception of cyclical sedimentation during the Pennsylvanian period, *Bull. Illinois Geol. Survey*, **60**: 163–177.

698. ――――, 1931a, Sedimentary cycles in the Pennsylvanian strata: A reply, *Am. Jour. Sci.* (5) **21**: 311–320.

699. ――――, 1932 (See Wanless, H. R., and J. M. Weller, 1932).

700. ――――, 1934, Boundaries of Pennsylvanian cyclothems [Abstract], *Illinois State Acad. Sci. Trans.*, **27**: 121.

701. ――――, H. R. WANLESS, L. M. CLINE, and D. G. STOOKEY, 1942, Interbasin Pennsylvanian correlations, Illinois and Iowa, *Bull. Am. Assoc. Petroleum Geologists*, **26**: 1585–1593.

702. WELLER, S., 1899, A peculiar Devonian deposit in northeastern Illinois, *Jour. Geology*, **7**: 483–488.

703. WELLS, A. K., 1923, The nomenclature of the spilitic suite. Part II. The problem of the spilites, *Geol. Mag.*, **60**: 62–74.

704. WENTWORTH, C. K., and H. WILLIAMS, 1932. The classification and terminology of the pyroclastic rocks, *Nat. Research Council, Rept. Comm. Sedimentation, Bull.*, **89**: 19–53.

705. WESTGATE, L. G., and R. P. FISCHER, 1933, Bone beds and crinoidal sands of the Delaware limestone of central Ohio, *Bull. Geol. Soc. Am.*, **44**: 1161–1172.

706. WHERRY, E. T., 1915, A peculiar oolite from Bethlehem, Pennsylvania, *U.S. Nat. Mus. Proc.*, **49**: 153–156.

707. WHITE, D., 1933, Informal communications, *Washington Acad. Sci. Jour.*, **23**: 567–568.

708. WHITEHEAD, W. L., 1920, The Chilean nitrate deposits, *Econ. Geology*, **15**: 187–224.

709. WHITFIELD, R. P., 1900, Observations on some "mud flow" markings on rocks from near Albany, New York, *Bull. Am. Mus. Nat. Hist.*, **12**: 183–187.

710. ———, 1904, Note on some worm (?) burrows in rocks of the Chemung group in New York, *Bull. Am. Mus. Nat. Hist.*, **20**: 473–474.

711. WILLARD, B., 1925, Mud cracks forming over water, *Jour. Geology*, **33**: 286–287.

712. WILLIAMS, H. S., 1881, Channel fillings in Upper Devonian shales, *Am. Jour. Sci.* (3) **21**: 318–320.

713. WILLIAMS, M. Y., 1927, Sandstone dikes in southeastern Alberta, *Royal Soc. Canada Trans.* (3) **21** (4): 153–174.

714. ———, 1936, Frost circles, *Royal Soc. Canada, Trans.* (3) **30** (4): 129–132.

715. WILLIS, B., and R. WILLIS, 1934, "Geologic Structures," 3d ed., McGraw-Hill Book Company, Inc., New York. 544 pp.

716. WILLS, L. J., 1938, The Pleistocene development of the Severn from Bridgnorth to the sea, *Geol. Soc. London Quart Jour.*, **94**: 161–242.

717. WILMARTH, M. G., 1938, Lexicon of geologic names of the United States (including Alaska), *U.S. Geol. Survey Bull.*, pp. 1–2396.

718. WILSON, G., 1947, The relationship of slaty cleavage and kindred structures to tectonics, *Proc. Geol. Assoc.*, **57**: 263–302, 1946.

719. WILSON, L. R., 1932, The Two Creeks forest bed, Manitowoc County, Wisconsin, *Wisconsin Acad. Sci. Trans.*, **27**: 31–46.

720. WILSON, M. E., 1911, Kawagama Lake map-area, Pontiac and Abitibi, Quebec, *Geol. Survey Canada Summary Rept.*, **1911**: 273–279.

721. ———, 1939, 1942, Structural features of the Keewatin volcanic rocks of western Quebec, *Bull. Geol. Soc. Am.*, **50**: 1943 (Abstract), **53**: 53–70.

722. ———, 1941, Noranda district, Quebec, *Geol. Survey Canada Mem.*, **229**: 1–162.

723. ———, 1945, The regional structural relations of the ore deposits of the Noranda district, western Quebec, *N.Y. Acad. Sci. Trans.* (2) **8**: 43–44.

724. WINCHELL, H., 1947, Honolulu series, Oahu, Hawaii, *Bull. Geol. Soc. Am.*, **58**: 1–48.

725. WINCHESTER, D. E., 1919, Contorted bituminous shale of the Green River formation of northwestern Colorado, *Washington Acad. Sci. Jour.*, **9**: 295–296.

726. WOODFORD, A. O., 1935, Rhomboid ripple mark, *Am. Jour. Sci.* (5) **29**: 518–525.

727. WOODWARD, H. B., 1892, Remarks on the formation of landscape marble, *Geol. Mag.*, **9**: 110–114.

728. WOODWORTH, J. B., 1901, Original micaceous cross banding of strata by current action, *Am. Geologist*, **27**: 281–283.

729. ———, 1903, On the sedentary impression of the animal whose trail is known as Climactichnites, *Bull. N.Y. State Mus.*, **69**: 959–966.

730. WOOLNOUGH, W. G., 1910, "Stone rolls" in the Bulli coal seam of New South Wales, *Royal Soc. New South Wales Jour. and Proc.*, **44**: 334–340.

731. ———, 1918, The physiographic significance of laterite in western Australia, *Geol. Mag.*, **55**: 385–393.

732. ———, 1927, [The "Duricrust" of Australia], presidential address to the Royal Society of New South Wales, *Royal Soc. New South Wales Jour. and Proc.*, **61**: 1–53 (17–53).

733. ———, 1928, Origin of white clays and bauxite, and chemical criteria of peneplanation, *Econ. Geology*, **23**: 887–894.

734. ———, 1930, The influence of climate and topography in the formation and distribution of products of weathering, *Geol. Mag.*, **67**: 124–132.

735. ———, 1933, Pseudo-tectonic structures, *Bull. Am. Assoc. Petroleum Geologists*, **17**: 1098–1106.

735a. WRIGHT, J. F., 1932, Geology and mineral deposits of a part of southeastern Manitoba, *Geol. Survey Canada Mem.*, **169**: 1–150.

736. WYMAN, J., 1855, [On the formation of rain impressions in clay], *Boston Soc. Nat. History Proc.*, **5**: 253–254.

737. YOUNG, R. B., 1945, Stylolitic solution in Witwatersrand quartzites, *Geol. Survey South Africa Trans.*, **47**: 137–142.

INDEX

A

Accessory minerals, 89
  in Galesville sandstone, 89
  in Ironton sandstone, 89
  in Jordan sandstone, 89
  in Madison sandstone, 89
  volumetric variation in, 89
Accretionary lapilli, 13
Admiral formation, cephalopods in, 42
Agates, water-level, 377
Alamogordo member, bioherms in, 299
Algal structures, 286–290
  in Belt series, 289
  bun-shaped, 289, 290
  columnar, 290
  compared with wave ripple-mark, 121
  conical, 287, 289
  dentate, 289, 290
  versus fucoids, 188
  in Kona dolostone, 287, 288
  in Otavi system, 289, 290
  in Pre-Cambrian rocks, 287, 289
Allegheny sandstones, rill marks in, 131
Allentown formation, oölites in, 283–284, 285
Amygdales (see Amygdules), 354
Amygdaloids, microscopic, 8
Amygdules, 328, 349–356
  in Brighton flows, 380
  chalcedonic, in Columbia River basalts, 380
  in Columbia River basalts, 379, 380
  complete, 328, 350, 376
  composite, 328, 350, 376, 380
    bipartite nature of, 380
  incomplete, 328, 350, 376, 377, 380
  as indexes of top and bottom, 377
  pipe, 352–355
    bent, 354
    references to, 355

Amygdules, references to, 355, 451
  secondary, 386
  spheroidal, 351
  spike, 352
  in tilted flows, 380
  tubular, 352
  use of, for top and bottom determination, 352
Anchorage stones, furrows produced by, 173
Anhydrite, rhythmically laminated, 90
Anhydrock, definition of, 65
  rhythmically laminated, 90
Antidune, definition of, 112
  in Posidonomya formation, 113
  ripple-mark, 112
Appin quartzite, cross-lamination in, 246
Arcente member, 299
Archean rocks of Finland, ripple-mark in, 97
Arenicola, burrows of, 184
Arenicolites, 183, 184
  burrows of, 183, 184
  chemungensis, 184
Arkose, definition of, 65
Arthrophycus, 175, 176, 177
  alleghaniensis, 176
  mode of formation of, 176–177
Arthropods, buried alive, 302
  Balanus, 302
  Calymene, in Racine dolostone, 302
  trilobites, 302
Artinskian, cephalopods in, 42
Ash, volcanic, 330–331, 356
  at bottom of flows, 356
  deposits of, 330–331
  textural variation in, 330–331
  at top of flows, 356
Ashstone, definition of, 65
Atoka sandstone, clastic dikes in, 215

485